REFRIGERATING PRINCIPLES AND PRACTICES

REFRIGERATING PRINCIPLES AND PRACTICES

by

NORMAN SHARPE

Chairman of Refrigerating
and Air Conditioning Department
California State Polytechnic College

FIRST EDITION

McGRAW-HILL BOOK COMPANY, INC.

New York   Toronto   London
1949

REFRIGERATING PRINCIPLES AND PRACTICES

THE MAPLE PRESS COMPANY, YORK, PA.

PREFACE

This book is written for the purpose of assisting the student to integrate principles and practices of the refrigerating industry.

Refrigeration is not a new field, inasmuch as the ammonia compressor was introduced by Dr. Carl Linde in 1873. Furthermore, there has been little development in the theory of refrigeration since 1900. Closer studies of principles, practices, and the integration of the two have reduced the first cost, the operating cost, and the size of refrigerating equipment to such an extent that it is now practical for purposes not dreamed of two decades ago. Because of the rapid development in the last two decades, refrigeration is now considered a new and promising field by many people.

Material is presented in the order in which the engineer would make calculations for a typical installation. This order is a suitable one for instructional purposes. The first chapter, dealing with the refrigeration load, gives the student a review of the fundamental principles of physics required. The second chapter gives the chemical and thermodynamic properties of the common refrigerants. The third chapter presents thermodynamic cycles and their use with the various refrigerants. Throughout the rest of the book principles and practices are discussed in close relation with each other.

NORMAN SHARPE

SAN LUIS OBISPO, CALIF.
February, 1949

v

CONTENTS

LIST OF TABLES

LIST OF CHARTS

SYMBOLS AND ABBREVIATIONS

A	area, sq ft
API	American Petroleum Institute
ASA	American Standards Association
ASHVE	American Society of Heating and Ventilating Engineers
ASRE	American Society of Refrigerating Engineers
bhp	brake horsepower
Btu	British thermal unit
B.w.g.	Birmingham wire gauge
c	specific heat
C	conductance, Btu/(sq ft)(°FTD) (hr)
cfm	cubic feet per minute
cgs	centimeter-gram-second system of units
c_p	specific heat at constant pressure
c_v	specific heat at constant volume
d	diameter, in.
d	differential operator, change of
D	diameter, ft
e	mechanical efficiency, saturation efficiency, or volumetric efficiency
f	film conductance Btu/(sq ft)(°FTD) (hr)
f	frequency, cycles/sec
F	friction factor
°F	degrees Fahrenheit
fpm	feet per minute
fps	feet per second
°FTD	degrees Fahrenheit temperature difference
g	gravitational constant, 4.18×10^8 ft/hr^2
G	mass velocity, lb/(hr)(sq ft)
gpm	gallons per minute
h	specific enthalpy, Btu/lb
H	specific enthalpy of superheated vapor, Btu/lb
hp	horsepower
i.d.	inner diameter
ime	ice-melting equivalent
J	mechanical equivalent of heat, 778

k thermal conductivity, Btu/(sq ft)(hr) (°FTD per in.) for building materials and insulations, Btu/(hr)(sq ft)(°FTD per ft) for other materials

l latent heat of evaporation, Btu/lb

L linear dimension, ft

mph   miles per hour

n number of rows of tubes

n revolutions per minute

NEMA   National Electrical Manufacturers Association

o.d.   outer diameter

p pressure, psi

p number of poles of an electric motor

P pressure, psf

P barometric pressure, inches of mercury

psf   pounds per square foot

psi   pounds per square inch

q heat per pound involved in a process, Btu/lb

Q transferred heat, Btu

r resistance to heat flow, $1/f$, x/k, or $1/C$

R compression ratio

R gas constant Pv/T

R_1 resistance to heat flow, $1/U$

°R   degrees Rankine

Re   Reynolds number, $Dv\rho/\mu$

rpm   revolutions per minute

s specific entropy, Btu/(lb)(°R)

S specific entropy of superheated vapor, Btu/(lb)(°R)

S stress, psi

SSU   seconds Saybolt Universal

t temperature, °F

T absolute temperature, °R

t' wet-bulb temperature

Δt temperature difference or increment of temperature, °FTD

v velocity, mph, fpm, or fps

v volume, cu ft

V specific volume, cu ft/lb

U over-all transmittance, Btu/(sq ft)(hr)(°FTD)

w weight, lb

W rate of flow, lb/hr

W work, ft/lb

x thickness, in.

Z viscosity, centipoises

Z_k	kinematic viscosity, centistokes
γ	(gamma) ratio of specific heats c_p/c_v
Δ	(delta) increment of
μ	(mu) absolute viscosity in the British system, lb/(hr)(ft)
ρ	(rho) density, lb/cu ft
Σ	(sigma) sigma heat function
τ_s	(tau) viscosity in seconds Saybolt Universal, SSU

CHAPTER 1

THE REFRIGERATION LOAD

DEFINITIONS AND GENERAL PRINCIPLES

Refrigeration is that branch of engineering which deals with the pumping of heat from a lower to a higher temperature. In order to understand this process it is necessary to study the fundamental principles of heat, heat transfer, and thermodynamics.

Heat. Heat is the energy of molecular activity. All substances, whether they are solid, liquid, or gas, are composed of molecules in motion, unless the temperature of the body is lowered to absolute zero. At absolute zero all molecular activity ceases, and hence at this temperature the body has no heat content.

Quantity of Heat. The unit of heat generally used in refrigeration is the British thermal unit, abbreviated Btu. The Btu is usually defined as the quantity of heat required to raise the temperature of 1 lb of water 1°F. More accurately, it is the $\frac{1}{180}$ part of the heat required to raise the temperature of 1 lb of water from 32 to 212°F. This is equal to the heat required to raise 1 lb of water from 63 to 64°F.

Specific Heat of Solids and Liquids. The specific heat of a substance is generally defined as the ratio of the quantity of heat required to raise a given quantity of a substance through a given temperature range to the quantity of heat required to raise the same weight of water through the same temperature range. More accurately, it is the Btu required to raise the temperature of 1 lb of a substance 1°F. The specific heat of ice is not the same as that of water. The Smithsonian Physical Tables give the following values:

TABLE 1-1. SPECIFIC HEAT OF ICE*

Temperature, °F	Specific Heat
32	0.487
− 30	0.434
−112	0.350

* Smithsonian Physical Tables, 8th rev. ed., The Smithsonian Institution, Washington, D. C., 1934.

Since food products contain a large portion of water, their specific heats below freezing should not be expected to be the same as above freezing.

Table 1-2 gives the specific heats of many comestibles.

TABLE 1-2. SPECIFIC HEATS OF COMESTIBLES*

Comestible	Above freezing	Below freezing	Comestible	Above freezing	Below freezing
Fruits and vegetables:			Fish, meat, and poultry:		
Apples.............	0.92		try:		
Asparagus.........	0.95	0.44	Bacon.............	0.55	0.31
Bananas...........	0.80		Beef, dried........	0.34	0.26
Beans, green.......	0.92	0.47	Beef, fat..........	0.60	0.35
Berries, fresh.......	0.89	0.46	Beef, lean.........	0.77	0.40
Cabbage...........	0.93	0.47	Fish, dried........	0.56	0.34
Cantaloupes.......	0.92		Fish, fresh........	0.82	0.41
Carrots...........	0.87	0.45	Liver, fresh........	0.72	0.40
Cherries..........	0.85		Mutton...........	0.81	0.39
Cranberries.......	0.91		Poultry...........	0.80	0.41
Dried fruit........	0.42	0.27	Pork, fresh........	0.60	0.38
Grapefruit........	0.92		Veal.............	0.71	0.39
Grapes...........	0.92		Miscellaneous:		
Lemons...........	0.91		Butter............	0.64	
Oranges..........	0.89		Cheese...........	0.64	
Peaches..........	0.92		Eggs.............	0.76	0.40
Pears............	0.90		Honey............	0.35	0.26
Peas, green........	0.80	0.42	Milk, sweet........	0.90	0.46
Plums............	0.83				
Potatoes..........	0.77	0.44			
Raspberries........	0.89				
Strawberries.......	0.92				

* ASRE Data Book, 5th ed., vol. 1, pp. 127, 171, The American Society of Refrigerating Engineers, New York, 1944.

For fruits and vegetables above freezing an approximation of the specific heat may be obtained as follows:[1]

$$c = (0.008)(\text{per cent water}) + 0.20 \qquad (1\text{-}1)$$

Specific Heat of Gases. If heat is added to a gas at constant pressure, it will expand, or if the volume is constant, it will increase in pressure. The heat required to raise 1 lb of the gas 1°F is not the same in the two cases. The heat required at constant pressure is slightly greater than that at constant volume since work is done in expanding the gas. A gas has, therefore, two specific heats—the specific heat at constant pressure, designated c_p, and the specific heat at constant volume, designated c_v.

Change of Phase. Most substances can exist in three phases—solid, liquid, and gas. A substance in the gaseous phase near its condensing

[1] ROSE, DEAN H., R. C. WRIGHT, and T. M. WHITEMAN, The Commercial Storage of Fruits, Vegetables, and Florists' Stocks, *U. S. Dept. Agr. Circ. 278*, November, 1941.

temperature is called a *vapor*. The temperature at which a substance changes from liquid to vapor is called its *boiling point* or *condensing temperature*. The temperature at which a substance changes from liquid to solid is called its *freezing point*.

Latent Heat. A change from the solid to the liquid phase involves the *latent heat of fusion*. The latent heat of fusion of ice at normal atmospheric pressure is 144 Btu/lb; that is, 144 Btu must be removed from 1 lb of water at 32°F to change it to ice at 32°F. The latent heat of evaporation of water when the barometric pressure is 14.7 psi is 970 Btu/lb. In the freezing of food products, it is only the water within the material that is involved. The latent heat involved in freezing a product is, therefore,

$$Q_l = 144(w)(\text{per cent water}) \tag{1-2}$$

where Q_l is the latent heat involved, Btu, and w is the weight, lb.

The percentage water content, the freezing point, and the optimum storage conditions are given in Tables 1-3 and 1-4.[1]

Sensible Heat. Sensible heat is the heat, other than the latent heat, involved in cooling a substance through a temperature range. From the definitions of the Btu and of specific heat, Eq. (1-3) follows directly.

$$Q_s = wc\,(t_1 - t_2) \tag{1-3}$$

where Q_s = sensible heat involved, Btu
  w = weight, lb
  c = specific heat
  t_1 = initial temperature, °F
  t_2 = final temperature, °F

The First Law of Thermodynamics. The first law of thermodynamics is the same as the law of conservation of energy. Energy can be neither created nor destroyed but can be converted from one form to another. Thus 778 ft-lb when changed to heat units is equal to 1 Btu. The conversion factor, 778, is called the *mechanical equivalent of heat*, or *Joule's constant*, and is designated J. Other importance conversion factors are as follows:

$$1 \text{ hp} = 42.42 \text{ Btu/min}$$
$$1 \text{ hp} = 2{,}546 \text{ Btu/hr}$$
$$1 \text{ watt} = 3.415 \text{ Btu/hr}$$
$$1 \text{ hp} = 745.7 \text{ watts/hr}$$

Temperature. Temperature is a measure, on an arbitrary scale, of the ability of heat to transfer from one substance to another or from one

[1] Rose, Wright, and Whiteman, *op. cit.*

TABLE 1-3. RECOMMENDED TEMPERATURE, RELATIVE HUMIDITY, AND APPROXIMATE LENGTH OF STORAGE PERIOD FOR THE COMMERCIAL STORAGE OF FRESH, DRIED, AND FROZEN FRUITS, AND NUTS, AND THE AVERAGE FREEZING POINTS

Commodity	Temperature, °F	Relative humidity, per cent	Approximate length of storage period	Average freezing point, °F	Water content per cent,
Apples..................	30–32*	85–88	*	28.4	84.1
Apricots...............	31–32	80–85	1– 2 weeks	28.1	85.4
Avocados..............	*	85–90	*	27.2	*
Bananas...............	*	*	*	†	74.8
Blackberries..........	31–32	80–85	7–10 days	28.9	85.3
Cherries..............	31–32	80–85	10–14 days	‡	83.0
Coconuts.............	32–35	80–85	1– 2 months	25.5	
Cranberries..........	36–40	85–90	1– 3 months	27.3	87.4
Dates................	28–32	*	*	−4.1	20.0
Dewberries..........	31–32	80–85	7–10 days		
Grapefruit...........	*	85–90	6– 8 weeks	28.4	88.8
Grapes:					
Vinifera..........	30–31	85–90	3– 6 months	24.9	81.6
American.........	31–32	80–85	3– 8 weeks	27.5	81.9
Lemons..............	55–58	85–90	1– 4 months	28.1	89.3
Limes...............	45–48	85–90	6– 8 weeks	29.3	86.0
Logan blackberries....	31–32	80–85	7–10 days	29.5	82.9
Olives (fresh)..........	45–50	85–90	4– 6 weeks	28.5	75.2
Oranges.............	*	85–90	8–10 weeks	§	87.2
Peaches.............	31–32	80–85	2– 4 weeks	29.4	86.9
Pears:					
Bartlett..........	29–30	85–90	*	28.5	83.5
Fall and winter varieties	30–31	85–90	*	‖	
Pineapples:					
Mature green........	50–60	85–90	3– 4 weeks	29.1	
Ripe.............	40–45	85–90	2– 4 weeks	29.9	85.3
Plums (including prunes)..	31–32	80–85	3– 8 weeks*	28.0	85.7
Quinces..............	31–32	80–85	2– 3 months	28.1	85.3
Raspberries..........	31–32	80–85	7–10 days	29.9	80.7
Strawberries.........	31–32	80–85	7–10 days	29.9	90.0
Dried fruits..........	*	*	9–12 months		
Frozen fruits.........	*	*	6–12 months		
Nuts................	32–50*	65–75	8–12 months	¶	3–6

* See Appendix 1.
† Green: flesh, 30.2°F; peel, 29.8°F.   Ripe: flesh, 26.0°F; peel, 29.4°F.
‡ Eastern sour, 28.0°F; eastern sweet, 24.7°F; California sweet, 24.2°F.
§ Flesh, 28.0°F; peel, 27.4°F.
‖ Winter Nelis, 27.2°F; Anjou, 26.9°F.
¶ Persian (English) walnuts, 20.0°F; pecans, 19.6°F; chestnuts (Italian), 23.8°F.

TABLE 1-4.   RECOMMENDED TEMPERATURE, RELATIVE HUMIDITY, AND APPROXIMATE
LENGTH OF STORAGE PERIOD FOR THE STORAGE OF VARIOUS VEGETABLES, AND
THE AVERAGE FREEZING POINTS

Commodity	Temperature, °F	Relative humidity, per cent	Approximate length of storage period	Average freezing point, °F	Water content, per cent
Asparagus.............	32	85–90	3– 4 weeks	29.8	93.0
Beans:					
Green or snap.........	32–40	85–90	2– 4 weeks	29.7	88.9
Lima................	32–40	85–90	2– 4 weeks	30.1	66.5
Beets:					
Topped..............	32	95–98	1– 3 months	26.9	87.6
Bunch...............	32	85–90	10–14 days		
Broccoli (Italian or sprouting).................	32–35	90–95	7–10 days	29.2	89.9
Brussels sprouts.........	32–35	90–95	3– 4 weeks	....	84.9
Cabbage................	32	90–95	3– 4 months	31.2	92.4
Carrots:					
Topped..............	32	95–98	4– 5 months	29.6	88.2
Bunch...............	32	85–90	10–14 days		
Cauliflower.............	32	85–90	2– 3 weeks	30.1	91.7
Celeriac...............	32	95–98	3– 4 months	....	88.3
Celery.................	31–32	90–95	2– 4 months	29.7	93.7
Corn (green)...........	31–32	85–90	‡	28.9	73.9
Cucumbers.............	45–50	80–85	10–14 days	30.5	96.1
Eggplants..............	45–50	85–90	10 days	30.4	92.7
Endive................	32	90–95	2– 3 weeks	30.9	93.3
Garlic (dry)...........	32	70–75	6– 8 months	25.4	74.2
Horse-radish...........	32	95–98	10–12 months	26.4	73.4
Jerusalem artichokes......	31–32	90–95	2– 5 months	27.5	79.5
Kohlrabi...............	32	95–98	2– 4 weeks	30.0	90.1
Leeks (green)...........	32	85–90	1– 3 months	29.2	88.2
Lettuce................	32	90–95	2– 3 weeks	31.2	94.8
Melons:					
Watermelon...........	36–40	75–85	2– 3 weeks	29.2* 28.8†	92.1
Muskmelon (cantaloupe)	32–34	75–78	7–10 days	29.0* 28.4†	92.7
Honeydew and Honeyball.	36–38	75–85	2– 4 weeks	29.0* 28.8†	
Casaba and Persian.....	36–40	75–85	4– 6 weeks		
Mushrooms (cultivated)...	32–35	80–85	2– 3 days	30.2	91.1
Onions.................	32	70–75	6– 8 months	30.1	87.5
Onion sets.............	32	70–75	6– 8 months	29.5	87.5
Parsnips...............	32	90–95	2– 4 months	28.9	78.6
Peas (green)...........	32	85–90	1– 2 weeks	30.0	74.3

TABLE 1-4. RECOMMENDED TEMPERATURE, RELATIVE HUMIDITY, AND APPROXIMATE LENGTH OF STORAGE PERIOD FOR THE STORAGE OF VARIOUS VEGETABLES, AND THE AVERAGE FREEZING POINTS.—(*Continued*)

Commodity	Temperature, °F	Relative humidity, per cent	Approximate length of storage period	Average freezing point, °F	Water content, per cent
Peppers:					
Chili (dry).............	‡	70–75	6– 9 months		
Sweet.................	32	85–90	4– 6 weeks	30.1	92.4
Potatoes.................	36–50‡	85–90	‡	28.9	77.8
Pumpkins................	50–55	70–75	2– 6 months	30.1	90.5
Radishes (winter)........	32	95–98	2– 4 months		93.6
Rhubarb.................	32	90–95	2– 3 weeks	28.4	94.9
Rutabagas...............	32	95–98	2– 4 months	29.5	89.1
Salsify..................	32	95–98	2– 4 months	28.4	79.1
Spinach.................	32	90–95	10–14 days	30.3	92.7
Squashes (winter)........	50–55	70–75	2– 6 months	29.3	90.5
Sweet potatoes...........	55–60	75–80‡	4– 6 months	28.5	68.5
Tomatoes:					
Ripe.................	40–50	85–90	7–10 days	30.4	94.1
Mature green...........	55–70‡	85–90	3– 5 weeks	30.4	94.7
Turnips.................	32	95–98	4– 5 months	30.5	90.9

* Flesh.
† Rind.
‡ See Appendix 1

position in a substance to another position within the substance. This definition is essentially the second law of thermodynamics, which may be stated as follows: Heat always flows from the substance of higher temperature to the substance of lower temperature regardless of what its heat content may be. To calibrate a thermometer, the freezing and boiling points of water are used. On the Fahrenheit scale, when the barometric pressure is 14.7 psi, water freezes at 32°F and boils at 212°F. Absolute temperature is measured in degrees Rankine, designated °R. To convert from degrees Fahrenheit to degrees Rankine, add 459.6 to the Fahrenheit reading. At 0°R (−459.6°F) a substance has no heat content; that is, all molecular activity within it has ceased. This point is termed *absolute zero* to indicate that lower temperatures are not possible.

Heat Transfer. Heat is transferred from one substance to another by three methods—conduction, convection, and radiation. *Conduction* is the transfer of heat through a substance by virtue of molecular activity within the substance. Some substances are better conductors than others. Poor conductors are good insulators. *Convection* is the transfer of heat within a substance by the process of mixing. *Radiation* is the transfer of heat by waves of the electromagnetic family. Radiant heat is similar to light, being capable of reflection and transmission in straight lines. Gases are quite transparent to the passage of radiant heat, while solids either absorb or reflect most of the radiant heat that falls upon them. We will deal with all three types of heat transfer.

Conducted Heat. The quantity of heat conducted through a substance per unit of time is proportional to the area through which the heat passes and to the temperature head causing the heat to flow. This principle is stated in the following formula:

$$Q = UA \, \Delta t \tag{1-4}$$

where Q = quantity of heat transmitted
U = proportionality constant, call the *over-all coefficient of heat transfer*
A = area through which the heat passes
Δt = temperature difference causing the heat to flow

The units generally used in this formula are Q in Btu per hour, U in Btu per hour per square feet of surface per degree Fahrenheit temperature difference,[1] and Δt in degrees fahrenheit. In calculating the areas of cold-storage spaces, the dimensions should be taken from center to center of partitions, ceiling, and floor.

For a single substance, U depends on the thermal conductivity and on the thickness of the material. It is directly proportional to the thermal conductivity and inversely proportional to its thickness, or

$$U = \frac{k}{x}$$

where k is the thermal conductivity and x is the thickness of the material

The factor U is a measure of the ability of heat to transfer through a substance. The resistance to heat flow, designated R, is the reciprocal of U; that is,

$$R = \frac{1}{U}$$

The total resistance to heat flow through a substance of several layers is the sum of the resistance of the various layers.

$$R = r_1 + r_2 + r_3 + \cdots \tag{1-5}$$

where R is the total resistance, and r_1, r_2, r_3, . . . , are the resistances of the several layers.

[1] Abbreviated hereafter °FTD.

If Eq. (1-5) is stated in terms of thermal conductivities, it becomes

$$\frac{1}{U} = \frac{x_1}{k_1} + \frac{x_2}{k_2} + \frac{x_3}{k_3} + \cdots \tag{1-6}$$

In case a fluid such as air or water is in contact with the substance on both sides, the film formed at the surface offers additional resistance. If r_i is the resistance of the inside film and r_o is the resistance of the outside film, Eq. (1-5) becomes

$$R = r_i + r_o + r_1 + r_2 + r_3 + \cdots \tag{1-7}$$

If f_i is the conductance of the inside film and f_0 is the conductance of the outside film, Eq. (1-7) may be rewritten as follows:

$$\frac{1}{U} = \frac{1}{f_i} + \frac{1}{f_o} + \frac{x_1}{k_1} + \frac{x_2}{k_2} + \frac{x_3}{k_3} + \cdots \tag{1-8}$$

Solving this equation for U, we obtain

$$U = \frac{1}{\dfrac{1}{f_i} + \dfrac{1}{f_o} + \dfrac{x_1}{k_1} + \dfrac{x_2}{k_2} + \dfrac{x_3}{k_3} + \cdots} \tag{1-9}$$

The units generally used in this formula are f_i and f_o in Btu/(sq ft)-(hr)(FTD° per in.), x in inches, and k in Btu/(sq ft surface)(in. thickness)(°FTD per hr).

Values of k can be obtained from the Refrigerating Data Book, ASHVE Guide, Smithsonian Physical Tables, etc. A few values are listed in Table 1-5.

Conductance. For some building materials of irregular cross section, such as hollow tile or shingles, it is difficult to compute the amount of heat that will flow per unit of time from their conductivities. For such materials the conductance rather than the conductivity is used. The conductance of a sample of material is the amount of heat that will flow through unit area of the material from one of its surfaces to the other. The conductance of a building material is designated C, and the conductance of a fluid film that adheres to a surface is designated f. In either case, the usual unit is Btu/(sq ft)(hr)(°F).

Table 1-6[1] gives conductances of various building materials and Table 1-7 gives air-film conductances.

Values of f for air have been determined by Rowley, Algren, and Blackshaw as shown in Table 1-7.

[1] ASRE Data Book, p. 156, The American Society of Refrigerating Engineers, New York, 1942.

TABLE 1-5. CONDUCTIVITY OF INSULATING AND BUILDING MATERIALS*
Btu/(sq ft)(hr)(°FTD per in.)

Material	Density, lb/cu ft	Mean temperature, °F	Conductivity, k	Authority†
Insulating materials				
Asbestos:				
Packed.............................	43.8	32	1.62	2
Loose...............................	29.3	32	1.07	2
Asbestos paper, thin layers, organic binder	31.2	86	0.49	1
Asbestos millboard....................	60.5	86	0.84	1
Asbestos wood........................	23.0	86	2.70	1
Asphalt roofing (felt).................	55.0	86	0.70	1
Balsa................................	7.36	86	0.35	1
Cement wood (sawdust and Portland cement)..............................	44.6	68	0.97	3
Charcoal (hardwoods), coarse...........	13.2	90	0.36	1
Corkboard...........................	6.7	−22	0.22	5
Typical...........................	8.3	35	0.27	4
	8.3	60	0.28	4
Cork:				
Granulated, coarse...................	8.1	90	0.31	1
Regranulated.......................	6.5	77	0.27	5
Cotton...............................	5.06	32	0.39	3
Diatomaceous earth.............	30.0	30	0.56	5
Eelgrass.............................	9.4	86	0.31	5
Glass wool:				
High grade........................	1.76	85	0.265	4
	3.61	74	0.237	4
	5.37	75	0.224	4
Commercial grade...................	2.49	65	0.26	4
Hair felt, not compressed..............	13.0	90	0.26	1
Insulation boards, fiber various..........	15–21	70	0.32–0.38	4
Kapok, loosely packed.................	0.87	84	0.24	1
Planer shavings, various woods..........	8.7	86	0.40	1
Rock wool............................	10.0	90	0.27	1
	14.0	90	0.28	1
Rubber, expanded.....................	4.85	72	0.21	4
Sawdust, various woods.................	12.0	90	0.41	1
Miscellaneous materials:				
Glass, window.......................	......	....	5.5	
Gravel.............................	115.0	68	2.6	2
Peanut, 2.6% water.................	......	68	7.5	5
Ice................................	57.5	32	15.6	

TABLE 1-5.   CONDUCTIVITY OF INSULATING AND BUILDING MATERIALS.*—(Continued)

Material	Density, lb/cu ft	Mean temperature, °F	Conductivity, k	Authority†
Soil, clay, 14% moisture:				
Loosely packed....................	75	68	2.6	5
Loaded 1 cwt/sq ft................	80	68	4.9	5
Loaded 1 ton/sq ft................	96	68	8.4	5
Loam over sand and gravel, 3 ft deep, seasonal change due to variation of moisture content.................	......	....	7.8–10.7	5
Snow.............................	34.7	....	3.2	
Water............................	......	50	4.3	5
Building materials				
Brick:				
Low density........................	......	....	5.0	
High density.......................	......	....	9.2	
Cement mortar........................	......	....	12.0	
Cement plaster, typical..................	......	....	12.0	
Concrete:				
Typical............................	......	....	12.0	
Typical fiber gypsum, 87.5% gypsum, 12.5% wood chips.................	51.2	74	1.66	6
Sand and gravel.....................	142	75	12.6	
Limestone.........................	132	75	10.8	6
Cinder............................	97	75	4.9	6
Cinders, boiler (½ to ¾ in.).............	60	71	1.23	4
Stucco, typical......................	......	....	12.0	
Tile or terrazzo, typical.................	......	....	12.0	
Asbestos building board.................	123	86	2.7	1
Gypsum:				
Between layers of heavy paper........	62.8	70	1.41	7
Plaster, typical......................	......	....	3.30	
Wood, across grain, typical:	......	....	1.0	
Balsa.............................	8.8	90	0.38	1
Redwood, California, 16% moisture....	22	75	0.74	6
Fir, Douglas, 16% moisture...........	26	75	0.76	6
Pine, yellow shortleaf, 16% moisture...	26	75	0.84	6
Pine, yellow shortleaf, 16% moisture...	36	75	1.04	6
Pine, yellow shortleaf, 16% moisture...	36	75	1.04	6

* ASRE Data Book, pp. 155–156, The American Society of Refrigerating Engineers, New York, 1942.

† Authorities: (1) Bureau of Standards; (2) Groeber; (3) Nusselt; (4) Hechler and Queer; (5) Griffiths; (6) Rowley; (7) Peebles.

TABLE 1-6. CONDUCTANCE OF BUILDING MATERIALS AND CONSTRUCTIONS
Btu/(sq ft)(hr)(°FTD) for Thickness Indicated

Material	Density, lb/cu ft	Mean temperature, °F	Conductance, c	Authority*
Plasterboard:				
⅜ in. thick	...	..	3.73	
½ in. thick	...	..	2.82	
Roofs:				
Asphalt, composition or prepared roofing	70	75	6.50	1
Shingles, asbestos	65	75	6.00	1
Shingles, asphalt	70	75	6.50	1
Shingles, slate	201	..	10.4	
Metal lath and plaster, total thickness ¾ in	...	..	4.40	
Wood lath and plaster, total thickness ¾ in	...	70	2.50	2
Fir sheathing, 1 in., and building paper	...	30	0.86	2
And yellow-pine siding	...	20	0.50	2
And stucco	...	20	0.82	2
Air spaces over ¾ in. faced ordinary building materials	...	40	1.10	2
Typical hollow clay tile:				
4 in	...	..	1.00	
6 in	...	..	0.64	
8 in	...	..	0.60	
10 in	...	..	0.58	
12 in	...	..	0.40	
16 in	...	..	0.31	
Concrete block, sand and gravel, typical:				
8 in	...	..	1.00	
12 in	...	..	0.80	
Concrete block, cinder aggregate, typical:				
8 in	...	..	0.60	
12 in	...	..	0.53	

* Authorities: (1) Peebles; (2) Rowley.

TABLE 1-7. AIR FILM CONDUCTANCES*
Btu/(hr)(sq ft)(°FTD)

Surface	f†
Very smooth	$1.4 + 0.28v$
Smooth wood or plaster	$1.6 + 0.3v$
Cast concrete	$2.0 + 0.4v$
Rough stucco	$2.1 + 0.5v$

* ROWLEY, F. B., A. B. ALGREN, and J. L. BLACKSHAW, Surface Conductances as Affected by Air Velocity, Temperature, and Character of Surface, *Trans. ASHVE*, vol. 36, pp. 429–446, 1930.
† v is measured in miles per hour.

Temperature Head for Conducted Heat. For a refrigerated space the temperature head Δt causing the heat to flow through the walls would be the temperature difference between the inside and the outside of the refrigerated space if the temperatures were constant. Unfortunately, this condition is seldom met. In some sections of our country there is as much as 40°F difference between maximum and minimum temperature for the day. Tests by the author indicate that where the wall has low thermal diffusivity[1] and appreciable thickness, Δt may be taken as the mean temperature difference for the day without introducing appreciable error. If Δt is to be taken as the mean temperature difference, the quantity $k/x\rho c$ should be less than 0.0078, where x is the thickness in feet, k is the thermal conductivity in Btu/(hr)(ft thickness) ρ is the density in lb/cu ft, and c is the specific heat. In calculating the cooling load, the warmest day should be considered.

Radiant Heat. Radiant energy from the sun affects the refrigeration load appreciably. The intensity of this energy on a clear day is approximately 400 Btu/hr per sq ft of surface normal to the sun's rays. Upon

TABLE 1-8. TEMPERATURE INCREMENTS FOR SOLAR-HEAT GAIN

Surface	Finish of surface	Δt_s,* °F
Northeast, south, or northwest walls	Unpainted brick or concrete	15
	Painted with aluminum or white paint	8
East, southeast, west, or southwest walls	Unpainted brick or concrete	20
	Painted with aluminum or white paint	10
Roof	Black tar	60
	Graveled	40
	Aluminum painted	20

* Δt_s is the temperature head that should be added to the temperature head used for shaded surfaces to allow for solar-heat gain.

striking a surface, part of this energy is reflected, and the balance is absorbed. The portion that is absorbed heats the outside surface of the wall. If the outside surface becomes warmer than the surroundings, a portion of the absorbed heat is conducted to the air film and carried away by convection; a second portion is radiated into space or to sur-

[1] Thermal diffusivity is defined by the expression $k/\rho c$, in which k is the thermal conductivity measured in Btu/(sq ft)(ft thickness)(°FTD per hr), ρ is the density measured in lb/cu ft, and c is the specific heat. The resulting unit for thermal diffusivity is square feet per hour.

rounding objects; a third portion is conducted through the wall. It is possible to compute the radiated heat that will ultimately be conducted through the wall for a steady heat-transfer condition. However, the variable direction of the sun's rays, the varying air currents, and the varying temperature gradient in the wall, caused by varying temperature heads, make an accurate solution extremely complex. Safe values are, therefore, used. To allow for solar-heat gain, it is customary to add an additional temperature head to the temperature head that is used for shaded surfaces. Table 1-8 gives suggested safe values for roofs and walls of low diffusivity such as are used for refrigerated spaces.

The total solar-heat gains during the day on horizontal roofs, east walls, and west walls are nearly the same for all parts of the United States. The solar-heat gain on south walls is about 30 per cent less for 30°N latitude than for 40°N latitude, and correction in Δt_s may be made accordingly if desired.

Convected Heat. Convection plays a large part in heat transfer. Refrigerated rooms are maintained at proper temperatures and humidities by mixing the room air with air that has been cooled and dehumidified. Upon opening of doors, heat enters the room by infiltration of warm moisture-laden air. The heat content of the air is affected by the moisture content, since it is necessary to add heat to water in order to evaporate it. In order to study the convection problem, it is therefore necessary to study the properties of air.

Product Load. The product load is the amount of heat that must be removed from the product to lower its temperature to the temperature of the room in which it is to be stored. The Btu added to the room is the weight of the product times its specific heat times its temperature reduction. The nature of the product largely determines the temperature at which it will enter the room. Where fruits or vegetables are to be taken directly from the field, their temperature may be taken as the mean temperature of the warmest day. Fruits and vegetables from refrigerated cars using ice without salt in bunkers are usually at about 45°F. If crates of vegetables are surrounded with crushed ice or snow ice during shipping, their temperature will be very little above 32°F. Meat entering the chilling room directly after being killed will be at body temperature. Meat entering the aging room after being chilled may be considered to have a temperature about 5°F above the chilling-room temperature.

In loading a cold-storage room, ample space should be provided for the circulation of air around the produce. One side and one end of each of the boxes should be on an aisle, and ample space should be allowed above the boxes for air circulation. When the boxes are stacked in this manner, about one-half the total space in the room will be filled with the boxed produce. The following data, compiled from the Deciduous Fruit Dealer Service Manual published by the California Fruit Exchange, will be useful in computing the number of tons of produce held in a cold-storage room.

TABLE 1-9. WEIGHTS OF BOXED PRODUCE

Produce	Type of box	Size inside, in.	Gross weight, lb	Net weight, lb
Apples............	Standard	$10\frac{1}{2} \times 11\frac{1}{2} \times 18$	50–53	44–47
Apricots..........	Standard 4-basket crate	$(4–5) \times 16 \times 16\frac{1}{8}$	26–31	22–28
Apricots..........	Special or Winters	$4\frac{5}{8} \times 13\frac{1}{2} \times 16\frac{1}{8}$	26	23
Cherries..........	Bulk or Calex	$4 \times 13\frac{1}{2} \times 16\frac{1}{8}$	21	18
Figs..............	Filler type	$2 \times 11 \times 16\frac{1}{8}$	7	5
Grapes...........	Display lug	$5\frac{3}{4} \times 13\frac{1}{2} \times 16\frac{1}{8}$	31	28
Grapes...........	Sawdust lug	$7\frac{3}{4} \times 13\frac{1}{2} \times 16\frac{1}{8}$	35	22
Nectarines........	Standard peach box	$4\frac{1}{2} \times 11\frac{1}{2} \times 18$	20–22	18
Peaches..........	Standard	$4\frac{1}{2} \times 11\frac{1}{2} \times 18$	$21\frac{1}{2}$	18
Pears.............	Standard	$8\frac{1}{2} \times 11\frac{1}{2} \times 18$	53–55	47–49
Persimmons.......	One-layer peach box	$(3–4\frac{3}{4}) \times 11\frac{1}{2} \times 18$	$21\frac{1}{2}$	18
Plums.............	Standard peach box	$4\frac{1}{2} \times 11\frac{1}{2} \times 18$	$21\frac{1}{2}$	18
Pomegranates......	Half orange box	$5\frac{3}{4} \times 11\frac{1}{2} \times 24\frac{5}{8}$	35–40	30–35

The time of loading will depend on the duty of the refrigerated space. If the warehouse handles a single product, such as oranges or apples, and is located where the product is grown, the warehouse will be loaded in about two-thirds of the picking season. If a terminal warehouse located where the produce is consumed is considered, loading and unloading will be nearly continuous. The average length of storage is about 3 months.

Heat of Evolution. Fruits and vegetables are alive and carry on many of the processes characteristic of living things. Both before and after harvest, fruit constantly takes in oxygen and gives off carbon dioxide. This respiration process is basically the same as that of animals. The produce is kept alive by burning a portion of its stored food. The function of cold storage in holding produce in its fresh state is not to stop the life processes but only to reduce the rate at which they take place. In carrying on these life processes, heat is involved. Table 1-10 gives the heat of evolution of fruits and vegetables.[1] Meats in cold storage are dead, and no heat of evolution need be considered.

[1] ROSE, WRIGHT, and WHITEMAN, *op. cit.*

TABLE 1-10. APPROXIMATE RATE OF EVOLUTION OF HEAT BY CERTAIN FRESH FRUITS AND VEGETABLES WHEN STORED AT THE TEMPERATURE INDICATED

Commodity	Temperature, °F	Heat evolved per ton of fruits or vegetables per 24 hr, Btu*
Apples...	32	660– 880
	40	1,110– 1,760
	60	4,400– 6,600
	85	6,600–15,400
Bananas:		
Green.................................	54	3,300
	68	8,360
Turning................................	68	9,240
Ripe...................................	68	8,360
Beets....................................	32	1,170†
	40	1,870†
	60	3,480†
Cantaloupes.............................	32	2,200†
	50	4,400†
	74	24,200†
Carrots..................................	32	810†
	40	1,410†
	60	3,810†
Celery...................................	32	700†
	40	2,610†
	60	5,960†
Cherries (sour)..........................	32	1,320– 1,760
	60	11,000–13,200
Grapefruit...............................	32	460
	40	1,070
	60	2,770
	80	4,180
Grapes:		
Cornichon and Flame Tokay..............	36	660– 1,100
	60	2,200– 2,640
	80	5,500– 6,600

TABLE 1-10. APPROXIMATE RATE OF EVOLUTION OF HEAT BY CERTAIN FRESH FRUITS AND VEGETABLES WHEN STORED AT THE TEMPERATURES INDICATED.—(*Continued*)

Commodity	Temperature, °F	Heat evolved per ton of fruits or vegetables per 24 hr, Btu*
Sultanina.................................	32	430‡
	43	1,050‡
	53	16,920‡
Emperor.............................	32	350‡
	43	850‡
	53	18,130‡
Ohanez.............................	32	300‡
	43	740‡
	53	15,730‡
Lemons.................................	32	580
	40	810
	60	2,970
	80	6,200
	77	2,200– 3,300
Lettuce.................................	32	640†
	40	7,400†
	60	22,660†
Mushrooms (cultivated)...................	32	6,160†
	50	22,000†
	70	58,000†
Onions (Yellow Globe)....................	32	660– 1,100†
	50	1,760– 1,980†
	70	3,080– 4,180†
Oranges................................	32	690– 900
	40	1,400
	60	5,000
	80	8,000
Peaches...............................	36	1,540– 1,980
	60	6,600– 8,800
	80	15,400–22,000
	32	850– 1,370
	40	1,440– 2,030
	60	7,260– 9,310
	80	17,930–22,460

TABLE 1-10. APPROXIMATE RATE OF EVOLUTION OF HEAT BY CERTAIN FRESH FRUITS
AND VEGETABLES WHEN STORED AT THE TEMPERATURES INDICATED.—(*Continued*)

Commodity	Temperature, °F	Heat evolved per ton of fruits or vegetables per 24 hr, Btu*
Pears (Bartlett)	32	660– 880
	60	8,800–13,200
Peppers	32	550†
	40	1,520†
	60	3,320†
Potatoes (Irish Cobbler)	32	440– 880†
	40	1,100– 1,760†
	50	1,100– 1,540†
	70	2,200– 3,520†
Raspberries	36	4,400– 6,600
	60	15,400–17,600
Strawberries	36	3,300
	60	13,200–15,400
	32	2,730– 3,800
	40	5,130– 6,600
	60	15,640–19,140
	80	37,220–46,440
String beans	32	1,690†
	40	2,710†
	60	10,800†
Sweet corn	32	2,640†
	40	3,810†
	60	8,120†
Sweet potatoes	40	880– 1,320
	85	6,600– 8,800
Tomatoes (mature green)	32	0†
	40	130†
	60	2,570†
Turnips	32	70†
	40	570†
	60	680†

* The figures in this column were obtained by assuming that the heat liberated by respiration is produced by the respiration of a hexose sugar and by multiplying the milligrams of carbon dioxide produced per hour by each kilogram of respiring material by the factor 220.

† Unpublished work on the respiration of vegetables by R. C. Wright and T. M. Whiteman.

‡ Unpublished work by W. T. Pentzer.

PSYCHROMETRY

Air is composed of several relatively noncondensable gases and water vapor. The relatively noncondensable gases are termed *dry gases,* and that portion of the air composed of these dry gases is termed *dry air.* The average composition of dry air is as follows: 78 per cent nitrogen, 21 per cent oxygen, and 1 per cent of other gases. *Psychrometry* is the study of these dry gases in relation to their water vapor content.

Properties of Air. The properties of air of interest in psychrometry are its temperature, humidity, vapor pressure, and heat content. In order to study these properties the following measurements are involved: dry-bulb temperature, wet-bulb temperature, dew-point temperature, absolute humidity, specific humidity, relative humidity, sensible heat, latent heat, total heat, and specific volume. With nearly any two of these measurements known, the others can be calculated or read from a psychrometric chart.

Dry-bulb Temperature. The dry-bulb temperature is the temperature of air as determined by an ordinary thermometer. It is indicative of the sensible heat content of the air.

Dew-point Temperature. If heat is removed from the air until dew starts to form, the temperature at which condensation starts is called the *dew-point temperature.* Since the air is saturated under this condition and since no moisture has been added, the dew-point temperature is indicative of the moisture content of the air in grains per cubic foot.

Water-vapor Content of the Air. The water-vapor content of the air in grains per cubic feet is called its *absolute humidity.* It is a function only of the dew-point temperature for any altitude and can be read directly from the steam tables. The water content in grams of water per pound of dry air is called its *specific humidity.* Specific humidity equals the absolute humidity times the specific volume of the dry air. *Relative humidity* is the ratio of the absolute humidity in the air to what it would be if the air were saturated at its dry-bulb temperature. It is also the ratio of the vapor pressure in the air to what it would be if the air were saturated at the dry-bulb temperature.

Water-vapor Pressure. According to Dalton's law of partial pressures, if we have a mixture of gases, each will exert a pressure independent of all other gases present and the total pressure will be the sum of the pressures of the separate gases. The barometric pressure is the sum of the water-vapor pressure and the pressure of the dry gases. If air is cooled at atmospheric pressure to its dew point, the vapor pressure will be that of saturated water vapor at its dew-point temperature. But the vapor pressure has remained constant, since the atmospheric pressure is constant. Therefore, the vapor pressure in the air is the pressure of saturated water vapor and can be read directly from the steam tables. Table 1-11[1] gives vapor pressures for various dew-point temperatures.

Adiabatic Saturation of Air with Water. Suppose that unsaturated air is passed through water in a perfectly insulated chamber for sufficient distance to saturate it completely. Heat transfer will occur between the air and the water until the water in the chamber is at the same temperature as the air leaving it. At this time an equilibrium will be established. The transfer of sensible heat from the air to the water results in the evaporation of water. The sensible heat transferred equals the increase in latent heat. This principle was stated mathematically by W. H. Carrier[2] as follows:

$$C_{pa}(t - t') + WC_{ps}(t - t') = h_{fc}(W_{t'} - W) \qquad (1\text{-}10)$$

where t = initial temperature of the air

t' = final temperature of the air (wet-bulb temperature)

C_{pa} = specific heat of air at constant pressure (0.240)*

C_{ps} = mean specific heat of steam between temperatures t and t'

$W_{t'}$ = pound of water in 1 lb of dry air saturated with water at temperature t'

W = lbs of water in 1 lb of dry air at its initial condition

h_{fg} = latent heat of evaporation at temperature t'

During this process the sum of the sensible heats of the gases and the latent heat of evaporation of the water remains a constant. This sum is called the sigma heat function and is designated Σ.

$$\Sigma = C_{pa}(t - 0) + WC_{ps}(t - t') + Wh_{fg} \qquad (1\text{-}11)$$

When saturation is reached, $t = t'$, and Eq. (1-11) becomes

$$\Sigma = C_{pa}t' + W_{t'}h_{fg} \qquad (1\text{-}12)$$

Since Σ has not changed during the process, its value can be readily computed for the temperature of saturation without knowing the initial temperature and humidity condition of the air. The quantities $W_{t'}$ and h_{fg} are direct functions of the saturation temperature; therefore, Σ is a direct function of the temperature of saturation of the air regardless of what its initial temperature and humidity may be.

[1] Abstracted by permission from "Thermodynamic Properties of Steam" by J. H. Keenan and F. G. Keyes, published by John Wiley & Sons, Inc., 1936.

[2] CARRIER, W. H., Rational Psychrometric Formulae, *Trans. ASME*, vol. 33, pp. 1005–1053, 1911.

* International Critical Tables, vol. 5, p. 81, McGraw-Hill Book Company, Inc., New York.

TABLE 1-11. VAPOR PRESSURES

Temperature, °F	Vapor pressure, inches of mercury	Temperature, °F	Vapor pressure, inches of mercury	Temperature, °F	Vapor pressure, inches of mercury
Over ice					
−40	0.0039	5	0.0488	20	0.1028
−35	0.0052	6	0.0514	21	0.1078
−30	0.0070	7	0.0542	22	0.1131
−25	0.0094	8	0.0570	23	0.1186
−20	0.0126	9	0.0599	24	0.1243
−15	0.0167	10	0.0629	25	0.1303
−10	0.0220	11	0.0661	26	0.1366
− 5	0.0289	12	0.0695	27	0.1432
0	0.0377	13	0.0730	28	0.1500
1	0.0397	14	0.0767	29	0.1571
2	0.0419	15	0.0806	30	0.1645
3	0.0441	16	0.0847	31	0.1723
4	0.0464	17	0.0889	32	0.1803
		18	0.0933		
		19	0.0979		
Over water					
20	0.1096	35	0.2035	50	0.3626
21	0.1144	36	0.2118	51	0.3764
22	0.1194	37	0.2203	52	0.3906
23	0.1245	38	0.2292	53	0.4052
24	0.1298	39	0.2383	54	0.4203
25	0.1353	40	0.2478	55	0.4359
26	0.1410	41	0.2576	56	0.4520
27	0.1470	42	0.2677	57	0.4686
28	0.1532	43	0.2782	58	0.4858
29	0.1597	44	0.2891	59	0.5035
30	0.1663	45	0.3004	60	0.5218
31	0.1732	46	0.3120	61	0.5407
32	0.1803	47	0.3240	62	0.5601
33	0.1878	48	0.3364	63	0.5802
34	0.1955	49	0.3493	64	0.6009

TABLE 1-11. VAPOR PRESSURES.—(*Continued*)

Temperature, °F	Vapor pressure, inches of mercury	Temperature, °F	Vapor pressure, inches of mercury	Temperature, °F	Vapor pressure, inches of mercury
Over water					
65	0.6222	100	1.933	160	9.65
66	0.6442	101	1.992	162	10.12
67	0.6669	102	2.052	164	10.61
68	0.6903	103	2.114	166	11.12
69	0.7144	104	2.178	168	11.65
70	0.7392	105	2.24	170	12.20
71	0.7648	106	2.31	172	12.77
72	0.7912	107	2.38	174	13.37
73	0.8183	108	2.45	176	13.98
74	0.8462	109	2.52	178	14.63
75	0.8750	110	2.60	180	15.29
76	0.9046	112	2.75	182	15.98
77	0.9352	114	2.91	184	16.70
78	0.9666	116	3.08	186	17.44
79	0.9989	118	3.26	188	18.21
80	1.032	120	3.45	190	19.01
81	1.066	122	3.64	192	19.84
82	1.102	124	3.85	194	20.70
83	1.138	126	4.06	196	21.59
84	1.175	128	4.29	198	22.52
85	1.213	130	4.53	200	23.47
86	1.253	132	4.77	202	24.46
87	1.293	134	5.03	204	25.48
88	1.335	136	5.30	206	26.53
89	1.378	138	5.59	208	27.63
90	1.422	140	5.88	210	28.76
91	1.467	142	6.19	212	29.92
92	1.513	144	6.51	214	31.13
93	1.561	146	6.85	216	32.38
94	1.610	148	7.20	218	33.66
95	1.660	150	7.57	220	34.99
96	1.712	152	7.95	222	36.37
97	1.765	154	8.35	224	37.78
98	1.819	156	8.77	226	39.24
99	1.875	158	9.20	228	40.75

TABLE 1-11. VAPOR PRESSURES.—(*Continued*)

Temperature, °F	Vapor pressure, inches of mercury	Temperature, °F	Vapor pressure, inches of mercury	Temperature, °F	Vapor pressure, inches of mercury
			Over water		
230	42.31	245	55.11	280	100.18
232	43.91	250	60.73	285	108.42
234	45.56	255	66.24	290	117.19
236	47.27	260	72.13	295	126.54
238	49.03			300	136.44
240	50.84	265	78.47	305	146.99
		270	85.23		
		275	92.47		

This process of saturation has been termed *adiabatic*, since no heat is transferred to or from the chamber.   It should be pointed out, however, that heat is gained during the process.   The water being evaporated is at the temperature of saturation of the air and hence has heat content.   As this water is added to the air, the heat of the liquid water is carried over into the air stream.   The total heat, or enthalpy, therefore changes. The enthalpy of the air is given as follows:

$$h = \Sigma + Wh_f \tag{1-13}$$

where h = enthalpy of the air, Btu per pound of dry air

h_f = enthalpy of the liquid water at the saturation temperature

W = actual weight of the water per pound of dry air, depending on the degree of saturation of the air (weight of water at the dew-point temperature of the air)

In the use of these formulas the datum is taken as 0°F for the dry gases and as 32°F for the water.   Accurate values of h_f and h_{fg} can be obtained from steam tables.   If only approximate values of h_f and h_{fg} are required, $h_f = t - 32$ and $h_{fg} = 1{,}091 - 0.56t$.

Wet-bulb Temperature. A wet-bulb thermometer is an ordinary thermometer with its bulb covered with a clean cloth wick that is wet with water.   It has been shown by W. H. Carrier[1] that if the thermometer is whirled vigorously in the air, the temperature reading will drop until the temperature of adiabatic saturation (as described in the foregoing paragraphs) has been reached, at which point the reading will remain constant.   This reading is subject to a slight radiation error; however,

---

[1] CARRIER, *loc. cit.*

for most engineering purposes the error is so slight that it may be neglected. The aspiration-type psychrometer largely avoids this error; the wet bulb is shielded with a chromium-plated shield, and air is drawn over it by a small fan. The temperature thus measured is called the *wet-bulb temperature*. Since the wet-bulb temperature is the temperature of adiabatic saturation, there will be a definite Σ in the air regardless of what its degree of saturation may be. Wet-bulb-temperature lines are therefore plotted with constant Σ heat content, on the psychrometric chart. Values of Σ heat content are not tabulated on the chart, since it is not used in computing heat changes.

Heat Change during a Psychrometric Process. The heat involved in a psychrometric process is the difference in enthalpies at the beginning and the end of the process times the weight of air involved. Enthalpies at saturation may be read directly from the chart as extensions of the wet-bulb lines. For conditions other than saturation, corrections must be made in accordance with the correction curves appearing on the chart.

Specific Volume. The specific volume of a gas is the volume of 1 lb of the gas. The specific volume of dry air is the cubic feet per pound of dry air, regardless of whether this dry air is mixed with water vapor or not. The specific volume of dry air containing no water vapor is not the same as if it is saturated with water vapor. In either case the specific volume may be calculated by the gas formula

$$Pv = wRT \qquad (1\text{-}14)$$

where P = pressure, psf

v = volume, cu ft

w = weight, lb

R = gas constant, 53.34 for dry air

T = absolute temperature, °R

If we consider dry air at 0 per cent relative humidity, Eq. (1-14) becomes

$$v = \frac{53.34T}{P} \qquad (1\text{-}15)$$

where P is the barometric pressure, psf.

If we consider dry air containing water vapor, Eq. (1-14) becomes

$$v = \frac{53.34T}{P - e} \qquad (1\text{-}16)$$

where e is the vapor pressure, psf.

From Eq. (1-15) and (1-16), it is obvious that the specific volume of dry air saturated with water vapor will be greater than the specific volume of dry air containing no water vapor.

The Psychrometric Chart. The psychrometric chart is a graphical presentation of the foregoing principles. On the psychrometric charts included in the pocket in the back of the book (Figs. 1-1, 1-2, and 1-3) the dry-bulb temperatures are plotted as abscissas and the specific humidities as ordinates. Relative-humidity lines sweep from the upper right-hand portion of each chart to the lower left-hand portion. The 100 per cent humidity curve is called the *saturation curve*. Wet-bulb and dew-point temperatures are labeled on the saturation curve. The dew-point lines extend from the saturation curve parallel to the base of each chart. The wet-bulb-temperature lines extend diagonally downward from the saturation curve to the lower right-hand portion of each chart. The specific volume of dry air is given by lines extending across the charts more steeply than the wet-bulb lines. Enthalpy at saturation is read as an extension of the wet-bulb lines. For conditions other than saturation, corrections must be made in accordance with the correction curves appearing on the charts. Since the specific humidity is a function of the dew-point temperature, it is read from the dew-point lines. The absolute humidity in grains of moisture per cubic foot is obtained by dividing the specific humidity by the specific volume. The vapor pressure is a function of the dew point and is read from Table 1-11. Corrections for altitude are given on the upper left portions of the charts.

Calculations Involving a Change of Volume. Air approximates a perfect gas and, as such, follows the gas equation. Since the pressure involved when cooling air nearly always remains constant at the barometric pressure, the volume of the air varies directly as the absolute temperature. The volume of the air is, therefore, less after cooling than before cooling. This characteristic causes complications if psychrometric problems are computed on a volume basis. This difficulty may be avoided by computing values on the basis of pounds of dry air. After suitable calculations have been made on this basis, the values thus obtained may be changed to the volume basis by multiplying by the specific volume.

Use of the Psychrometric Chart at Altitudes. Psychrometric charts are constructed for standard barometric pressure. Corrections must be made if the user is working at an altitude. The common instruments for determining psychrometric properties either at sea level or at altitudes are the wet- and dry-bulb thermometers. In the use of the chart, a correction table for h and W is placed at its upper left corner. These corrections are made at the wet-bulb temperature of the air. The vapor pressure, dew point, relative humidity, and specific volume cannot be read directly from the chart. The vapor pressure is determined by the formula

$$e = \frac{WP}{4,355 + W} \tag{1-17}$$

where P is the barometric pressure in inches of mercury and W is the specific humidity in grains of moisture per pound of dry air. The dew point is dependent only on the vapor pressure and can be read directly from the vapor-pressure table. The relative humidity, by definition, is equal to the quotient $e \div e_t$ where e is the vapor pressure actually in the air and e_t is the vapor pressure if the air were saturated at the dry-bulb temperature. Its value can, therefore, be readily computed. The specific volume of dry air at any degree of saturation can be calculated by Eq. (1-16).

Infiltration. When doors into refrigerated spaces are opened, cold air will flow out of the bottom of the doorway, and warm air will flow in the top to replace it. Maximum air velocities are reached at the bottom and at the top of the doorway, whereas at the center the velocity is zero. The velocity depends upon the height of the door and the temperature difference between inside and outside of the room. It varies, as the square root of the heights of doorways and as the square root of the temperature differences is involved. For a 7-ft open doorway at a 60°FTD, the average velocity for either the bottom or the top half of the door is about 100 fpm. For reach-in doors, with shelves immediately inside, the infiltration is usually less than half of that with an open doorway. The door is usually open about 15 sec per time opened. A great deal of judgment must be used in estimating the infiltration. For walk-in boxes in grocery stores and meat markets, or for general storage rooms in warehouses, the door is usually not open more than 1 min/hr. Cold-storage rooms that are used to store a specific product, such as oranges or apples, are seldom opened except on loading and unloading. In such cases the infiltration may be considered negligible. If there is frequent passage through the doorway, the cold-storage room should be entered through a vestibule or through light swinging doors. If swinging doors are used, they should be used in addition to the insulated door. Either of these devices will reduce the infiltration to about one-half of what it would be otherwise. The heat due to infiltration is calculated as the pounds of air infiltrated times the enthalpy difference of the air inside and outside of the room during the warmest hour of the year that is normal to the locality.

Heat Gain Due to Air Used for Ventilation. If comestibles are maintained in a frozen condition, or at a temperature only slightly above their freezing point, their life processes will be slowed down to such a degree that few odors or gases will be given off. In such cases the air that normally infiltrates through the doorway will supply ample ventilation. Certain produce, notably some varieties of apples and citrus fruits,[1] must be stored at temperatures considerably above their freezing points. In such cases odors, carbon dioxide, and ethylene gas are given off. While carbon dioxide may have beneficial effects, the other two are definitely detrimental. It is therefore advisable to ventilate rooms storing this produce at the rate of about one air change per 6 hr. The heat gain due to air used for ventilation should be calculated as the pounds of air involved times the enthalpy difference of the air inside and outside the room during the warmest hour of the year that is normal to the locality.

SUMMARY

The refrigeration load is usually measured in Btu per hour. It usually consists of a combination of the following factors:

1. Heat given up by the product owing to the lowering of its temperature, called the *product load*.

2. Heat given up by the product during the freezing process, called the *latent heat of fusion*.

3. Heat given up by lights, motors, etc., within the refrigerated space.

4. Heat conducted through the walls, ceiling, and floor owing to a temperature head.

5. Solar-heat gain.

6. Heat gain due to infiltrated air.

7. Heat gain due to air used for ventilation.

8. Heat generated by the product owing to its respiration, called the *heat of evolution*.

Problems

1. Calculate the rate of removal of heat in Btu per hour in cooling a carcass of beef weighing 600 lb from 98 to 40°F in 24 hr.

2. Calculate the heat that must be removed from 1 ton of water at 32°F to change it to ice at 32°F.

3. Calculate the rate of heat removal in Btu per hour to change 1 ton of water at 70°F to ice at 15°F in 36 hr.

4. Calculate the heat that must be removed from 1,000 lb of green peas to lower their temperature from 80 to 0°F.

5. In a cold-storage room the blower requires 1.1 bhp. The motor driving it is 75 per cent efficient. Both blower and motor are located in the room. How much heat per hour is added to the room by the blower and its motor?

6. In Prob. 5, if the blower and its motor were located outside the room, the blower being insulated against heat gain and connected to the room by insulated ducts, how much heat per hour would be added to the room? (The motor is not in the air stream.)

7. From outside to inside a wall is constructed as follows: 8 in. concrete, 4 in. hollow clay tile, ½ in. smooth-finish cement plaster. The outside wind velocity is

[1] See Appendix 1.

10 mph, and the inside air velocity is nearly zero. Find the over-all coefficient of heat transfer.

8. From outside to inside a wall is constructed as follows: 8 in. concrete, 4 in. corkboard, ½ in. smooth-finish cement plaster. The outside wind velocity is 10 mph, and the inside air velocity is nearly zero. Find the over-all coefficient of heat transfer.

9. From outside to inside a wall is constructed as follows: 1 in. pine, 6 in. granulated cork, 1 in. pine. The outside wind velocity is 10 mph, and the inside air velocity is nearly zero. Find the over-all coefficient of heat transfer.

10. A cold-storage room has 900 sq ft of wall, facing north, exposed to the outside. Its construction is as described in Prob. 8. The maximum outside temperature for the warmest day is 100°F, and the minimum outside temperature for the warmest day is 70°F. The inside temperature is 31°F. Estimate the heat gain in Btu per hour through the wall.

11. If the wall in Prob. 10 were facing west and if it were unpainted, what would be the heat gain?

12. The roof of a cold-storage warehouse is constructed from outside to inside as follows: graveled composition roof, 6 in. concrete, and 6 in. corkboard with smooth mastic finish. The area is 1,500 sq ft. The maximum outside temperature for the warmest day is 90°F, and the minimum temperature for the same day is 75°F. The inside temperature is 31°F. The wind velocity is 10 mph. Find the heat gain through the roof in Btu per hour.

Solve Probs. 13 through 16 without use of the psychrometric chart.

13. Calculate the specific volume of dry air at 70°F, 50 per cent relative humidity, and 0 ft altitude.

14. Calculate the specific humidity of air at 70°F and 50 per cent relative humidity for 0 ft altitude.

15. Calculate the relative humidity of air at 100°F (dry bulb) and 60°F dew point for 0 ft altitude.

16. Calculate the relative humidity of air at 100°F (dry bulb) and 60°F dew point if the altitude is 4,800 ft.

17. Given: dry-bulb temperature, 100°F; wet-bulb temperature, 70°F; altitude, 0 ft. Find: relative humidity, dew point, absolute humidity, specific humidity, sigma heat content, enthalpy, specific volume, and vapor pressure.

18. Given: dry-bulb temperature, 70°F; wet-bulb temperature, 60°F; altitude, 4,800 ft. Find: dew-point temperature, absolute humidity, relative humidity, specific volume, specific humidity, vapor pressure, sigma heat content, and enthalpy.

19. Calculate the heat due to infiltration for a cold-storage room at 0 ft altitude, having a 7- by 4-ft door normally open 1 min/hr, with the inside held at 31°F (dry bulb) and 85 per cent relative humidity, if the outside temperatures are 100°F (dry bulb) and 70°F (wet bulb).

20. Calculate the heat gain due to infiltration for conditions as described in Prob. 19 if the elevation of the room were 2,700 ft.

21. A room having a volume of 50,000 cu ft is ventilated at the rate of one air change per 6 hr. The inside conditions are 33°F (dry bulb), 90 per cent relative humidity. The outside conditions are 95°F (dry bulb), 75°F (wet bulb). The altitude is 1,800 ft. Find the heat that is added to the room per hour by air used for ventilation. [Use the low-temperature chart for values at 32°F (wet bulb).]

22. An apple storage room having dimensions of 50 by 100 by 10 ft has half its volume filled with boxed apples. They are stored at 32°F. Find the heat of evolution in Btu per hour.

CHAPTER 2

PROPERTIES OF REFRIGERANTS

A refrigerant is a fluid in a refrigerating system that by its evaporating takes in heat at the cooling coils and gives up heat by condensing in the condenser. The common refrigerants with their chemical formulas and molecular weights are as follows:

TABLE 2-1

Refrigerant common name	Chemical formula	Molecular weight	Chemical name
Ammonia.............	NH_3	17.03	Ammonia
Freon 11..............	CCl_3F	137.37	Trichloromonofluoromethane
Freon 12..............	CCl_2F_2	120.91	Dichlorodifluoromethane
Freon 22..............	$CHClF_2$	86.47	Monochlorodifluoromethane
Freon 113.............	$CCl_2F—CClF_2$	187.39	Trichlorotrifluoromethane
Methyl chloride........	CH_3Cl	50.48	Methyl chloride
Sulfur dioxide..........	SO_2	64.06	Sulfur dioxide

The refrigerant properties of importance in engineering are

1. Toxicity
2. Inflammability
3. Chemical activity
4. Effect on refrigerated produce
5. Odor
6. Oil-solvent properties
7. Cost
8. Pressure-volume-temperature characteristics
9. Power required per unit of refrigeration
10. Specific heat
11. Viscosity
12. Thermal conductivity
13. Enthalpy and entropy

These properties will be discussed separately.

Toxicity. It is obviously desirable that the refrigerant have little effect on people. The importance of this item depends on the number of people present in the vicinity and the quantity of refrigerant in the system. Thus, ammonia is satisfactory for ice making but is entirely unsatisfactory for air conditioning in a theater. Sulfur dioxide is satisfactory in household refrigerators but is entirely unsatisfactory for systems of appreciable size. Table 2-2 gives the toxic properties of several refrigerants.

TABLE 2-2. TOXIC PROPERTIES OF REFRIGERANTS*

Refrigerant	Kills or seriously injures guinea pigs, per cent by volume	Poisonous decomposition products	Underwriters' Laboratory class
Ammonia	0.5–0.6	No	2
Freon 11	10	Yes	5
Freon 12	30	Yes	6
Freon 22	....	Yes	5a
Freon 113	....	Yes	5
Methyl chloride	2.0–2.5	Yes	4
Sulfur dioxide	0.7	No	1

* Compiled from Underwriters' Laboratory Reports MH 2375 and MH 3134.

Inflammability. Although refrigerants are entirely sealed from the atmosphere, leaks are bound to develop. If the refrigerant is inflammable and the system is located where ignition of the refrigerant may occur, a great hazard is involved. Inflammables should not be used except on small systems unless an operating engineer is present at all times. Table 2-3 gives the explosive properties of many refrigerants.

TABLE 2-3. EXPLOSIVE PROPERTIES OF REFRIGERANTS*

Refrigerant	Explosive-range concentration in atmospheric air, per cent by volume	Maximum explosion pressure, psi gauge	Time of development of pressure, sec
Ammonia	16–25	50	0.175
Freon 11	Noninflammable		
Freon 12	Noninflammable		
Freon 22	Noninflammable		
Freon 113	Noninflammable		
Methyl chloride	8.1–17.2	69	0.110
Sulfur dioxide	Noninflammable		

* Compiled from Underwriters' Laboratory Reports MH 2375 and MH 3134.

Chemical Activity. Refrigerants in their pure state must be chemically inert to the materials from which the system is made. In the presence of water, it is also desirable that they be chemically inert. Acid-forming refrigerants are more corrosive to metals than base-forming refrigerants. If a refrigerant is insoluble in water, it can be neither acid- or base-forming. Refrigerants that are relatively insoluble in water and neither acid- nor base-forming will have the least corrosive effect. It must not be inferred, however, that corrosion will not occur in such systems if water and air are present. With water, air, refrigerant, and oil present, it is hard to predict from theoretical consideration what the chemical action on metals may be. The problem of corrosion will be discussed separately for several refrigerants. The solubilities of several refrigerants, together with their acid- or base-forming properties, are listed in Table 2-4.

The corrosion problem with anhydrous or aqueous ammonia is slight. Ammonia has very little effect on steel but attacks copper readily. It also has a slight effect on galvanized and tinned surfaces. In the pres-

TABLE 2-4. SOLUBILITIES OF REFRIGERANTS IN WATER

Refrigerant	Temperature, °F	Solubility, g/g	Acid- or base-forming
Ammonia	68	0.525*	Base
Freon 11	32	0.006†	Neutral
Freon 12	32	0.006†	Neutral
Freon 22	32	0.05‡	Neutral
Freon 113	32	0.0039†	Neutral
Methyl chloride	64	0.0072*	Neutral
Sulfur dioxide	104	0.053*	Acid

* Computed from data of the International Critical Tables.
† THOMPSON, R. J., Properties and Characteristics of Refrigerants, *Refrig. Eng.*, November, 1942.
‡ THOMPSON, R. J., and W. W. RHODES, Freon 22, Kinetic Chemicals, Inc., Wilmington, January, 1944.

ence of moisture, it forms the weak base NH_4OH. The tendency of oils to go to the acid side is inhibited by this alkaline action. If both water and air are present in the system, a slight amount of scale will be formed.

The Freon refrigerants are noncorrosive to all metals used in refrigerating systems, such as brass, copper, iron, steel, aluminum, tin, lead, and zinc. However, if air and water are present in the system, an acid condition may be set up by the action of the air and water on the oil. Freon refrigerants will not inhibit this action. Since magnesium and aluminum are readily attacked by acids, they should not be used in Freon systems. The presence of moisture results in corrosion of the shaft seal, copper plating of the cylinder walls and bearings, and embrittlement of brass bellows or diaphragms. Since Freon refrigerants have low solubilities in water, freezing at the expansion valve readily occurs. Because of these factors, care should be taken to eliminate all air and moisture present in Freon systems. Freon has a high solvent action on all natural rubber binders used in gasket material. Several synthetic rubbers have been developed that are satisfactory.

The corrosion problem with methyl chloride is similar in all respects to that with the Freons.

Anhydrous sulfur dioxide is noncorrosive to all common engineering metals. In water solution it forms the weak acid H_2SO_3, which is corrosive to all common engineering metals, especially when air is also present. Common symptoms of the presence of water in the system are copper plating of cylinder walls and bearings, corrosion of the valves and shaft seal, and embrittlement of bellows and diaphragms.

Effect on Refrigerated Produce. Ammonia is readily dissolved by the water in most produce and is alkaline in reaction. Most fruits, vegetables, and meat are slightly acid. Ammonia, therefore, reacts readily with these products. In small concentrations the effect of ammonia is mild, but excessive exposure will result in rot or scald. Cooked or uncooked, foods contaminated with ammonia are so unpalatable they cannot be eaten.

Sulfur dioxide is readily dissolved by the moisture of most produce but is acid in reaction. Since most foods are also slightly acid, no chemical reaction takes place with them. It is not dangerous in foods; in fact, it has been approved as a food preservative. It kills or withers flowers. It is not injurious to textiles or furs but may tend to bleach some of the dyes in them.

Methyl chloride vapors do not harm furs, flowers, or other household articles. Methyl chloride may flavor foods to a very slight extent if they are sufficiently exposed to the vapors; however, there is no danger in eating foods that have been exposed to methyl chloride vapors.

Freons 11, 12, 22, and 113 are soluble in water only to a very limited extent. The vapors have, therefore, no effect on dairy products, meats, and vegetables. They have, further, no effect upon flowers, plant life, or the color and structure of textiles and furs.

Odor. Odor may be an advantage or a disadvantage to a refrigerant. Leaks can be easily detected if the refrigerant has a distinct odor. On the other hand, if a leak occurs in a refrigerated space, it may flavor the product and render it unsalable. Refrigerants having irritating odors may cause panic where numerous people are involved and should not be used under this condition. The odors of the various refrigerants will be discussed separately.

Sulfur dioxide has an irritating and obnoxious odor even at very small concentrations.

Ammonia has a rather pleasant, stimulating odor in very small concentrations, but becomes very unpleasant and irritating as the concentration increases.

Methly chloride has a very slight sweet odor. It is nonirritating and involves no panic hazard.

The Freons 11, 12, 22, and 113 are nearly odorless and cannot be smelled by most people.

Oil-solvent Properties. A refrigerant that is highly insoluble in oil offers fewer problems than one that is highly soluble in oil; however, the compressor is often better lubricated when oil-solvent refrigerants are used. The oil problems will be discussed in a later chapter. In order to design a refrigerating system, the degree of solubility must be known and taken into consideration. Ammonia and carbon dioxide are nearly insoluble in mineral lubricating oils. Freon 22 and sulfur dioxide have a limited solubility in mineral lubricating oil. The Freons 11, 12, and 113 and methyl chloride are highly soluble in mineral oil.

Pressure-volume-temperature Characteristics. The complete pressure-volume-temperature characteristics of the various refrigerants are tabulated in the tables that follow on the thermodynamic properties of refrigerants. Values at atmospheric pressure and at standard conditions (86°F condensing temperature, 5°F evaporating temperature) are taken from these tables and tabulated in Table 2-5 for comparison purposes.

TABLE 2-5. PRESSURE-VOLUME-TEMPERATURE COMPARISON OF REFRIGERANTS

Refrigerant	Critical temp., °F	Critical pressure, psi	Boiling point,* °F	Freezing point,* °F	Vapor displacement,† cu ft/(min) (ton)	Saturation pressures, psi		Superheated temp.,‡ °F
						Cond. temp., 86°F	Evap. temp., 5°F	
Ammonia........	271	1,651	−28	−108	3.44	169	24.3	210
Freon 11.......	388	635	75	−168	36.3	18.3	2.9	116
Freon 12.......	233	582	−22	−252	5.82	108	26.5	100
Freon 22.......	205	716	−41	−256	.....	174.5	43.0	131
Freon 113......	417	495	118	−31	100.7	7.9	0.98	
Methyl chloride	290	969	−11	−144	6.09	95.5	20.9	182
Sulfur dioxide...	315	1,142	14	−99	9.08	66.5	11.8	190

* At normal atmospheric pressure.
† At standard conditions (86°F condensing temperature and 5°F evaporating temperature).
‡ The superheated temperature is the temperature after compression, based on standard conditions with the vapor entering the compressor in the saturated condition.

The critical temperature and pressure of a refrigerant is the temperature and pressure at which the liquid and vapor have identical properties. A suitable refrigerant will have a critical temperature and pressure well above the condensing temperature and pressure of the refrigerating system.

The freezing point should be well below the lowest evaporating temperature at which the system operates.

The required displacement is a large factor in determining the type of compressor that should be used. For given space requirements, reciprocating compressors are suitable for pumping relatively small volumes through relatively large pressure differences. Rotary compressors are suitable for pumping moderate volumes through moderate pressure differences. Centrifugal compressors are suitable for pumping large volumes through low pressure differences. Thus, reference to Table 2-5 shows that reciprocating compressors would be suitable for ammonia, Freon 12, Freon 22, and methyl chloride; rotary compressors would be suitable for Freon 22 and sulfur dioxide; centrifugal compressors would be suitable for Freon 11 and Freon 113.

The saturation pressures at the evaporating and condensing temperatures give information required in the selection of a suitable refrigerant for a given compressor. If the evaporating pressure of a refrigerant is below normal atmospheric pressure, special caution should be used to keep air or moisture from entering the system. Either special shaft-seal devices should be used, or the motor should be sealed in the compressor case. If common shaft-seal devices are used, it is desirable that the evaporating temperature be only slightly above atmospheric pressure. In this case, the condensing pressure will also be moderate, and relatively light construction of the compressor may be used.

It is desirable that the superheated temperature of the refrigerant upon compression be low, in order that special methods need not be used to cool the head of the compressor. If the temperature of the gas after compression is above 200°F, the head of the compressor should be water-cooled.

Power Required per Unit of Refrigeration. The theoretical horsepower per ton of refrigeration is nearly the same for all common refrigerants under a given set of temperature and operating conditions.[1] The greatest factors in reducing horsepower are good engineering and proper maintenance.

Cost. The cost of the entire system, when using various refrigerants, is always an item of major importance. Analysis of this item can be made only for separate installations. Development of refrigerants that require moderate-cost equipment for small- and medium-sized installations has been one of the greatest factors in furthering the refrigeration field since 1925.

Specific Heats. The specific heats of refrigerants in their liquid and vapor phases are of importance in many heat-transfer and thermodynamic computations. Table 2-6 gives the specific heat of many liquid

[1] McGovern, E. W., "Methyl Chloride—A Practical Refrigerant Measured by the Theoretical Ideal," *Refrig. Eng.*, p. 33, July, 1937.

TABLE 2-6. SPECIFIC HEATS OF LIQUID REFRIGERANTS

Refrigerant	Temperature, °F	c	Reference*
Ammonia.............................	0	1.080	1
	10	1.085	1
	20	1.091	1
	30	1.097	1
	40	1.104	1
	50	1.112	1
	60	1.120	1
	70	1.129	1
	80	1.138	1
	90	1.147	1
	100	1.156	1
Freon 11..........................	11	0.208	2
	148	0.220	2
Freon 12................................	−40	0.21	3
	60	0.25	3
Freon 22...............................	20	0.275	4
	130	0.329	4
Freon 113.............................	11	0.212	5
	73	0.220	5
	146	0.228	5
Methyl chloride.......................	0	0.370	1
	20	0.373	1
	40	0.379	1
	60	0.383	1
	80	0.388	1
	100	0.392	1
	150	0.405	1
Sulfur dioxide.........................	0	0.305	1
	10	0.300	1
	20	0.327	1
	30	0.330	1
	40	0.342	1
	50	0.350	1
	60	0.361	1
	70	0.370	1
	80	0.387	1

* References: (1) International Critical Tables, vol. 5, pp. 79–80; (2) BENNING, A. F., and R. C. McHARNESS, Thermodynamic Properties of Freon 11, Kinetic Chemicals, Inc., Wilmington, 1938; (3) BUFFINGTON, R. M., and W. K. GILKEY, Thermodynamic Properties of Freon 12, *ASRE Circ.* 12, 1931; (4) GRAHAM, D. P., and R. C. McHARNESS, Thermodynamic Properties of Freon 22, Kinetic Chemicals, Inc., Wilmington, 1945; (5) BENNING, A. F., and R. C. McHARNESS, Thermodynamic Properties of Freon 113, Kinetic Chemicals, Inc., Wilmington, 1938.

refrigerants. The specific heat of a liquid is relatively independent of temperature and pressure. Table 2-7 gives the specific heats of vapors and gases at 1 atm pressure and at various temperatures.

Specific heats of liquid refrigerants can be readily computed over a wide range of temperatures from the enthalpy of the liquid in tables of thermodynamic properties of refrigerants.

TABLE 2-7.   SPECIFIC HEATS OF REFRIGERANT GASES AND VAPORS AT 1 ATM PRESSURE

Refrigerant	Temperature, °F	c_p	c_v	c_p/c_v	Reference*
Ammonia..........	73–212	0.5102	0.3975	1.3172	1
Freon 11..........	32	0.130	0.113	......	4
	110	0.1374	0.1213	1.133	2
	160	0.1422	0.1265	1.124	2
Freon 12..........	−40	0.1314	0.1131	1.161	3
	0	0.1366	0.1183	1.155	3
	40	0.1417	0.1263	1.146	3
	80	0.1468	0.1289	1.139	3
	120	0.1520	0.1342	1.132	3
	160	0.1571	0.1395	1.126	3
Freon 22..........	32	0.145	0.121	......	4
	117	†	†	1.178	4
	212	†	†	1.166	4
Freon 113..........	32	0.149	0.137	......	4
	171	†	†	1.081	4
	212	†	†	1.077	4
Methyl chloride....	66–86	0.24	0.20	1.1991	5
Sulfur dioxide......	59	0.1516	0.1175	1.29	6

* References: (1) Smithsonian Physical Tables, 8th rev. ed., p. 293, The Smithsonian Institution, Washington, D. C., 1934; (2) BENNING, A. F., and R. C. McHARNESS, Thermodynamic Properties of Freon 11, Kinetic Chemicals, Inc., Wilmington, 1938; (3) Direct communication with Kinetic Chemicals, Inc., 1947; (4) BENNING, A. F., R. C. McHARNESS, W. H. MARKWOOD, JR., and W. J. SMITH, Thermodynamic Properties of Fluorochloromethanes and -ethanes, *Ind. Eng. Chem.*, vol. 32, pp., 976–980, 1940; (5) LANGE, "Handbook of Chemistry," p. 1383, Handbook Publishers, Inc., Sandusky, Ohio, 1944; (6) *ibid.*, p. 1491.

† The heat capacities in calories per mole per degree centigrade can be computed by the following formulas in which t is measured in degrees centigrade (reference 4). The specific heat equals the heat capacity divided by the molecular weight.

$$\text{Freon 11: } c_p \text{ (1 atm)} = 17.83 + .0240t$$
$$\text{Freon 22: } c_p \text{ (1 atm)} = 12.52 + .0220t$$
$$\text{Freon 113: } c_p \text{ (1 atm)} = 27.92 + .0374t$$

TABLE 2-8. VISCOSITY OF AMMONIA*

Pressure, psi	Temperature, °F						
	−4	14	32	50	68	113	176
	Viscosity, centipoises × 10²†						
14.70	0.88	0.92	0.95	0.99	1.02	1.12	1.24
29.40	25.78	0.98	0.98	1.01	1.04	1.12	1.24
58.80	26.47	25.52	1.09	1.06	1.09	1.13	1.25
88.20	27.02	26.16	24.98	1.20	1.16	1.15	1.26
117.6	27.52	26.67	25.58	24.10	1.27	1.19	1.29
140.7	27.89	27.10	26.07	24.64	22.81	1.23	1.31
170.1	28.20	27.44	26.45	25.08	23.33	1.30	1.36
205.8	28.45	27.75	26.77	25.43	23.72	1.39	1.41
235.2	28.66	27.98	27.02	25.70	24.03	1.49	1.49
264.6	28.85	28.18	27.24	25.93	24.28	....	1.60
281.4	29.02	28.36	27.42	26.13	24.49	....	1.73

* VON STAKELBECK, H., Über die Zähigkeit verschiedener Kältemittel in flüssigen und dampfförmigen Zustand in Abhängigkeit von Druck und Temperatur, *Z. ges. Kälte-Ind.*, March, 1933, p. 37.
† Values above the line are for vapor; those below are for liquid.

TABLE 2-9. VISCOSITIES OF FREON REFRIGERANTS*

Temperature, °F	Freon 11		Freon 12		Freon 22		Freon 113	
	Vapor	Liquid	Vapor	Liquid	Vapor	Liquid	Vapor	Liquid
	Viscosity, centipoises × 10²†							
−40	0.88	98.0	1.06	42.3	1.05	35.1		
−20	0.92	80.1	1.09	37.1	1.09	31.6	0.90	156.6
0	0.96	67.7	1.13	33.5	1.13	29.1	0.93	126.3
20	0.99	58.6	1.16	30.8	1.18	27.1	0.95	104.3
40	1.03	51.7	1.19	28.6	1.22	25.6	0.98	87.6
60	1.06	46.1	1.23	26.9	1.26	24.3	1.01	74.7
80	1.10	41.7	1.26	25.5	1.30	23.2	1.03	64.6
100	1.13	38.0	1.29	24.2	1.33	22.3	1.06	56.4
120	1.16	34.9	1.32	23.2	1.37	21.4	1.08	49.7
140	1.20	32.3	1.35	22.2	1.41	20.7	1.11	44.2
160	1.23	30.0	1.38	21.4	1.45	20.1	1.13	39.5
180	1.26	28.1	1.40	20.7	1.48	19.5	1.16	35.6
200	1.29	26.3	1.43	20.0	1.52	....	1.18	32.2

* BENNING, A. F., and W. H. MARKWOOD, JR., The Viscosities of Freon Refrigerants, *Refrig. Eng.*, April, 1939.
† The measured viscosities from which the above values were computed were measured at 1 atm in the case of all gases except Freon 113, the pressure in this case being 0.1 atm.

TABLE 2-10. VISCOSITY OF METHYL CHLORIDE*

Pressure, psi	Temperature, °F					
	−4	14	32	50	68	86
	Viscosity, centipoises × 10²					
7.35	0.89	0.96	0.99	1.04	1.09	1.13
14.70	0.95	0.99	1.02	1.05	1.10	1.13
22.05	31.77	1.05	1.05	1.06	1.10	1.14
29.40	32.15	30.91	1.09	1.08	1.11	1.14
36.75	32.48	31.24	1.14	1.11	1.13	1.15
44.10	32.74	31.55	30.15	1.15	1.15	1.16
51.45	32.97	31.80	30.42	1.21	1.18	1.18
58.80	33.18	32.03	30.65	28.90	1.22	1.21
66.15	33.36	32.23	30.87	29.15	1.27	1.24
73.50	33.53	32.40	31.05	29.36	27.53	1.29
80.85	33.66	32.54	31.18	29.55	27.72	1.36
88.20	33.77	32.67	31.32	29.70	27.87	1.43
95.55	33.85	32.78	31.42	29.82	27.98	1.54
102.9	33.90	32.84	31.50	29.90	28.06	25.90

* Values above the line are for vapor; those below are for liquid.

TABLE 2-11. VISCOSITY OF SULFUR DIOXIDE*

Pressure, psi	Temperature, °F						
	−4	14	0	50	68	86	104
	Viscosity, centipoises × 10²						
7.35	1.07	1.11	1.15	1.21	1.26	1.32	1.39
14.70	50.00	1.14	1.19	1.24	1.28	1.33	1.40
22.05	50.60	45.20	1.24	1.28	1.31	1.34	1.41
29.40	51.20	45.85	40.00	1.33	1.36	1.36	1.43
36.75	51.63	46.33	40.57	33.95	1.41	1.38	1.45
44.10	52.00	46.80	41.05	34.48	1.48	1.42	1.47
51.45	52.30	47.20	41.45	34.95	27.94	1.47	1.50
58.80	52.55	47.55	41.83	35.35	28.40	1.55	1.54
66.15	52.82	47.86	42.13	35.72	28.85	1.66	1.59
73.50	53.02	48.15	42.43	36.00	29.24	....	1.65
80.85	53.20	48.41	42.70	36.28	29.55	....	1.72
88.20	53.35	48.65	42.92	36.50	29.88	....	1.80
95.55	53.48	48.85	43.13	36.72	30.12		
102.9	53.62	49.05	43.32	36.90	30.37		
110.2	53.74	49.25	43.50	36.06	30.60		
117.6	53.85	49.44	43.65	37.25	30.80		

* Values above the line are for vapor; those below are for liquid.

Viscosity. Absolute viscosity is the resisting force offered by a layer of fluid of unit area, moving at unit velocity, to another layer of fluid at unit distance from it. In cgs units the unit of absolute viscosity is known as the *poise* and is equal to the force in dynes per square centimeter at a velocity of 1 cm/sec at a distance of 1 cm. For practical purposes the unit is quite large so one-hundredth of it, the *centipoise*, is commonly used. It happens that the viscosity of water at 68.4°C is 1 centipoise.

TABLE 2-12.   THERMAL CONDUCTIVITIES OF LIQUID REFRIGERANTS*

Refrigerant	Temperature, °F	k	Reference†
Ammonia.............................	5–86	0.29	1
Freon 11.............................	32	0.0680	2
	104	0.0586	2
Freon 12.............................	32	0.0559	2
	104	0.0469	2
Freon 21.............................	32	0.0770	2
	104	0.0673	2
Freon 22.............................	32	0.0704	2
	104	0.0559	2
Freon 113............................	32	0.0576	2
	104	0.0503	2
Methyl chloride......................	5	0.111	1
	86	0.089	1
Sulfur dioxide.......................	5	0.128	1
	86	0.111	1

* The above values are for refrigerants at their saturation pressures.
† References: (1) McADAMS, W. H., "Heat Transmission," 2d ed., p. 389, McGraw-Hill Book Company, Inc., New York, 1942; (2) MARKWOOD, W. H., JR., and A. F. BENNING, Thermal Conductances and Heat Transmission Coefficients of Freon Refrigerants, Kinetic Chemicals, Inc., Wilmington, 1942.

The viscosity of a refrigerant is of importance in determining its heat-transfer characteristics and its resistance to flow through pipes. A refrigerant having a low viscosity tends to have good heat-transfer characteristics and will flow through pipes with a minimum friction. Values of the viscosities of refrigerants in the liquid and gaseous phases are given in the foregoing tables. The viscosity of a gas is nearly independent of pressure except as the gas approaches its boiling point.

Saturated vapors may have a viscosity considerably greater than that of the superheated gas.

Thermal Conductivity. The thermal conductivity is the heat that flows through unit thickness of a material per unit area per unit time per unit temperature difference. Throughout this text, except for building materials, the thermal conductivity is measured in the consistent unit

TABLE 2-13. THERMAL CONDUCTIVITIES OF GASES AND VAPORS

Refrigerant	Temperature, °F	k	Reference*
Ammonia..........................	−76	0.0095	1
	32	0.0128	1
	122	0.0157	1
	212	0.0185	1
Freon 11.............................	86	0.00484	2
	194	0.00557	2
Freon 12.............................	86	0.00557	2
	194	0.00702	2
Freon 22.............................	86	0.00678	2
	194	0.00799	2
Freon 113.............................	86	0.00450	2
	194	0.00586	2
Methyl chloride......................	32	0.0053	1
	115	0.0072	1
	212	0.0094	1
	363	0.0130	1
Sulfur dioxide.......................	32	0.0050	1
	212	0.0069	1

* References: (1) McADAMS, W. H., "Heat Transmission," 2d ed., p. 391, McGraw-Hill Book Company, Inc., New York, 1942; (2) MARKWOOD, W. H., JR., and A. F. BENNING, Thermal Conductances and Heat Transmission Coefficients of Freon Refrigerants, Kinetic Chemicals, Inc., Wilmington, 1942.

Btu/(sq ft)(hr)(°FTD per ft). For building materials, the unit is Btu/(sq ft)(hr)(°FTD per in.).

The thermal conductivity of refrigerant liquids and gases is important in calculating the film coefficients of heat transfer when the refrigerant is evaporating, condensing, or flowing through a pipe. Thermal conductivities of refrigerants are given in Tables 2-12 and 2-13. Thermal conductivities are relatively independent of pressure for moderate pressures.

Enthalpy and Entropy. The thermodynamic properties of a refrigerant are its temperature, pressure, volume, enthalpy, and entropy characteristics. Of these, temperature, pressure, and volume have already been discussed. The enthalpy and entropy are of importance in determining the amount of refrigerant that must be pumped and the power required to do it. Enthalpy, designated h, is the energy content of 1 lb of a fluid above some datum. In refrigeration, it is the energy content above saturated liquid at $-40°F$. The enthalpy of vaporization is the energy required to evaporate 1 lb of refrigerant at a constant designated temperature.

Change of entropy is defined as transferred heat divided by absolute temperature. In the tables on the thermodynamic properties, entropy, designated s, is the transferred heat required to bring the refrigerant to its designated state from saturated liquid at $-40°F$, divided by the absolute temperature in degrees Rankine.

TABLE 2-14. SATURATED AMMONIA: TEMPERATURE TABLE*

Temp. °F.	Absolute Pressure. lbs./in.²	Volume vapor. ft³/lb.	Density vapor. lbs./ft.³	Heat content. Liquid. Btu./lb.	Heat content. Vapor. Btu./lb.	Latent heat. Btu./lb.	Entropy. Liquid. Btu./lb.°F.	Entropy. Vapor. Btu./lb.°F.	Temp. °F.
−60	5.55	44.73	0.02235	−21.2	589.6	610.8	−0.0517	1.4769	−60
−59	5.74	43.37	.02306	−20.1	590.0	610.1	−.0490	.4741	−59
−58	5.93	42.05	.02378	−19.1	590.4	609.5	−.0464	.4713	−58
−57	6.13	40.79	.02452	−18.0	590.8	608.8	−.0438	.4686	−57
−56	6.33	39.56	.02528	−17.0	591.2	608.2	−.0412	.4658	−56
−55	6.54	38.38	0.02605	−15.9	591.6	607.5	−0.0386	1.4631	−55
−54	6.75	37.24	.02685	−14.8	592.1	606.9	.0360	.4604	−54
−53	6.97	36.15	.02766	−13.8	592.4	606.2	−.0334	.4577	−53
−52	7.20	35.09	.02850	−12.7	592.9	605.6	−.0307	.4551	−52
−51	7.43	34.06	.02936	−11.7	593.2	604.9	−.0281	.4524	−51
−50	7.67	33.08	0.03023	−10.6	593.7	604.3	−0.0256	1.4497	−50
−49	7.91	32.12	.03113	−9.6	594.0	603.6	−.0230	.4471	−49
−48	8.16	31.20	.03205	−8.5	594.4	602.9	−.0204	.4445	−48
−47	8.42	30.31	.03299	−7.4	594.9	.602.3	−.0179	.4419	−47
−46	8.68	29.45	.03395	−6.4	595.2	601.6	−.0153	.4393	−46
−45	8.95	28.62	0.03494	−5.3	595.6	600.9	−0.0127	1.4368	−45
−44	9.23	27.82	.03595	−4.3	596.0	600.3	−.0102	.4342	−44
−43	9.51	27.04	.03698	−3.2	596.4	599.6	−.0076	.4317	−43
−42	9.81	26.29	.03804	−2.1	596.8	598.9	−.0051	.4292	−42
−41	10.10	25.56	.03912	−1.1	597.2	598.3	−.0025	.4267	−41
−40	10.41	24.86	0.04022	0.0	597.6	597.6	0.0000	1.4242	−40
−39	10.72	24.18	.04135	1.1	598.0	596.9	.0025	.4217	−39
−38	11.04	23.53	.04251	2.1	598.3	596.2	.0051	.4193	−38
−37	11.37	22.89	.04369	3.2	598.7	595.5	.0076	.4169	−37
−36	11.71	22.27	.04489	4.3	599.1	594.8	.0101	.4144	−36
−35	12.05	21.68	0.04613	5.3	599.5	594.2	0.0126	1.4120	−35
−34	12.41	21.10	.04739	6.4	599.9	593.5	.0151	.4096	−34
−33	12.77	20.54	.04868	7.4	600.2	592.8	.0176	.4072	−33
−32	13.14	20.00	.04999	8.5	600.6	592.1	.0201	.4048	−32
−31	13.52	19.48	.05134	9.6	601.0	591.4	.0226	.4025	−31
−30	13.90	18.97	0.05271	10.7	601.4	590.7	0.0250	1.4001	−30
−29	14.30	18.48	.05411	11.7	601.7	590.0	.0275	.3978	−29
−28	14.71	18.00	.05555	12.8	602.1	589.3	.0300	.3955	−28
−27	15.12	17.54	.05701	13.9	602.5	588.6	.0325	.3932	−27
−26	15.55	17.09	.05850	14.9	602.8	587.9	.0350	.3909	−26
−25	15.98	16.66	0.06003	16.0	603.2	587.2	0.0374	1.3886	−25
−24	16.42	16.24	.06158	17.1	603.6	586.5	.0399	.3863	−24
−23	16.88	15.83	.06317	18.1	603.9	585.8	.0423	.3840	−23
−22	17.34	15.43	.06479	19.2	604.3	585.1	.0448	.3818	−22
−21	17.81	15.05	.06644	20.3	604.6	584.3	.0472	.3796	−21
−20	18.30	14.68	0.06813	21.4	605.0	583.6	0.0497	1.3774	−20
−19	18.79	14.32	.06985	22.4	605.3	582.9	.0521	.3752	−19
−18	19.30	13.97	.07161	23.5	605.7	582.2	.0545	.3729	−18
−17	19.81	13.62	.07340	24.6	606.1	581.5	.0570	.3708	−17
−16	20.34	13.29	.07522	25.6	606.4	580.8	.0594	.3686	−16
−15	20.88	12.97	0.07709	26.7	606.7	580.0	0.0618	1.3664	−15
−14	21.43	12.66	.07898	27.8	607.1	579.3	.0642	.3643	−14
−13	21.99	12.36	.08092	28.9	607.5	578.6	.0666	.3621	−13
−12	22.56	12.06	.08289	30.0	607.8	577.8	.0690	.3600	−12
−11	23.15	11.78	.08490	31.0	608.1	577.1	.0714	.3579	−11
−10	23.74	11.50	0.08695	32.1	608.5	576.4	0.0738	1.3558	−10

* Department of Commerce, Bureau of Standards Circular 142. See Fig. 2-1.

TABLE 2-14. SATURATED AMMONIA: TEMPERATURE TABLE (*Continued*)

Temp. °F.	Absolute Pressure. lbs./in.²	Volume vapor. ft³/lb.	Density vapor. lbs./ft.³	Heat content. Liquid. Btu./lb.	Vapor. Btu./lb.	Latent heat. Btu./lb.	Entropy. Liquid. Btu./lb.°F.	Vapor. Btu./lb.°F.	Temp. °F.
−10	23.74	11.50	0.08695	32.1	608.5	576.4	0.0738	1.3558	−10
−9	24 35	11.23	.08904	33.2	608.8	575.6	.0762	.3537	−9
−8	24.97	10.97	.09117	34.3	609.2	574.9	.0786	.3516	−8
−7	25.61	10.71	.09334	35.4	609.5	574.1	.0809	.3495	−7
−6	26.26	10.47	.09555	36.4	609.8	573.4	.0833	.3474	−6
−5	26.92	10.23	0.09780	37.5	610.1	572.6	0.0857	1.3454	−5
−4	27.59	9.991	.1001	38.6	610.5	571.9	.0880	.3433	−4
−3	28.28	9.763	.1024	39.7	610.8	571.1	.0904	.3413	−3
−2	28.98	9.541	.1048	40.7	611.1	570.4	.0928	.3393	−2
−1	29.69	9.326	.1072	41.8	611.4	569.6	.0951	.3372	−1
0	30.42	9.116	0.1097	42.9	611.8	568.9	0.0975	1.3352	0
1	31.16	8.912	.1122	44.0	612.1	568.1	.0998	.3332	1
2	31.92	8.714	.1148	45.1	612.4	567.3	.1022	.3312	2
3	32.69	8.521	.1174	46.2	612.7	566.5	.1045	.3292	3
4	33.47	8.333	.1200	47.2	613.0	565.8	.1069	.3273	4
5	34.27	8.150	0.1227	48.3	613.3	565.0	0.1092	1.3253	5
6	35.09	7.971	.1254	49.4	613.6	564.2	.1115	.3234	6
7	35.92	7.798	.1282	50.5	613.9	563.4	.1138	.3214	7
8	36.77	7.629	.1311	51.6	614.3	562.7	.1162	.3195	8
9	37.63	7.464	.1340	52.7	614.6	561.9	.1185	.3176	9
10	38.51	7.304	0.1369	53.8	614.9	561.1	0.1208	1.3157	10
11	39.40	7.148	.1399	54.9	615.2	560.3	.1231	.3137	11
12	40.31	6.996	.1429	56.0	615.5	559.5	.1254	.3118	12
13	41.24	6.847	.1460	57.1	615.8	558.7	.1277	.3099	13
14	42.18	6.703	.1492	58.2	616.1	557.9	.1300	.3081	14
15	43.14	6.562	0.1524	59.2	616.3	557.1	0.1323	1.3062	15
16	44.12	6.425	.1556	60.3	616.6	556.3	.1346	.3043	16
17	45.12	6.291	.1590	61.4	616.9	555 5	.1369	.3025	17
18	46.13	6.161	.1623	62.5	617.2	554.7	.1392	.3006	18
19	47.16	6.034	.1657	63.6	617.5	553.9	.1415	.2988	19
20	48.21	5.910	0.1692	64.7	617.8	553.1	0.1437	1.2969	20
21	49.28	5.789	.1728	65.8	618.0	552.2	.1460	.2951	21
22	50.36	5.671	.1763	66.9	618.3	551.4	.1483	.2933	22
23	51.47	5.556	.1800	68.0	618.6	550.6	.1505	.2915	23
24	52.59	5.443	.1837	69.1	618.9	549.8	.1528	.2897	24
25	53.73	5.334	0.1875	70.2	619.1	548.9	0.1551	1.2879	25
26	54.90	5.227	.1913	71.3	619.4	548.1	.1573	.2861	26
27	56.08	5.123	.1952	72.4	619.7	547.3	.1596	.2843	27
28	57.28	5.021	.1992	73.5	619.9	546.4	.1618	.2825	28
29	58.50	4.922	.2032	74.6	620.2	545.6	.1641	.2808	29
30	59.74	4.825	0.2073	75.7	620.5	544.8	0.1663	1.2790	30
31	61.00	4.730	.2114	76.8	620.7	543.9	.1686	.2773	31
32	62.29	4.637	.2156	77.9	621.0	543.1	.1708	.2755	32
33	63.59	4.547	.2199	79.0	621.2	542.2	.1730	.2738	33
34	64.91	4.459	.2243	80.1	621.5	541.4	.1753	.2721	34
35	66.26	4.373	0.2287	81.2	621.7	540.5	0.1775	1.2704	35
36	67.63	4.289	.2332	82.3	622.0	539.7	.1797	.2686	36
37	69.02	4.207	.2377	83.4	622.2	538.8	.1819	.2669	37
38	70.43	4.126	.2423	84.6	622.5	537.9	.1841	.2652	38
39	71.87	4.048	.2470	85.7	622.7	537.0	.1863	.2635	39
40	73.32	3.971	0.2518	86.8	623.0	536.2	0.1885	1,2618	40

TABLE 2-14. SATURATED AMMONIA: TEMPERATURE TABLE (*Continued*)

Temp. °F.	Absolute Pressure. lbs./in.³	Volume vapor. ft.³/lb.	Density vapor. lbs./ft.³	Heat content.		Latent heat. Btu./lb.	Entropy.		Temp. °F.
				Liquid. Btu./lb.	Vapor. Btu./lb.		Liquid. Btu./lb.°F.	Vapor. Btu./lb.°F.	
40	73.32	3.971	0.2518	86.8	623.0	536.2	0.1885	1.2618	**40**
41	74.80	3.897	.2566	87.9	623.2	535.3	.1908	.2602	41
42	76.31	3.823	.2616	89.0	623.4	534.4	.1930	.2585	42
43	77.83	3.752	.2665	90.1	623.7	533.6	.1952	.2568	43
44	79.38	3.682	.2716	91.2	623.9	532.7	.1974	.2552	44
45	80.96	3.614	0.2767	92.3	624.1	531.8	0.1996	1.2535	**45**
46	82.55	3.547	.2819	93.5	624.4	530.9	.2018	.2519	46
47	84.18	3.481	.2872	94.6	624.6	530.0	.2040	.2502	47
48	85.82	3.418	.2926	95.7	624.8	529.1	.2062	.2486	48
49	87.49	3.355	.2981	96.8	625.0	528.2	.2083	.2469	49
50	89.19	3.294	0.3036	97.9	625.2	527.3	0.2105	1.2453	**50**
51	90.91	3.234	.3092	99.1	625.5	526.4	.2127	.2437	51
52	92.66	3.176	.3149	100.2	625.7	525.5	.2149	.2421	52
53	94.43	3.119	.3207	101.3	625.9	524.6	.2171	.2405	53
54	96.23	3.063	.3265	102.4	626.1	523.7	.2192	.2389	54
55	98.06	3.008	0.3325	103.5	626.3	522.8	0.2214	1.2373	**55**
56	99.91	2.954	.3385	104.7	626.5	521.8	.2236	.2357	56
57	101.8	2.902	.3446	105.8	626.7	520.9	.2257	.2341	57
58	103.7	2.851	.3508	106.9	626.9	520.0	.2279	.2325	58
59	105.6	2.800	.3571	108.1	627.1	519.0	.2301	.2310	59
60	107.6	2.751	0.3635	109.2	627.3	518.1	0.2322	1.2294	**60**
61	109.6	2.703	.3700	110.3	627.5	517.2	.2344	.2278	61
62	111.6	2.656	.3765	111.5	627.7	516.2	.2365	.2262	62
63	113.6	2.610	.3832	112.6	627.9	515.3	.2387	.2247	63
64	115.7	2.565	.3899	113.7	628.0	514.3	.2408	.2231	64
65	117.8	2.520	0.3968	114.8	628.2	513.4	0.2430	1.2216	**65**
66	120.0	2.477	.4037	116.0	628.4	512.4	.2451	.2201	66
67	122.1	2.435	.4108	117.1	628.6	511.5	.2473	.2186	67
68	124.3	2.393	.4179	118.3	628.8	510.5	.2494	.2170	68
69	126.5	2.352	.4251	119.4	628.9	509.5	.2515	.2155	69
70	128.8	2.312	0.4325	120.5	629.1	508.6	0.2537	1.2140	**70**
71	131.1	2.273	.4399	121.7	629.3	507.6	.2558	.2125	71
72	133.4	2.235	.4474	122.8	629.4	506.6	.2579	.2110	72
73	135.7	2.197	.4551	124.0	629.6	505.6	.2601	.2095	73
74	138.1	2.161	.4628	125.1	629.8	504.7	.2622	.2080	74
75	140.5	2.125	0.4707	126.2	629.9	503.7	0.2643	1.2065	**75**
76	143.0	2.089	.4786	127.4	630.1	502.7	.2664	.2050	76
77	145.4	2.055	.4867	128.5	630.2	501.7	.2685	.2035	77
78	147.9	2.021	.4949	129.7	630.4	500.7	.2706	.2020	78
79	150.5	1.988	.5031	130.8	630.5	499.7	.2728	.2006	79
80	153.0	1.955	0.5115	132.0	630.7	498.7	0.2749	1.1991	**80**
81	155.6	1.923	.5200	133.1	630.8	497.7	.2769	.1976	81
82	158.3	1.892	.5287	134.3	631.0	496.7	.2791	.1962	82
83	161.0	1.861	.5374	135.4	631.1	495.7	.2812	.1947	83
84	163.7	1.831	.5462	136.6	631.3	494.7	.2833	.1933	84
85	166.4	1.801	0.5552	137.8	631.4	493.6	0.2854	1.1918	**85**

TABLE 2-14. SATURATED AMMONIA: TEMPERATURE TABLE (*Concluded*)

Temp. °F.	Absolute Pressure. lbs./in.²	Volume vapor. ft.³/lb.	Density vapor. lbs./ft.³	Heat content.		Latent heat. Btu./lb.	Entropy.		Temp. °F.
				Liquid. Btu./lb.	Vapor. Btu./lb.		Liquid. Btu./lb.°F.	Vapor. Btu./lb.°F.	
85	166.4	1.801	0.5552	137.8	631.4	493.6	0.2854	1.1918	85
86	169.2	1.772	.5643	138.9	631.5	492.6	.2875	.1904	86
87	172.0	1.744	.5735	140.1	631.7	491.6	.2895	.1889	87
88	174.8	1.716	.5828	141.2	631.8	490.6	.2917	.1875	88
89	177.7	1.688	.5923	142.4	631.9	489.5	.2937	.1860	89
90	180.6	1.661	0.6019	143.5	632.0	488.5	0.2958	1.1846	90
91	183.6	1.635	.6116	144.7	632.1	487.4	.2979	.1832	91
92	186.6	1.609	.6214	145.8	632.2	486.4	.3000	.1818	92
93	189.6	1.584	.6314	147.0	632.3	485.3	.3021	.1804	93
94	192.7	1.559	.6415	148.2	632.5	484.3	.3041	.1789	94
95	195.8	1.534	0.6517	149.4	632.6	483.2	0.3062	1.1775	95
96	198.9	1.510	.6620	150.5	632.6	482.1	.3083	.1761	96
97	202.1	1.487	.6725	151.7	632.8	481.1	.3104	.1747	97
98	205.3	1.464	.6832	152.9	632.9	480.0	.3125	.1733	98
99	208.6	1.441	.6939	154.0	632.9	478.9	.3145	.1719	99
100	211.9	1.419	0.7048	155.2	633.0	477.8	0.3166	1.1705	100
101	215.2	1.397	.7159	156.4	633.1	476.7	.3187	.1691	101
102	218.6	1.375	.7270	157.6	633.2	475.6	.3207	.1677	102
103	222.0	1.354	.7384	158.7	633.3	474.6	.3228	.1663	103
104	225.4	1.334	.7498	159.9	633.4	473.5	.3248	.1649	104
105	228.9	1.313	0.7615	161.1	633.4	472.3	0.3269	1.1635	105
106	232.5	1.293	.7732	162.3	633.5	471.2	.3289	.1621	106
107	236.0	1.274	.7852	163.5	633.6	470.1	.3310	.1607	107
108	239.7	1.254	.7972	164.6	633.6	469.0	.3330	.1593	108
109	243.3	1.235	.8095	165.8	633.7	467.9	.3351	.1580	109
110	247.0	1.217	0.8219	167.0	633.7	466.7	0.3372	1.1566	110
111	250.8	1.198	.8344	168.2	633.8	465.6	.3392	.1552	111
112	254.5	1.180	.8471	169.4	633.8	464.4	.3413	.1538	112
113	258.4	1.163	.8600	170.6	633.9	463.3	.3433	.1524	113
114	262.2	1.145	.8730	171.8	633.9	462.1	.3453	.1510	114
115	266.2	1.128	0.8862	173.0	633.9	460.9	0.3474	1.1497	115
116	270.1	1.112	.8996	174.2	634.0	459.8	.3495	.1483	116
117	274.1	1.095	.9132	175.4	634.0	458.6	.3515	.1469	117
118	278.2	1.079	.9269	176.6	634.0	457.4	.3535	.1455	118
119	282.3	1.063	.9408	177.8	634.0	456.2	.3556	.1441	119
120	286.4	1.047	0.9549	179.0	634.0	455.0	0.3576	1.1427	120
121	290.6	1.032	.9692	180.2	634.0	453.8	.3597	.1414	121
122	294.8	1.017	.9837	181.4	634.0	452.6	.3618	.1400	122
123	299.1	1.002	.9983	182.6	634.0	451.4	.3638	.1386	123
124	303.4	0.987	1.0132	183.9	634.0	450.1	.3659	.1372	124
125	307.8	0.973	1.028	185.1	634.0	448.9	0.3679	1.1358	125

TABLE 2-15. SATURATED AMMONIA: ABSOLUTE PRESSURE TABLE

Pressure (abs.). lbs./in.³	Temp. °F.	Volume vapor. ft.³/lb.	Density vapor. lbs./ft.³	Heat content. Liquid. Btu./lb.	Heat content. Vapor. Btu./lb.	Latent heat. Btu./lb.	Entropy. Liquid. Btu./lb. °F.	Entropy. Evap. Btu./lb.°F.	Entropy. Vapor. Btu./lb.°F.	Pressure (abs.). lbs./in.³
5.0	−63.11	49.31	0.02029	−24.5	588.3	612.8	−0.0599	1.5456	1.4857	5.0
5.5	−60.27	45.11	.02217	−21.5	589.5	611.0	− .0524	.5301	.4777	5.5
6.0	−57.64	41.59	.02405	−18.7	590.6	609.3	− .0455	.5158	.4703	6.0
6.5	−55.18	38.59	.02591	−16.1	591.6	607.7	− .0390	.5026	.4636	6.5
7.0	−52.88	36.01	.02777	−13.7	592.5	606.2	− .0330	.4904	.4574	7.0
7.5	−50.70	33.77	0.02962	−11.3	593.4	604.7	−0.0274	1.4790	1.4516	7.5
8.0	−48.64	31.79	.03146	− 9.2	594.2	603.4	− .0221	.4683	.4462	8.0
8.5	−46.69	30.04	.03329	− 7.1	595.0	602.1	− .0171	.4582	.4411	8.5
9.0	−44.83	28.48	.03511	− 5.1	595.7	600.8	− .0123	.4486	.4363	9.0
9.5	−43.05	27.08	.03693	− 3.2	596.4	599.6	− .0077	.4396	.4319	9.5
10.0	−41.34	25.81	0.03874	− 1.4	597.1	598.5	−0.0034	1.4310	1.4276	10.0
10.5	−39.71	24.66	.04055	+ 0.3	597.7	597.4	+ .0007	.4228	.4235	10.5
11.0	−38.14	23.61	.04235	2.0	598.3	596.3	.0047	.4149	.4196	11.0
11.5	−36.62	22.65	.04414	3.6	598.9	595.3	.0085	.4074	.4159	11.5
12.0	−35.16	21.77	.04593	5.1	599.4	594.3	.0122	.4002	.4124	12.0
12.5	−33.74	20.96	0.04772	6.7	600.0	593.3	0.0157	1.3933	1.4090	12.5
13.0	−32.37	20.20	.04950	8.1	600.5	592.4	.0191	.3866	.4057	13.0
13.5	−31.05	19.50	.05128	9.6	601.0	591.4	.0225	.3801	.4026	13.5
14.0	−29.76	18.85	.05305	10.9	601.4	590.5	.0257	.3739	.3996	14.0
14.5	−28.51	18.24	.05482	12.2	601.9	589.7	.0288	.3679	.3967	14.5
15.0	−27.29	17.67	0.05658	13.6	602.4	588.8	0.0318	1.3620	1.3938	15.0
15.5	−26.11	17.14	.05834	14.8	602.8	588.0	.0347	.3564	.3911	15.5
16.0	−24.95	16.64	.06010	16.0	603.2	587.2	.0375	.3510	.3885	16.0
16.5	−23.83	16.17	.06186	17.2	603.6	586.4	.0403	.3456	.3859	16.5
17.0	−22.73	15.72	.06361	18.4	604.0	585.6	.0430	.3405	.3835	17.0
17.5	−21.66	15.30	0.06535	19.6	604.4	584.8	0.0456	1.3354	1.3810	17.5
18.0	−20.61	14.90	.06710	20.7	604.8	584.1	.0482	.3305	.3787	18.0
18.5	−19.59	14.53	.06884	21.8	605.1	583.3	.0507	.3258	.3765	18.5
19.0	−18.58	14.17	.07058	22.9	605.5	582.6	.0531	.3211	.3742	19.0
19.5	−17.60	13.83	.07232	23.9	605.8	581.9	.0555	.3166	.3721	19.5
20.0	−16.64	13.50	0.07405	25.0	606.2	581.2	0.0578	1.3122	1.3700	20.0
20.5	−15.70	13.20	.07578	26.0	606.5	580.5	.0601	.3078	.3679	20.5
21.0	−14.78	12.90	.07751	27.0	606.8	579.8	.0623	.3036	.3659	21.0
21.5	−13.87	12.62	.07924	27.9	607.1	579.2	.0645	.2995	.3640	21.5
22.0	−12.98	12.35	.08096	28.9	607.4	578.5	.0666	.2955	.3621	22.0
22.5	−12.11	12.09	0.08268	29.8	607.7	577.9	0.0687	1.2915	1.3602	22.5
23.0	−11.25	11.85	.08440	30.8	608.1	577.3	.0708	.2876	.3584	23.0
23.5	−10.41	11.61	.08612	31.7	608.3	576.6	.0728	.2838	.3566	23.5
24.0	− 9.58	11.39	.08783	32.6	608.6	576.0	.0748	.2801	.3549	24.0
24.5	− 8.76	11.17	.08955	33.5	608.9	575.4	.0768	.2764	.3532	24.5
25.0	− 7.96	10.96	0.09126	34.3	609.1	574.8	0.0787	1.2728	1.3515	25.0
25.5	− 7.17	10.76	.09297	35.2	609.4	574.2	.0805	.2693	.3498	25.5
26.0	− 6.39	10.56	.09468	36.0	609.7	573.7	.0824	.2658	.3482	26.0
26.5	− 5.63	10.38	.09638	36.8	609.9	573.1	.0842	.2625	.3467	26.5
27.0	− 4.87	10.20	.09809	37.7	610.2	572.5	.0860	.2591	.3451	27.0
27.5	− 4.13	10.02	0.09979	38.4	610.4	572.0	0.0878	1.2558	1.3436	27.5
28.0	− 3.40	9.853	.1015	39.3	610.7	571.4	.0895	.2526	.3421	28.0
28.5	− 2.68	9.691	.1032	40.0	610.9	570.9	.0912	.2494	.3406	28.5
29.0	− 1.97	9.534	.1049	40.8	611.1	570.3	.0929	.2463	.3392	29.0
29.5	− 1.27	9.383	.1066	41.6	611.4	569.8	.0945	.2433	.3378	29.5
30.0	− 0.57	9.236	0.1083	42.3	611.6	569.3	0.0962	1.2402	1.3364	30.0

TABLE 2-15. SATURATED AMMONIA: ABSOLUTE PRESSURE TABLE (*Continued*)

Pressure (abs.). lbs./in.²	Temp. °F.	Volume vapor. ft.³/lb.	Density vapor. lbs./ft.³	Heat content. Liquid. Btu./lb.	Heat content. Vapor. Btu./lb.	Latent heat. Btu./lb.	Entropy. Liquid. Btu./lb. °F.	Entropy. Evap. Btu./lb.°F.	Entropy. Vapor. Btu./lb.°F.	Pressure (abs.). lbs./in.²
30	−0.57	9.236	0.1083	42.3	611.6	569.3	0.0962	1.2402	1.3364	30
31	+0.79	8.955	.1117	43.8	612.0	568.2	.0993	.2343	.3336	31
32	2.11	8.693	.1150	45.2	612.4	567.2	.1024	.2286	.3310	32
33	3.40	8.445	.1184	46.6	612.8	566.2	.1055	.2230	.3285	33
34	4.66	8.211	.1218	48.0	613.2	565.2	.1084	.2176	.3260	34
35	5.89	7.991	0.1251	49.3	613.6	564.3	0.1113	1.2123	1.3236	35
36	7.09	7.782	.1285	50.6	614.0	563.4	.1141	.2072	.3213	36
37	8.27	7.584	.1319	51.9	614.3	562.4	.1168	.2022	.3190	37
38	9.42	7.396	.1352	53.2	614.7	561.5	.1195	.1973	.3168	38
39	10.55	7.217	.1386	54.4	615.0	560.6	.1221	.1925	.3146	39
40	11.66	7.047	0.1419	55.6	615.4	559.8	0.1246	1.1879	1.3125	40
41	12.74	6.885	.1452	56.8	615.7	558.9	.1271	.1833	.3104	41
42	13.81	6.731	.1486	57.9	616.0	558.1	.1296	.1788	.3084	42
43	14.85	6.583	.1519	59.1	616.3	557.2	.1320	.1745	.3065	43
44	15.88	6.442	.1552	60.2	616.6	556.4	.1343	.1703	.3046	44
45	16.88	6.307	0.1586	61.3	616.9	555.6	0.1366	1.1661	1.3027	45
46	17.87	6.177	.1619	62.4	617.2	554.8	.1389	.1620	.3009	46
47	18.84	6.053	.1652	63.4	617.4	554.0	.1411	.1580	.2991	47
48	19.80	5.934	.1685	64.5	617.7	553.2	.1433	.1540	.2973	48
49	20.74	5.820	.1718	65.5	618.0	552.5	.1454	.1502	.2956	49
50	21.67	5.710	0.1751	66.5	618.2	551.7	0.1475	1.1464	1.2939	50
51	22.58	5.604	.1785	67.5	618.5	551.0	.1496	.1427	.2923	51
52	23.48	5.502	.1818	68.5	618.7	550.2	.1516	.1390	.2906	52
53	24.36	5.404	.1851	69.5	619.0	549.5	.1536	.1354	.2890	53
54	25.23	5.309	.1884	70.4	619.2	548.8	.1556	.1319	.2875	54
55	26.09	5.218	0.1917	71.4	619.4	548.0	0.1575	1.1284	1.2859	55
56	26.94	5.129	.1950	72.3	619.7	547.4	.1594	.1250	.2844	56
57	27.77	5.044	.1983	73.3	619.9	546.6	.1613	.1217	.2830	57
58	28.59	4.962	.2015	74.2	620.1	545.9	.1631	.1184	.2815	58
59	29.41	4.882	.2048	75.0	620.3	545.3˙	.1650	.1151	.2801	59
60	30.21	4.805	0.2081	75.9	620.5	544.6	0.1668	1.1119	1.2787	60
61	31.00	4.730	.2114	76.8	620.7	543.9	.1685	.1088	.2773	61
62	31.78	4.658	.2147	77.7	620.9	543.2	.1703	.1056	.2759	62
63	32.55	4.588	.2180	78.5	621.1	542.6	.1720	.1026	.2746	63
64	33.31	4.519	.2213	79.4	621.3	541.9	.1737	.0996	.2733	64
65	34.06	4.453	0.2245	80.2	621.5	541.3	0.1754	1.0966	1.2720	65
66	34.81	4.389	.2278	81.0	621.7	540.7	.1770	.0937	.2707	66
67	35.54	4.327	.2311	81.8	621.9	540.1	.1787	.0907	.2694	67
68	36.27	4.267	.2344	82.6	622.0	539.4	.1803	.0879	.2682	68
69	36.99	4.208	.2377	83.4	622.2	538.8	.1819	.0851	.2670	69
70	37.70	4.151	0.2409	84.2	622.4	538.2	0.1835	1.0823	1.2658	70
71	38.40	4.095	.2442	85.0	622.6	537.6	.1850	.0795	.2645	71
72	39.09	4.041	.2475	85.8	622.8	537.0	.1866	.0768	.2634	72
73	39.78	3.988	.2507	86.5	622.9	536.4	.1881	.0741	.2622	73
74	40.46	3.937	.2540	87.3	623.1	535.8	.1896	.0715	.2611	74
75	41.13	3.887	0.2573	88.0	623.2	535.2	0.1910	1.0689	1.2599	75
76	41.80	3.838	.2606	88.8	623.4	534.6	.1925	.0663	.2588	76
77	42.46	3.790	.2638	89.5	623.5	534.0	.1940	.0637	.2577	77˙
78	43.11	3.744	.2671	90.2	623.7	533.5	.1954	.0612	.2566	78
79	43.76	3.699	.2704	90.9	623.8	532.9	.1968	.0587	.2555	79
80	44.40	3.655	0.2736	91.7	624.0	532.3	0.1982	1.0563	1.2545	80

TABLE 2-15. SATURATED AMMONIA: ABSOLUTE PRESSURE TABLE (*Continued*)

Pressure (abs.). lbs./in.²	Temp. °F.	Volume vapor. ft.³/lb.	Density vapor. lbs./ft.³	Heat content.		Latent heat. Btu./lb.	Entropy.			Pressure (abs.). lbs./in.²
				Liquid. Btu./lb.	Vapor. Btu./lb.		Liquid. Btu./lb.·°F.	Evap. Btu./lb.°F.	Vapor. Btu./lb.°F.	
80	44. 40	3. 655	0. 2736	91. 7	624. 0	532. 3	0. 1982	1. 0563	1. 2545	80
81	45. 03	3. 612	. 2769	92. 4	624. 1	531. 7	. 1996	. 0538	. 2534	81
82	45. 66	3. 570	. 2801	93. 1	624. 3	531. 2	. 2010	. 0514	. 2524	82
83	46. 28	3. 528	. 2834	93. 8	624. 4	530. 6	. 2024	. 0490	. 2514	83
84	46. 89	3. 488	. 2867	94. 5	624. 6	530. 1	. 2037	. 0467	. 2504	84
85	47. 50	3. 449	0. 2899	95. 1	624. 7	529. 6	0. 2051	1. 0443	1. 2494	85
86	48. 11	3. 411	. 2932	95. 8	624. 8	529. 0	. 2064	. 0420	. 2484	86
87	48. 71	3. 373	. 2964	96. 5	625. 0	528. 5	. 2077	. 0397	. 2474	87
88	49. 30	3 337	. 2997	97. 2	625. 1	527. 9	. 2090	. 0375	. 2465	88
89	49. 89	3. 301	. 3030	97. 8	625. 2	527. 4	. 2103	. 0352	. 2455	89
90	50. 47	3. 266	0. 3062	98. 4	625. 3	526. 9	0. 2115	1. 0330	1. 2445	90
91	51. 05	3. 231	. 3095	99. 1	625. 5	526. 4	. 2128	. 0308	. 2436	91
92	51. 62	3. 198	. 3127	99. 8	625. 6	525. 8	. 2141	. 0286	. 2427	92
93	52. 19	3. 165	. 3160	100. 4	625. 7	525. 3	. 2153	. 0265	. 2418	93
94	52. 76	3. 132	. 3192	101. 0	625. 8	524. 8	. 2165	. 0243	. 2408	94
95	53. 32	3. 101	0. 3225	101. 6	625. 9	524. 3	0. 2177	1. 0222	1. 2399	95
96	53. 87	3. 070	. 3258	102. 3	626. 1	523. 8	. 2190	. 0201	. 2391	96
97	54. 42	3. 039	. 3290	102. 9	626. 2	523. 3	. 2201	. 0181	. 2382	97
98	54. 97	3. 010	. 3323	103. 5	626. 3	522. 8	. 2213	. 0160	. 2373	98
99	55. 51	2. 980	. 3355	104. 1	626. 4	522. 3	. 2225	. 0140	. 2365	99
100	56. 05	2. 952	0. 3388	104. 7	626. 5	521. 8	0. 2237	1. 0119	1. 2356	100
102	57. 11	2. 896	. 3453	105. 9	626. 7	520. 8	. 2260	. 0079	. 2339	102
104	58. 16	2. 843	. 3518	107. 1	626. 9	519. 8	. 2282	. 0041	. 2323	104
106	59. 19	2. 791	. 3583	108. 3	627. 1	518. 8	. 2305	1. 0002	. 2307	106
108	60. 21	2. 741	. 3648	109. 4	627. 3	517. 9	. 2327	0. 9964	. 2291	108
110	61. 21	2. 693	0. 3713	110. 5	627. 5	517. 0	0. 2348	0. 9927	1. 2275	110
112	62. 20	2. 647	. 3778	111. 7	627. 7	516. 0	. 2369	. 9890	. 2259	112
114	63. 17	2. 602	. 3843	112. 8	627. 9	515. 1	. 2390	. 9854	. 2244	114
116	64. 13	2. 559	. 3909	113. 9	628. 1	514. 2	. 2411	. 9819	. 2230	116
118	65. 08	2. 517	. 3974	114.·9	628. 2	513. 3	. 2431	. 9784	. 2215	118
120	66. 02	2. 476	0. 4039	116. 0	628. 4	512. 4	0. 2452	0. 9749	1. 2201	120
122	66. 94	2. 437	. 4104	117. 1	628. 6	511. 5	. 2471	. 9715	. 2186	122
124	67. 86	2. 399	. 4169	118. 1	628. 7	510. 6	. 2491	. 9682	. 2173	124
126	68. 76	2. 362	. 4234	119. 1	628. 9	509. 8	. 2510	. 9649	. 2159	126
128	69. 65	2. 326	. 4299	120. 1	629. 0	508. 9	. 2529	. 9616	. 2145	128
130	70. 53	2. 291	0. 4364	121. 1	629. 2	508. 1	0. 2548	0. 9584	1. 2132	130
132	71. 40	2. 258	. 4429	122. 1	629. 3	507. 2	. 2567	. 9552	. 2119	132
134	72. 26	2. 225	. 4494	123. 1	629. 5	506. 4	. 2585	. 9521	. 2106	134
136	73. 11	2. 193	. 4559	124. 1	629. 6	505. 5	. 2603	. 9490	. 2093	136
138	73. 95	2. 162	. 4624	125. 1	629. 8	504. 7	. 2621	. 9460	. 2081	138
140	74. 79	2. 132	0. 4690	126. 0	629. 9	503. 9	0. 2638	0. 9430	1. 2068	140
142	75. 61	2. 103	. 4755	126. 9	630. 0	503. 1	. 2656	. 9400	. 2056	142
144	76. 42	2. 075	. 4820	127. 9	630. 2	502. 3	. 2673	. 9371	. 2044	144
146	77. 23	2. 047	. 4885	128. 8	630. 3	501. 5	. 2690	. 9342	. 2032	146
148	78. 03	2. 020	. 4951	129. 7	630. 4	500. 7	. 2707	. 9313	. 2020	148
150	78. 81	1. 994	0. 5016	130. 6	630. 5	499. 9	0. 2724	0. 9285	1. 2009	150

TABLE 2-15. SATURATED AMMONIA: ABSOLUTE PRESSURE TABLE (Concluded)

Pressure (abs.). lbs./in.²	Temp. °F.	Volume vapor. ft.³/lb.	Density vapor. lbs./ft.³	Heat content. Liquid. Dtu./lb.	Vapor. Btu./lb.	Latent heat. Btu./lb.	Entropy. Liquid. Dtu./lb. °F.	Evap. Btu./lb.°F.	Vapor. Btu./lb.°F.	Pressure (abs.). lbs./in.²
150	78.81	1.994	0.5016	130.6	630.5	499.9	0.2724	0.9285	1.2009	**150**
152	79.60	1.968	.5081	131.5	630.6	499.1	.2740	.9257	.1997	152
154	80.37	1.943	.5147	132.4	630.7	498.3	.2756	.9229	.1985	154
156	81.13	1.919	.5212	133.3	630.9	497.6	.2772	.9202	.1974	156
158	81.89	1.895	.5277	134.2	631.0	496.8	.2788	.9175	.1963	158
160	82.64	1.872	0.5343	135.0	631.1	496.1	0.2804	0.9148	1.1952	**160**
162	83.39	1.849	.5408	135.9	631.2	495.3	.2820	.9122	.1942	162
164	84.12	1.827	.5473	136.8	631.3	494.5	.2835	.9096	.1931	164
166	84.85	1.805	.5539	137.6	631.4	493.8	.2850	.9070	.1920	166
168	85.57	1.784	.5604	138.4	631.5	493.1	.2866	.9044	.1910	168
170	86.29	1.764	0.5670	139.3	631.6	492.3	0.2881	0.9019	1.1900	**170**
172	87.00	1.744	.5735	140.1	631.7	491.6	.2895	.8994	.1889	172
174	87.71	1.724	.5801	140.9	631.7	490.8	.2910	.8969	.1879	174
176	88.40	1.705	.5866	141.7	631.8	490.1	.2925	.8944	.1869	176
178	89.10	1.686	.5932	142.5	631.9	489.4	.2939	.8920	.1859	178
180	89.78	1.667	0.5998	143.3	632.0	488.7	0.2954	0.8896	1.1850	**180**
182	90.46	1.649	.6063	144.1	632.1	488.0	.2968	.8872	.1840	182
184	91.14	1.632	.6129	144.8	632.1	487.3	.2982	.8848	.1830	184
186	91.80	1.614	.6195	145.6	632.2	486.6	.2996	.8825	.1821	186
188	92.47	1.597	.6261	146.4	632.3	485.9	.3010	.8801	.1811	188
190	93.13	1.581	0.6326	147.2	632.4	485.2	0.3024	0.8778	1.1802	**190**
192	93.78	1.564	.6392	147.9	632.4	484.5	.3037	.8755	.1792	192
194	94.43	1.548	.6458	148.7	632.5	483.8	.3050	.8733	.1783	194
196	95.07	1.533	.6524	149.5	632.6	483.1	.3064	.8710	.1774	196
198	95.71	1.517	.6590	150.2	632.6	482.4	.3077	.8688	.1765	198
200	96.34	1.502	0.6656	150.9	632.7	481.8	0.3090	0.8666	1.1756	**200**
205	97.90	1.466	.6821	152.7	632.8	480.1	.3122	.8612	.1734	205
210	99.43	1.431	.6986	154.6	633.0	478.4	.3154	.8559	.1713	210
215	100.94	1.398	.7152	156.3	633.1	476.8	.3185	.8507	.1692	215
220	102.42	1.367	.7318	158.0	633.2	475.2	.3216	.8455	.1671	220
225	103.87	1.336	0.7484	159.7	633.3	473.6	0.3246	0.8405	1.1651	**225**
230	105.30	1.307	.7650	161.4	633.4	472.0	.3275	.8356	.1631	230
235	106.71	1.279	.7817	163.1	633.5	470.4	.3304	.8307	.1611	235
240	108.09	1.253	.7984	164.7	633.6	468.9	.3332	.8260	.1592	240
245	109.46	1.227	.8151	166.4	633.7	467.3	.3360	.8213	.1573	245
250	110.80	1.202	0.8319	168.0	633.8	465.8	0.3388	0.8167	1.1555	**250**
255	112.12	1.178	.8487	169.5	633.8	464.3	.3415	.8121	.1536	255
260	113.42	1.155	.8655	171.1	633.9	462.8	.3441	.8077	.1518	260
265	114.71	1.133	.8824	172.6	633.9	461.3	.3468	.8033	.1501	265
270	115.97	1.112	.8993	174.1	633.9	459.8	.3494	.7989	.1483	270
275	117.22	1.091	0.9162	175.6	634.0	458.4	0.3519	0.7947	1.1466	**275**
280	118.45	1.072	.9332	177.1	634.0	456.9	.3545	.7904	.1449	280
285	119.66	1.052	.9502	178.6	634.0	455.4	.3569	.7863	.1432	285
290	120.86	1.034	.9672	180.0	634.0	454.0	.3594	.7821	.1415	290
295	122.05	1.016	.9843	181.5	634.0	452.5	.3618	.7781	.1399	295
300	123.21	0.999	1.0015	182.9	634.0	451.1	0.3642	0.7741	1.1383	**300**

TABLE 2-16. PROPERTIES OF LIQUID AMMONIA

Temp. °F.	Pressure (abs.). lbs./in.²	Volume. ft.³/lb.	Density. lbs./ft.³	Specific heat. Btu./lb. °F.	Heat content. Btu./lb.	Latent heat. Btu./lb.	Latent heat of pressure variation. Btu./lb. lb./in.³	Variation of h with p (t constant). Btu./lb. lb./in.²	Compressibility. per lb./in.²×10⁶	Temp. °F.
Triple point.	{ 0. 88	0. 01961* .02182	51. 00* 45. 83	....	....	....	....	....	....	−107. 86
−100	1. 24	0. 02197	45. 52	(1. 040)	(−63. 0)	(633)	....	....	....	−100
−95	1. 52	. 02207	45. 32	(1. 042)	(−57. 8)	(631)	....	....	....	−95
−90	1. 86	. 02216	45. 12	(1. 043)	(−52. 6)	(628)	....	....	....	−90
−85	2. 27	. 02226	44. 92	(1. 045)	(−47. 4)	(625)	....	....	....	−85
−80	2. 74	. 02236	44. 72	(1. 046)	(−42. 2)	(622)	....	....	....	−80
−75	3. 29	0. 02246	44. 52	(1. 048)	(−36. 9)	(619)	....	....	....	−75
−70	3. 94	. 02256	44. 32	(1. 050)	(−31. 7)	(616)	....	....	....	−70
−65	4. 69	. 02267	44. 11	(1. 052)	(−26. 4)	(613)	....	....	....	−65
−60	5. 55	. 02278	43. 91	1. 054	−21. 18	610. 8	−0. 0016	0. 0026	4. 4	−60
−55	6. 54	. 02288	43. 70	1. 056	−15. 90	607. 5	−. 0016	. 0026	4. 5	−55
−50	7. 67	0. 02299	43. 49	1. 058	−10. 61	604. 3	−0. 0017	0. 0026	4. 6	−50
−45	8. 95	. 02310	43. 28	1. 060	−5. 31	600. 9	−. 0017	. 0026	4. 7	−45
−40	10. 41	. 02322	43. 08	1. 062	0. 00	597. 6	−. 0018	. 0025	4. 8	−40
−35	12. 05	. 02333	42. 86	1. 064	+5. 32	594. 2	−. 0018	. 0025	5. 0	−35
−30	13. 90	. 02345	42. 65	1. 066	10. 66	590. 7	−. 0019	. 0025	5. 1	−30
−25	15. 98	0. 02357	42. 44	1. 068	16. 00	587. 2	−0. 0019	0. 0024	5. 2	−25
−20	18. 30	. 02369	42. 22	1. 070	21. 36	583. 6	−. 0020	. 0024	5. 4	−20
−15	20. 88	. 02381	42. 00	1. 073	26. 73	580. 0	−. 0020	. 0024	5. 5	−15
−10	23. 74	. 02393	41. 78	1. 075	32. 11	576. 4	−. 0021	. 0023	5. 7	−10
−5	26. 92	. 02406	41. 56	1. 078	37. 51	572. 6	−. 0022	. 0023	5. 8	−5
0	30. 42	0. 02419	41. 34	1. 080	42. 92	568. 9	−0. 0022	0. 0022	6. 0	0
5	34. 27	. 02432	41. 11	1. 083	48. 35	565. 0	−. 0023	. 0022	6. 2	5
10	38. 51	. 02446	40. 89	1. 085	53. 79	561. 1	−. 0024	. 0021	6. 4	10
15	43. 14	. 02460	40. 66	1. 088	59. 24	557. 1	−. 0025	. 0021	6. 6	15
20	48. 21	. 02474	40. 43	1. 091	64. 71	553. 1	−. 0025	. 0020	6. 8	20
25	53. 73	0. 02488	40. 20	1. 094	70. 20	548. 9	−0. 0026	0. 0020	7. 0	25
30	59. 74	. 02503	39. 96	1. 097	75. 71	544. 8	−. 0027	. 0019	7. 3	30
35	66. 26	. 02518	39. 72	1. 100	81. 23	540. 5	−. 0028	. 0019	7. 5	35
40	73. 32	. 02533	39. 49	1. 104	86. 77	536. 2	−. 0029	. 0018	7. 8	40
45	80. 96	. 02548	39. 24	1. 108	92. 34	531. 8	−. 0030	. 0017	8. 1	45
50	89. 19	0. 02564	39. 00	1. 112	97. 93	527. 3	−0. 0031	0. 0017	8. 4	50
55	98. 06	. 02581	38. 75	1. 116	103. 54	522. 8	−. 0032	. 0016	8. 8	55
60	107. 6	. 02597	38. 50	1. 120	109. 18	518. 1	−. 0033	. 0015	9. 1	60
65	117. 8	. 02614	38. 25	1. 125	114. 85	513. 4	−. 0034	. 0014	9. 5	65
70	128. 8	. 02632	38. 00	1. 129	120. 54	508. 6	−. 0035	. 0013	10. 0	70
75	140. 5	0. 02650	37. 74	1. 133	126. 25	503. 7	−0. 0037	0. 0012	10. 4	75

* Properties of solid ammonia at the triple point (−107.86°F.)

TABLE 2-16. PROPERTIES OF LIQUID AMMONIA (Concluded)

Temp. °F.	Pressure (abs.). lbs./in.²	Volume. ft.³/lb.	Density. lbs./ft.³	Specific heat. Btu./lb. °F	Heat content. Btu./lb.	Latent heat. Btu./lb.	Latent heat of pressure variation. Btu./lb. lb./in.²	Variation of h with p (t constant). Btu./lb. lb./in.²	Compressibility. per lb./in.²×10⁶	Temp. °F.
				Saturation.						
75	140.5	0.02650	37.74	1.133	126.25	503.7	−0.0037	0.0012	10.4	75
80	153.0	.02668	37.48	1.138	131.99	498.7	− .0038	.0011	10.9	80
85	166.4	.02687	37.21	1.142	137.75	493.6	− .0040	.0010	11.4	85
90	180.6	.02707	36.95	1.147	143.54	488.5	− .0041	.0009	12.0	90
95	195.8	.02727	36.67	1.151	149.36	483.2	− .0043	.0008	12.6	95
100	211.9	0.02747	36.40	1.156	155.21	477.8	−0.0045	0.0006	13.3	100
105	228.9	.02769	36.12	1.162	161.09	472.3	− .0047	.0005	14.1	105
110	247.0	.02790	35.84	1.168	167.01	466.7	− .0049	.0003	14.9	110
115	266.2	.02813	35.55	1.176	172.97	460.9	− .0051	.0001	15.8	115
120	286.4	.02836	35.26	1.183	178.98	455.0	− .0053	.0000	16.7	120
125	307.8	0.02860	34.96	(1.189)	(185)	(449)	....	....	....	125
130	330.3	.02885	34.66	(1.197)	(191)	(443)	....	....	....	130
135	354.1	.02911	34.35	(1.205)	(197)	(436)	....	....	....	135
140	379.1	.02938	34.04	(1.213)	(203)	(430)	....	....	....	140
145	405.5	.02966	33.72	(1.222)	(210)	(423)	....	....	....	145
150	433.2	0.02995	33.39	(1.23)	(216)	(416)	....	....	....	150
155	462.3	.03025	33.06	(1.24)	(222)	(409)	....	....	....	155
160	492.8	.03056	32.72	(1.25)	(229)	(401)	....	....	....	160
165	524.8	.03089	32.37	(1.26)	(235)	(394)	....	....	....	165
170	558.4	.03124	32.01	(1.27)	(241)	(386)	....	....	....	170
175	593.5	0.03160	31.65	(1.29)	(248)	(377)	....	....	....	175
180	630.3	.03198	31.27	(1.30)	(255)	(369)	....	....	....	180
185	668.7	.03238	30.88	(1.32)	(262)	(360)	....	....	....	185
190	708.9	.03281	30.48	(1.34)	(269)	(351)	....	....	....	190
195	750.9	.03326	30.06	(1.36)	(276)	(342)	....	....	....	195
200	794.7	0.03375	29.63	(1.38)	(283)	(332)	....	....	....	200
210	888.1	.03482	28.72	(1.43)	(297)	(310)	....	....	....	210
220	989.5	.0361	27.7	(1.49)	(313)	(287)	....	....	....	220
230	1099.5	.0376	26.6	(1.57)	(329)	(260)	....	....	....	230
240	1218.5	ʼ.0395	25.3	(1.70)	(346)	(229)	....	....	....	240
250	1347	.0422	23.7	(1.90)	(365)	(192)	....	....	....	250
260	1486	.0463	21.6	(2.33)	(387)	(142)	....	....	....	260
270	1635	.0577	17.3	(5.30)	(419)	(52)	....	....	....	270
Critical.	1657	.0686	14.6	∞	(433)	0	−∞	−∞	∞	271.4

NOTE.—The figures in parentheses were calculated from empirical equations given in Bureau of Standards Scientific Papers Nos. 313 and 315 and represent values obtained by extrapolation beyond the range covered in the experimental work.

Table 2-17 appears on pages 52–67.

TABLE 2-17. PROPERTIES OF SUPERHEATED AMMONIA VAPOR

[V = volume in ft.^{3}/lb.; H = heat content in Btu./lb.; S = entropy in Btu./lb. °F.]

Temp. °F.	Absolute pressure in lbs./in.^{2} (Saturation temperature in italics.)									Temp. °F.
	5 −63.11°			**6** −57.64°			**7** −53.88°			
	V	H	S	V	H	S	V	H	S	
Sat.	*49.31*	*588.3*	*1.4857*	*41.59*	*590.6*	*1.4703*	*36.01*	*592.5*	*1.4574*	*Sat.*
−50	51.05	595.2	1.5025	42.44	594.6	1.4803	36.29	594.0	1.4611	−50
−40	52.36	600.3	.5149	43.55	599.8	.4928	37.25	599.3	.4739	−40
−30	53.67	605.4	.5269	44.64	604.9	.5049	38.19	604.5	.4861	−30
−20	54.97	610.4	.5385	45.73	610.0	.5166	39.13	609.6	.4979	−20
−10	56.26	615.4	.5498	46.82	615.1	.5280	40.07	614.7	.5094	−10
0	57.55	620.4	1.5608	47.90	620.1	1.5391	41.00	619.8	1.5206	0
10	58.84	625.4	.5716	48.98	625.2	.5499	41.93	624.9	.5314	10
20	60.12	630.4	.5821	50.05	630.2	.5605	42.85	629.9	.5421	20
30	61.41	635.4	.5925	51.12	635.2	.5708	43.77	635.0	.5525	30
40	62.69	640.4	.6026	52.19	640.2	.5810	44.69	640.0	.5627	40
50	63.96	645.5	1.6125	53.26	645.2	1.5910	45.61	645.0	1.5727	50
60	65.24	650.5	.6223	54.32	650.3	.6008	46.53	650.1	.5825	60
70	66.51	655.5	.6319	55.39	655.3	.6104	47.44	655.2	.5921	70
80	67.79	660.6	.6413	56.45	660.4	.6199	48.36	660.2	.6016	80
90	69.06	665.6	.6506	57.51	665.5	.6292	49.27	665.3	.6110	90
100	70.33	670.7	1.6598	58.58	670.6	1.6384	50.18	670.4	1.6202	100
110	71.60	675.8	.6689	59.64	675.7	.6474	51.09	675.5	.6292	110
120	72.87	680.9	.6778	60.70	680.8	.6563	52.00	680.7	.6382	120
130	74.14	686.1	.6865	61.76	685.9	.6651	52.91	685.8	.6470	130
140	75.41	691.2	.6952	62.82	691.1	.6738	53.82	691.0	.6557	140
150	76.68	696.4	1.7038	63.87	696.3	1.6824	54.73	696.2	1.6643	150
160	77.95	701.6	.7122	64.93	701.5	.6909	55.63	701.4	.6727	160
170	79.21	706.8	.7206	65.99	706.7	.6992	56.54	706.6	.6811	170
180	80.48	712.1	.7289	67.05	712.0	.7075	57.45	711.9	.6894	180

Temp. °F.	**10** −41.34°			**11** −38.14°			**12** −35.16°			Temp. °F.
Sat.	*25.81*	*597.1*	*1.4276*	*23.61*	*598.3*	*1.4196*	*21.77*	*599.4*	*1.4124*	*Sat.*
−30	26.58	603.2	1.4420	24.12	602.7	1.4300	22.07	602.3	1.4190	−30
−20	27.26	608.5	.4542	24.74	608.1	.4423	22.64	607.7	.4314	−20
−10	27.92	613.7	.4659	25.35	613.3	.4542	23.20	613.0	.4434	−10
0	28.58	618.9	1.4773	25.95	618.5	1.4656	23.75	618.2	1.4549	0
10	29.24	624.0	.4884	26.55	623.7	.4768	24.31	623.4	.4661	10
20	29.90	629.1	.4992	27.15	628.9	.4876	24.86	628.6	.4770	20
30	30.55	634.2	.5097	27.74	634.0	.4982	25.41	633.7	.4877	30
40	31.20	639.3	.5200	28.34	639.1	.5085	25.95	638.9	.4980	40
50	31.85	644.4	1.5301	28.93	644.2	1.5187	26.49	644.0	1.5082	50
60	32.49	649.5	.5400	29.52	649.3	.5286	27.03	649.1	.5182	60
70	33.14	654.6	.5497	30.10	654.4	.5383	27.57	654.3	.5279	70
80	33.78	659.7	.5593	30.69	659.6	.5479	28.11	659.4	.5375	80
90	34.42	664.8	.5687	31.28	664.7	.5573	28.65	664.5	.5470	90
100	35.07	670.0	1.5779	31.86	669.8	1.5666	29.19	669.7	1.5562	100
110	35.71	675.1	.5870	32.44	675.0	.5757	29.72	674.8	.5654	110
120	36.35	680.3	.5960	33.03	680.1	.5847	30.26	680.0	.5744	120
130	36.99	685.4	.6049	33.61	685.3	.5936	30.79	685.2	.5833	130
140	37.62	690.6	.6136	34.19	690.5	.6023	31.33	690.4	.5920	140
150	38.26	695.8	1.6222	34.77	695.7	1.6109	31.86	695.6	1.6006	150
160	38.90	701.1	.6307	35.35	700.9	.6194	32.39	700.8	.6092	160
170	39.54	706.3	.6391	35.93	706.2	.6278	32.92	706.1	.6176	170
180	40.17	711.6	.6474	36.51	711.5	.6362	33.46	711.4	.6259	180
190	40.81	716.9	.6556	37.09	716.8	.6444	33.99	716.7	.6341	190
200	41.45	722.2	1.6637	37.67	722.1	1.6525	34.52	722.0	1.6422	200

TABLE 2-17. PROPERTIES OF SUPERHEATED AMMONIA VAPOR (*Continued*)
[V = volume in ft.³/lb.; H = heat content in Btu./lb.; S = entropy in Btu./lb. °F.]

Temp. °F.	Absolute pressure in lbs./in.² (Saturation temperature in italics.)									Temp. °F.
	8 *−48.64°*			**9** *−44.33°*			**10** *−41.34°*			
	V	*H*	*S*	*V*	*H*	*S*	*V*	*H*	*S*	
Sat.	*31.79*	*594.2*	*1.4462*	*28.48*	*595.7*	*1.4363*	*25.81*	*597 1*	*1.4276*	*Sat.*
−50										−50
−40	32.52	598.8	1.4573	28.85	598.3	1.4426	25.90	597.8	1.4293	−40
−30	33.36	604.1	.4697	29.59	603.6	.4551	26.58	603.2	.4420	−30
−20	34.19	609.3	.4816	30.34	608.9	.4672	27.26	608.5	.4542	−20
−10	35.01	614.4	.4932	31.07	614.0	.4788	27.92	613.7	.4659	−10
0	35.83	619.5	1.5044	31.80	619.2	1.4902	28.58	618.9	1.4773	0
10	36.64	624.6	.5154	32.53	624.3	.5012	29.24	624.0	.4884	10
20	37.45	629.7	.5261	33.26	629.4	.5119	29.90	629.1	.4992	20
30	38.26	634.7	.5365	33.98	634.5	.5224	30.55	634.2	.5097	30
40	39.07	639.8	.5467	34.70	639.5	.5327	31.20	639.3	.5200	40
50	39.88	644.8	1.5568	35.42	644.6	1.5427	31.85	644.4	1.5301	50
60	40.68	649.9	.5666	36.13	649.7	.5526	32.49	649.5	.5400	60
70	41.48	655.0	.5763	36.85	654.8	.5623	33.14	654.6	.5497	70
80	42.28	660.1	.5858	37.56	659.9	.5718	33.78	659.7	.5593	80
90	43.08	665.2	.5952	38.27	665.0	.5812	34.42	664.8	.5687	90
100	43.88	670.3	1.6044	38.98	670.1	1.5904	35.07	670.0	1.5779	100
110	44.68	675.4	.6135	39.70	675.3	.5995	35.71	675.1	.5870	110
120	45.48	680.5	.6224	40.40	680.4	.6085	36.35	680.3	.5960	120
130	46.27	685.7	.6312	41.11	685.6	.6173	36.99	685.4	.6049	130
140	47.07	690.9	.6399	41.82	690.7	.6260	37.62	690.6	.6136	140
150	47.87	696.1	1.6485	42.53	695.9	1.6346	38.26	695.8	1.6222	150
160	48.66	701.3	.6570	43.24	701.2	.6431	38.90	701.1	.6307	160
170	49.46	706.5	.6654	43.95	706.4	.6515	39.54	706.3	.6391	170
180	50.25	711.8	.6737	44.65	711.7	.6598	40.17	711.6	.6474	180

Temp. °F.	**13** *−32.37°*			**14** *−29.76°*			**15** *−27.29°*			Temp. °F.
Sat.	*20.20*	*600.5*	*1.4057*	*18.85*	*601.4*	*1.3996*	*17.67*	*602.4*	*1.3938*	*Sat.*
−30	20.33	601.8	1.4088							−30
−20	20.86	607.2	.4213	19.33	606.8	1.4119	18.01	606.4	1.4031	−20
−10	21.38	612.6	.4334	19.82	612.2	.4241	18.47	611.9	.4154	−10
0	21.90	617.9	1.4450	20.30	617.6	1.4358	18.92	617.2	1.4272	0
10	22.41	623.1	.4563	20.78	622.8	.4472	19.37	622.5	.4386	10
20	22.92	628.3	.4672	21.26	628.0	.4582	19.82	627.8	.4497	20
30	23.43	633.5	.4779	21.73	633.2	.4688	20.26	633.0	.4604	30
40	23.93	638.6	.4883	22.20	638.4	.4793	20.70	638.2	.4709	40
50	24.43	643.8	1.4985	22.67	643.6	1.4896	21.14	643.4	1.4812	50
60	24.94	648.9	.5085	23.14	648.7	.4996	21.58	648.5	.4912	60
70	25.43	654.1	.5183	23.60	653.9	.5094	22.01	653.7	.5011	70
80	25.93	659.2	.5279	24.06	659.0	.5191	22.44	658.9	.5108	80
90	26.43	664.4	.5374	24.53	664.2	.5285	22.88	664.0	.5203	90
100	26.93	669.5	1.5467	24.99	669.4	1.5378	23.31	669.2	1.5296	100
110	27.42	674.7	.5558	25.45	674.5	.5470	23.74	674.4	.5388	110
120	27.92	679.9	.5649	25.91	679.7	.5560	24.17	679.6	.5478	120
130	28.41	685.1	.5737	26.37	884.9	.5649	24.60	684.8	.5567	130
140	28.90	690.3	.5825	26.83	690.1	.5737	25.03	690.0	.5655	140
150	29.40	695.5	1.5911	27.29	695.4	1.5824	25.46	695.3	1.5742	150
160	29.89	700.7	.5997	27.74	700.6	.5909	25.88	700.5	.5827	160
170	30.38	706.0	.6081	28.20	705.9	.5993	26.31	705.8	.5911	170
180	30.87	711.3	.6164	28.66	711.2	.6076	26.74	711.1	.5995	180
190	31.36	716.6	.6246	29.11	716.5	.6159	27.16	716.4	.6077	190
200	31.85	721.9	1.6328	29.57	721.8	1.6240	27.59	721.7	1.6158	**200**

TABLE 2-17. PROPERTIES OF SUPERHEATED AMMONIA VAPOR (*Continued*)
[V = volume in ft.³/lb.; H = heat content in Btu./lb.; S = entropy in Btu./lb. °F.]

Temp. °F.	Absolute pressure in lbs./in.² (Saturation temperature in italics.)									Temp. °F.
	15 −27.29°			**16** −24.95°			**17** −22.73°			
	V	H	S	V	H	S	V	H	S	
Sat.	*17.67*	*602.4*	*1.3938*	*16.64*	*603.2*	*1.3885*	*15.72*	*604.0*	*1.3835*	Sat.
−20	18.01	606.4	1.4031	16.86	606.0	1.3948	15.83	605.6	1.3870	−20
−10	18.47	611.9	.4154	17.29	611.5	.4072	16.24	611.1	.3994	−10
0	18.92	617.2	1.4272	17.72	616.9	1.4191	16.65	616.6	1.4114	0
10	19.37	622.5	.4386	18.14	622.2	.4306	17.05	621.9	.4230	10
20	19.82	627.8	.4497	18.56	627.5	.4417	17.45	627.2	.4342	20
30	20.26	633.0	.4604	18.97	632.7	.4525	17.84	632.5	.4450	30
40	20.70	638.2	.4709	19.39	638.0	.4630	18.23	637.7	.4556	40
50	21.14	643.4	1.4812	19.80	643.2	1.4733	18.62	642.9	1.4659	50
60	21.58	648.5	.4912	20.21	648.3	.4834	19.01	648.1	.4761	60
70	22.01	653.7	.5011	20.62	653.5	.4933	19.39	653.3	.4860	70
80	22.44	658.9	.5108	21.03	658.7	.5030	19.78	658.5	.4957	80
90	22.88	664.0	.5203	21.43	663.9	.5125	20.16	663.7	.5052	90
100	23.31	669.2	1.5296	21.84	669.1	1.5218	20.54	668.9	1.5146	100
110	23.74	674.4	.5388	22.24	674.3	.5310	20.92	674.1	.5238	110
120	24.17	679.6	.5478	22.65	679.5	.5401	21.30	679.3	.5328	120
130	24.60	684.8	.5567	23.05	684.7	.5490	21.68	684.5	.5418	130
140	25.03	690.0	.5655	23.45	689.9	.5578	22.06	689.8	.5506	140
150	25.46	695.3	1.5742	23.86	695.1	1.5665	22.44	695.0	1.5593	150
160	25.88	700.5	.5827	24.26	700.4	.5750	22.82	700.3	.5678	160
170	26.31	705.8	.5911	24.66	705.7	.5835	23.20	705.6	.5763	170
180	26.74	711.1	.5995	25.06	711.0	.5918	23.58	710.9	.5846	180
190	27.16	716.4	.6077	25.46	716.3	.6001	23.95	716.2	.5929	190
200	27.59	721.7	1.6158	25.86	721.6	1.6082	24.33	721.5	1.6010	200
220	28.44	732.4	.6318	26.66	732.3	.6242	25.08	732.2	.6170	220

Temp. °F.	**20** −16.64°			**21** −14.78°			**22** −12.98°			Temp. °F.
	V	H	S	V	H	S	V	H	S	
Sat.	*13.50*	*606.2*	*1.3700*	*12.90*	*606.8*	*1.3659*	*12.35*	*607.4*	*1.3621*	Sat.
−10	13.74	610.0	1.3784	13.06	609.6	1.3720	12.45	609.2	1.3659	−10
0	14.09	615.5	1.3907	13.40	615.2	1.3844	12.77	614.8	1.3784	0
10	14.44	621.0	.4025	13.73	620.7	.3962	13.09	620.4	.3903	10
20	14.78	626.4	.4138	14.06	626.1	.4077	13.40	625.8	.4018	20
30	15.11	631.7	.4248	14.38	631.5	.4187	13.71	631.2	.4129	30
40	15.45	637.0	.4356	14.70	636.8	.4295	14.02	636.6	.4237	40
50	15.78	642.3	1.4460	15.02	642.1	1.4400	14.32	641.9	1.4342	50
60	16.12	647.5	.4562	15.34	647.3	.4502	14.63	647.1	.4445	60
70	16.45	652.8	.4662	15.65	652.6	.4602	14.93	652.4	.4545	70
80	16.78	658.0	.4760	15.97	657.3	.4700	15.23	657.7	.4643	80
90	17.10	663.2	.4856	16.28	663.1	.4796	15.53	662.9	.4740	90
100	17.43	668.5	1.4950	16.59	668.3	1.4891	15.83	668.1	1.4834	100
110	17.76	673.7	.5042	16.90	673.5	.4983	16.12	673.4	.4927	110
120	18.08	678.9	.5133	17.21	678.8	.5075	16.42	678.6	.5019	120
130	18.41	684.2	.5223	17.52	684.0	.5165	16.72	683.9	.5109	130
140	18.73	689.4	.5312	17.83	689.3	.5253	17.01	689.2	.5197	140
150	19.05	694.7	1.5399	18.14	694.6	1.5340	17.31	694.4	1.5285	150
160	19.37	700.0	.5485	18.44	699.8	.5426	17.60	699.7	.5371	160
170	19.70	705.3	.5569	18.75	705.1	.5510	17.89	705.0	.5456	170
180	20.02	710.6	.5653	19.06	710.5	.5595	18.19	710.4	.5539	180
190	20.34	715.9	.5736	19.36	715.8	.5678	18.48	715.7	.5622	190
200	20.66	721.2	1.5817	19.67	721.1	1.5759	18.77	721.1	1.5704	200
220	21.30	732.0	.5978	20.28	731.9	.5920	19.35	731.8	.5865	220
240	21.94	742.8	.6135	20.89	742.7	.6077	19.94	742.7	.6022	240

TABLE 2-17. PROPERTIES OF SUPERHEATED AMMONIA VAPOR (*Continued*)
[V = volume in ft.³/lb.; H = heat content in Btu./lb.; S = entropy in Btu./lb. °F.]

Temp. °F.	Absolute pressure in lbs./in.² (Saturation temperature in italics.)									Temp. °F.
	18 −20.61°			19 −18.58°			20 −16.64°			
	V	H	S	V	H	S	V	H	S	
Sat.	*14.90*	*604.8*	*1.3787*	*14.17*	*605.5*	*1.3742*	*13.50*	*606.2*	*1.3700*	*Sat.*
−20	14.93	605.1	1.3795							−20
−10	15.32	610.7	.3921	14.49	610.3	1.3851	13.74	610.0	1.3784	−10
0	15.70	616.2	1.4042	14.85	615.9	1.3973	14.09	615.5	1.3907	0
10	16.08	621.6	.4158	15.21	621.3	.4090	14.44	621.0	.4025	10
20	16.46	626.9	.4270	15.57	626.7	.4203	14.78	626.4	.4138	20
30	16.83	632.2	.4380	15.93	632.0	.4312	15.11	631.7	.4248	30
40	17.20	637.5	.4486	16.28	637.3	.4419	15.45	637.0	.4356	40
50	17.57	642.7	1.4590	16.63	642.5	1.4523	15.78	642.3	1.4460	50
60	17.94	647.9	.4691	16.98	647.7	.4625	16.12	647.5	.4562	60
70	18.30	653.1	.4790	17.33	653.0	.4724	16.45	652.8	.4662	70
80	18.67	658.4	.4887	17.67	658.2	.4822	16.78	858.0	.4760	80
90	19.03	663.6	.4983	18.02	663.4	.4918	17.10	663.2	.4856	90
100	19.39	668.8	1.5077	18.36	668.6	1.5012	17.43	668.5	1.4950	100
110	19.75	674.0	.5169	18.70	673.8	.5104	17.76	673.7	.5042	110
120	20.11	679.2	.5260	19.04	679.1	.5195	18.08	678.9	.5133	120
130	20.47	684.4	.5349	19.38	684.3	.5285	18.41	684.2	.5223	130
140	20.83	689.7	.5438	19.72	689.5	.5373	18.73	689.4	.5312	140
150	21.19	694.9	1.5525	20.06	694.8	1.5460	19.05	694.7	1.5399	150
160	21.54	700.2	.5610	20.40	700.1	.5546	19.37	700.0	.5485	160
170	21.90	705.5	.5695	20.74	705.4	.5631	19.70	705.3	.5569	170
180	22.26	710.8	.5778	21.08	710.7	.5714	20.02	710.6	.5653	180
190	22.61	716.1	.5861	21.42	716.0	·.5797	20.34	715.9	.5736	190
200	22.97	721.4	1.5943	21.75	721.3	1.5878	20.66	721.2	1.5817	200
220	23.68	732.2	.6103	22.43	732.1	.6039	21.30	732.0	.5978	220

Temp. °F.	23 −11.25°			24 −9.58°			25 −7.96°			Temp. °F.
	V	H	S	V	H	S	V	H	S	
Sat.	*11.85*	*608.1*	*1.3584*	*11.39*	*608.8*	*1.3549*	*10.96*	*609.1*	*1.3515*	*Sat.*
−10	11.89	608.8	1.3600							−10
0	12.20	614.5	1.3726	11.67	614.1	1.3670	11.19	613.8	1.3616	0
10	12.50	620.0	.3846	11.96	619.7	.3791	11.47	619.4	.3738	10
20	12.80	625.5	.3961	12.25	625.2	.3907	11.75	625.0	.3855	20
30	13.10	630.9	.4073	12.54	630.7	.4019	12.03	630.4	.3967	30
40	13.40	636.3	.4181	12.82	636.1	.4128	12.30	635.8	.4077	40
50	13.69	641.6	1.4287	13.11	641.4	1.4234	12.57	641.2	1.4183	50
60	13.98	646.9	.4390	13.39	646.7	.4337	12.84	646.5	.4287	60
70	14.27	652.2	.4491	13.66	652.0	.4438	13.11	651.8	.4388	70
80	14.56	657.5	.4589	13.94	657.3	.4537	13.37	657.1	.4487	80
90	14.84	662.7	.4686	14.22	662.6	.4634	13.64	662.4	.4584	90
100	15.13	668.0	1.4780	14.49	667.8	1.4729	13.90	667.7	1.4679	100
110	15.41	673.2	.4873	14.76	673.1	.4822	14.17	673.0	.4772	110
120	15.70	678.5	.4965	15.04	678.4	.4914	14.43	678.2	.4864	120
130	15.98	683.8	.5055	15.31	683.6	.5004	14.69	683.5	.4954	130
140	16.26	689.0	.5144	15.58	688.9	.5093	14.95	688.8	.5043	140
150	16.55	694.3	1.5231	15.85	694.2	1.5180	15.21	694.1	1,5131	150
160	16.83	699.6	.5317	16.12	699.5	;5266	15.47	699.4	.5217	160
170	17.11	704.9	.5402	16.39	704.8	.5352	15.73	704.7	.5303	170
180	17.39	710.3	.5486	16.66	710.2	.5436	15.99	710.1	.5387	180
190	17.67	715.6	.5569	16.93	715.5	.5518	16.25	715.4	.5470	190
200	17.95	721.0	1.5651	17.20	720.9	1.5600	16.50	720.8	1.5552	200
220	18.51	731.7	.5812	17.73	731.7	.5761	17.02	731.6	.5713	220
240	19.07	742.6	.5969	18.27	742.6	.5919	17.53	742.5	.5870	240

TABLE 2-17. PROPERTIES OF SUPERHEATED AMMONIA VAPOR (*Continued*)
[V = volume in ft.³/lb.; H = heat content in Btu./lb.; S = entropy in Btu./lb. °F.]

Temp. °F.	Absolute pressure in lbs./in.² (Saturation temperature in italics.)									Temp. °F.
	25 −7.96°			26 −6.39°			27 −4.87°			
	V	H	S	V	H	S	V	H	S	
Sat.	*10.96*	*609.1*	*1.3515*	*10.56*	*609.7*	*1.3482*	*10.20*	*610.2*	*1.3451*	*Sat.*
0	11.19	613.8	1.3616	10.74	613.4	1.3564	10.33	613.0	1.3513	0
10	11.47	619.4	.3738	11.01	619.1	.3686	10.59	618.8	.3637	10
20	11.75	625.0	.3855	11.28	624.7	.3804	10.85	624.4	.3755	20
30	12.03	630.4	.3967	11.55	630.2	.3917	11.11	629.9	.3869	30
40	12.30	635.8	.4077	11.81	635.6	.4027	11.37	635.4	.3979	40
50	12.57	641.2	1.4183	12.08	641.0	1.4134	11.62	640.8	1.4087	50
60	12.84	646.5	.4287	12.34	646.3	.4238	11.87	646.1	.4191	60
70	13.11	651.8	.4388	12.59	651.6	.4339	12.12	651.5	.4292	70
80	13.37	657.1	.4487	12.85	656.9	.4439	12.37	656.8	.4392	80
90	13.64	662.4	.4584	13.11	662.2	.4536	12.61	662.1	.4489	90
100	13.90	667.7	1.4679	13.36	667.5	1.4631	12.86	667.4	1.4585	100
110	14.17	673.0	.4772	13.61	672.8	.4725	13.10	672.7	.4679	110
120	14.43	678.2	.4864	13.87	678.1	.4817	13.34	678.0	.4771	120
130	14.69	683.5	.4954	14.12	683.4	.4907	13.59	683.3	.4861	130
140	14.95	688.8	.5043	14.37	688.7	.4996	13.83	688.6	.4950	140
150	15.21	694.1	1.5131	14.62	694.0	1.5084	14.07	693.9	1.5038	150
160	15.47	699.4	.5217	14.87	699.3	.5170	14.31	699.2	.5125	160
170	15.73	704.7	.5303	15.12	704.6	.5256	14.55	704.5	.5210	170
180	15.99	710.1	.5387	15.37	710.0	.5340	14.79	709.9	.5295	180
190	16.25	715.4	.5470	15.62	715.3	.5423	15.03	715.2	.5378	190
200	16.50	720.8	1.5552	15.86	720.7	1.5505	15.27	720.6	1.5460	200
220	17.02	731.6	.5713	16.36	731.5	.5666	15.75	731.4	.5621	220
240	17.53	742.5	.5870	16.85	742.4	.5824	16.23	742.3	.5779	240
260	18.04	753.4	.6025	17.35	753.3	.5978	16.70	753.2	.5933	260

Temp. °F.	30 −0.57°			31 +0.79°			32 +2.11°			Temp. °F.
Sat.	*9.236*	*611.6*	*1.3384*	*8.955*	*612.0*	*1.3338*	*8.693*	*612.4*	*1.3310*	*Sat.*
10	9.492	617.8	1.3497	9.173	617.4	1.3453	8.874	617.1	1.3411	10
20	9.731	623.5	.3618	9.405	623.2	.3574	9.099	622.9	.3532	20
30	9.966	629.1	.3733	9.633	628.8	.3691	9.321	628.5	.3649	30
40	10.20	634.6	.3845	9.858	634.4	.3803	9.540	634.1	.3762	40
50	10.43	640.1	1.3953	10.08	639.9	1.3912	9.757	639.6	1.3871	50
60	10.65	645.5	.4059	10.30	645.3	.4017	9.972	645.1	.3977	60
70	10.88	650.9	.4161	10.52	650.7	.4120	10.18	650.5	.4080	70
80	11.10	656.2	.4261	10.74	656.1	.4221	10.40	655.9	.4181	80
90	11.33	661.6	.4359	10.96	661.4	.4319	10.61	661.2	.4280	90
100	11.55	666.9	1.4456	11.17	666.7	1.4415	10.81	666.6	1.4376	100
110	11.77	672.2	.4550	11.38	672.1	.4510	11.02	671.9	.4470	110
120	11.99	677.5	.4642	11.60	677.4	.4602	11.23	677.3	.4563	120
130	12.21	682.9	.4733	11.81	682.7	.4693	11.44	682.6	.4655	130
140	12.43	688.2	.4823	12.02	688.1	.4783	11.64	687.9	.4744	140
150	12.65	693.5	1.4911	12.23	693.4	1.4871	11.85	693.3	1.4833	150
160	12.87	698.8	.4998	12.44	698.7	.4958	12.05	698.6	.4920	160
170	13.08	704.2	.5083	12.66	704.1	.5044	12.26	704.0	.5006	170
180	13.30	709.6	.5168	12.87	709.5	.5129	12.46	709.4	.5090	180
190	13.52	714.9	.5251	13.07	714.8	.5212	12.66	714.7	.5174	190
200	13.73	720.3	1.5334	13.28	720.2	1.5294	12.86	720.1	1.5256	200
220	14.16	731.1	.5495	13.70	731.1	.5456	13.27	731.0	.5418	220
240	14.59	742.0	.5653	14.12	742.0	.5614	13.67	741.9	.5576	240
260	15.02	753.0	.5808	14.53	752.9	.5769	14.08	752.9	.5731	260
280	15.45	764.1	.5960	14.95	764.0	.5921	14.48	763.9	.5883	280

TABLE 2-17. PROPERTIES OF SUPERHEATED AMMONIA VAPOR (*Continued*)
[V = volume in ft.³/lb.; H = heat content in Btu./lb.; S = entropy in Btu./lb. °F.]

Temp. °F.	Absolute pressure in lbs./in.² (Saturation temperature in italics.)									Temp. °F.
	28 −3.40°			29 −1.97°			30 −0.57°			
	V	*H*	*S*	*V*	*H*	*S*	*V*	*H*	*S*	
Sat.	*9.853*	*610.7*	*1.3421*	*9.534*	*611.1*	*1.3392*	*9.236*	*611.6*	*1.3364*	*Sat.*
0	9.942	612.7	1.3465	9.584	612.3	1.3417	9.250	611.9	1.3371	0
10	10.20	618.4	.3589	9.834	618.1	.3542	9.492	617.8	.3497	10
20	10.45	624.1	.3708	10.08	623.8	.3662	9.731	623.5	.3618	20
30	10.70	629.6	.3822	10.32	629.4	.3777	9.966	629.1	.3733	30
40	10.95	635.1	.3933	10.56	634.9	.3888	10.20	634.6	.3845	40
50	11.19	640.5	1.4041	10.80	640.3	1.3996	10.43	640.1	1.3953	50
60	11.44	645.9	.4145	11.03	645.7	..4101	10.65	645.5	.4059	60
70	11.68	651.2	.4247	11.26	651.1	.4204	10.88	650.9	.4161	70
80	11.92	656.6	.4347	11.50	656.4	.4304	11.10	656.2	.4261	80
90	12.15	661.9	.4445	11.73	661.7	.4401	11.33	661.6	.4359	90
100	12.39	667.2	1.4540	11.96	667.1	1.4497	11.55	666.9	1.4456	100
110	12.63	672.5	.4634	12.18	672.4	.4591	11.77	672.2	.4550	110
120	12.86	677.8	.4726	12.41	677.7	.4684	11.99	677.5	.4642	120
130	13.10	683.1	.4817	12.64	683.0	.4775	12.21	682.9	.4733	130
140	13.33	688.4	.4906	12.86	688.3	.4864	12.43	688.2	.4823	140
150	13.56	693.7	1.4994	13.09	693.6	1.4952	12.65	693.5	1.4911	150
160	13.80	699.1	.5081	13.31	699.0	.5039	12.87	698.8	.4998	160
170	14.03	704.4	.5167	13.54	704.3	.5124	13.08	704.2	.5083	170
180	14.26	709.8	.5251	13.76	709.7	.5209	13.30	709.6	.5168	180
190	14.49	715.1	.5334	13.99	715.0	.5292	13.52	714.9	.5251	190
200	14.72	720.5	1.5416	14.21	720.4	1.5374	13.73	720.3	1.5334	200
220	15.18	731.3	.5578	14.65	731.2	.5536	14.16	731.1	.5495	220
240	15.64	742.2	.5736	15.10	742.2	.5694	14.59	742.0	.5653	240
260	16.10	753.2	.5890	15.54	753.1	.5848	15.02	753.0	.5808	260

Temp. °F.	33 3.40°			34 4.66°			35 5.89°			Temp. °F.
	V	*H*	*S*	*V*	*H*	*S*	*V*	*H*	*S*	
Sat.	*8.445*	*612.8*	*1.3285*	*8.211*	*613.2*	*1.3260*	*7.991*	*613.6*	*1.3238*	*Sat.*
10	8.592	616.8	1.3369	8.328	616.4	1.3328	8.078	616.1	1.3289	10
20	8.812	622.6	.3492	8.542	622.3	.3452	8.287	622.0	.3413	20
30	9.028	628.3	.3609	8.753	628.0	.3570	8.493	627.7	.3532	30
40	9.242	633.9	.3722	8.960	633.6	.3684	8.695	633.4	.3646	40
50	9.452	639.4	1.3832	9.166	639.2	1.3793	8.895	638.9	1.3756	50
60	9.661	644.9	.3938	9.369	644.7	.3900	9.093	644.4	.3863	60
70	9.868	650.3	.4042	9.570	650.1	.4004	9.289	649.9	.3967	70
80	10.07	655.7	.4143	9.770	655.5	.4105	9.484	655.3	.4069	80
90	10.28	661.1	.4241	9.969	660.9	.4204	9.677	660.7	.4168	90
100	10.48	666.4	1.4338	10.17	666.3	1.4301	9.869	666.1	1.4265	100
110	10.68	671.8	.4433	10.36	671.6	.4396	10.06	671.5	.4360	110
120	10.88	677.1	.4526	10.56	677.0	.4489	10.25	676.8	.4453	120
130	11.08	682.5	.4617	10.75	682.3	.4581	10.44	682.2	.4545	130
140	11.28	687.8	.4707	10.95	687.7	.4671	10.63	687.6	.4635	140
150	11.48	693.2	1.4795	11.14	693.0	1.4759	10.82	692.9	1.4724	150
160	11.68	698.5	.4883	11.33	698.4	.4846	11.00	698.3	.4811	160
170	11.88	703.9	.4968	11.53	703.8	.4932	11.19	703.7	.4897	170
180	12.08	709.3	.5053	11.72	709.2	.5017	11.38	709.1	.4982	180
190	12.27	714.6	.5137	11.91	714.5	.5101	11.56	714.5	.5066	190
200	12.47	720.0	1.5219	12.10	720.0	1.5183	11.75	719.9	1.5148	200
220	12.86	730.9	.5381	12.48	730.8	.5346	12.12	730.7	.5311	220
240	13.26	741.8	.5540	12.86	741.7	.5504	12.49	741.7	.5469	240
260	13.65	752.8	.5695	13.24	752.7	.5659	12.86	752.7	.5624	260
280	14.04	763.9	.5846	13.62	763.8	.5811	13.23	763.7	.5776	280

TABLE 2-17. PROPERTIES OF SUPERHEATED AMMONIA VAPOR (*Continued*)
[V = volume in ft.³/lb.; H = heat content in Btu./lb.; S = entropy in Btu./lb. °F.]

Temp. °F.	Absolute pressure in lbs./in.³ (Saturation temperature in italics.)									Temp. °F.
	35 5.89°			**36** 7.09°			**37** 8.27°			
	V	H	S	V	H	S	V	H	S	
Sat.	*7.991*	*613.6*	*1.3236*	*7.782*	*614.0*	*1.3213*	*7.584*	*614.3*	*1.3190*	*Sat.*
10	8.078	616.1	1.3289	7.842	615.7	1.3250	7.619	615.4	1.3212	10
20	8.287	622.0	.3413	8.046	621.7	.3375	7.819	621.4	.3338	20
30	8.493	627.7	.3532	8.247	627.4	.3494	8.015	627.2	.3458	30
40	8.695	633.4	.3646	8.445	633.1	.3609	8.208	632.9	.3573	40
50	8.895	638.9	1.3756	8.640	638.7	1.3720	8.398	638.5	1.3684	**50**
60	9.093	644.4	.3863	8.833	644.2	.3827	8.587	644.0	.3792	60
70	9.289	649.9	.3967	9.024	649.7	.3932	8.773	649.5	.3897	70
80	9.484	655.3	.4069	9.214	655.2	.4033	8.958	655.0	.3999	80
90	9.677	660.7	.4168	9.402	660.6	.4133	9.142	660.4	.4098	90
100	9.869	666.1	1.4265	9.589	666.0	1.4230	9.324	665.8	1.4196	**100**
110	10.06	671.5	.4360	9.775	671.3	.4325	9.506	671.2	.4291	110
120	10.25	676.8	.4453	9.961	676.7	.4419	9.686	676.6	.4385	120
130	10.44	682.2	.4545	10.15	682.1	.4510	9.866	681.9	.4477	130
140	10.63	687.6	.4635	10.33	687.4	.4601	10.05	687.3	.4567	140
150	10.82	692.9	1.4724	10.51	692.8	1.4689	10.22	692.7	1.4656	**150**
160	11.00	698.3	.4811	10.69	698.2	.4777	10.40	698.1	.4744	160
170	11.19	703.7	.4897	10.88	703.6	.4863	10.58	703.5	.4830	170
180	11.38	709.1	.4982	11.06	709.0	.4948	10.76	708.9	.4915	180
190	11.56	714.5	.5066	11.24	714.4	.5032	10.93	714.3	.4999	190
200	11.75	719.9	1.5148	11.42	719.8	1.5115	11.11	719.7	1.5082	**200**
220	12.12	730.7	.5311	11.78	730.6	.5277	11.46	730.6	.5244	220
240	12.49	741.7	.5469	12.14	741.6	.5436	11.81	741.5	.5403	240
260	12.86	752.7	.5624	12.50	752.6	.5591	12.16	752.5	.5558	260
280	13.23	763.7	.5776	12.86	763.7	.5743	12.51	763.6	.5710	280
	40 11.66°			**42** 13.81°			**44** 15.88°			
Sat.	*7.047*	*615.4*	*1.3125*	*6.731*	*616.0*	*1.3084*	*6.442*	*616.6*	*1.3046*	*Sat.*
20	7.203	620.4	1.3231	6.842	619.8	1.3164	6.513	619.1	1.3099	20
30	7.387	626.3	.3353	7.019	625.8	.3287	6.683	625.2	.3224	30
40	7.568	632.1	.3470	7.192	631.6	.3405	6.850	631.1	.3343	40
50	7.746	637.8	1.3583	7.363	637.3	1.3519	7.014	636.8	1.3457	**50**
60	7.922	643.4	.3692	7.531	643.0	.3628	7.176	642.5	.3567	60
70	8.096	648.9	.3797	7.697	648.5	.3734	7.336	648.1	.3674	70
80	8.268	654.4	.3900	7.862	654.1	.3838	7.494	653.7	.3778	80
90	8.439	659.9	.4000	8.026	659.5	.3939	7.650	659.2	.3880	90
100	8.609	665.3	1.4098	8.188	665.0	1.4037	7.806	664.7	1.3978	**100**
110	8.777	670.7	.4194	8.349	670.4	.4133	7.960	670.1	.4075	110
120	8.945	676.1	.4288	8.510	675.9	.4228	8.114	675.6	.4170	120
130	9.112	681.5	.4381	8.669	681.3	.4320	8.267	681.0	.4263	130
140	9.278	686.9	.4471	8.828	686.7	.4411	8.419	686.4	.4354	140
150	9.444	692.3	1.4561	8.986	692.1	1.4501	8.570	691.9	1.4444	**150**
160	9.609	697.7	.4648	9.144	697.5	.4589	8.721	697.3	.4532	160
170	9.774	703.1	.4735	9.301	702.9	.4676	8.871	702.7	.4619	170
180	9.938	708.5	.4820	9.458	708.3	.4761	9.021	708.1	.4704	180
190	10.10	714.0	.4904	9.614	713.8	.4845	9.171	713.6	.4789	190
200	10.27	719.4	1.4987	9.770	719.2	1.4928	9.320	719.0	1.4872	**200**
220	10.59	730.3	.5150	10.08	730.1	.5091	9.617	730.0	.5035	220
240	10.92	741.3	.5309	10.39	741.1	.5251	9.913	741.0	.5195	240
260	11.24	752.3	.5465	10.70	752.2	.5406	10.21	752.0	.5350	260
280	11.56	763.4	.5617	11.01	763.3	.5559	10.50	763.1	.5503	280
300	11.88	774.6	.5766	11.31	774.5	1.5708	10.80	774.3	1.5652	**300**

TABLE 2-17. PROPERTIES OF SUPERHEATED AMMONIA VAPOR (*Continued*)

[V = volume in ft.³/lb.; H = heat content in Btu./lb.; S = entropy in Btu./lb. °F.]

Absolute pressure in lbs./in.² (Saturation temperature in italics.)

Temp. °F.	38 9.42° V	H	S	39 10.55° V	H	S	40 11.66° V	H	S	Temp. °F.
Sat.	*7.396*	*614.7*	*1.3168*	*7.217*	*615.0*	*1.3146*	*7.047*	*615.4*	*1.3125*	Sat.
10	7.407	615.0	1.3175	....			....			10
20	7.603	621.0	.3301	7.398	620.7	1.3266	7.203	620.4	1.3231	20
30	7.795	626.9	.3422	7.586	626.6	.3387	7.387	626.3	.3353	30
40	7.983	632.6	.3538	7.770	632.4	.3504	7.568	632.1	.3470	40
50	8.170	638.3	1.3650	7.952	638.0	1.3616	7.746	637.8	1.3583	50
60	8.353	643.8	.3758	8.132	643.6	.3724	7.922	643.4	.3692	60
70	8.535	649.3	.3863	8.310	649.1	.3830	8.096	648.9	.3797	70
80	8.716	654.8	.3965	8.486	654.6	.3932	8.268	654.4	.3900	80
90	8.895	660.2	.4065	8.661	660.1	.4032	8.439	659.9	.4000	90
100	9.073	665.6	1.4163	8.835	665.5	1.4130	8.609	665.3	1.4098	100
110	9.250	671.0	.4258	9.008	670.9	.4226	8.777	670.7	.4194	110
120	9.426	676.4	.4352	9.179	676.3	.4320	8.945	676.1	.4288	120
130	9.602	681.8	.4444	9.351	681.7	.4412	9.112	681.5	.4381	130
140	9.776	687.2	.4534	9.521	687.1	.4503	9.278	686.9	.4471	140
150	9.950	692.6	1.4623	9.691	692.5	1.4592	9.444	692.3	1.4561	150
160	10.12	698.0	.4711	9.860	697.8	.4679	9.609	697.7	.4648	160
170	10.30	703.3	.4797	10.03	703.2	.4766	9.774	703.1	.4735	170
180	10.47	708.7	.4883	10.20	708.6	.4851	9.938	708.5	.4820	180
190	10.64	714.2	.4966	10.36	714.1	.4935	10.10	714.0	.4904	190
200	10.81	719.6	1.5049	10.53	719.5	1.5018	10.27	719.4	1.4987	200
220	11.16	730.5	.5212	10.87	730.4	.5181	10.59	730.3	.5150	220
240	11.50	741.4	.5371	11.20	741.3	.5340	10.92	741.3	.5309	240
260	11.84	752.4	.5526	11.53	752.4	.5495	11.24	752.3	.5465	260
280	12.18	763.5	.5678	11.86	763.5	.5647	11.56	763.4	.5617	280

Temp. °F.	46 17.87° V	H	S	48 19.80° V	H	S	50 21.67° V	H	S	Temp. °F.
Sat.	*6.177*	*617.2*	*1.3009*	*5.934*	*617.7*	*1.2973*	*5.710*	*618.2*	*1.2939*	Sat.
20	6.213	618.5	1.3036	5.937	617.8	1.2976	....			20
30	6.377	624.6	.3162	6.096	624.0	.3103	5.838	623.4	1.3046	30
40	6.538	630.5	.3283	6.251	630.0	.3225	5.988	629.5	.3169	40
50	6.696	636.4	1.3398	6.404	635.9	1.3341	6.135	635.4	1.3286	50
60	6.851	642.1	.3509	6.554	641.6	.3453	6.280	641.2	.3399	60
70	7.005	647.7	.3617	6.702	647.3	.3561	6.423	646.9	.3508	70
80	7.157	653.3	.3721	6.848	652.9	.3666	6.564	652.6	.3613	80
90	7.308	658.9	.3823	6.993	658.5	.3768	6.704	658.2	.3716	90
100	7.457	664.4	1.3922	7.137	664.0	1.3868	6.843	663.7	1.3816	100
110	7.605	669.8	.4019	7.280	669.5	.3965	6.980	669.2	.3914	110
120	7.753	675.3	.4114	7.421	675.0	.4061	7.117	674.7	.4009	120
130	7.899	680.7	.4207	7.562	680.5	.4154	7.252	680.2	.4103	130
140	8.045	686.2	.4299	7.702	685.9	.4246	7.387	685.7	.4195	140
150	8.190	691.6	1.4389	7.842	691.4	1.4336	7.521	691.1	1.4286	150
160	8.335	697.1	.4477	7.981	696.8	.4425	7.655	696.6	.4374	160
170	8.479	702.5	.4564	8.119	702.3	.4512	7.788	702.1	.4462	170
180	8.623	707.9	.4650	8.257	707.7	.4598	7.921	707.5	.4548	180
190	8.766	713.4	.4735	8.395	713.2	.4683	8.053	713.0	.4633	190
200	8.909	718.8	1.4818	8.532	718.7	1.4766	8.185	718.5	1.4716	200
220	9.194	729.8	.4981	8.805	729.6	.4930	8.448	729.4	.4880	220
240	9.477	740.8	.5141	9.077	740.6	.5090	8.710	740.5	.5040	240
260	9.760	751.9	.5297	9.348	751.7	.5246	8.970	751.6	.5197	260
280	10.04	763.0	.5450	9.619	762.9	.5399	9.230	762.7	.5350	280
300	10.32	774.2	1.5599	9.888	774.1	1.5548	9.489	774.0	1.5500	300

TABLE 2-17. PROPERTIES OF SUPERHEATED AMMONIA VAPOR (*Continued*)

[V = volume in ft.³/lb.; H = heat content in Btu./lb.; S = entropy in Btu./lb. °F.]

Temp. °F.	Absolute pressure in lbs./in.² (Saturation temperatures in italics.)									Temp. °F.
	50 *21.67°*			52 *23.48°*			54 *25.33°*			
	V	H	S	V	H	S	V	H	S	
Sat.	*5.710*	*618.2*	*1.2939*	*5.502*	*618.7*	*1.2906*	*5.309*	*619.2*	*1.2875*	*Sat.*
30	5.838	623.4	1.3046	5.599	622.8	1.2991	5.378	622.2	1.2937	30
40	5.988	629.5	.3169	5.744	629.0	.3114	5.519	628.4	.3062	40
50	6.135	635.4	1.3286	5.887	634.9	1.3233	5.657	634.4	1.3181	50
60	6.280	641.2	.3399	6.027	640.8	.3346	5.793	640.3	.3295	60
70	6.423	646.9	.3508	6.165	646.5	.3456	5.927	646.1	.3406	70
80	6.564	652.6	.3613	6.302	652.2	.3562	6.059	651.8	.3513	80
90	6.704	658.2	.3716	6.437	657.8	.3665	6.190	657.5	.3616	90
100	6.843	663.7	1.3816	6.571	663.4	1.3766	6.319	663.1	1.3717	100
110	6.980	669.2	.3914	6.704	668.9	.3864	6.447	668.6	.3816	110
120	7.117	674.7	.4009	6.835	674.4	.3960	6.575	674.2	.3912	120
130	7.252	680.2	.4103	6.966	679.9	.4054	6.701	679.7	.4006	130
140	7.387	685.7	.4195	7.096	685.4	.4146	6.827	685.2	.4099	140
150	7.521	691.1	1.4286	7.225	690.9	1.4237	6.952	690.7	1.4190	150
160	7.655	696.6	.4374	7.354	696.4	.4326	7.076	696.1	.4279	160
170	7.788	702.1	.4462	7.483	701.8	.4413	7.200	701.6	.4367	170
180	7.921	707.5	.4548	7.611	707.3	.4500	7.323	707.1	.4453	180
190	8.053	713.0	.4633	7.738	712.8	.4585	7.446	712.6	.4538	190
200	8.185	718.5	1.4716	7.865	718.3	1.4668	7.569	718.1	1.4622	200
210	8.317	724.0	.4799	7.992	723.8	.4751	7.691	723.6	.4705	210
220	8.448	729.4	.4880	8.118	729.3	.4833	7.813	729.1	.4787	220
240	8.710	740.5	.5040	8.370	740.3	.4993	8.056	740.2	.4947	240
260	8.970	751.6	.5197	8.621	751.4	.5149	8.298	751.3	.5104	260
280	9.230	762.7	1.5350	8.871	762.6	1.5303	8.539	762.5	1.5257	280
300	9.489	774.0	.5500	9.120	773.8	.5453	8.779	773.7	.5407	300

Temp. °F.	60 *30.21°*			62 *31.78°*			64 *33.31°*			Temp. °F.
	V	H	S	V	H	S	V	H	S	
Sat.	*4.805*	*620.5*	*1.2787*	*4.658*	*620.9*	*1.2759*	*4.519*	*621.3*	*1.2733*	*Sat.*
40	4.933	626.8	1.2913	4.762	626.2	1.2866	4.602	625.6	1.2820	40
50	5.060	632.9	1.3035	4.886	632.4	1.2989	4.723	631.9	1.2944	50
60	5.184	639.0	.3152	5.007	638.5	.3107	4.842	638.0	.3063	60
70	5.307	644.9	.3265	5.127	644.4	.3220	4.958	644.0	.3177	70
80	5.428	650.7	.3373	5.244	650.3	.3330	5.072	649.9	.3287	80
90	5.547	656.4	.3479	5.360	656.0	.3435	5.185	655.7	.3393	90
100	5.665	662.1	1.3581	5.474	661.7	1.3538	5.296	661.4	1.3496	100
110	5.781	667.7	.3681	5.588	667.4	.3638	5.406	667.1	.3597	110
120	5.897	673.3	.3778	5.700	673.0	.3736	5.516	672.7	.3695	120
130	6.012	678.9	.3873	5.811	678.6	.3831	5.624	678.3	.3791	130
140	6.126	684.4	.3966	5.922	684.2	.3925	5.731	683.9	.3885	140
150	6.239	689.9	1.4058	6.032	689.7	1.4017	5.838	689.5	1.3977	150
160	6.352	695.5	.4148	6.142	695.2	.4107	5.944	695.0	.4067	160
170	6.464	701.0	.4236	6.250	700.8	.4195	6.050	700.5	.4156	170
180	6.576	706.5	.4323	6.359	706.3	.4282	6.155	706.1	.4243	180
190	6.687	712.0	.4409	6.467	711.8	.4368	6.260	711.6	.4329	190
200	6.798	717.5	1.4493	6.574	717.3	1.4453	6.364	717.2	1.4413	200
210	6.909	723.1	.4576	6.681	722.9	.4536	6.468	722.7	.4497	210
220	7.019	728.6	.4658	6.788	728.4	.4618	6.572	728.3	.4579	220
230	7.129	734.1	.4739	6.895	734.0	.4699	6.675	733.8	.4660	230
240	7.238	739.7	.4819	7.001	739.5	.4779	6.778	739.4	.4741	240
260	7.457	750.9	1.4976	7.213	750.7	1.4937	6.984	750.6	1.4898	260
280	7.675	762.1	.5130	7.424	761.9	.5091	7.188	761.8	.5052	280
300	7.892	773.3	.5281	7.634	773.2	.5241	7.392	773.1	.5203	300

TABLE 2-17. PROPERTIES OF SUPERHEATED AMMONIA VAPOR (*Continued*)
[V = volume in ft.³/lb.; H = heat content in Btu./lb.; S = entropy in Btu./lb. °F.]

Temp. °F.	Absolute pressure in lbs./in.² (Saturation temperature in italics.)									Temp. °F.
	56 *26.94°*			**58** *28.59°*			**60** *30.21°*			
	V	H	S	V	H	S	V	H	S	
Sat.	*5.129*	*619.7*	*1.2844*	*4.962*	*620.1*	*1.2815*	*4.805*	*620.5*	*1.2787*	Sat.
30	5.172	621.6	1.2884	4.981	621.0	1.2834	....	....	....	30
40	5.310	627.9	.3011	5.115	627.3	.2961	4.933	626.8	1.2913	40
50	5.444	633.9	1.3131	5.245	633.4	1.3082	5.060	632.9	1.3035	50
60	5.576	639.9	.3246	5.373	639.4	.3199	5.184	639.0	.3152	60
70	5.706	645.7	.3357	5.499	645.3	.3310	5.307	644.9	.3265	70
80	5.834	651.4	.3465	5.624	651.1	.3418	5.428	650.7	.3373	80
90	5.960	657.1	.3569	5.746	656.8	.3523	5.547	656.4	.3479	90
100	6.085	662.7	1.3670	5.868	662.4	1.3625	5.665	662.1	1.3581	100
110	6.209	668.3	.3769	5.988	668.0	.3724	5.781	667.7	.3681	110
120	6.333	673.9	.3866	6.107	673.6	.3821	5.897	673.3	.3778	120
130	6.455	679.4	.3961	6.226	679.1	.3916	6.012	678.9	.3873	130
140	6.576	684.9	.4053	6.343	684.7	.4009	6.126	684.4	.3966	140
150	6.697	690.4	1.4144	6.460	690.2	1.4100	6.239	689.9	1.4058	150
160	6.817	695.9	.4234	6.577	695.7	.4190	6.352	695.5	.4148	160
170	6.937	701.4	.4322	6.692	701.2	.4278	6.464	701.0	.4236	170
180	7.056	706.9	.4408	6.808	706.7	.4365	6.576	706.5	.4323	180
190	7.175	712.4	.4494	6.923	712.2	.4450	6.687	712.0	.4409	190
200	7.294	717.9	1.4578	7.037	717.7	1.4535	6.798	717.5	1.4493	200
210	7.412	723.4	.4661	7.151	723.2	.4618	6.909	723.1	.4576	210
220	7.529	728.9	.4743	7.265	728.8	.4700	7.019	728.6	.4658	220
240	7.764	740.0	.4903	7.492	739.9	.4860	7.238	739.7	.4819	240
260	7.998	751.1	.5060	7.718	751.0	.5017	7.457	750.9	.4976	260
280	8.230	762.3	1.5213	7.943	762.2	1.5171	7.675	762.1	1.5130	280
300	8.462	773.6	.5364	8.167	773.5	.5321	7.892	773.3	.5281	300
	66 *34.81°*			**68** *36.27°*			**70** *37.70°*			
Sat.	*4.389*	*621.7*	*1.2707*	*4.267*	*622.0*	*1.2682*	*4.151*	*622.4*	*1.2658*	Sat.
40	4.452	625.1	1.2775	4.310	624.5	1.2731	4.177	623.9	1.2688	40
50	4.570	631.4	1.2900	4.426	630.9	1.2858	4.290	630.4	1.2816	50
60	4.686	637.6	.3020	4.539	637.1	.2978	4.401	636.6	.2937	60
70	4.799	643.6	.3135	4.650	643.2	.3094	4.509	642.7	.3054	70
80	4.910	649.5	.3245	4.758	649.1	.3205	4.615	648.7	.3166	80
90	5.020	655.3	.3352	4.865	655.0	.3312	4.719	654.6	.3274	90
100	5.129	661.1	1.3456	4.971	660.7	1.3417	4.822	660.4	1.3378	100
110	5.236	666.8	.3557	5.075	666.5	.3518	4.924	666.1	.3480	110
120	5.342	672.4	.3655	5.179	672.1	.3617	5.025	671.8	.3579	120
130	5.447	678.0	.3751	5.281	677.8	.3713	5.125	677.5	.3676	130
140	5.552	683.6	.3846	5.383	683.4	.3807	5.224	683.1	.3770	140
150	5.656	689.2	1.3938	5.484	689.0	1.3900	5.323	688.7	1.3863	150
160	5.759	694.8	.4028	5.585	694.5	.3991	5.420	694.3	.3954	160
170	5.862	700.3	.4117	5.685	700.1	.4080	5.518	699.9	.4043	170
180	5.964	705.9	.4205	5.784	705.7	.4167	5.615	705.5	.4131	180
190	6.066	711.4	.4291	5.883	711.2	.4254	5.711	711.0	.4217	190
200	6.167	717.0	1.4375	5.982	716.8	1.4338	5.807	716.6	1.4302	200
210	6.268	722.5	.4459	6.080	722.3	.4422	5.902	722.2	.4386	210
220	6.369	728.1	.4541	6.179	727.9	.4505	5.998	727.7	.4469	220
230	6.470	733.7	.4623	6.275	733.5	.4586	6.093	733.3	.4550	230
240	6.570	739.2	.4703	6.373	739.1	.4666	6.187	738.9	.4631	240
260	6.769	750.4	1.4861	6.567	750.3	1.4824	6.376	750.1	1.4789	260
280	6.968	761.7	.5015	6.760	761.5	.4979	6.563	761.4	.4943	280
300	7.165	773.0	.5166	6.952	772.8	.5130	6.750	772.7	.5095	300

TABLE 2-17.   PROPERTIES OF SUPERHEATED AMMONIA VAPOR (*Continued*)
[V = volume in ft.³/lb.; H = heat content in Btu./lb.; S = entropy in Btu./lb. °F.]

Temp. °F.	Absolute pressure in lbs./in.² (Saturation temperature in italics.)									Temp. °F.
	75 *41.13°*			80 *44.40°*			85 *47.50°*			
	V	H	S	V	H	S	V	H	S	
Sat.	*3.887*	*623.2*	*1.2599*	*3.655*	*624.0*	*1.2545*	*3.449*	*624.7*	*1.2494*	*Sat.*
50	3.982	629.1	1.2715	3.712	627.7	1.2619	3.473	626.4	1.2527	50
60	4.087	635.5	.2839	3.812	634.3	.2745	3.569	633.0	.2656	60
70	4.189	641.7	.2957	3.909	640.6	.2866	3.662	639.5	.2779	70
80	4.289	647.7	.3071	4.005	646.7	.2981	3.753	645.7	.2896	80
90	4.388	653.7	.3180	4.098	652.8	.3092	3.842	651.8	.3008	90
100	4.485	659.6	1.3286	4.190	658.7	1.3199	3.930	657.8	1.3117	100
110	4.581	665.4	.3389	4.281	664.6	.3303	4.016	663.8	.3221	110
120	4.676	671.1	.3489	4.371	670.4	.3404	4.101	669.6	.3323	120
130	4.770	676.8	.3586	4.460	676.1	.3502	4.186	675.4	.3422	130
140	4.863	682.5	.3682	4.548	681.8	.3598	4.269	681.2	.3519	140
150	4.956	688.1	1.3775	4.635	687.5	1.3692	4.352	686.9	1.3614	150
160	5.048	693.7	.3866	4.722	693.2	.3784	4.434	692.6	.3706	160
170	5.139	699.3	.3956	4.808	698.8	.3874	4.515	698.2	.3797	170
180	5.230	704.9	.4044	4.893	704.4	.3963	4.596	703.9	.3886	180
190	5.320	710.5	.4131	4.978	710.0	.4050	4.677	709.5	.3974	190
200	5.410	716.1	1.4217	5.063	715.6	1.4136	4.757	715.2	1.4060	200
210	5.500	721.7	.4301	5.147	721.3	.4220	4.836	720.8	.4145	210
220	5.589	727.3	.4384	5.231	726.9	.4304	4.916	726.4	.4228	220
230	5.678	732.9	.4466	5.315	732.5	.4386	4.995	732.1	.4311	230
240	5.767	738.5	.4546	5.398	738.1	.4467	5.074	737.7	.4392	240
250	5.855	744.1	1.4625	5.482	743.8	1.4547	5.152	743.4	1.4472	250
260	5.943	749.8	.4705	5.565	749.4	.4626	5.230	749.0	.4551	260
280	6.119	761.1	.4860	5.730	760.7	.4781	5.386	760.4	.4707	280
300	6.294	772.4	.5011	5.894	772.1	.4933	5.541	771.8	.4859	300

Temp. °F.	100 *56.05°*			105 *58.67°*			110 *61.21°*			Temp. °F.
	V	H	S	V	H	S	V	H	S	
Sat.	*2.952*	*626.5*	*1.2356*	*2.817*	*627.0*	*1.2314*	*2.693*	*627.5*	*1.2275*	*Sat.*
70	3.068	636.0	1.2539	2.907	634.9	1.2464	2.761	633.7	1.2392	70
80	3.149	642.6	.2661	2.985	641.5	.2589	2.837	640.5	.2519	80
90	3.227	649.0	.2778	3.061	648.0	.2708	2.910	647.0	.2640	90
100	3.304	655.2	1.2891	3.135	654.3	1.2822	2.981	653.4	1.2755	100
110	3.380	661.3	.2999	3.208	660.5	.2931	3.051	659.7	.2866	110
120	3.454	667.3	.3104	3.279	666.6	.3037	3.120	665.8	.2972	120
130	3.527	673.3	.3206	3.350	672.6	.3139	3.188	671.9	.3076	130
140	3.600	679.2	.3305	3.419	678.5	.3239	3.255	677.8	.3176	140
150	3.672	685.0	1.3401	3.488	684.4	1.3336	3.321	683.7	1.3274	150
160	3.743	690.8	.3495	3.556	690.2	.3431	3.386	689.6	.3370	160
170	3.813	696.6	.3588	3.623	696.0	.3524	3.451	695.4	.3463	170
180	3.883	702.3	.3678	3.690	701.8	.3615	3.515	701.2	.3555	180
190	3.952	708.0	.3767	3.757	707.5	.3704	3.579	707.0	.3644	190
200	4.021	713.7	1.3854	3.823	713.3	1.3792	3.642	712.8	1.3732	200
210	4.090	719.4	.3940	3.888	719.0	.3878	3.705	718.5	.3819	210
220	4.158	725.1	.4024	3.954	724.7	.3963	3.768	724.3	.3904	220
230	4.226	730.8	.4108	4.019	730.4	.4046	3.830	730.0	.3988	230
240	4.294	736.5	.4190	4.083	736.1	.4129	3.892	735.7	.4070	240
250	4.361	742.2	1.4271	4.148	741.9	1.4210	3.954	741.5	1.4151	250
260	4.428	747.9	.4350	4.212	747.6	.4290	4.015	747.2	.4232	260
270	4.495	753.6	.4429	4.276	753.3	.4369	4.076	752.9	.4311	270
280	4.562	759.4	.4507	4.340	759.0	.4447	4.137	758.7	.4389	280
290	4.629	765.1	.4584	4.403	764.8	.4524	4.198	764.5	.4466	290
300	4.695	770.8	1.4660	4.466	770.5	1.4600	4.259	770.2	1.4543	300

TABLE 2-17. PROPERTIES OF SUPERHEATED AMMONIA VAPOR (*Continued*)
[V = volume in ft.³/lb.; H = heat content in Btu./lb.; S = entropy in Btu./lb. °F.]

Temp. °F.	Absolute pressure in lbs./in.² (Saturation temperature in italics.)									Temp. °F.
	90 *50.47°*			95 *53.32°*			100 *56.05°*			
	V	H	S	V	H	S	V	H	S	
Sat.	*3.266*	*625.3*	*1.2445*	*3.101*	*625.9*	*1.2399*	*2.952*	*626.5*	*1.2356*	*Sat.*
50	....	....	....	....	....	....	....	....	....	50
60	3.353	631.8	1.2571	3.160	630.5	1.2489	2.985	629.3	1.2409	60
70	3.442	638.3	.2695	3.245	637.2	.2616	3.068	636.0	.2539	70
80	3.529	644.7	.2814	3.329	643.6	.2736	3.149	642.6	.2661	80
90	3.614	650.9	.2928	3.411	649.9	.2852	3.227	649.0	.2778	90
100	3.698	657.0	1.3038	3.491	656.1	1.2963	3.304	655.2	1.2891	100
110	3.780	663.0	.3144	3.570	662.1	.3070	3.380	661.3	.2999	110
120	3.862	668.9	.3247	3.647	668.1	.3174	3.454	667.3	.3104	120
130	3.942	674.7	.3347	3.724	674.0	.3275	3.527	673.3	.3206	130
140	4.021	680.5	.3444	3.799	679.8	.3373	3.600	679.2	.3305	140
150	4.100	686.3	1.3539	3.874	685.6	1.3469	3.672	685.0	1.3401	150
160	4.178	692.0	.3633	3.949	691.4	.3562	3.743	690.8	.3495	160
170	4.255	697.7	.3724	4.022	697.1	.3654	3.813	696.6	.3588	170
180	4.332	703.4	.3813	4.096	702.8	.3744	3.883	702.3	.3678	180
190	4.408	709.0	.3901	4.168	708.5	.3833	3.952	708.0	.3767	190
200	4.484	714.7	1.3988	4.241	714.2	1.3919	4.021	713.7	1.3854	200
210	4.560	720.4	.4073	4.313	719.9	.4005	4.090	719.4	.3940	210
220	4.635	726.0	.4157	4.384	725.6	.4089	4.158	725.1	.4024	220
230	4.710	731.7	.4239	4.455	731.3	.4172	4.226	730.8	.4108	230
240	4.785	737.3	.4321	4.526	736.9	.4254	4.294	736.5	.4190	240
250	4.859	743.0	1.4401	4.597	742.6	1.4334	4.361	742.2	1.4271	250
260	4.933	748.7	.4481	4.668	748.3	.4414	4.428	747.9	.4350	260
280	5.081	760.0	.4637	4.808	759.7	.4570	4.562	759.4	.4507	280
300	5.228	771.5	.4789	4.947	771.2	.4723	4.695	770.8	.4660	300

Temp. °F.	115 *63.65°*			120 *66.02°*			125 *68.31°*			Temp. °F.
	V	H	S	V	H	S	V	H	S	
Sat.	*2.580*	*628.0*	*1.2237*	*2.476*	*628.4*	*1.2201*	*2.380*	*628.8*	*1.2166*	*Sat.*
70	2.628	632.5	1.2323	2.505	631.3	1.2255	2.392	630.0	1.2189	70
80	2.701	639.4	.2451	2.576	638.3	.2386	2.461	637.2	.2322	80
90	2.772	646.0	.2574	2.645	645.0	.2510	2.528	644.0	.2448	90
100	2.841	652.5	1.2690	2.712	651.6	1.2628	2.593	650.7	1.2568	100
110	2.909	658.8	.2802	2.778	658.0	.2741	2.657	657.1	.2682	110
120	2.975	665.0	.2910	2.842	664.2	.2850	2.719	663.5	.2792	120
130	3.040	671.1	.3015	2.905	670.4	.2956	2.780	669.7	.2899	130
140	3.105	677.2	.3116	2.967	676.5	.3058	2.840	675.8	.3002	140
150	3.168	683.1	1.3215	3.029	682.5	1.3157	2.900	681.8	1.3102	150
160	3.231	689.0	.3311	3.089	688.4	.3254	2.958	687.8	.3199	160
170	3.294	694.9	.3405	3.149	694.3	.3348	3.016	693.7	.3294	170
180	3.355	700.7	.3497	3.209	700.2	.3441	3.074	699.6	.3387	180
190	3.417	706.5	.3587	3.268	706.0	.3531	3.131	705.5	.3478	190
200	3.477	712.3	1.3675	3.326	711.8	1.3620	3.187	711.3	1.3567	200
210	3.538	718.1	.3762	3.385	717.6	.3707	3.243	717.2	.3654	210
220	3.598	723.8	.3847	3.442	723.4	.3793	3.299	723.0	.3740	220
230	3.658	729.6	.3931	3.500	729.2	.3877	3.354	728.8	.3825	230
240	3.717	735.3	.4014	3.557	734.9	.3960	3.409	734.5	.3908	240
250	3.776	741.1	1.4096	3.614	740.7	1.4042	3.464	740.3	1.3990	250
260	3.835	746.8	.4176	3.671	746.5	.4123	3.519	746.1	.4071	260
270	3.894	752.6	.4256	3.727	752.2	.4202	3.573	751.9	.4151	270
280	3.952	758.4	.4334	3.783	758.0	.4281	3.627	757.7	.4230	280
290	4.011	764.1	.4411	3.839	763.8	.4359	3.681	763.5	.4308	290
300	4.069	769.9	1.4488	3.895	769.6	1.4435	3.735	769.3	1.4385	300

TABLE 2-17. PROPERTIES OF SUPERHEATED AMMONIA VAPOR (Continued)
[V = volume in ft.³/lb.; H = heat content in Btu./lb.; S = entropy in Btu./lb. °F.]

Temp. °F.	125 68.31°			130 70.53°			135 72.69°			Temp. °F.
	V	H	S	V	H	S	V	H	S	
Sat.	2.380	628.8	1.2166	2.291	629.2	1.2132	2.209	629.6	1.2100	Sat.
80	2.461	637.2	1.2322	2.355	636.0	1.2260	2.257	634.9	1.2199	80
90	2.528	644.0	.2448	2.421	643.0	.2388	2.321	642.0	.2329	90
100	2.593	650.7	1.2568	2.484	649.7	1.2509	2.382	648.8	1.2452	100
110	2.657	657.1	.2682	2.546	656.3	.2625	2.442	655.4	.2569	110
120	2.719	663.5	.2792	2.606	662.7	.2736	2.501	661.9	.2681	120
130	2.780	669.7	.2899	2.665	668.9	.2843	2.559	668.2	.2790	130
140	2.840	675.8	.3002	2.724	675.1	.2947	2.615	674.4	.2894	140
150	2.900	681.8	1.3102	2.781	681.2	1.3048	2.671	680.5	1.2996	150
160	2.958	687.8	.3199	2.838	687.2	.3146	2.726	686.6	.3094	160
170	3.016	693.7	.3294	2.894	693.2	.3241	2.780	692.6	.3191	170
180	3.074	699.6	.3387	2.949	699.1	.3335	2.834	698.6	.3284	180
190	3.131	705.5	.3478	3.004	705.0	.3426	2.887	704.5	.3376	190
200	3.187	711.3	1.3567	3.059	710.9	1.3516	2.940	710.4	1.3466	200
210	3.243	717.2	.3654	3.113	716.7	.3604	2.992	716.2	.3554	210
220	3.299	723.0	.3740	3.167	722.5	.3690	3.044	722.1	.3641	220
230	3.354	728.8	.3825	3.220	728.3	.3775	3.096	727.9	.3726	230
240	3.409	734.5	.3908	3.273	734.1	.3858	3.147	733.7	.3810	240
250	3.464	740.3	1.3990	3.326	739.9	1.3941	3.198	739.6	1.3893	250
260	3.519	746.1	.4071	3.379	745.7	.4022	3.249	745.4	.3974	260
270	3.573	751.9	.4151	3.431	751.5	.4102	3.300	751.2	.4054	270
280	3.627	757.7	.4230	3.483	757.3	.4181	3.350	757.0	.4133	280
290	3.681	763.5	.4308	3.535	763.1	.4259	3.400	762.8	.4212	290
300	3.735	769.3	1.4385	3.587	769.0	1.4336	3.450	768.6	1.4289	300
320	3.842	780.9	.4536	3.690	780.6	.4487	3.550	780.3	.4441	320
	150 78.81°			160 82.64°			170 86.29°			
Sat.	1.994	630.5	1.2009	1.872	631.1	1.1952	1.764	631.6	1.1900	Sat.
90	2.061	638.8	1.2161	1.914	636.6	1.2055	1.784	634.4	1.1952	90
100	2.118	645.9	1.2289	1.969	643.9	1.2186	1.837	641.9	1.2087	100
110	2.174	652.8	.2410	2.023	651.0	.2311	1.889	649.1	.2215	110
120	2.228	659.4	.2526	2.075	657.8	.2429	1.939	656.1	.2336	120
130	2.281	665.9	.2638	2.125	664.4	.2542	1.988	662.8	.2452	130
140	2.334	672.3	.2745	2.175	670.9	.2652	2.035	669.4	.2563	140
150	2.385	678.6	1.2849	2.224	677.2	1.2757	2.081	675.9	1.2669	150
160	2.435	684.8	.2949	2.272	683.5	.2859	2.127	682.3	.2773	160
170	2.485	690.9	.3047	2.319	689.7	.2958	2.172	688.5	.2873	170
180	2.534	696.9	.3142	2.365	695.8	.3054	2.216	694.7	.2971	180
190	2.583	702.9	.3236	2.411	701.9	.3148	2.260	700.8	.3066	190
200	2.631	708.9	1.3327	2.457	707.9	1.3240	2.303	706.9	1.3159	200
210	2.679	714.8	.3416	2.502	713.9	.3331	2.346	713.0	.3249	210
220	2.726	720.7	.3504	2.547	719.9	.3419	2.389	719.0	.3338	220
230	2.773	726.6	.3590	2.591	725.8	.3506	2.431	724.9	.3426	230
240	2.820	732.5	.3675	2.635	731.7	.3591	2.473	730.9	.3512	240
250	2.866	738.4	1.3758	2.679	737.6	1.3675	2.514	736.8	1.3596	250
260	2.912	744.3	.3840	2.723	743.5	.3757	2.555	742.8	.3679	260
270	2.958	750.1	.3921	2.766	749.4	.3838	2.596	748.7	.3761	270
280	3.004	756.0	.4001	2.809	755.3	.3919	2.637	754.6	.3841	280
290	3.049	761.8	.4079	2.852	761.2	.3998	2.678	760.5	.3921	290
300	3.095	767.7	1.4157	2.895	767.1	1.4076	2.718	766.4	1.3999	300
320	3.185	779.4	.4310	2.980	778.9	.4229	2.798	778.3	.4153	320
340	3.274	791.2	.4459	3.064	790.7	.4379	2.878	790.1	.4303	340

TABLE 2-17. PROPERTIES OF SUPERHEATED AMMONIA VAPOR (*Continued*)
[V = volume in ft.³/lb.; H = heat content in Btu./lb.; S = entropy in Btu./lb. °F.]

	Absolute pressure in lbs./in.² (Saturation temperature in italics.)									
Temp. °F.	**140** 74.79°			**145** 76.83°			**150** 78.81°			Temp. °F.
	V	H	S	V	H	S	V	H	S	
Sat.	*2.132*	*629.9*	*1.2068*	*2.061*	*630.2*	*1.2038*	*1.994*	*630.5*	*1.2009*	Sat.
80	2.166	633.8	1.2140	2.080	632.6	1.2082	2.001	631.4	1.2025	80
90	2.228	640.9	.2272	2.141	639.9	.2216	2.061	638.8	.2161	90
100	2.288	647.8	1.2396	2.200	646.9	1.2342	2.118	645.9	1.2289	100
110	2.347	654.5	.2515	2.257	653.6	.2462	2.174	652.8	.2410	110
120	2.404	661.1	.2628	2.313	660.2	.2577	2.228	659.4	.2526	120
130	2.460	667.4	.2738	2.368	666.7	.2687	2.281	665.9	.2638	130
140	2.515	673.7	.2843	2.421	673.0	.2793	2.334	672.3	.2745	140
150	2.569	679.9	1.2945	2.474	679.2	1.2896	2.385	678.6	1.2849	150
160	2.622	686.0	.3045	2.526	685.4	.2996	2.435	684.8	.2949	160
170	2.675	692.0	.3141	2.577	691.4	.3093	2.485	690.9	.3047	170
180	2.727	698.0	.3236	2.627	697.5	.3188	2.534	696.9	.3142	180
190	2.779	704.0	.3328	2.677	703.4	.3281	2.583	702.9	.3236	190
200	2.830	709.9	1.3418	2.727	709.4	1.3372	2.631	708.9	1.3327	200
210	2.880	715.8	.3507	2.776	715.3	.3461	2.679	714.8	.3416	210
220	2.931	721.6	.3594	2.825	721.2	.3548	2.726	720.7	.3504	220
230	2.981	727.5	.3679	2.873	727.1	.3634	2.773	726.6	.3590	230
240	3.030	733.3	.3763	2.921	732.9	.3718	2.820	732.5	.3675	240
250	3.080	739.2	1.3846	2.969	738.8	1.3801	2.866	738.4	1.3758	250
260	3.129	745.0	.3928	3.017	744.6	.3883	2.912	744.3	.3840	260
270	3.179	750.8	.4008	3.064	750.5	.3964	2.958	750.1	.3921	270
280	3.227	756.7	.4088	3.111	756.3	.4043	3.004	756.0	.4001	280
290	3.275	762.5	.4166	3.158	762.2	.4122	3.049	761.8	.4079	290
300	3.323	768.3	1.4243	3.205	768.0	1.4199	3.095	767.7	1.4157	300
320	3.420	780.0	.4395	3.298	779.7	.4352	3.185	779.4	.4310	320
	180 89.78°			**190** 93.13°			**200** 96.34°			
Sat.	*1.667*	*632.0*	*1.1850*	*1.581*	*632.4*	*1.1802*	*1.502*	*632.7*	*1.1756*	Sat.
90	1.668	632.2	1.1853	....	....	....	....	....	....	90
100	1.720	639.9	1.1992	1.615	637.8	1.1899	1.520	635.6	1.1809	100
110	1.770	647.3	.2123	1.663	645.4	.2034	1.567	643.4	.1947	110
120	1.818	654.4	.2247	1.710	652.6	.2160	1.612	650.9	.2077	120
130	1.865	661.3	.2364	1.755	659.7	.2281	1.656	658.1	.2200	130
140	1.910	668.0	.2477	1.799	666.5	.2396	1.698	665.0	.2317	140
150	1.955	674.6	1.2586	1.842	673.2	1.2506	1.740	671.8	1.2429	150
160	1.999	681.0	.2691	1.884	679.7	.2612	1.780	678.4	.2537	160
170	2.042	687.3	.2792	1.925	686.1	.2715	1.820	684.9	.2641	170
180	2.084	693.6	.2891	1.966	692.5	.2815	1.859	691.3	.2742	180
190	2.126	699.8	.2987	2.005	698.7	.2912	1.897	697.7	.2840	190
200	2.167	705.9	1.3081	2.045	704.9	1.3007	1.935	703.9	1.2935	200
210	2.208	712.0	.3172	2.084	711.1	.3099	1.972	710.1	.3029	210
220	2.248	718.1	.3262	2.123	717.2	.3189	2.009	716.3	.3120	220
230	2.288	724.1	.3350	2.161	723.2	.3278	2.046	722.4	.3209	230
240	2.328	730.1	.3436	2.199	729.3	.3365	2.082	728.4	.3296	240
250	2.367	736.1	1.3521	2.236	735.3	1.3450	2.118	734.5	1.3382	250
260	2.407	742.0	.3605	2.274	741.3	.3534	2.154	740.5	.3467	260
270	2.446	748.0	.3687	2.311	747.3	.3617	2.189	746.5	.3550	270
280	2.484	753.9	.3768	2.348	753.2	.3698	2.225	752.5	.3631	280
290	2.523	759.9	.3847	2.384	759.2	.3778	2.260	758.5	.3712	290
300	2.561	765.8	1.3926	2.421	765.2	1.3857	2.295	764.5	1.3791	300
320	2.637	777.7	.4081	2.493	777.1	.4012	2.364	776.5	.3947	320
340	2.713	789.6	.4231	2.565	789.0	.4163	2.432	788.5	.4099	340

TABLE 2-17. PROPERTIES OF SUPERHEATED AMMONIA VAPOR (*Continued*)

[V = volume in ft.³/lb.; H = heat content in Btu./lb.; S = entropy in Btu./lb. °F.]

Temp. °F.	Absolute pressure in lbs./in.² (Saturation temperature in italics.)									Temp. °F.
	200 *96.34°*			**210** *99.43°*			**220** *102.42°*			
	V	*H*	*S*	*V*	*H*	*S*	*V*	*H*	*S*	
Sat.	*1.502*	*632.7*	*1.1756*	*1.431*	*633.0*	*1.1713*	*1.367*	*633.2*	*1.1671*	*Sat.*
110	1.567	643.4	1.1947	1.480	641.5	1.1863	1.400	639.4	1.1781	110
120	1.612	650.9	.2077	1.524	649.1	.1996	1.443	647.3	.1917	120
130	1.656	658.1	.2200	1.566	656.4	.2121	1.485	654.8	.2045	130
140	1.698	665.0	.2317	1.608	663.5	.2240	1.525	662.0	.2167	140
150	1.740	671.8	1.2429	1.648	670.4	1.2354	1.564	669.0	1.2281	**150**
160	1.780	678.4	.2537	1.687	677.1	.2464	1.601	675.8	.2394	160
170	1.820	684.9	.2641	1.725	683.7	.2569	1.638	682.5	.2501	170
180	1.859	691.3	.2742	1.762	690.2	.2672	1.675	689.1	.2604	180
190	1.897	697.7	.2840	1.799	696.6	.2771	1.710	695.5	.2704	190
200	1.935	703.9	1.2935	1.836	702.9	1.2867	1.745	701.9	1.2801	**200**
210	1.972	710.1	.3029	1.872	709.2	.2961	1.780	708.2	.2896	210
220	2.009	716.3	.3120	1.907	715.3	.3053	1.814	714.4	.2989	220
230	2.046	722.4	.3209	1.942	721.5	.3143	1.848	720.6	.3079	230
240	2.082	728.4	.3296	1.977	727.6	.3231	1.881	726.8	.3168	240
250	2.118	734.5	1.3382	2.011	733.7	1.3317	1.914	732.9	1.3255	**250**
260	2.154	740.5	.3467	2.046	739.8	.3402	1.947	739.0	.3340	260
270	2.189	746.5	.3550	2.080	745.8	.3486	1.980	745.1	.3424	270
280	2.225	752.5	.3631	2.113	751.8	.3568	2.012	751.1	.3507	280
290	2.260	758.5	.3712	2.147	757.9	.3649	2.044	757.2	.3588	290
300	2.295	764.5	1.3791	2.180	763.9	1.3728	2.076	763.2	1.3668	**300**
320	2.364	776.5	.3947	2.246	775.9	.3884	2.140	775.3	.3825	320
340	2.432	788.5	.4099	2.312	787.9	.4037	2.203	787.4	.3978	340
360	2.500	800.5	.4247	2.377	800.0	.4186	2.265	799.5	.4127	360
380	2.568	812.5	.4392	2.442	812.0	.4331	2.327	811.6	.4273	380

Temp. °F.	**250** *110.80°*			**260** *113.48°*			**270** *115.97°*			Temp. °F.
Sat.	*1.202*	*633.8*	*1.1555*	*1.155*	*633.9*	*1.1518*	*1.112*	*633.9*	*1.1483*	*Sat.*
120	1.240	641.5	1.1690	1.182	639.5	1.1617	1.128	637.5	1.1544	120
130	1.278	649.6	.1827	1.220	647.8	.1757	1.166	645.9	.1689	130
140	1.316	657.2	.1956	1.257	655.6	.1889	1.202	653.9	.1823	140
150	1.352	664.6	1.2078	1.292	663.1	1.2014	1.236	661.6	1.1950	**150**
160	1.386	671.8	.2195	1.326	670.4	.2132	1.269	669.0	.2071	160
170	1.420	678.7	.2306	1.359	677.5	.2245	1.302	676.2	.2185	170
180	1.453	685.5	.2414	1.391	684.4	.2354	1.333	683.2	.2296	180
190	1.486	692.2	.2517	1.422	691.1	.2458	1.364	690.0	.2401	190
200	1.518	698.8	1.2617	1.453	697.7	1.2560	1.394	696.7	1.2504	**200**
210	1.549	705.3	.2715	1.484	704.3	.2658	1.423	703.3	.2603	210
220	1.580	711.7	.2810	1.514	710.7	.2754	1.452	709.8	.2700	220
230	1.610	718.0	.2902	1.543	717.1	.2847	1.481	716.2	.2794	230
240	1.640	724.3	.2993	1.572	723.4	.2938	1.509	722.6	.2885	240
250	1.670	730.5	1.3081	1.601	729.7	1.3027	1.537	728.9	1.2975	**250**
260	1.699	736.7	.3168	1.630	736.0	.3115	1.565	735.2	.3063	260
270	1.729	742.9	.3253	1.658	742.2	.3200	1.592	741.4	.3149	270
280	1.758	749.1	.3337	1.686	748.4	.3285	1.620	747.7	.3234	280
290	1.786	755.2	.3420	1.714	754.5	.3367	1.646	753.9	.3317	290
300	1.815	761.3	1.3501	1.741	760.7	1.3449	1.673	760.0	1.3399	**300**
320	1.872	773.5	.3659	1.796	772.9	.3608	1.726	772.3	.3559	320
340	1.928	785.7	.3814	1.850	785.2	.3763	1.778	784.6	.3714	340
360	1.983	797.9	.3964	1.904	797.4	.3914	1.830	796.9	.3866	360
380	2.038	810.1	.4111	1.957	809.6	.4062	1.881	809.1	.4014	380
400	2.093	822.3	1.4255	2.009	821.9	1.4206	1.932	821.4	1.4158	**400**

TABLE 2-17. PROPERTIES OF SUPERHEATED AMMONIA VAPOR (*Concluded*)
[V = volume in ft.^{3}/lb.; H = heat content in Btu./lb.; S = entropy in Btu./lb. °F.]

Temp. °F.	Absolute pressure in lbs./in.^{2} (Saturation temperature in italics.)									Temp. °F.
	230 *105.30°*			240 *108.09°*			250 *110.80°*			
	V	*H*	*S*	*V*	*H*	*S*	*V*	*H*	*S*	
Sat.	*1.307*	*633.4*	*1.1631*	*1.253*	*633.6*	*1.1592*	*1.202*	*633.8*	*1.1555*	*Sat.*
110	1.328	637.4	1.1700	1.261	635.3	1.1621	....	.....	......	110
120	1.370	645.4	.1840	1.302	643.5	.1764	1.240	641.5	1.1690	120
130	1.410	653.1	.1971	1.342	651.3	.1898	1,278	649.6	.1827	130
140	1.449	660.4	.2095	1.380	658.8	.2025	1.316	657.2	.1956	140
150	1.487	667.6	1.2213	1.416	666.1	1.2145	1.352	664.6	1,2078	150
160	1.524	674.5	.2325	1.452	673.1	.2259	1.386	671.8	.2195	160
170	1.559	681.3	.2434	1.487	680.0	.2369	1.420	678.7	.2306	170
180	1.594	687.9	.2538	1.521	686.7	.2475	1.453	685.5	.2414	180
190	1.629	694.4	.2640	1.554	693.3	.2577	1.486	692.2	.2517	190
200	1.663	700.9	1.2738	1.587	699.8	1.2677	1.518	698.8	1.2617	200
210	1.696	707.2	.2834	1.619	706.2	.2773	1.549	705.3	.2715	210
220	1.729	713.5	.2927	1.651	712.6	.2867	1.580	711.7	.2810	220
230	1.762	719.8	.3018	1.683	718.9	.2959	1.610	718.0	.2902	230
240	1.794	726.0	.3107	1.714	725.1	.3049	1.640	724.3	.2993	240
250	1.826	732.1	1.3195	1.745	731.3	1.3137	1.670	730.5	1.3081	250
260	1.857	738.3	.3281	1.775	737.5	.3224	1.699	736.7	.3168	260
270	1.889	744.4	.3365	1.805	743.6	.3308	1.729	742.9	.3253	270
280	1.920	750.5	.3448	1.835	749.8	.3392	1.758	749.1	.3337	280
290	1.951	756.5	.3530	1.865	755.9	.3474	1.786	755.2	.3420	290
300	1.982	762.6	1.3610	1.895	762.0	1.3554	1.815	761.3	1.3501	300
320	2.043	774.7	.3767	1.954	774.1	.3712	1.872	773.5	.3659	320
340	2.103	786.8	.3921	2.012	786.3	.3866	1.928	785.7	.3814	340
360	2.163	798.9	.4070	2.069	798.4	.4016	1.983	797.9	.3964	360
380	2.222	811.1	.4217	2.126	810.6	.4163	2.038	810.1	.4111	380
	280 *118.45°*			290 *120.86°*			300 *123.21°*			
Sat.	*1.072*	*634.0*	*1.1449*	*1.034*	*634.0*	*1.1415*	*0.999*	*634.0*	*1.1383*	*Sat.*
120	1.078	635.4	1.1473	....	.....	......				120
130	1.115	644.0	.1621	1.068	642.1	1.1554	1.023	640.1	1.1487	130
140	1.151	652.2	.1759	1.103	650.5	.1695	1.058	648.7	.1632	140
150	1.184	660.1	1.1888	1.136	658.5	1.1827	1.091	656.9	1.1767	150
160	1.217	667.6	.2011	1.168	666.1	.1952	1.123	664.7	.1894	160
170	1.249	674.9	.2127	1.199	673.5	.2070	1.153	672.2	.2014	170
180	1.279	681.9	.2239	1.229	680.7	.2183	1.183	679.5	.2129	180
190	1.309	688.9	.2346	1.259	687.7	.2292	1.211	686.5	.2239	190
200	1.339	695.6	1.2449	1.287	694.6	1.2396	1.239	693.5	1.2344	200
210	1.367	702.3	.2550	1.315	701.3	.2497	1.267	700.3	.2447	210
220	1.396	708.8	.2647	1.343	707.9	.2596	1.294	706.9	.2546	220
230	1.424	715.3	.2742	1.370	714.4	.2691	1.320	713.5	.2642	230
240	1.451	721.8	.2834	1.397	720.9	.2784	1.346	720.0	.2736	240
250	1.478	728.1	1.2924	1.423	727.3	1.2875	1.372	726.5	1.2827	250
260	1.505	734.4	.3013	1.449	733.7	.2964	1.397	732.9	.2917	260
270	1.532	740.7	.3099	1.475	740.0	.3051	1.422	739.2	.3004	270
280	1.558	747.0	.3184	1.501	746.3	.3137	1.447	745.5	.3090	280
290	1.584	753.2	.3268	1.526	752.5	.3221	1.472	751.8	.3175	290
300	1.610	759.4	1.3350	1.551	758.7	1.3303	1.496	758.1	1.3257	300
320	1.661	771.7	.3511	1.601	771.1	.3464	1.544	770.5	.3419	320
340	1.712	784.0	.3667	1.650	783.5	.3621	1.592	782.9	.3576	340
360	1.762	796.3	.3819	1.698	795.8	.3773	1.639	795.3	.3729	360
380	1.811	808.7	.3967	1.747	808.2	.3922	1.686	807.7	.3878	380
400	1.861	821.0	1.4112	1.794	820.5	1.4067	1.732	820.1	1.4024	400

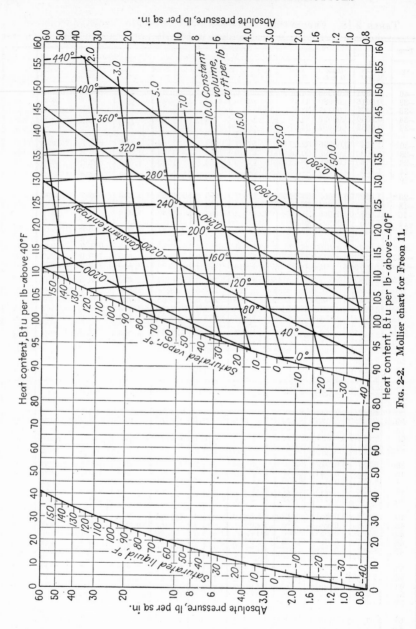

Fig. 2-2.   Mollier chart for Freon 11.

TABLE 2-18. FREON 11: PROPERTIES OF SATURATED VAPOR AND LIQUID*

Temp.	Abs. Pressure lb./in.²	Volume		Density		Heat Content from —40°			Entropy from —40°		Temp.
°F.		Liquid ft.³/lb.	Vapor ft.³/lb.	Liquid lb./ft.²	Vapor lb./ft.²	Liquid Btu./lb.	Latent Btu./lb.	Vapor Btu./lb.	Liquid Btu./lb.°F.	Vapor Btu./lb.°F.	°F.
—40	0.7391	0.00988	44.21	101.25	0.02262	0.00	87.48	87.48	0.0000	0.2085	—40
—38	0.7916	.00989	41.47	101.10	.02411	0.39	87.33	87.72	.0009	.2081	—38
—36	0.8471	.00991	38.93	100.96	.02569	0.79	87.17	87.96	.0019	.2076	—36
—34	0.9060	.00992	36.57	100.81	.02735	1.18	87.02	88.20	.0028	.2072	—34
—32	0.9682	.00993	34.37	100.66	.02910	1.58	86.86	88.44	.0037	.2068	—32
—30	1.034	0.00995	32.33	100.52	0.03093	1.97	86.70	88.67	0.0046	0.2064	—30
—28	1.103	.00996	30.44	100.37	.03285	2.36	86.55	88.91	.0055	.2060	—28
—26	1.176	.00998	28.68	100.22	.03487	2.75	86.40	89.15	.0064	.2057	—26
—24	1.253	.00999	27.03	100.07	.03700	3.15	86.24	89.39	.0073	.2053	—24
—22	1.334	.01001	25.50	99.92	.03922	3.55	86.08	89.63	.0082	.2049	—22
—20	1.420	0.01002	24.06	99.77	0.04157	3.94	85.93	89.87	0.0091	0.2046	—20
—18	1.510	.01004	22.72	99.63	.04401	4.33	85.78	90.11	.0100	.2043	—18
—16	1.605	.01005	21.47	99.48	.04658	4.73	85.62	90.35	.0109	.2040	—16
—14	1.705	.01007	20.30	99.33	.04927	5.12	85.47	90.59	.0118	.2036	—14
—12	1.810	.01008	19.20	99.18	.05209	5.52	85.31	90.83	.0127	.2033	—12
—10	1.920	0.01010	18.17	99.03	0.05503	5.91	85.16	91.07	0.0136	0.2030	—10
— 8	2.035	.01011	17.21	98.87	.05810	6.31	85.00	91.31	.0145	.2027	— 8
— 6	2.156	.01013	16.32	98.72	.06129	6.70	84.85	91.55	.0153	.2024	— 6
— 4	2.283	.01015	15.47	98.57	.06464	7.10	84.69	91.79	.0162	.2021	— 4
— 2	2.416	.01016	14.68	98.42	.06813	7.49	84.54	92.03	.0171	.2018	— 2
0	2.555	0.01018	13.94	98.27	0.07176	7.89	84.38	92.27	0.0179	0.2015	0
2	2.700	.01019	13.24	98.11	.07554	8.28	84.23	92.51	.0188	.2013	2
4	2.852	.01021	12.58	97.96	.07949	8.68	84.07	92.75	.0197	.2010	4
5†	2.931	.01022	12.27	97.88	.08152	8.88	84.00	92.88	.0201	.2009	5†
6	3.012	.01022	11.96	97.81	.08361	9.08	83.92	93.00	.0205	.2008	6
8	3.179	.01024	11.38	97.65	.08790	9.48	83.76	93.24	.0213	.2005	8
10	3.352	0.01026	10.83	97.50	0.09233	9.88	83.60	93.48	0.0222	0.2003	10
12	3.534	.01027	10.31	97.34	.09697	10.28	83.45	93.72	.0231	.2000	12
14	3.724	.01029	9.823	97.19	.1018	10.68	83.29	93.97	.0239	.1998	14
16	3.923	.01031	9.359	97.03	.1068	11.07	83.14	94.21	.0248	.1996	16
18	4.129	.01032	8.925	96.88	.1120	11.47	82.98	94.45	.0256	.1993	18
20	4.342	0.01034	8.519	96.72	0.1174	11.87	82.82	94.69	0.0264	0.1991	20
22	4.567	.01036	8.129	96.57	.1230	12.27	82.66	94.94	.0273	.1989	22
24	4.801	.01037	7.760	96.41	.1289	12.68	82.50	95.18	.0281	.1987	24
26	5.043	.01039	7.414	96.25	.1349	13.08	82.34	95.42	.0289	.1985	26
28	5.294	.01041	7.087	96.10	.1411	13.48	82.18	95.66	.0297	.1983	28
30	5.557	0.01042	6.776	95.94	0.1476	13.88	82.03	95.91	0.0306	0.1981	30
32	5.830	.01044	6.481	95.78	.1543	14.28	81.87	96.15	.0314	.1979	32
34	6.115	.01046	6.200	95.62	.1613	14.68	81.71	96.39	.0322	.1977	34
36	6.411	.01048	5.934	95.46	.1685	15.08	81.55	96.63	.0330	.1976	36
38	6.718	.01049	5.682	95.30	.1760	15.49	81.38	96.87	.0338	.1974	38
40	7.032	0.01051	5.447	95.14	0.1836	15.89	81.22	97.11	0.0346	0.1972	40
42	7.362	.01053	5.220	94.98	.1916	16.30	81.06	97.36	.0354	.1970	42
44	7.702	.01055	5.006	94.82	.1998	16.70	80.90	97.60	.0362	.1969	44
46	8.055	.01056	4.802	94.66	.2083	17.11	80.73	97.84	.0370	.1967	46
48	8.422	.01058	4.607	94.50	.2170	17.52	80.57	98.08	.0378	.1966	48
50	8.804	0.01060	4.421	94.34	0.2262	17.92	80.40	98.32	0.0386	0.1964	50
52	9.199	.01062	4.245	94.18	.2356	18.33	80.24	98.56	.0394	.1963	52
54	9.605	.01064	4.078	94.02	.2452	18.74	80.07	98.81	.0402	.1961	54
56	10.02	.01066	3.921	93.85	.2550	19.15	79.90	99.05	.0410	.1960	56
58	10.45	.01067	3.770	93.69	.2652	19.56	79.73	99.29	.0418	.1959	58
60	10.90	0.01069	3.626	93.53	0.2758	19.96	79.57	99.53	0.0426	0.1958	60
62	11.37	.01071	3.487	93.36	.2868	20.37	79.40	99.77	.0434	.1956	62
64	11.85	.01073	3.356	93.20	.2980	20.78	79.23	100.01	.0442	.1955	64
66	12.35	.01075	3.229	93.04	.3097	21.19	79.06	100.25	.0450	.1954	66
68	12.87	.01077	3.107	92.87	.3219	21.61	78.88	100.49	.0457	.1953	68

* Courtesy Kinetic Chemicals, Inc., Wilmington, Del. See Fig. 2-2.
† Standard ton temperature.

TABLE 2-18.   FREON 11: PROPERTIES OF SATURATED VAPOR AND LIQUID (*Concluded*)

Temp.	Abs. Pressure	Volume		Density		Heat Content from —40°			Entropy from —40°		Temp.
°F.	lb./in.²	Liquid ft.³/lb.	Vapor ft.³/lb.	Liquid lb./ft.³	Vapor lb./ft.³	Liquid Btu./lb.	Latent Btu./lb.	Vapor Btu./lb.	Liquid Btu./lb.°F.	Vapor Btu./lb.°F.	°F.
70	13.40	0.01079	2.993	92.71	0.3342	22.02	78.71	100.73	0.0465	0.1951	70
72	13.95	.01081	2.883	92.54	.3469	22.43	78.54	100.97	.0473	.1950	72
74	14.51	.01083	2.779	92.38	.3598	22.84	78.37	101.21	.0481	.1949	74
76	15.09	.01085	2.679	92.21	.3732	23.26	78.19	101.45	.0489	.1948	76
78	15.69	.01086	2.584	92.04	.3870	23.68	78.01	101.69	.0496	.1947	78
80	16.31	0.01088	2.492	91.88	0.4012	24.09	77.84	101.93	0.0504	0.1947	80
82	16.94	.01090	2.406	91.71	.4157	24.51	77.66	102.17	.0512	.1946	82
84	17.60	.01092	2.322	91.54	.4307	24.93	77.48	102.41	.0519	.1945	84
86†	18.28	.01094	2.242	91.38	.4461	25.34	77.31	102.65	.0527	.1944	86†
88	18.97	.01096	2.165	91.21	.4619	25.76	77.13	102.89	.0535	.1943	88
90	19.69	0.01098	2.091	91.04	0.4783	26.18	76.95	103.12	0.0542	0.1942	90
92	20.43	.01101	2.020	90.87	.4950	26.60	76.76	103.36	.0550	.1941	92
94	21.19	.01103	1.952	90.70	.5122	27.01	76.58	103.59	.0557	.1941	94
96	21.97	.01105	1.887	90.53	.5299	27.43	76.40	103.83	.0565	.1940	96
98	22.77	.01107	1.825	90.36	.5480	27.85	76.21	104.07	.0572	.1939	98
100	23.60	0.01109	1.765	90.19	0.5666	28.27	76.03	104.30	0.0580	0.1938	100
102	24.45	.01111	1.707	90.02	.5857	28.70	75.84	104.54	.0587	.1938	102
104	25.33	.01113	1.652	89.85	.6054	29.12	75.65	104.77	.0595	.1937	104
106	26.23	.01115	1.599	89.68	.6256	29.54	75.46	105.00	.0602	.1937	106
108	27.15	.01117	1.548	89.51	.6461	29.97	75.27	105.24	.0610	.1936	108
110	28.09	0.01119	1.499	89.34	0.6671	30.40	75.08	105.47	0.0617	0.1935	110
112	29.05	.01122	1.452	89.16	.6885	30.82	74.89	105.71	.0625	.1935	112
114	30.04	.01124	1.407	88.99	.7107	31.24	74.70	105.94	.0632	.1935	114
116	31.07	.01126	1.363	88.82	.7335	31.67	74.50	106.17	.0639	.1934	116
118	32.11	.01128	1.321	88.65	.7570	32.10	74.30	106.40	.0647	.1933	118
120	33.20	0.01130	1.281	88.47	0.7808	32.53	74.10	106.63	0.0654	0.1933	120
122	34.29	.01133	1.243	88.30	.8049	32.95	73.91	106.86	.0661	.1932	122
124	35.42	.01135	1.206	88.12	.8296	33.38	73.71	107.09	.0669	.1932	124
126	36.56	.01137	1.170	87.95	.8550	33.81	73.51	107.32	.0676	.1931	126
128	37.74	.01139	1.135	87.77	.8811	34.24	73.31	107.55	.0683	.1931	128
130	38.96	0.01142	1.101	87.60	0.9080	34.67	73.11	107.78	0.0691	0.1931	130
132	40.23	.01144	1.068	87.42	.9361	35.10	72.90	108.00	.0698	.1930	132
134	41.50	.01146	1.037	87.25	.9646	35.54	72.69	108.23	.0705	.1929	134
136	42.80	.01149	1.007	87.07	0.9927	35.97	72.49	108.46	.0712	.1929	136
138	44.12	.01151	0.9785	86.88	1.022	36.40	72.28	108.68	.0719	.1929	138
140	45.50	0.01154	0.9505	86.69	1.052	36.84	72.07	108.91	0.0727	0.1929	140
142	46.92	.01156	.9231	86.50	1.083	37.28	71.85	109.13	.0734	.1928	142
144	48.35	.01159	.8970	86.32	1.115	37.71	71.64	109.35	.0741	.1928	144
146	49.81	.01161	.8719	86.14	1.147	38.15	71.43	109.58	.0748	.1928	146
148	51.31	.01163	.8476	85.96	1.180	38.59	71.21	109.80	.0755	.1927	148
150	52.85	0.01166	0.8240	85.78	1.214	39.02	71.00	110.02	0.0763	0.1927	150
152	54.41	.01168	.8014	85.60	1.248	39.46	70.78	110.24	.0770	.1927	152
154	56.01	.01171	.7794	85.41	1.283	39.91	70.56	110.47	.0777	.1927	154
156	57.65	.01173	.7581	85.23	1.319	40.35	70.34	110.69	.0784	.1927	156
158	59.32	.01176	.7376	85.04	1.356	40.79	70.12	110.90	.0791	.1926	158
160	61.04	0.01179	0.7176	84.85	1.394	41.23	69.89	111.12	0.0798	0.1926	160

† Standard ton temperature.

TABLE 2-19. FREON 11: PROPERTIES OF SUPERHEATED VAPOR

Temp. °F. t	Abs. Pressure 0.7 lb./in.² (Sat'n. Temp. −41.6°F.)			Abs. Pressure 0.8 lb./in.² (Sat'n. Temp. −37.7°F.)			Abs. Pressure 0.9 lb./in.² (Sat'n. Temp. −34.2°F.)			Abs. Pressure 1.0 lb./in.² (Sat'n. Temp. −31.0°F.)		
	V	H	S	V	H	S	V	H	S	V	H	S
(at sat'n)	(46.54)	(87.29)	(0.2090)	(41.09)	(87.76)	(0.2080)	(36.81)	(88.18)	(0.2073)	(33.37)	(88.55)	(0.2066)
−40	46.69	87.49	0.2093	....	....	....	....	....	....	....	....	....
−30	47.81	88.69	.2121	41.82	88.69	0.2102	37.16	88.68	0.2085	33.43	88.67	0.2069
−20	48.93	89.91	.2149	42.80	89.91	.2130	38.03	89.90	.2113	34.22	89.90	.2097
−10	50.06	91.14	.2177	43.78	91.14	.2158	38.90	91.13	.2141	35.00	91.13	.2125
0	51.18	92.38	0.2204	44.77	92.37	0.2185	39.78	92.37	0.2168	35.79	92.36	0.2153
10	52.30	93.63	.2231	45.74	93.62	.2212	40.65	93.62	.2195	36.57	93.61	.2180
20	53.42	94.89	.2258	46.73	94.88	.2238	41.52	94.88	.2221	37.36	94.87	.2206
30	54.54	96.16	.2284	47.70	96.15	.2265	42.39	96.15	.2247	38.14	96.14	.2232
40	55.66	97.44	.2310	48.69	97.43	.2291	43.26	97.43	.2273	38.93	97.42	.2258
50	56.77	98.73	0.2335	49.66	98.72	0.2316	44.14	98.72	0.2299	39.71	98.71	0.2284
60	57.89	100.03	.2361	50.65	100.03	.2341	45.01	100.02	.2324	40.50	100.02	.2309
70	59.01	101.34	.2386	51.62	101.34	.2366	45.88	101.33	.2349	41.28	101.33	.2334
80	60.13	102.67	.2411	52.60	102.67	.2391	46.75	102.66	.2374	42.07	102.66	.2359
90	61.25	104.00	.2435	53.58	104.00	.2416	47.62	103.99	.2398	42.85	103.99	.2383
100	62.37	105.34	0.2459	54.56	105.34	0.2440	48.49	105.33	0.2423	43.63	105.33	0.2407
110	63.49	106.69	.2483	55.54	106.69	.2464	49.36	106.68	.2447	44.42	106.68	.2431
120	64.60	108.06	.2507	56.52	108.06	.2487	50.23	108.05	.2470	45.20	108.05	.2455
130	65.72	109.43	.2531	57.50	109.43	.2511	51.10	109.43	.2494	45.98	109.42	.2478
140	66.84	110.82	.2554	58.48	110.81	.2534	51.97	110.81	.2517	46.77	110.80	.2502
150	67.96	112.22	0.2577	59.46	112.21	0.2557	52.84	112.21	0.2540	47.55	112.20	0.2525
160	69.08	113.62	.2600	60.44	113.61	.2580	53.71	113.61	.2563	48.33	113.60	.2548
170	70.20	115.04	.2622	61.42	115.03	.2603	54.58	115.03	.2586	49.12	115.05	.2571
180	71.32	116.47	.2645	62.40	116.46	.2625	55.45	116.46	.2608	49.90	116.45	.2593
190	72.43	117.90	.2667	63.37	117.89	.2648	56.32	117.89	.2631	50.68	117.89	.2615
200	73.55	119.35	0.2689	64.35	119.34	0.2670	57.19	119.34	0.2653	51.47	119.34	0.2637
210	74.67	120.81	.2711	65.33	120.80	.2692	58.06	120.80	.2675	52.25	120.80	.2659
220	75.79	122.27	.2733	66.31	122.26	.2713	58.93	122.26	.2696	53.03	122.26	.2681
230	76.90	123.75	.2754	67.28	123.74	.2735	59.80	123.74	.2718	53.82	123.74	.2703
240	78.02	125.24	.2776	68.26	125.24	.2756	60.67	125.23	.2739	54.60	125.23	.2724
250	79.14	126.74	0.2797	69.24	126.74	0.2778	61.54	126.73	0.2761	55.38	126.73	0.2745
260	80.26	128.25	.2818	70.22	128.25	.2799	62.41	128.24	.2782	56.16	128.24	.2766
270	....	....	....	71.20	129.77	.2820	63.28	129.76	.2803	56.95	129.76	.2787.

TABLE 2-19. FREON 11: PROPERTIES OF SUPERHEATED VAPOR (Continued)

Temp. °F.	Abs. Pressure 1.1 lb./in.² (Sat'n. Temp. −28.1°F.)			Abs. Pressure 1.2 lb./in.² (Sat'n. Temp. −25.4°F.)			Abs. Pressure 1.3 lb./in.² (Sat'n. Temp. −22.8°F.)			Abs. Pressure 1.4 lb./in.² (Sat'n. Temp. −20.5°F.)		
(at sat'n)	(30.52)	(88.90)	(0.2061)	(28.15)	(89.23)	(0.2056)	(26.13)	(89.53)	(0.2051)	(24.39)	(89.81)	(0.2047)
−20	31.09	89.89	0.2084	28.49	89.88	0.2071	26.29	89.88	0.2060	24.41	89.87	0.2049
−10	31.81	91.12	.2111	29.15	91.11	.2099	26.90	91.11	.2087	24.97	91.10	.2076
0	32.52	92.35	0.2139	29.80	92.35	0.2126	27.50	92.34	0.2114	25.53	92.34	0.2104
10	33.24	93.60	.2166	30.46	93.60	.2153	28.11	93.59	.2141	26.09	93.59	.2131
20	33.95	94.87	.2192	31.11	94.86	.2179	28.71	94.86	.2168	26.65	94.85	.2157
30	34.66	96.14	.2218	31.77	96.13	.2205	29.32	96.13	.2194	27.21	96.12	.2183
40	35.38	97.42	.2244	32.42	97.41	.2231	29.92	97.41	.2220	27.78	97.40	.2209
50	36.09	98.71	0.2270	33.08	98.70	0.2257	30.52	98.70	0.2246	28.34	98.69	0.2235
60	36.81	100.01	.2295	33.73	100.01	.2282	31.13	100.00	.2271	28.90	100.00	.2260
70	37.52	101.32	.2320	34.39	101.32	.2307	31.73	101.31	.2296	29.46	101.31	.2285
80	38.23	102.65	.2345	35.04	102.65	.2332	32.34	102.64	.2321	30.02	102.64	.2310
90	38.95	103.98	.2369	35.69	103.98	.2357	32.94	103.97	.2345	30.58	103.97	.2334
100	39.66	105.32	0.2393	36.35	105.32	0.2381	33.54	105.32	0.2369	31.14	105.31	0.2358
110	40.37	106.68	.2417	37.00	106.67	.2405	34.15	106.67	.2393	31.70	106.66	.2382
120	41.08	108.05	.2441	37.65	108.04	.2429	34.75	108.04	.2417	32.26	108.03	.2406
130	41.80	109.42	.2465	38.31	109.41	.2452	35.35	109.41	.2440	32.82	109.40	.2430
140	42.51	110.80	.2488	38.96	110.79	.2475	35.96	110.79	.2464	33.38	110.79	.2453
150	43.22	112.20	0.2511	39.61	112.19	0.2498	36.56	112.19	0.2487	33.94	112.19	0.2476
160	43.93	113.60	.2534	40.27	113.60	.2521	37.16	113.59	.2510	34.51	113.59	.2499
170	44.65	115.02	.2557	40.92	115.02	.2544	37.77	115.01	.2532	35.07	115.01	.2522
180	45.36	116.45	.2579	41.57	116.45	.2567	38.37	116.44	.2555	35.63	116.44	.2544
190	46.07	117.88	.2602	42.23	117.88	.2589	38.97	117.87	.2577	36.19	117.87	.2567
200	46.78	119.33	0.2624	42.88	119.33	0.2611	39.58	119.32	0.2599	36.75	119.32	0.2589
210	47.50	120.79	.2646	43.53	120.79	.2633	40.18	120.78	.2621	37.31	120.78	.2611
220	48.21	122.25	.2667	44.19	122.25	.2655	40.78	122.25	.2643	37.87	122.24	.2632
230	48.92	123.73	.2689	44.84	123.73	.2676	41.39	123.73	.2665	38.43	123.72	.2654
240	49.63	125.22	.2710	45.49	125.22	.2698	41.99	125.22	.2686	38.99	125.21	.2675
250	50.34	126.72	0.2731	46.14	126.72	0.2719	42.59	126.72	0.2707	39.55	126.71	0.2697
260	51.06	128.24	.2753	46.80	128.23	.2740	43.19	128.23	.2728	40.11	128.23	.2718
270	51.77	129.76	.2774	47.45	129.75	.2761	43.80	129.75	.2749	40.67	129.75	.2739
280	52.48	131.29	0.2794	48.10	131.28	0.2782	44.40	131.28	0.2770	41.23	131.28	0.2760

Temp. °F.	Abs. Pressure 1.6 lb./in.² (Sat'n. Temp.-16.1°F.)			Abs. Pressure 1.8 lb./in.² (Sat'n. Temp.-12.2°F.)			Abs. Pressure 2.0 lb./in.² (Sat'n. Temp.-8.6°F.)			Abs. Pressure 2.2 lb./in.² (Sat'n. Temp.-5.3°F.)		
t (at sat'n)	V (21.53)	H (90.34)	S (0.2057)	V (19.30)	H (90.81)	S (0.2033)	V (17.50)	H (91.24)	S (0.2028)	V (16.02)	H (91.63)	S (0.2023)
—10	21.83	91.09	0.2057	19.39	91.08	0.2040	17.50	91.24	0.2028	....	....	....
0	22.32	92.33	.2084	19.83	92.32	.2067	17.83	92.31	.2052	16.20	92.29	0.2038
10	22.82	93.58	.2111	20.27	93.57	.2094	18.23	93.56	.2079	16.56	93.54	.2065
20	23.31	94.84	.2138	20.71	94.83	.2120	18.62	94.82	.2105	16.92	94.81	.2091
30	23.80	96.11	.2164	21.14	96.10	.2147	19.02	96.09	.2131	17.28	96.08	.2117
40	24.29	97.39	.2190	21.58	97.38	.2173	19.41	97.37	.2157	17.64	97.36	.2143
50	24.78	98.68	0.2215	22.02	98.67	0.2198	19.81	98.66	0.2183	17.99	98.65	0.2169
60	25.27	99.99	.2241	22.46	99.98	.2223	20.20	99.97	.2208	18.35	99.96	.2194
70	25.77	101.30	.2266	22.89	101.29	.2248	20.59	101.28	.2233	18.71	101.27	.2219
80	26.26	102.63	.2290	23.33	102.62	.2273	20.99	102.61	.2258	19.07	102.60	.2244
90	26.75	103.96	.2315	23.77	103.95	.2298	21.38	103.94	.2282	19.43	103.93	.2269
100	27.24	105.30	0.2339	24.20	105.29	0.2322	21.77	105.28	0.2307	19.79	105.27	0.2293
110	27.73	106.65	.2363	24.64	106.65	.2346	22.17	106.64	.2331	20.14	106.63	.2317
120	28.22	108.02	.2387	25.08	108.02	.2370	22.56	108.01	.2354	20.50	108.00	.2340
130	28.71	109.40	.2410	25.51	109.39	.2393	22.95	109.38	.2378	20.86	109.37	.2364
140	29.20	110.78	.2434	25.95	110.77	.2417	23.35	110.76	.2401	21.22	110.75	.2387
150	29.59	112.18	0.2457	26.39	112.17	0.2440	23.74	112.17	0.2424	21.57	112.16	0.2410
160	30.18	113.58	.2480	26.82	113.57	.2463	24.13	113.57	.2447	21.93	113.56	.2433
170	30.67	115.00	.2502	27.26	114.99	.2485	24.52	114.98	.2470	22.29	114.98	.2456
180	31.16	116.43	.2525	27.69	116.42	.2508	24.92	116.41	.2492	22.65	116.41	.2479
190	31.66	117.86	.2547	28.13	117.86	.2530	25.31	117.85	.2515	23.00	117.85	.2501
200	32.15	119.31	0.2569	28.57	119.31	0.2552	25.70	119.30	0.2537	23.36	119.29	0.2523
210	32.64	120.77	.2591	29.00	120.77	.2574	26.10	120.76	.2559	23.72	120.75	.2545
220	33.13	122.24	.2613	29.44	122.23	.2596	26.49	122.22	.2581	24.07	122.22	.2567
230	33.62	123.72	.2634	29.87	123.71	.2617	26.88	123.70	.2602	24.43	123.70	.2588
240	34.11	125.21	.2656	30.31	125.20	.2639	27.27	125.19	.2624	24.79	125.19	.2610
250	34.60	126.71	0.2677	30.75	126.70	0.2660	27.66	126.69	0.2645	25.15	126.69	0.2631
260	35.09	128.22	.2698	31.18	128.21	.2681	28.06	128.21	.2666	25.50	128.20	.2652
270	35.58	129.74	.2719	31.62	129.73	.2702	28.45	129.73	.2687	25.86	129.72	.2673
280	36.07	131.27	.2740	32.05	131.26	.2723	28.84	131.26	.2708	26.21	131.25	.2694
290	36.56	132.81	.2761	32.49	132.81	.2744	29.23	132.80	.2728	26.57	132.79	.2715
300	....	....	....	....	....	....	29.62	134.35	0.2749	26.93	134.35	0.2735

TABLE 2-19. FREON 11: PROPERTIES OF SUPERHEATED VAPOR (Continued)

Temp. °F	Abs. Pressure 2.4 lb./in.² (Sat'n. Temp. -2.2°F.)			Abs. Pressure 2.6 lb./in.² (Sat'n. Temp. +0.6°F.)			Abs. Pressure 2.8 lb./in.² (Sat'n. Temp. 3.3°F.)			Abs. Pressure 3.0 lb./in.² (Sat'n. Temp. 5.9°F.)		
(at sat'n)	(14.77)	(92.00)	(0.2018)	(13.71)	(92.34)	(0.2015)	(12.81)	(92.67)	(0.2011)	(12.01)	(92.98)	(0.2008)
0	14.84	92.28	0.2025	.....	.....	.....	.....	.....	.....	.....	.....	.....
10	15.17	93.53	.2052	13.99	93.52	0.2040	12.99	93.51	0.2029	12.11	93.50	0.2019
20	15.50	94.80	.2078	14.30	94.78	.2067	13.27	94.77	.2056	12.38	94.76	.2046
30	15.83	96.07	.2105	14.60	96.06	.2093	13.55	96.05	.2082	12.64	96.04	.2072
40	16.16	97.35	.2131	14.91	97.34	.2119	13.84	97.33	.2108	12.91	97.32	.2098
50	16.49	98.64	0.2156	15.21	98.63	0.2144	14.12	98.62	0.2134	13.17	98.61	0.2123
60	16.82	99.95	.2181	15.52	99.94	.2170	14.40	99.93	.2159	13.43	99.92	.2149
70	17.14	101.26	.2206	15.82	101.25	.2195	14.68	101.24	.2184	13.70	101.23	.2174
80	17.47	102.59	.2231	16.12	102.58	.2220	14.96	102.57	.2209	13.96	102.56	.2199
90	17.80	103.92	.2256	16.43	103.91	.2244	15.25	103.90	.2233	14.22	103.90	.2223
100	18.13	105.27	0.2280	16.73	105.26	0.2268	15.53	105.25	0.2258	14.49	105.24	0.2247
110	18.46	106.63	.2304	17.03	106.62	.2292	15.81	106.61	.2282	14.75	106.60	.2271
120	18.79	108.00	.2328	17.34	107.99	.2316	16.09	107.98	.2305	15.01	107.97	.2295
130	19.11	109.37	.2351	17.64	109.36	.2340	16.37	109.35	.2329	15.28	109.34	.2319
140	19.44	110.75	.2375	17.94	110.74	.2363	16.65	110.73	.2352	15.54	110.72	.2342
150	19.77	112.15	0.2398	18.24	112.14	0.2386	16.94	112.13	0.2375	15.80	112.12	0.2365
160	20.10	113.55	.2421	18.55	113.54	.2409	17.22	113.54	.2398	16.06	113.53	.2388
170	20.43	114.97	.2443	18.85	114.96	.2432	17.50	114.95	.2421	16.33	114.95	.2411
180	20.75	116.40	.2466	19.15	116.39	.2454	17.78	116.38	.2444	16.59	116.38	.2433
190	21.08	117.83	.2488	19.45	117.83	.2477	18.06	117.82	.2466	16.85	117.81	.2456
200	21.41	119.28	0.2510	19.76	119.28	0.2499	18.34	119.27	0.2488	17.11	119.26	0.2478
210	21.74	120.74	.2532	20.06	120.74	.2521	18.62	120.73	.2510	17.38	120.72	.2500
220	22.06	122.21	.2554	20.36	122.20	.2542	18.90	122.19	.2532	17.64	122.19	.2522
230	22.39	123.69	.2576	20.66	123.68	.2564	19.18	123.67	.2553	17.90	123.67	.2543
240	22.72	125.18	.2597	20.97	125.17	.2585	19.47	125.17	.2575	18.16	125.16	.2565
250	23.05	126.68	0.2618	21.27	126.67	0.2607	19.75	126.67	0.2596	18.43	126.66	0.2586
260	23.37	128.18	.2639	21.57	128.19	.2628	20.03	128.18	.2617	18.69	128.17	.2607
270	23.70	129.71	.2660	21.87	129.71	.2649	20.31	129.70	.2638	18.95	129.70	.2628
280	24.03	131.25	.2681	22.18	131.24	.2670	20.59	131.23	.2659	19.21	131.23	.2649
290	24.35	132.79	.2702	22.48	132.78	.2690	20.87	132.77	.2680	19.47	132.77	.2670
300	24.68	134.34	0.2723	22.78	134.33	0.2711	21.15	134.33	0.2700	19.74	134.32	0.2690
310	.....	.....	.....	23.08	135.89	.2731	21.43	135.89	.2721	20.00	135.88	0.2711

Temp. °F.	Abs. Pressure 3.5 lb./in.² (Sat'n Temp. 11.6°F.)			Abs. Pressure 4.0 lb./in.² (Sat'n Temp. 16.7°F.)			Abs. Pressure 4.5 lb./in.² (Sat'n Temp. 21.4°F.)			Abs. Pressure 5.0 lb./in.² (Sat'n Temp. 25.6°F.)		
t	V	H	S	V	H	S	V	H	S	V	H	S
(at sat'n)	(10.41)	(93.67)	(0.2001)	(9.194)	(94.30)	(0.1995)	(8.243)	(94.87)	(0.1990)	(7.475)	(95.38)	(0.1985)
20	10.60	94.74	0.2023	9.256	94.71	0.2003	....	....	....	....	....	....
30	10.82	96.01	.2049	9.455	95.99	.2030	8.393	95.96	0.2012	7.543	95.94	0.1997
40	11.05	97.29	.2075	9.655	97.27	.2056	8.570	97.24	.2038	7.703	97.22	.2023
50	11.28	98.59	0.2101	9.853	98.56	.2081	8.747	98.54	0.2064	7.863	98.51	0.2048
60	11.50	99.89	.2126	10.05	99.87	.2107	8.924	99.84	.2089	8.023	99.82	.2074
70	11.73	101.21	.2151	10.25	101.18	.2132	9.101	101.16	.2114	8.182	101.14	.2099
80	11.95	102.54	.2176	10.45	102.51	.2157	9.278	102.49	.2139	8.341	102.47	.2124
90	12.18	103.87	.2201	10.65	103.84	.2181	9.454	103.83	.2164	8.500	103.80	.2148
100	12.41	105.22	0.2225	10.84	105.20	0.2205	9.631	105.18	0.2188	8.659	105.16	0.2173
110	12.63	106.58	.2249	11.04	106.56	.2229	9.807	106.54	.2212	8.818	106.51	.2197
120	12.86	107.95	.2273	11.24	107.93	.2253	9.983	107.91	.2236	8.977	107.88	.2220
130	13.08	109.32	.2296	11.44	109.30	.2277	10.16	109.28	.2260	9.135	109.26	.2244
140	13.31	110.70	.2320	11.64	110.68	.2300	10.34	110.66	.2283	9.294	110.65	.2267
150	13.53	112.10	0.2343	11.83	112.08	0.2323	10.51	112.06	0.2306	9.452	112.05	0.2290
160	13.76	113.51	.2366	12.03	113.49	.2346	10.69	113.47	.2329	9.610	113.45	.2313
170	13.98	114.93	.2388	12.23	114.91	.2369	10.86	114.89	.2352	9.769	114.87	.2336
180	14.21	116.36	.2411	12.43	116.34	.2391	11.04	116.32	.2374	9.927	116.30	.2359
190	14.44	117.79	.2433	12.62	117.77	.2414	11.21	117.76	.2396	10.09	117.74	.2381
200	14.66	119.24	0.2455	12.82	119.22	0.2436	11.39	119.21	0.2419	10.25	119.19	0.2403
210	14.89	120.70	.2477	13.02	120.68	.2458	11.56	120.67	.2441	10.40	120.65	.2425
220	15.11	122.17	.2499	13.22	122.15	.2480	11.74	122.13	.2462	10.56	122.12	.2447
230	15.34	123.65	.2521	13.41	123.63	.2501	11.92	123.61	.2484	10.72	123.60	.2469
240	15.56	125.14	.2542	13.61	125.13	.2523	12.09	125.11	.2506	10.88	125.09	.2490
250	15.79	126.64	0.2563	13.81	126.63	0.2544	12.27	126.61	0.2527	11.04	126.59	0.2511
260	16.01	128.16	.2585	14.00	128.14	.2565	12.44	128.12	.2548	11.19	128.11	.2533
270	16.24	129.68	.2606	14.20	129.66	.2586	12.62	129.65	.2569	11.35	129.63	.2554
280	16.46	131.21	.2626	14.40	131.20	.2607	12.79	131.18	.2590	11.51	131.16	.2574
290	16.69	132.76	.2647	14.59	132.74	.2628	12.97	132.73	.2611	11.67	132.71	.2595
300	16.91	134.31	0.2668	14.79	134.30	0.2648	13.14	134.28	0.2631	11.82	134.27	0.2616
310	17.13	135.87	.2688	14.99	135.86	.2669	13.32	135.84	.2652	11.98	135.83	.2636
320	17.36	137.44	.2708	15.18	137.43	.2689	13.49	137.41	.2672	12.14	137.40	.2656
330	....	....	....	....	....	....	13.67	138.99	0.2692	12.30	138.98	0.2677

TABLE 2-19. FREON 11: PROPERTIES OF SUPERHEATED VAPOR (Continued)

Temp. °F.	Abs. Pressure 5.5 lb./in.² (Sat'n. Temp. 29.6°F.)			Abs. Pressure 6.0 lb./in.² (Sat'n. Temp. 33.2°F.)			Abs. Pressure 6.5 lb./in.² (Sat'n. Temp. 36.6°F.)			Abs. Pressure 7.0 lb./in.² (Sat'n. Temp. 39.8°F.)		
(at sat'n)	(6.842)	(95.86)	(0.1982)	(6.313)	(96.29)	(0.1978)	(5.861)	(96.70)	(0.1975)	(5.470)	(97.09)	(0.1972)
30	6.847	95.91	0.1983	....	....	....	....	....	....	....	....	....
40	6.993	97.19	.2009	6.401	97.16	0.1996	5.901	97.14	0.1984	5.472	97.11	0.1973
50	7.138	98.49	0.2034	6.534	98.46	0.2021	6.024	98.44	0.2009	5.587	98.41	0.1998
60	7.283	99.80	.2060	6.668	99.77	.2047	6.148	99.75	.2035	5.702	99.72	.2024
70	7.428	101.11	.2085	6.802	101.09	.2072	6.271	101.07	.2060	5.817	101.04	.2049
80	7.573	102.44	.2110	6.936	102.42	.2097	6.395	102.40	.2085	5.932	102.37	.2074
90	7.718	103.78	.2134	7.069	103.76	.2121	6.518	103.73	.2110	6.046	103.71	.2099
100	7.863	105.13	0.2159	7.202	105.11	0.2146	6.641	105.08	0.2134	6.161	105.06	0.2123
110	8.008	106.49	.2183	7.335	106.47	.2170	6.764	106.44	.2158	6.275	106.42	.2147
120	8.153	107.86	.2206	7.467	107.84	.2194	6.887	107.81	.2182	6.389	107.79	.2171
130	8.297	109.24	.2230	7.600	109.22	.2217	7.009	109.19	.2205	6.503	109.17	.2194
140	8.442	110.63	.2253	7.733	110.61	.2241	7.131	110.58	.2229	6.617	110.56	.2218
150	8.586	112.03	0.2276	7.865	112.01	0.2264	7.254	111.99	0.2252	6.730	111.97	0.2241
160	8.731	113.43	.2299	7.998	113.41	.2287	7.377	113.40	.2275	6.844	113.38	.2264
170	8.875	114.85	.2322	8.130	114.83	.2309	7.499	114.82	.2298	6.958	114.80	.2287
180	9.020	116.28	.2345	8.263	116.26	.2332	7.622	116.25	.2320	7.072	116.23	.2309
190	9.164	117.72	.2367	8.395	117.70	.2354	7.745	117.69	.2343	7.186	117.67	.2332
200	9.307	119.17	0.2389	8.527	119.15	0.2376	7.867	119.14	0.2365	7.300	119.12	0.2354
210	9.451	120.63	.2411	8.659	120.61	.2398	7.989	120.60	.2387	7.413	120.58	.2376
220	9.595	122.10	.2433	8.791	122.08	.2420	8.111	122.07	.2409	7.527	122.05	.2398
230	9.739	123.58	.2455	8.923	123.56	.2442	8.233	123.55	.2430	7.641	123.53	.2419
240	9.883	125.07	.2476	9.056	125.06	.2463	8.355	125.04	.2452	7.755	125.02	.2441
250	10.03	126.58	0.2498	9.188	126.56	0.2485	8.477	126.54	0.2473	7.868	126.53	0.2462
260	10.17	128.09	.2519	9.319	128.07	.2506	8.599	128.06	.2494	7.981	128.04	.2483
270	10.31	129.62	.2540	9.451	129.60	.2527	8.720	129.59	.2515	8.094	129.57	.2504
280	10.46	131.15	.2560	9.583	131.13	.2548	8.841	131.12	.2536	8.207	131.10	.2525
290	10.60	132.70	.2581	9.714	132.68	.2568	8.962	132.67	.2557	8.320	132.65	.2546
300	10.74	134.25	0.2602	9.845	134.24	0.2589	9.084	134.22	0.2577	8.432	134.21	0.2567
310	10.89	135.81	.2622	9.976	135.80	.2609	9.205	135.79	.2598	8.545	135.77	.2587
320	11.03	137.38	.2642	10.11	137.37	.2630	9.327	137.36	.2618	8.658	137.34	.2607
330	11.17	138.96	.2663	10.24	138.95	.2650	9.448	138.94	.2638	8.771	138.92	.2627
340	....	....	....	10.37	140.54	0.2670	9.570	140.53	0.2658	8.884	140.51	0.2647

Temp. °F. t (at sat'n)	Abs. Pressure 7.5 lb./in.² (Sat'n. Temp. 42.8°F.)			Abs. Pressure 8.0 lb./in.² (Sat'n. Temp. 45.7°F.)			Abs. Pressure 9.0 lb./in.² (Sat'n. Temp. 51.0°F.)			Abs. Pressure 10.0 lb./in.² (Sat'n. Temp. 55.9°F.)		
	V	H	S	V	H	S	V	H	S	V	H	S
(at sat'n)	(5.132)	(97.46)	(0.1970)	(4.833)	(97.80)	(0.1968)	(4.333)	(98.44)	(0.1964)	(3.928)	(99.04)	(0.1960)
50	5.207	98.39	0.1988	4.875	98.36	0.1979	.....	.....	.....	.....	.....	.....
60	5.314	99.70	.2014	4.976	99.67	.2004	4.412	99.62	0.1986	3.961	99.57	0.1970
70	5.422	101.02	.2039	5.077	100.99	.2029	4.502	100.94	.2012	4.042	100.89	.1996
80	5.530	102.35	.2064	5.178	102.32	.2054	4.592	102.28	.2037	4.123	102.23	.2021
90	5.637	103.69	.2088	5.279	103.66	.2079	4.682	103.62	.2061	4.204	103.57	.2045
100	5.745	105.04	0.2113	5.380	105.02	0.2103	4.772	104.98	0.2086	4.285	104.93	0.2070
110	5.851	106.40	.2137	5.480	106.38	.2127	4.862	106.34	.2110	4.366	106.29	.2094
120	5.957	107.77	.2161	5.580	107.75	.2151	4.951	107.71	.2134	4.447	107.67	.2118
130	6.064	109.15	.2184	5.680	109.13	.2175	5.041	109.09	.2157	4.528	109.05	.2141
140	6.170	110.54	.2208	5.780	110.52	.2198	5.131	110.48	.2181	4.609	110.44	.2165
150	6.277	111.94	0.2231	5.880	111.92	0.2221	5.220	111.89	0.2204	4.690	111.85	0.2188
160	6.384	113.35	.2254	5.980	113.34	.2244	5.309	113.30	.2227	4.771	113.26	.2211
170	6.490	114.78	.2277	6.081	114.76	.2267	5.398	114.72	.2250	4.851	114.69	.2234
180	6.597	116.21	.2299	6.181	116.19	.2290	5.487	116.15	.2272	4.932	116.12	.2257
190	6.703	117.65	.2322	6.281	117.63	.2312	5.576	117.59	.2295	5.012	117.56	.2279
200	6.809	119.10	0.2344	6.380	119.08	0.2334	5.665	119.04	0.2317	5.092	119.01	0.2301
210	6.915	120.56	.2366	6.480	120.55	.2356	5.753	120.51	.2339	5.171	120.48	.2323
220	7.021	122.03	.2387	6.579	122.02	.2378	5.842	121.98	.2361	5.251	121.95	.2345
230	7.127	123.51	.2409	6.679	123.50	.2400	5.930	123.46	.2382	5.331	123.43	.2367
240	7.233	125.01	.2431	6.779	124.99	.2421	6.019	124.96	.2404	5.411	124.92	.2388
250	7.339	126.51	0.2452	6.878	126.50	0.2442	6.107	126.46	0.2425	5.491	126.43	0.2409
260	7.445	128.03	.2473	6.977	128.01	.2464	6.196	127.98	.2446	5.571	127.95	.2431
270	7.550	129.55	.2494	7.076	129.54	.2485	6.285	129.51	.2467	5.650	129.48	.2452
280	7.656	131.09	.2515	7.175	131.07	.2506	6.373	131.04	.2488	5.730	131.01	.2473
290	7.761	132.64	.2536	7.274	132.62	.2526	6.461	132.59	.2509	5.809	132.56	.2494
300	7.867	134.19	0.2556	7.373	134.18	0.2547	6.549	134.15	0.2530	5.889	134.12	0.2514
310	7.972	135.76	.2577	7.471	135.74	.2567	6.637	135.71	.2550	5.969	135.68	.2535
320	8.078	137.33	.2597	7.570	137.31	.2588	6.725	137.28	.2570	6.048	137.26	.2555
330	8.183	138.91	.2617	7.668	138.89	.2608	6.813	138.86	.2591	6.127	138.84	.2575
340	8.289	140.50	.2637	7.767	140.49	.2628	6.901	140.46	.2611	6.206	140.43	.2595
350	8.394	142.11	0.2657	7.866	142.10	0.2648	6.988	142.07	0.2631	6.285	142.04	0.2615
360	.....	.....	.....	.....	.....	.....	7.076	143.69	.2651	6.365	143.66	.2635

TABLE 2-19. FREON 11: PROPERTIES OF SUPERHEATED VAPOR (Continued)

TABLE 11: PROPERTIES OF SUPERHEATED VAPOR (Continued)

Temp. °F.	Abs. Pressure 11.0 lb./in.² (Sat'n. Temp. 60.4°F.)			Abs. Pressure 12.0 lb./in.² (Sat'n. Temp. 64.6°F.)			Abs. Pressure 13 lb./in.² (Sat'n. Temp. 68.5°F.)			Abs. Pressure 14 lb./in.² (Sat'n. Temp. 72.2°F.)		
(at sat'n)	(99.58)	(3.596)	(0.1957)	(100.08)	(3.317)	(0.1955)	(100.55)	(3.079)	(0.1952)	(100.99)	(2.873)	(0.1950)
70	100.85	3.666	0.1982	100.80	3.354	0.1969	100.75	3.088	0.1956			
80	102.18	3.740	.2007	102.13	3.421	.1993	102.09	3.152	.1981	102.04	2.920	0.1970
90	103.52	3.814	.2031	103.48	3.489	.2018	103.43	3.215	.2006	103.38	2.978	.1995
100	104.88	3.888	0.2056	104.84	3.557	0.2042	104.79	3.278	0.2030	104.74	3.037	0.2019
110	106.24	3.962	.2080	106.20	3.625	.2066	106.16	3.341	.2055	106.11	3.095	.2043
120	107.62	4.036	.2104	107.58	3.693	.2090	107.54	3.405	.2079	107.49	3.154	.2067
130	109.01	4.110	.2127	108.97	3.761	.2114	108.92	3.468	.2102	108.88	3.212	.2091
140	110.40	4.184	.2151	110.36	3.829	.2138	110.32	3.531	.2126	110.28	3.271	.2114
150	111.80	4.257	0.2174	111.76	3.897	0.2161	111.73	3.594	0.2149	111.69	3.329	0.2138
160	113.22	4.331	.2197	113.18	3.964	.2184	113.15	3.656	.2172	113.11	3.388	.2161
170	114.65	4.404	.2220	114.61	4.032	.2207	114.58	3.719	.2195	114.54	3.446	.2184
180	116.08	4.477	.2242	116.04	4.099	.2230	116.01	3.781	.2218	115.97	3.504	.2206
190	117.52	4.551	.2265	117.48	4.166	.2252	117.45	3.843	.2240	117.41	3.562	.2229
200	118.97	4.624	0.2287	118.94	4.233	0.2274	118.90	3.905	0.2262	118.87	3.620	0.2251
210	120.44	4.697	.2309	120.41	4.300	.2296	120.37	3.967	.2284	120.34	3.677	.2273
220	121.91	4.769	.2331	121.88	4.367	.2318	121.84	4.029	.2306	121.81	3.735	.2295
230	123.39	4.842	.2352	123.36	4.433	.2340	123.33	4.090	.2328	123.29	3.792	.2317
240	124.89	4.914	.2374	124.86	4.500	.2361	124.83	4.152	.2349	124.79	3.850	.2338
250	126.40	4.987	0.2395	126.36	4.567	0.2383	126.33	4.214	0.2371	126.30	3.907	0.2360
260	127.92	5.060	.2417	127.88	4.634	.2404	127.85	4.276	.2392	127.82	3.965	.2381
270	129.45	5.132	.2438	129.41	4.701	.2425	129.38	4.337	.2413	129.35	4.022	.2402
280	130.98	5.205	.2459	130.95	4.768	.2446	130.92	4.399	.2434	130.89	4.080	.2423
290	132.53	5.278	.2479	132.50	4.834	.2467	132.47	4.460	.2455	132.44	4.137	.2444
300	134.09	5.350	0.2500	134.06	4.900	0.2487	134.03	4.522	0.2475	134.00	4.195	0.2464
310	135.65	5.422	.2521	135.62	4.966	.2508	135.59	4.583	.2496	135.56	4.252	.2485
320	137.23	5.494	.2541	137.20	5.033	.2528	137.17	4.644	.2516	137.14	4.308	.2505
330	138.81	5.566	.2561	138.78	5.100	.2548	138.75	4.705	.2537	138.72	4.365	.2526
340	140.41	5.639	.2581	140.38	5.166	.2568	140.35	4.767	.2557	140.32	4.422	.2546
350	142.02	5.711	0.2601	141.99	5.232	0.2588	141.96	4.828	0.2577	141.94	4.479	0.2566
360	143.64	5.783	.2621	143.61	5.299	.2608	143.58	4.889	.2597	143.56	4.536	.2586
370	145.26	5.855	.2641	145.23	5.365	.2628	145.21	4.950	.2616	145.19	4.593	.2605
380										146.83	4.651	0.2625

Temp. °F. t	Abs. Pressure 16 lb./in.² (Sat'n. Temp. 79.0°F.)			Abs. Pressure 18 lb./in.² (Sat'n. Temp. 85.2°F.)			Abs. Pressure 20 lb./in.² (Sat'n. Temp. 90.8°F.)			Abs. Pressure 22 lb./in.² (Sat'n. Temp. 96.1°F.)		
	V	H	S	V	H	S	V	H	S	V	H	S
(at sat'n)	(2.537)	(101.81)	(0.1947)	(2.274)	(102.55)	(0.1943)	(2.061)	(103.22)	(0.1942)	(1.885)	(103.84)	(0.1940)
80	2.543	101.94	0.1949	.....	.....	.....	.....	.....	.....	.....	.....	.....
90	2.594	103.29	.1974	2.295	103.20	0.1956	.....	.....	.....	.....	.....	.....
100	2.645	104.65	0.1999	2.342	104.56	0.1980	2.099	104.47	0.1964	1.900	104.38	0.1949
110	2.696	106.02	.2023	2.388	105.93	.2005	2.140	105.84	.1989	1.938	105.75	.1974
120	2.748	107.40	.2047	2.434	107.32	.2029	2.182	107.23	.2013	1.976	107.14	.1998
130	2.800	108.80	.2071	2.480	108.71	.2053	2.224	108.63	.2036	2.015	108.54	.2022
140	2.852	110.20	.2094	2.526	110.11	.2076	2.266	110.03	.2060	2.053	109.94	.2045
150	2.903	111.61	0.2118	2.572	111.53	0.2100	2.307	111.44	0.2083	2.091	111.36	0.2069
160	2.954	113.03	.2141	2.618	112.95	.2123	2.349	112.87	.2107	2.129	112.79	.2092
170	3.006	114.46	.2164	2.663	114.38	.2146	2.390	114.31	.2130	2.166	114.23	.2115
180	3.057	115.90	.2186	2.709	115.82	.2168	2.431	115.75	.2152	2.204	115.67	.2138
190	3.108	117.34	.2209	2.755	117.26	.2191	2.473	117.19	.2175	2.242	117.11	.2160
200	3.159	118.79	0.2231	2.801	118.72	0.2213	2.514	118.65	0.2197	2.280	118.57	0.2183
210	3.209	120.26	.2253	2.846	120.19	.2235	2.555	120.12	.2219	2.317	120.05	.2205
220	3.259	121.74	.2275	2.891	121.67	.2257	2.596	121.60	.2241	2.355	121.53	.2227
230	3.310	123.23	.2297	2.936	123.16	.2279	2.637	123.09	.2263	2.392	123.02	.2248
240	3.361	124.73	.2318	2.981	124.66	.2301	2.678	124.59	.2285	2.429	124.53	.2270
250	3.411	126.24	0.2340	3.027	126.17	0.2322	2.719	126.11	0.2306	2.466	126.04	0.2292
260	3.462	127.76	.2361	3.072	127.69	.2343	2.760	127.63	.2328	2.504	127.57	.2313
270	3.513	129.29	.2382	3.117	129.22	.2364	2.800	129.16	.2349	2.541	129.10	.2334
280	3.563	130.83	.2403	3.162	130.76	.2385	2.841	130.70	.2370	2.578	130.64	.2355
290	3.614	132.37	.2424	3.207	132.31	.2406	2.881	132.25	.2391	2.615	132.19	.2376
300	3.664	133.94	0.2445	3.252	133.88	0.2427	2.922	133.82	0.2411	2.652	133.76	0.2397
310	3.714	135.50	.2465	3.296	135.45	.2447	2.962	135.39	.2432	2.689	135.33	.2417
320	3.764	137.08	.2486	3.341	137.03	.2468	3.003	136.97	.2452	2.726	136.91	.2438
330	3.814	138.67	.2506	3.385	138.61	.2488	3.043	138.56	.2472	2.763	138.50	.2458
340	3.864	140.27	.2526	3.430	140.21	.2508	3.084	140.16	.2493	2.800	140.10	.2478
350	3.914	141.88	0.2546	3.475	141.83	0.2528	3.124	141.77	0.2513	2.837	141.72	0.2498
360	3.964	143.50	.2566	3.520	143.45	.2548	3.164	143.40	.2532	2.874	143.34	.2518
370	4.015	145.13	.2586	3.565	145.08	.2568	3.205	145.03	.2552	2.910	144.97	.2538
380	4.066	146.78	.2605	3.610	146.73	.2588	3.245	146.68	.2572	2.947	146.62	.2558
390	.....	.....	.....	3.654	148.38	.2607	3.286	148.33	.2592	2.984	148.28	.2577
400	.....	.....	.....	.....	.....	.....	3.326	149.99	0.2611	3.021	149.94	0.2597

TABLE 2-19. FREON 11: PROPERTIES OF SUPERHEATED VAPOR (Continued)

Temp. °F.	Abs. Pressure 24 lb./in.² (Sat'n. Temp. 100.9°F.)			Abs. Pressure 26 lb./in.² (Sat'n. Temp. 105.5°F.)			Abs. Pressure 28 lb./in.² (Sat'n. Temp. 109.8°F.)			Abs. Pressure 30 lb./in.² (Sat'n. Temp. 113.9°F.)		
(at sat'n)	(1.738)	(104.41)	(0.1938)	(1.612)	(104.94)	(0.1937)	(1.504)	(105.45)	(0.1935)	(1.409)	(105.93)	(0.1935)
110	1.769	105.66	0.1960	1.626	105.57	0.1947	1.504	105.48	0.1936	....	....	....
120	1.805	107.05	.1984	1.659	106.96	.1972	1.535	106.87	.1960	1.426	106.79	0.1949
130	1.840	108.45	.2008	1.692	108.36	.1996	1.566	108.27	.1984	1.455	108.19	.1973
140	1.875	109.86	.2032	1.725	109.77	.2019	1.596	109.69	.2008	1.484	109.60	.1997
150	1.910	111.28	0.2055	1.757	111.19	0.2043	1.626	111.11	0.2031	1.513	111.02	0.2020
160	1.945	112.70	.2079	1.790	112.62	.2066	1.657	112.54	.2054	1.541	112.45	.2044
170	1.980	114.14	.2102	1.822	114.06	.2089	1.687	113.98	.2077	1.569	113.90	.2067
180	2.015	115.59	.2124	1.854	115.51	.2112	1.717	115.43	.2100	1.598	115.35	.2090
190	2.049	117.04	.2147	1.887	116.96	.2135	1.747	116.88	.2123	1.626	116.81	.2112
200	2.084	118.50	0.2169	1.919	118.42	0.2157	1.777	118.35	0.2146	1.654	118.27	0.2135
210	2.119	119.98	.2192	1.951	119.90	.2179	1.807	119.83	.2168	1.682	119.75	.2157
220	2.154	121.46	.2214	1.983	121.39	.2201	1.837	121.32	.2190	1.711	121.24	.2179
230	2.188	122.96	.2235	2.015	122.88	.2223	1.867	122.81	.2212	1.739	122.74	.2201
240	2.222	124.46	.2257	2.047	124.39	.2245	1.897	124.32	.2233	1.767	124.25	.2223
250	2.256	125.97	0.2279	2.079	125.91	0.2266	1.926	125.84	0.2255	1.794	125.77	0.2244
260	2.291	127.50	.2300	2.111	127.44	.2288	1.956	127.37	.2276	1.822	127.30	.2266
270	2.325	129.03	.2321	2.142	128.97	.2309	1.986	128.91	.2298	1.850	128.84	.2287
280	2.359	130.58	.2342	2.174	130.52	.2330	2.015	130.46	.2319	1.878	130.39	.2308
290	2.393	132.13	.2363	2.206	132.07	.2351	2.045	132.01	.2340	1.905	131.95	.2329
300	2.427	133.70	0.2384	2.238	133.64	0.2372	2.074	133.58	0.2360	1.933	133.52	0.2350
310	2.461	135.27	.2404	2.269	135.22	.2392	2.103	135.16	.2381	1.960	135.10	.2370
320	2.495	136.85	.2425	2.300	136.80	.2413	2.133	136.74	.2401	1.988	136.68	.2391
330	2.529	138.44	.2445	2.332	138.39	.2433	2.162	138.33	.2422	2.015	138.28	.2411
340	2.563	140.04	.2465	2.363	139.99	.2453	2.192	139.94	.2442	2.043	139.89	.2431
350	2.597	141.66	0.2485	2.394	141.61	0.2473	2.221	141.56	0.2462	2.070	141.51	0.2452
360	2.631	143.29	.2505	2.426	143.24	.2493	2.250	143.19	.2482	2.097	143.14	.2472
370	2.665	144.92	.2525	2.457	144.87	.2513	2.279	144.83	.2502	2.125	144.78	.2491
380	2.699	146.57	.2545	2.488	146.52	.2533	2.308	146.48	.2522	2.152	146.43	.2511
390	2.733	148.23	.2564	2.520	148.18	.2552	2.337	148.14	.2541	2.179	148.09	.2531
400	2.767	149.90	0.2584	2.551	149.85	0.2572	2.367	149.80	0.2561	2.207	149.75	0.2550
410	2.801	151.58	.2603	2.583	151.53	.2591	2.396	151.48	.2580	2.234	151.43	.2570
420	....	....	....	....	....	....	....	....	....	2.261	153.12	0.2589

Temp. °F. (t)	Abs. Pressure 35 lb./in.² (Sat'n. Temp. 123.3°F.) v	H	s	Abs. Pressure 40 lb./in.² (Sat'n. Temp. 131.6°F.) v	H	s	Abs. Pressure 45 lb./in.² (Sat'n. Temp. 139.3°F.) v	H	s	Abs. Pressure 50 lb./in.² (Sat'n. Temp. 146.3°F.) v	H	s
(at sat'n)	(1.219)	(107.01)	(0.1932)	(1.074)	(107.96)	(0.1930)	(0.9608)	(108.84)	(0.1929)	(0.8689)	(109.62)	(0.1928)
130	1.235	107.97	.1948	1.092	109.17	0.1950						
140	1.260	109.39	.1972				0.9621	108.95	0.1931			
150	1.285	110.81	0.1996	1.115	110.60	0.1974	0.9824	110.39	0.1955	0.8756	110.16	0.1937
160	1.310	112.25	.2019	1.137	112.04	.1997	1.002	111.83	.1978	.8937	111.61	.1960
170	1.335	113.70	.2042	1.159	113.49	.2021	1.022	113.29	.2001	.9118	113.08	.1984
180	1.360	115.15	.2065	1.181	114.95	.2044	1.042	114.75	.2024	.9299	114.55	.2007
190	1.384	116.61	.2088	1.202	116.42	.2067	1.061	116.22	.2047	.9477	116.03	.2030
200	1.409	118.08	0.2111	1.224	117.89	0.2089	1.081	117.70	0.2070	0.9656	117.52	0.2053
210	1.433	119.57	.2133	1.246	119.38	.2112	1.100	119.20	.2093	0.9835	119.02	.2075
220	1.458	121.06	.2155	1.268	120.88	.2134	1.120	120.70	.2115	1.002	120.52	.2098
230	1.482	122.57	.2177	1.289	122.39	.2156	1.139	122.21	.2137	1.019	122.04	.2120
240	1.506	124.08	.2199	1.311	124.91	.2178	1.159	123.73	.2159	1.037	123.56	.2142
250	1.530	125.61	0.2220	1.332	125.44	0.2199	1.178	125.27	0.2181	1.054	125.10	0.2164
260	1.554	127.14	.2242	1.353	126.97	.2221	1.197	126.81	.2202	1.072	126.64	.2185
270	1.578	128.68	.2263	1.374	128.52	.2242	1.216	128.36	.2224	1.089	128.20	.2207
280	1.602	130.23	.2284	1.396	130.08	.2263	1.235	129.92	.2245	1.106	129.76	.2228
290	1.626	131.80	.2305	1.417	131.64	.2284	1.254	131.49	.2266	1.124	131.33	.2249
300	1.650	133.37	0.2326	1.438	133.22	0.2305	1.273	133.07	0.2287	1.141	132.91	0.2270
310	1.674	134.95	.2347	1.459	134.80	.2326	1.292	134.65	.2307	1.158	134.50	.2291
320	1.698	136.54	.2367	1.480	136.40	.2347	1.311	136.25	.2328	1.175	136.10	.2311
330	1.721	138.14	.2388	1.501	138.00	.2367	1.330	137.86	.2349	1.192	137.71	.2332
340	1.745	139.75	.2408	1.522	139.61	.2387	1.348	139.47	.2369	1.209	139.33	.2352
350	1.769	141.38	0.2428	1.543	141.24	0.2407	1.367	141.10	0.2389	1.226	140.96	0.2373
360	1.792	143.01	.2448	1.564	142.88	.2427	1.386	142.74	.2409	1.243	142.61	.2393
370	1.816	144.65	.2468	1.584	144.52	.2447	1.404	144.39	.2429	1.260	144.26	.2413
380	1.840	146.30	.2488	1.605	146.18	.2467	1.423	146.05	.2449	1.277	145.92	.2433
390	1.863	147.96	.2507	1.626	147.83	.2487	1.442	147.71	.2469	1.294	147.58	.2452
400	1.887	149.63	0.2527	1.647	149.51	0.2506	1.460	149.38	0.2488	1.311	149.26	0.2472
410	1.910	151.31	.2546	1.668	151.19	.2526	1.479	151.07	.2508	1.328	150.95	.2492
420	1.934	153.00	.2566	1.688	152.89	.2545	1.498	152.77	.2527	1.345	152.65	.2511
430	1.957	154.70	0.2585	1.709	154.59	.2564	1.516	154.47	.2547	1.361	154.36	.2530
440	.....	.....	.....	1.729	156.30	.2583	1.534	156.19	.2566	1.378	156.07	.2549
450	.....	.....	.....	.....	.....	.....	.....	.....	.....	1.395	157.80	0.2569

TABLE 2-19.   FREON 11: PROPERTIES OF SUPERHEATED VAPOR (Concluded)

Temp. °F.	Abs. Pressure 55 lb./in.² (Sat'n. Temp. 152.8°F.)			Abs. Pressure 60 lb./in.² (Sat'n. Temp. 158.8°F.)			Abs. Pressure 65 lb./in.² (Sat'n. Temp. 164.5°F.)		
(at.sat'n)	(0.7933)	(110.33)	(0.1927)	(0.7297)	(110.99)	(0.1926)	(0.6755)	(111.61)	(0.1926)
160	0.8054	111.39	0.1944	0.7314	111.17	0.1929	.....	.....	.....
170	.8222	112.86	.1968	.7471	112.65	.1953	0.6835	112.44	0.1939
180	.8389	114.34	.1991	.7627	114.14	.1976	.6982	113.93	.1963
190	.8554	115.83	.2014	.7782	115.63	.1999	.7129	115.42	.1986
200	0.8720	117.33	0.2037	0.7937	117.13	0.2022	0.7273	116.93	0.2009
210	.8884	118.83	.2060	.8090	118.64	.2045	.7417	118.44	.2032
220	.9048	120.34	.2082	.8241	120.16	.2068	.7561	119.96	.2054
230	.9210	121.86	.2104	.8391	121.68	.2090	.7701	121.49	.2077
240	.9372	123.39	.2126	.8541	123.21	.2112	.7841	123.04	.2099
250	0.9534	124.93	0.2148	0.8691	124.76	0.2134	0.7980	124.59	0.2121
260	.9695	126.48	.2170	.8839	126.31	.2156	.8119	126.15	.2142
270	.9853	128.04	.2191	.8987	127.87	.2177	.8255	127.71	.2164
280	1.001	129.60	.2213	.9134	129.44	.2198	.8391	129.27	.2185
290	1.017	131.17	.2234	.9281	131.01	.2220	.8529	130.85	.2207
300	1.033	132.76	0.2255	0.9427	132.60	0.2241	0.8667	132.45	0.2228
310	1.049	134.35	.2276	.9574	134.20	.2262	.8803	134.05	.2249
320	1.065	135.96	.2296	.9719	135.81	.2282	.8939	135.66	.2269
330	1.080	137.57	.2317	.9863	137.42	.2303	.9073	137.28	.2290
340	1.096	139.19	.2337	1.001	139.05	.2323	.9207	138.91	.2311
350	1.111	140.83	0.2358	1.015	140.69	0.2344	0.9341	140.55	0.2331
360	1.127	142.47	.2378	1.030	142.33	.2364	.9474	142.20	.2351
370	1.142	144.12	.2398	1.044	143.98	.2384	.9608	143.85	.2371
380	1.158	145.78	.2418	1.059	145.65	.2404	.9742	145.52	.2391
390	1.173	147.45	.2437	1.073	147.32	.2424	0.9875	147.19	.2411
400	1.189	149.13	0.2457	1.087	149.01	0.2443	1.001	148.88	0.2431
410	1.204	150.83	.2477	1.101	150.70	.2463	1.014	150.58	.2450
420	1.220	152.53	.2496	1.115	152.41	.2483	1.027	152.29	.2470
430	1.235	154.24	.2515	1.130	154.12	.2502	1.040	154.01	.2489
440	1.250	155.96	.2535	1.144	155.84	.2521	1.053	155.73	.2509
450	1.265	157.68	0.2554	1.158	157.57	0.2540	1.066	157.46	0.2528
460	1.281	159.42	.2573	1.172	159.31	.2559	1.080	159.20	.2547
470							1.093	160.96	0.2566

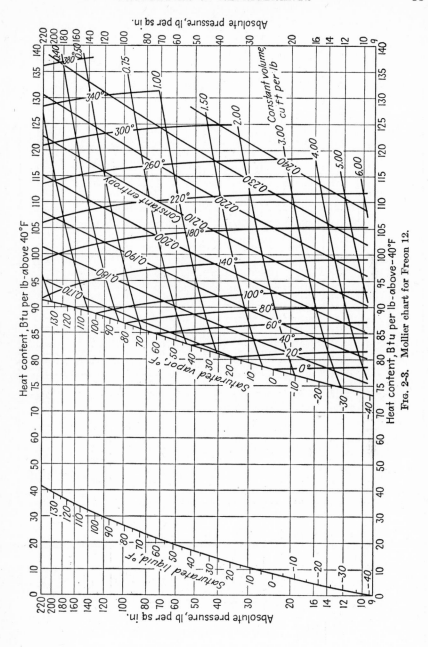

Fig. 2-3. Mollier chart for Freon 12.

TABLE 2-20. FREON 12: PROPERTIES OF SATURATED VAPOR*

Temp.	Pressure		Volume		Density		Heat content from −40°			Entropy from −40°		Temp.
°F.	Abs. lb./in.²	Gage lb./in.²	Liquid ft.³/lb.	Vapor ft.³/lb.	Liquid lb./ft.³	Vapor lb./ft.³	Liquid Btu./lb.	Latent Btu./lb.	Vapor Btu./lb.	Liquid Btu./lb. °F	Vapor Btu./lb. °F	°F.
−40	9.32	10.92†	0.0106	3.911	94.58	0.2557	0	73.50	73.50	0	0.17517	−40
−38	9.82	9.91†	.0106	3.727	94.39	.2683	0.40	73.34	73.74	0.00094	.17490	−38
−36	10.34	8.87†	.0106	3.553	94.20	.2815	0.81	73.17	73.98	.00188	.17463	−36
−34	10.87	7.80†	.0106	3.389	93.99	.2951	1.21	73.01	74.22	.00282	.17438	−34
−32	11.43	6.66†	.0107	3.234	93.79	.3092	1.62	72.84	74.46	.00376	.17412	−32
−30	12.02	5.45†	0.0107	3.088	93.59	0.3238	2.03	72.67	74.70	0.00471	0.17387	−30
−28	12.62	4.23†	.0107	2.950	93.39	.3390	2.44	72.50	74.94	.00565	.17364	−28
−26	13.26	2.93†	.0107	2.820	93.18	.3546	2.85	72.33	75.18	.00659	.17340	−26
−24	13.90	1.63†	.0108	2.698	92.98	.3706	3.25	72.16	75.41	.00753	.17317	−24
−22	14.58	0.24†	.0108	2.583	92.78	.3871	3.66	71.98	75.64	.00846	.17296	−22
−20	15.28	0.58	0.0108	2.474	92.58	0.4042	4.07	71.80	75.87	0.00940	0.17275	−20
−18	16.01	1.31	.0108	2.370	92.38	.4219	4.48	71.63	76.11	.01033	.17253	−18
−16	16.77	2.07	.0108	2.271	92.18	.4403	4.89	71.45	76.34	.01126	.17232	−16
−14	17.55	2.85	.0109	2.177	91.97	.4593	5.30	71.27	76.57	.01218	.17212	−14
−12	18.37	3.67	.0109	2.088	91.77	.4789	5.72	71.09	76.81	.01310	.17194	−12
−10	19.20	4.50	0.0109	2.003	91.57	0.4993	6.14	70.91	77.05	0.01403	0.17175	−10
−8	20.08	5.38	.0109	1.922	91.35	.5203	6.57	70.72	77.29	.01496	.17158	−8
−6	20.98	6.28	.0110	1.845	91.14	.5420	6.99	70.53	77.52	.01589	.17140	−6
−4	21.91	7.21	.0110	1.772	90.93	.5644	7.41	70.34	77.75	.01682	.17123	−4
−2	22.87	8.17	.0110	1.703	90.72	.5872	7.83	70.15	77.98	.01775	.17107	−2
0	23.87	9.17	0.0110	1.637	90.52	0.6109	8.25	69.96	78.21	0.01869	0.17091	0
2	24.89	10.19	.0110	1.574	90.31	.6352	8.67	69.77	78.44	.01961	.17075	2
4	25.96	11.26	.0111	1.514	90.10	.6606	9.10	69.57	78.67	.02052	.17060	4
5‡	26.51	11.81	.0111	1.485	90.00	.6735	9.32	69.47	78.79	.02097	.17052	5‡
6	27.05	12.35	.0111	1.457	89.88	.6864	9.53	69.37	78.90	.02143	.17045	6
8	28.18	13.48	.0111	1.403	89.68	.7129	9.96	69.17	79.13	.02235	.17030	8
10	29.35	14.65	0.0112	1.351	89.45	0.7402	10.39	68.97	79.36	0.02328	0.17015	10
12	30.56	15.86	.0112	1.301	89.24	.7687	10.82	68.77	79.59	.02419	.17001	12
14	31.80	17.10	.0112	1.253	89.03	.7981	11.26	68.56	79.82	.02510	.16987	14
16	33.08	18.38	.0112	1.207	88.81	.8288	11.70	68.35	80.05	.02601	.16974	16
18	34.40	19.70	.0113	1.163	88.58	.8598	12.12	68.15	80.27	.02692	.16961	18
20	35.75	21.05	0.0113	1.121	88.37	0.8921	12.55	67.94	80.49	0.02783	0.16949	20
22	37.15	22.45	.0113	1.081	88.13	.9251	13.00	67.72	80.72	.02873	.16938	22
24	38.58	23.88	.0113	1.043	87.91	.9588	13.44	67.51	80.95	.02963	.16926	24
26	40.07	25.37	.0114	1.007	87.68	.9930	13.89	67.29	81.17	.03053	.16913	26
28	41.59	26.89	.0114	0.973	87.47	1.028	14.32	67.07	81.39	.03143	.16900	28
30	43.16	28.46	0.0115	0.939	87.24	1.065	14.76	66.85	81.61	0.03233	0.16887	30
32	44.77	30.07	.0115	.908	87.02	1.102	15.21	66.62	81.83	.03323	.16876	32
34	46.42	31.72	.0115	.877	86.78	1.140	15.65	66.40	82.05	.03413	.16865	34
36	48.13	33.43	.0116	.848	86.55	1.180	16.10	66.17	82.27	.03502	.16854	36
38	49.88	35.18	.0116	.819	86.33	1.221	16.55	65.94	82.49	.03591	.16843	38
40	51.68	36.98	0.0116	0.792	86.10	1.263	17.00	65.71	82.71	0.03680	0.16833	40
42	53.51	38.81	.0116	.767	85.88	1.304	17.46	65.47	82.93	.03770	.16823	42
44	55.40	40.70	.0117	.742	85.66	1.349	17.91	65.24	83.15	.03859	.16813	44
46	57.35	42.65	.0117	.718	85.43	1.393	18.36	65.00	83.36	.03948	.16803	46
48	59.35	44.65	.0117	.695	85.19	1.438	18.82	64.74	83.57	.04037	.16794	48
50	61.39	46.69	0.0118	0.673	84.94	1.485	19.27	64.51	83.78	0.04126	0.16785	50
52	63.49	48.79	.0118	.652	84.71	1.534	19.72	64.27	83.99	.04215	.16776	52
54	65.63	50.93	.0118	.632	84.50	1.583	20.18	64.02	84.20	.04304	.16767	54
56	67.84	53.14	.0119	.612	84.28	1.633	20.64	63.77	84.41	.04392	.16758	56
58	70.10	55.40	.0119	.593	84.04	1.686	21.11	63.51	84.62	.04480	.16749	58
60	72.41	57.71	0.0119	0.575	83.78	1.740	21.57	63.25	84.82	0.04568	0.16741	60
62	74.77	60.07	.0120	.557	83.57	1.795	22.03	62.99	85.02	.04657	.16733	62
64	77.20	62.50	.0120	.540	83.34	1.851	22.49	62.73	85.22	.04745	.16725	64
66	79.67	64.97	.0120	.524	83.10	1.909	22.95	62.47	85.42	.04833	.16717	66
68	82.24	67.54	.0121	.508	82.86	1.968	23.42	62.20	85.62	.04921	.16709	68
70	84.82	70.12	0.0121	.0493	82.60	2.028	23.90	61.92	85.82	0.05009	0.16701	70

TABLE 2-20. FREON 12: PROPERTIES OF SATURATED VAPOR (*Concluded*)

Temp.	Pressure		Volume		Density		Heat content from −40°			Entropy from −40°		Temp.
°F.	Abs. lb./ in.²	Gage lb./in.²	Liquid ft.³/ lb.	Vapor ft.³/ lb.	Liquid lb./ ft.³	Vapor lb./ ft.³	Liquid Btu./ lb.	Latent Btu./ lb.	Vapor Btu./ lb.	Liquid Btu./ lb. °F	Vapor Btu./ lb. °F	°F
70	84.82	70.12	0.0121	0.493	82.60	2.028	23.90	61.92	85.82	0.05009	0.16701	**70**
72	87.50	72.80	.0121	.479	82.37	2.090	24.37	61.65	86.02	.05097	.16693	72
74	90.20	75.50	.0122	.464	82.12	2.153	24.84	61.38	86.22	.05185	.16685	74
76	93.00	78.30	.0122	.451	81.87	2.218	25.32	61.10	86.42	.05272	.16677	76
78	95.85	81.15	.0123	.438	81.62	2.284	25.80	60.81	86.61	.05359	.16669	78
80	98.76	84.06	0.0123	0.425	81.39	2.353	26.28	60.52	86.80	0.05446	0.16662	**80**
82	101.7	87.00	.0123	.413	81.12	2.423	26.76	60.23	86.99	.05534	.16655	82
84	104.8	90.1	.0124	.401	80.87	2.495	27.24	59.94	87.18	.05621	.16648	84
86‡	107.9	93.2	.0124	.389	80.63	2.569	27.72	59.65	87.37	.05708	.16640	86‡
88	111.1	96.4	.0124	.378	80.37	2.645	28.21	59.35	87.56	.05795	.16632	88
90	114.3	99.6	0.0125	0.368	80.11	2.721	28.70	59.04	87.74	0.05882	0.16624	**90**
92	117.7	103.0	.0125	.357	79.86	2.799	29.19	58.73	87.92	.05969	.16616	92
94	121.0	106.3	.0126	.347	79.60	2.880	29.68	58.42	88.10	.06056	.16608	94
96	124.5	109.8	.0126	.338	79.32	2.963	30.18	58.10	88.28	.06143	.16600	96
98	128.0	113.3	.0126	.328	79.06	3.048	30.67	57.78	88.45	.06230	.16592	98
100	131.6	116.9	0.0127	0.319	78.80	3.135	31.16	57.46	88.62	0.06316	0.16584	**100**
102	135.3	120.6	.0127	.310	78.54	3.224	31.65	57.14	88.79	.06403	.16576	102
104	139.0	124.3	.0128	.302	78.27	3.316	32.15	56.80	88.95	.06490	.16568	104
106	142.8	128.1	.0128	.293	78.00	3.411	32.65	56.46	89.11	.06577	.16560	106
108	146.8	132.1	.0129	.285	77.73	3.509	33.15	56.12	89.27	.06663	.16551	108
110	150.7	136.0	0.0129	0.277	77.46	3.610	33.65	55.78	89.43	0.06749	0.16542	**110**
112	154.8	140.1	.0130	.269	77.18	3.714	34.15	55.43	89.58	.06836	.16533	112
114	158.9	144.2	.0130	.262	76.89	3.823	34.65	55.08	89.73	.06922	.16524	114
116	163.1	148.4	.0131	.254	76.60	3.934	35.15	54.72	89.87	.07008	.16515	116
118	167.4	152.7	.0131	.247	76.32	4.049	36.65	54.36	90.01	.07094	.16505	118
120	171.8	157.1	0.0132	0.240	76.02	4.167	36.16	53.99	90.15	0.07180	0.16495	**120**
122	176.2	161.5	.0132	.233	75.72	4.288	36.66	53.62	90.28	.07266	.16484	122
124	180.8	166.1	.0133	.227	75.40	4.413	37.16	53.24	90.40	.07352	.16473	124
126	185.4	170.7	.0133	.220	75.10	4.451	37.67	52.85	90.52	.07437	.16462	126
128	190.1	175.4	.0134	.214	74.78	4.673	38.18	52.46	90.64	.07522	.16450	128
130	194.9	180.2	0.0134	0.208	74.46	4.808	38.69	52.07	90.76	0.07607	0.16438	**130**
132	199.8	185.1	.0135	.202	74.13	4.948	39.19	51.67	90.86	.07691	.16425	132
134	204.8	190.1	.0135	.196	73.81	5.094	39.70	51.26	90.96	.07775	.16411	134
136	209.9	195.2	.0136	.191	73.46	5.247	40.21	50.85	91.06	.07858	.16396	136
138	215.0	200.3	.0137	.185	73.10	5.405	40.72	50.43	91.15	.07941	.16380	138
140	220.2	205.5	0.0138	0.180	72.73	5.571	41.24	50.00	91.24	0.08024	0.16363	**140**

* Courtesy Kinetic Chemicals, Inc., Wilmington, Del.
† Inches of mercury below one atmosphere.
‡ Standard ton temperatures.

TABLE 2-21. FREON 12: PROPERTIES OF SUPERHEATED VAPOR

Temp. °F. (t)	Abs. Pressure 8 lb./in.^{2} (Sat'n. Temp. -45.8° F.)			Abs. Pressure 9 lb./in.^{2} (Sat'n. Temp. -41.4° F.)			Abs. Pressure 10 lb./in.^{2} (Sat'n. Temp. -37.3° F.)			Abs. Pressure 11 lb./in.^{2} (Sat'n. Temp. -33.5° F.)		
	V	H	S	V	H	S	V	H	S	V	H	S
(at sat'n)	(4.502)	(72.80)	(0.17596)	(4.036)	(73.32)	(0.17533)	(3.652)	(73.80)	(0.17480)	(3.356)	(74.27)	(0.17432)
-40	4.569	73.56	0.17777	4.050	73.51	0.17576						
-30	4.684	74.87	.18085	4.152	74.83	.17884	3.728	74.77	0.17704	3.383	74.73	0.17540
-20	4.799	76.20	.18390	4.255	76.15	.18188	3.821	76.11	.18008	3.467	76.06	.17845
-10	4.914	77.54	.18691	4.357	77.49	.18490	3.913	77.46	.18310	3.551	77.40	.18146
0	5.028	78.89	0.18991	4.460	78.84	0.18791	4.006	78.81	0.18611	3.635	78.75	0.18448
10	5.142	80.26	.19284	4.562	80.20	.19084	4.098	80.18	.18905	3.719	80.12	.18742
20	5.257	81.64	.19574	4.663	81.58	.19374	4.189	81.56	.19194	3.802	81.50	.19032
30	5.370	83.02	.19860	4.766	82.98	.19661	4.280	82.94	.19482	3.887	82.90	.19320
40	5.484	84.43	.20143	4.867	84.39	.19945	4.371	84.35	.19766	3.971	84.31	.19605
50	5.598	85.85	0.20425	4.969	85.80	0.20227	4.463	85.77	0.20047	4.055	85.73	0.19887
60	5.711	87.27	.20703	5.071	87.24	.20505	4.556	87.19	.20326	4.138	87.16	.20165
70	5.824	88.72	.20977	5.171	88.68	.20779	4.648	88.64	.20601	4.221	88.61	.20440
80	5.938	90.18	.21250	5.272	90.13	.21051	4.740	90.11	.20874	4.304	90.07	.20713
90	6.051	91.64	.21519	5.374	91.60	.21321	4.832	91.58	.21144	4.388	91.54	.20984
100	6.165	93.13	0.21786	5.475	93.09	0.21588	4.923	93.05	0.21411	4.471	93.03	0.21251
110	6.278	94.63	.22051	5.576	94.59	.21853	5.015	94.56	.21676	4.553	94.52	.21515
120	6.391	96.13	.22314	5.677	96.10	.22116	5.107	96.07	.21940	4.636	96.03	.21778
130	6.504	97.64	.22573	5.778	97.63	.22375	5.198	97.59	.22199	4.718	97.56	.22037
140	6.617	99.18	.22831	5.879	99.16	.22634	5.289	99.14	.22458	4.800	99.09	.22296
150	6.730	100.73	0.23087	5.979	100.70	0.22889	5.379	100.66	0.22713	4.882	100.63	0.22551
160	6.843	102.29	.23340	6.080	102.26	.23143	5.470	102.24	.22967	4.965	102.20	.22805
170	6.955	103.87	.23591	6.180	103.84	.23394	5.560	103.81	.23218	5.047	103.78	.23057
180	7.068	105.44	.23842	6.280	105.43	.23645	5.650	105.40	.23469	5.130	105.37	.23308
190	7.181	107.05	.24090	6.380	107.03	.23893	5.740	107.00	.23717	5.214	106.97	.23557
200	7.294	108.67	0.24337	6.481	108.64	0.24140	5.831	108.63	0.23963	5.297	108.58	0.23804
210	7.407	110.28	.24581	6.581	110.26	.24384	5.921	110.25	.24208	5.379	110.21	.24049
220	7.520	111.93	.24825	6.682	111.90	.24628	6.011	111.88	.24451	5.462	111.85	.24291
230	7.633	113.57	.25066	6.782	113.55	.24868	6.101	113.53	.24692	5.544	113.50	.24532
240										5.626	115.18	.24773

Temp. °F.	Abs. Pressure 12 lb./in.² (Sat'n. Temp. −30.0° F.)			Abs. Pressure 13 lb./in.² (Sat'n. Temp. −26.8° F.)			Abs. Pressure 14 lb./in.² (Sat'n. Temp. −23.7° F.)			Abs. Pressure 15 lb./in.² (Sat'n. Temp. −20.8° F.)		
(at sat'n)	(3.093)	(74.69)	(0.17389)	(2.875)	(75.08)	(0.17350)	(2.677)	(75.45)	(0.17314)	(2.518)	(75.78)	(0.17282)
−30	3.093	74.69	0.17389									
−20	3.172	76.02	.17695	2.920	75.98	0.17556	2.706	75.94	0.17427	2.521	75.89	0.17307
−10	3.250	77.37	.17998	2.992	77.32	.17859	2.773	77.28	.17731	2.583	77.23	.17611
0	3.328	78.73	0.18299	3.064	78.69	0.18160	2.841	78.64	0.18032	2.646	78.59	0.17913
10	3.405	80.10	.18594	3.136	80.05	.18455	2.908	80.01	.18328	2.708	79.97	.18208
20	3.483	81.48	.18884	3.207	81.43	.18746	2.974	81.40	.18618	2.771	81.37	.18499
30	3.560	82.87	.19173	3.278	82.83	.19034	3.041	82.80	.18907	2.833	82.77	.18788
40	3.637	84.28	.19458	3.349	84.23	.19319	3.107	84.21	.19192	2.895	84.18	.19074
50	3.714	85.71	0.19739	3.420	85.66	0.19601	3.173	85.63	0.19475	2.957	85.60	0.19357
60	3.790	87.14	.20018	3.491	87.10	.19880	3.239	87.06	.19753	3.019	87.03	.19635
70	3.867	88.59	.20293	3.562	88.54	.20156	3.303	88.51	.20028	3.081	88.48	.19911
80	3.943	90.05	.20566	3.632	90.01	.20428	3.369	89.97	.20302	3.143	89.94	.20185
90	4.019	91.52	.20836	3.703	91.48	.20699	3.435	91.44	.20572	3.204	91.41	.20455
100	4.095	93.00	0.21104	3.774	92.96	0.20967	3.501	92.93	0.20841	3.266	92.91	0.20723
110	4.170	94.50	.21367	3.844	94.47	.21231	3.567	94.43	.21106	3.327	94.41	.20989
120	4.246	96.01	.21631	3.915	95.98	.21495	3.633	95.95	.21369	3.388	95.91	.21252
130	4.323	97.53	.21891	3.986	97.50	.21755	3.699	97.48	.21630	3.450	97.44	.21513
140	4.400	99.07	.22151	4.056	99.04	.22014	3.763	99.01	.21889	3.510	98.98	.21772
150	4.474	100.62	0.22406	4.126	100.59	0.22270	3.828	100.56	0.22144	3.571	100.53	0.22028
160	4.549	102.18	.22659	4.196	102.16	.22524	3.894	102.13	.22400	3.632	102.10	.22282
170	4.624	103.75	.22911	4.266	103.73	.22775	3.960	103.71	.22651	3.694	103.68	.22535
180	4.700	105.34	.23162	4.337	105.32	.23027	4.025	105.30	.22902	3.755	105.27	.22786
190	4.774	106.94	.23409	4.408	106.92	.23276	4.090	106.90	.23150	3.816	106.87	.23034
200	4.850	108.55	0.23656	4.478	108.55	0.23523	4.155	108.52	0.23398	3.877	108.49	0.23282
210	4.926	110.18	.23901	4.547	110.16	.23767	4.220	110.14	.23643	3.938	110.12	.23527
220	5.000	111.82	.24144	4.617	111.81	.24011	4.285	111.78	.23886	3.998	111.77	.23770
230	5.076	113.47	.24385	4.686	113.45	.24252	4.350	113.44	.24128	4.059	113.42	.24011
240	5.152	115.15	.24626	4.755	115.13	.24492	4.414	115.11	.24368	4.120	115.10	.24253
250							4.479	116.79	0.24607	4.181	116.78	0.24491

TABLE 2-21. FREON 12: PROPERTIES OF SUPERHEATED VAPOR (Continued)

Temp. °F. t	Abs. Pressure 16 lb./in.² (Sat'n. Temp. −18.0° F.)			Abs. Pressure 17 lb./in.² (Sat'n. Temp. −15.4° F.)			Abs. Pressure 18 lb./in.² (Sat'n. Temp. −12.9° F.)			Abs. Pressure 19 lb./in.² (Sat'n. Temp. −10.5° F.)		
	V	H	S	V	H	S	V	H	S	V	H	S
(at sat'n)	(2.370)	(76.11)	(0.17254)	(2.240)	(76.41)	(0.17226)	(2.123)	(76.70)	(0.17202)	(2.019)	(76.99)	(0.17180)
−10	2.417	77.20	0.17498	2.268	77.15	0.17390	2.137	77.09	0.17289	2.022	77.05	0.17195
0	2.476	78.56	0.17800	2.325	78.52	0.17693	2.191	78.47	0.17592	2.072	78.42	0.17497
10	2.535	79.94	.18095	2.382	79.90	.17990	2.244	79.85	.17889	2.122	79.80	.17794
20	2.594	81.33	.18387	2.438	81.29	.18283	2.297	81.24	.18181	2.172	81.19	.18087
30	2.652	82.73	.18676	2.493	82.69	.18571	2.350	82.65	.18471	2.222	82.60	.18376
40	2.710	84.13	.18962	2.548	84.10	.18857	2.402	84.06	.18757	2.272	84.02	.18663
50	2.768	85.55	0.19244	2.603	85.52	0.19140	2.454	85.49	0.19041	2.321	85.45	0.18946
60	2.827	86.99	.19524	2.658	86.96	.19420	2.506	86.93	.19321	2.371	86.90	.19226
70	2.886	88.45	.19800	2.712	88.41	.19696	2.558	88.38	.19597	2.420	88.35	.19503
80	2.944	89.91	.20075	2.767	89.88	.19969	2.610	89.84	.19872	2.469	89.81	.19777
90	3.002	91.39	.20345	2.822	91.36	.20241	2.662	91.32	.20142	2.518	91.29	.20047
100	3.059	92.88	0.20613	2.876	92.85	0.20510	2.713	92.81	0.20411	2.567	92.78	0.20317
110	3.117	94.38	.20879	2.930	94.35	.20774	2.764	94.32	.20676	2.616	94.28	.20583
120	3.175	95.89	.21143	2.984	95.86	.21038	2.815	95.83	.20941	2.665	95.80	.20847
130	3.232	97.42	.21403	3.038	97.39	.21298	2.867	97.36	.21201	2.714	97.33	.21108
140	3.290	98.95	.21662	3.092	98.93	.21558	2.918	98.90	.21462	2.763	98.88	.21368
150	3.347	100.50	0.21917	3.147	100.48	0.21814	2.969	100.45	0.21717	2.812	100.43	0.21625
160	3.404	102.07	.22172	3.201	102.05	.22070	3.020	102.02	.21971	2.861	102.00	.21880
170	3.461	103.65	.22425	3.256	103.63	.22323	3.072	103.60	.22223	2.910	103.59	.22133
180	3.519	105.24	.22677	3.310	105.22	.22574	3.124	105.19	.22474	2.958	105.18	.22384
190	3.576	106.85	.22925	3.364	106.82	.22822	3.175	106.80	.22725	3.006	106.78	.22633
200	3.633	108.47	0.23173	3.417	108.44	0.23070	3.226	108.42	0.22973	3.054	108.39	0.22880
210	3.690	110.10	.23418	3.470	110.07	.23315	3.277	110.05	.23219	3.102	110.02	.23126
220	3.747	111.74	.23662	3.524	111.71	.23558	3.327	111.69	.23461	3.150	111.66	.23369
230	3.803	113.40	.23903	3.578	113.37	.23800	3.378	113.34	.23703	3.198	113.31	.23612
240	3.860	115.07	.24143	3.632	115.04	.24041	3.428	115.00	.23944	3.246	114.99	.23852
250	3.917	116.76	0.24382	3.686	116.72	0.24279	3.478	116.68	0.24182	3.294	116.68	0.24091
260	....	....	....	3.739	118.41	.24517	3.528	118.36	.24420	3.342	118.37	.24327

Temp. °F.	Abs. Pressure 20 lb./in.² (Sat'n. Temp. −8.2° F.)			Abs. Pressure 22 lb./in.² (Sat'n. Temp. −3.8° F.)			Abs. Pressure 24 lb./in.² (Sat'n. Temp. 0.3° F.)			Abs. Pressure 26 lb./in.² (Sat'n. Temp. 4.1° F.)		
(at sat'n)	(1.925)	(77.27)	(0.17160)	(1.762)	(77.77)	(0.17121)	(1.623)	(78.24)	(0.17089)	(1.510)	(78.68)	(0.17059)
0	1.965	78.39	0.17407	1.779	78.30	0.17237						
10	2.013	79.76	.17704	1.823	79.68	.17534	1.664	79.59	0.17378	1.530	79.50	0.17233
20	2.060	81.14	.17996	1.866	81.07	.17827	1.705	80.99	.17673	1.568	80.90	.17529
30	2.107	82.55	.18286	1.909	82.48	.18118	1.745	82.40	.17964	1.606	82.31	.17821
40	2.155	83.97	.18573	1.953	83.90	.18405	1.785	83.82	.18251	1.643	83.74	.18109
50	2.203	85.40	0.18858	1.997	85.33	0.18691	1.825	85.26	0.18536	1.680	85.19	0.18395
60	2.250	86.85	.19138	2.040	86.78	.18971	1.865	86.71	.18817	1.716	86.64	.18675
70	2.297	88.31	.19415	2.083	88.25	.19248	1.905	88.17	.19096	1.754	88.10	.18954
80	2.343	89.78	.19688	2.125	89.71	.19522	1.944	89.64	.19371	1.790	89.57	.19229
90	2.390	91.26	.19959	2.168	91.19	.19794	1.984	91.13	.19643	1.826	91.05	.19501
100	2.437	92.75	0.20229	2.211	92.68	0.20064	2.023	92.63	0.19912	1.863	92.55	0.19772
110	2.483	94.26	.20494	2.253	94.19	.20330	2.062	94.13	.20179	1.900	94.06	.20039
120	2.530	95.78	.20759	2.296	95.71	.20595	2.101	95.64	.20444	1.936	95.58	.20305
130	2.577	97.31	.21020	2.339	97.25	.20856	2.140	97.17	.20704	1.972	97.12	.20565
140	2.623	98.85	.21280	2.381	98.80	.21116	2.179	98.72	.20966	2.008	98.67	.20827
150	2.669	100.40	0.21537	2.423	100.35	0.21373	2.218	100.28	0.21223	2.045	100.23	0.21085
160	2.716	101.97	.21792	2.465	101.92	.21628	2.257	101.86	.21479	2.082	101.80	.21341
170	2.762	103.56	.22045	2.507	103.50	.21881	2.296	103.45	.21732	2.117	103.39	.21594
180	2.808	105.15	.22297	2.550	105.10	.22133	2.335	105.05	.21984	2.153	104.99	.21847
190	2.854	106.76	.22545	2.592	106.71	.22382	2.373	106.66	.22233	2.189	106.60	.22096
200	2.901	108.38	0.22794	2.634	108.33	0.22630	2.412	108.28	0.22481	2.224	108.23	0.22344
210	2.947	110.01	.23039	2.676	109.96	.22876	2.450	109.92	.22727	2.259	109.86	.22589
220	2.992	111.65	.23283	2.717	111.60	.23120	2.489	111.57	.22972	2.295	111.51	.22834
230	3.038	113.31	.23524	2.758	113.26	.23361	2.528	113.23	.23214	2.331	113.17	.23076
240	3.084	114.98	.23766	2.800	114.94	.23603	2.566	114.90	.23455	2.366	114.85	.23318
250	3.130	116.67	0.24005	2.842	116.62	0.23843	2.605	116.58	0.23695	2.402	116.54	0.23557
260	3.177	118.36	.24242	2.884	118.32	.24080	2.644	118.28	.23933	2.438	118.24	.23796
270	3.223	120.07	.24477	2.926	120.04	.24316	2.682	120.00	.24169	2.474	119.95	.24033
280										2.510	121.68	.24267

TABLE 2-21.　FREON 12: PROPERTIES OF SUPERHEATED VAPOR (Continued)

Temp. °F.	Abs. Pressure 28 lb./in.² (Sat'n. Temp. 7.7° F.)			Abs. Pressure 30 lb./in.² (Sat'n. Temp. 11.1° F.)			Abs. Pressure 32 lb./in.² (Sat'n. Temp. 14.3° F.)			Abs. Pressure 34 lb./in.² (Sat'n. Temp. 17.4° F.)		
t	V	H	S	V	H	S	V	H	S	V	H	S
(at sat'n)	(1.409)	(79.10)	(0.17032)	(1.323)	(79.47)	(0.17008)	(1.245)	(79.84)	(0.16985)	(1.175)	(80.20)	(0.16965)
10	1.415	79.41	0.17099									
20	1.450	80.81	.17393	1.350	80.73	0.17269	1.262	80.67	0.17152	1.183	80.58	0.17040
30	1.485	82.23	.17685	1.383	82.15	.17562	1.293	82.08	.17445	1.212	82.00	.17333
40	1.520	83.66	.17975	1.415	83.58	.17851	1.323	83.51	.17734	1.241	83.44	.17623
50	1.555	85.11	0.18261	1.448	85.03	0.18138	1.354	84.96	0.18022	1.270	84.88	0.17910
60	1.590	86.56	.18544	1.480	86.48	.18420	1.384	86.41	.18304	1.299	86.34	.18194
70	1.625	88.03	.18823	1.512	87.95	.18699	1.414	87.88	.18583	1.328	87.81	.18474
80	1.659	89.51	.19097	1.544	89.43	.18974	1.444	89.36	.18860	1.356	89.29	.18750
90	1.693	90.99	.19371	1.576	90.91	.19249	1.474	90.85	.19133	1.385	90.78	.19025
100	1.727	92.49	0.19642	1.608	92.41	0.19519	1.504	92.35	0.19404	1.413	92.29	0.19295
110	1.761	94.01	.19909	1.640	93.93	.19787	1.535	93.87	.19673	1.441	93.81	.19563
120	1.795	95.53	.20174	1.672	95.46	.20053	1.565	95.40	.19940	1.470	95.34	.19831
130	1.828	97.07	.20436	1.703	97.00	.20315	1.595	96.94	.20202	1.498	96.88	.20094
140	1.862	98.62	.20698	1.735	98.54	.20577	1.624	98.50	.20463	1.526	98.43	.20356
150	1.896	100.18	0.20956	1.767	100.11	0.20836	1.654	100.06	0.20721	1.554	100.00	0.20614
160	1.930	101.75	.21212	1.799	101.69	.21092	1.683	101.64	.20977	1.582	101.58	.20871
170	1.963	103.33	.21466	1.829	103.28	.21344	1.713	103.23	.21232	1.610	103.17	.21125
180	1.997	104.93	.21719	1.860	104.88	.21597	1.743	104.83	.21486	1.638	104.78	.21379
190	2.030	106.55	.21967	1.891	106.49	.21846	1.772	106.45	.21735	1.666	106.40	.21629
200	2.063	108.17	0.22216	1.923	108.12	0.22096	1.802	108.08	0.21985	1.693	108.03	0.21878
210	2.096	109.81	.22462	1.954	109.76	.22342	1.831	109.72	.22231	1.721	109.67	.22125
220	2.129	111.46	.22706	1.986	111.41	.22588	1.860	111.36	.22476	1.749	111.32	.22370
230	2.163	113.12	.22949	2.017	113.08	.22830	1.889	113.03	.22718	1.776	112.98	.22613
240	2.196	114.80	.23191	2.048	114.75	.23072	1.918	114.72	.22960	1.804	114.66	.22856
250	2.229	116.49	0.23430	2.079	116.44	0.23312	1.948	116.41	0.23200	1.833	116.35	0.23097
260	2.262	118.19	.23669	2.110	118.15	.23550	1.977	118.11	.23439	1.860	118.06	.23335
270	2.295	119.91	.23905	2.141	119.87	.23787	2.006	119.82	.23676	1.888	119.79	.23573
280	2.329	121.65	.24141	2.172	121.60	.24023	2.035	121.55	.23912	1.916	121.54	.23809
290							2.065	123.30	.24146	1.944	123.31	.24043

Temp. °F.	Abs. Pressure 36 lb./in.² (Sat'n. Temp. 20.4° F.)			Abs. Pressure 38 lb./in.² (Sat'n. Temp. 23.2° F.)			Abs. Pressure 40 lb./in.² (Sat'n. Temp. 25.9° F.)			Abs. Pressure 42 lb./in.² (Sat'n. Temp. 23.5° F.)		
(at sat'n)	(1.113)	(80.54)	(0.16947)	(1.058)	(80.86)	(0.16931)	(1.009)	(81.16)	(0.16914)	(0.963)	(81.44)	(0.16897)
30	1.140	81.90	0.17227	1.076	81.82	0.17126	1.019	81.76	0.17030	0.967	81.65	0.16939
40	1.168	83.35	.17518	1.103	83.27	.17418	1.044	83.20	.17322	0.991	83.10	.17231
50	1.196	84.81	0.17806	1.129	84.72	0.17706	1.070	84.65	0.17612	1.016	84.56	0.17521
60	1.223	86.27	.18089	1.156	86.19	.17991	1.095	86.11	.17896	1.040	86.03	.17806
70	1.250	87.74	.18369	1.182	87.67	.18272	1.120	87.60	.18178	1.063	87.51	.18086
80	1.278	89.22	.18647	1.208	89.16	.18551	1.144	89.09	.18455	1.087	89.00	.18365
90	1.305	90.71	.18921	1.234	90.66	.18826	1.169	90.58	.18731	1.110	90.50	.18640
100	1.332	92.22	0.19193	1.260	92.17	0.19096	1.194	92.09	0.19004	1.134	92.01	0.18913
110	1.359	93.75	.19462	1.285	93.69	.19365	1.218	93.62	.19272	1.158	93.54	.19184
120	1.386	95.28	.19729	1.310	95.22	.19631	1.242	95.15	.19538	1.181	95.09	.19451
130	1.412	96.82	.19991	1.336	96.76	.19895	1.267	96.70	.19803	1.204	96.64	.19714
140	1.439	98.37	.20254	1.361	98.32	.20157	1.291	98.26	.20066	1.227	98.20	.19979
150	1.465	99.93	0.20512	1.387	99.89	0.20416	1.315	99.83	0.20325	1.250	99.77	0.20237
160	1.492	101.51	.20770	1.412	101.47	.20673	1.340	101.42	.20583	1.274	101.36	.20496
170	1.518	103.11	.21024	1.437	103.07	.20929	1.364	103.02	.20838	1.297	102.96	.20751
180	1.545	104.72	.21278	1.462	104.67	.21183	1.388	104.63	.21092	1.320	104.57	.21005
190	1.571	106.34	.21528	1.487	106.29	.21433	1.412	106.25	.21343	1.343	106.19	.21256
200	1.597	107.97	0.21778	1.512	107.93	0.21681	1.435	107.88	0.21592	1.365	107.82	0.21505
210	1.623	109.61	.22024	1.537	109.57	.21928	1.459	109.52	.21840	1.388	109.47	.21754
220	1.650	111.27	.22270	1.562	111.22	.22176	1.482	111.17	.22085	1.411	111.12	.22000
230	1.676	112.94	.22513	1.587	112.89	.22419	1.506	112.84	.22329	1.434	112.80	.22244
240	1.702	114.62	.22756	1.612	114.58	.22662	1.530	114.52	.22572	1.457	114.49	.22486
250	1.728	116.31	0.22996	1.637	116.28	0.22903	1.554	116.21	0.22813	1.480	116.19	0.22728
260	1.754	118.02	.23235	1.662	117.99	.23142	1.577	117.92	.23052	1.502	117.90	.22967
270	1.780	119.74	.23472	1.687	119.71	.23379	1.601	119.65	.23289	1.524	119.62	.23204
280	1.807	121.47	.23708	1.712	121.45	.23616	1.625	121.40	.23526	1.547	121.36	.23441
290	1.833	123.22	.23942	1.737	123.20	.23850	1.649	123.15	.23760	1.570	123.11	.23675
300	...	...	...	1.762	124.95	0.24083	1.673	124.92	0.23994	1.592	124.87	0.23909

TABLE 2-21. FREON 12: PROPERTIES OF SUPERHEATED VAPOR (Continued)

Temp. °F. t	Abs. Pressure 44 lb./in.² (Sat'n. Temp. 31.0° F.) V	H	S	Abs. Pressure 46 lb./in.² (Sat'n. Temp. 33.5° F.) V	H	S	Abs. Pressure 48 lb./in.² (Sat'n. Temp. 35.8° F.) V	H	S	Abs. Pressure 50 lb./in.² (Sat'n. Temp. 38.3° F.) V	H	S
(at sat'n)	(0.922)	(81.72)	(0.16882)	(0.885)	(82.00)	(0.16867)	(0.849)	(82.25)	(0.16855)	(0.817)	(82.52)	(0.16841)
40	0.943	83.03	0.17142	0.899	82.94	0.17057	0.858	82.85	0.16974	0.821	82.76	0.16895
50	0.966	84.48	0.17432	0.921	84.40	0.17347	0.880	84.32	0.17266	0.842	84.24	0.17187
60	0.989	85.96	0.17717	0.943	85.88	0.17633	0.902	85.80	0.17554	0.863	85.72	0.17475
70	1.012	87.45	0.18000	0.965	87.37	0.17916	0.923	87.29	0.17837	0.884	87.22	0.17760
80	1.035	88.94	0.18279	0.988	88.88	0.18198	0.944	88.79	0.18117	0.904	88.72	0.18040
90	1.058	90.44	0.18556	1.010	90.39	0.18474	0.965	90.30	0.18394	0.924	90.23	0.18317
100	1.080	91.95	0.18828	1.031	91.90	0.18746	0.986	91.82	0.18668	0.944	91.75	0.18591
110	1.103	93.48	0.19099	1.053	93.43	0.19016	1.007	93.35	0.18939	0.964	93.29	0.18862
120	1.125	95.02	0.19367	1.074	94.96	0.19285	1.028	94.89	0.19208	0.984	94.83	0.19132
130	1.147	96.57	0.19630	1.096	96.51	0.19551	1.048	96.44	0.19472	1.004	96.39	0.19397
140	1.170	98.14	0.19895	1.117	98.08	0.19814	1.069	98.01	0.19737	1.024	97.96	0.19662
150	1.192	99.72	0.20154	1.139	99.66	0.20075	1.089	99.59	0.19997	1.044	99.54	0.19923
160	1.214	101.31	0.20412	1.160	101.25	0.20333	1.110	101.18	0.20256	1.064	101.14	0.20182
170	1.236	102.91	0.20667	1.181	102.85	0.20588	1.130	102.79	0.20513	1.084	102.75	0.20439
180	1.258	104.52	0.20922	1.202	104.46	0.20843	1.150	104.40	0.20766	1.103	104.36	0.20694
190	1.280	106.14	0.21173	1.223	106.09	0.21094	1.170	106.02	0.21017	1.123	105.98	0.20946
200	1.302	107.78	0.21424	1.244	107.73	0.21344	1.191	107.66	0.21269	1.142	107.62	0.21196
210	1.324	109.42	0.21672	1.265	109.38	0.21592	1.211	109.31	0.21517	1.162	109.28	0.21444
220	1.346	111.08	0.21918	1.286	111.04	0.21839	1.231	110.98	0.21763	1.181	110.95	0.21691
230	1.367	112.75	0.22161	1.307	112.71	0.22083	1.251	112.66	0.22007	1.200	112.62	0.21935
240	1.389	114.44	0.22405	1.327	114.39	0.22326	1.271	114.35	0.22251	1.220	114.31	0.22179
250	1.411	116.14	0.22646	1.348	116.09	0.22567	1.291	116.05	0.22492	1.239	116.00	0.22419
260	1.432	117.85	0.22885	1.369	117.81	0.22806	1.311	117.77	0.22731	1.258	117.71	0.22660
270	1.454	119.57	0.23123	1.390	119.54	0.23044	1.331	119.49	0.22970	1.277	119.44	0.22898
280	1.475	121.31	0.23359	1.410	121.27	0.23281	1.351	121.23	0.23207	1.296	121.18	0.23134
290	1.496	123.06	0.23592	1.431	123.02	0.23515	1.370	122.98	0.23440	1.314	122.93	0.23367
300	1.518	124.82	0.23826	1.452	124.79	0.23749	1.390	124.75	0.23674	1.332	124.69	0.23600
310	1.539	126.59	0.24058	1.472	126.57	0.23981	1.410	126.53	0.23907	1.350	126.45	0.23831

Temp. °F.	Abs. Pressure 52 lb./in.² (Sat'n. Temp. 40.4°F.)			Abs. Pressure 54 lb./in.² (Sat'n. Temp. 42.5° F.)			Abs. Pressure 56 lb./in.² (Sat'n. Temp. 44.6° F.)			Abs. Pressure 58 lb./in.² (Sat'n. Temp. 46.7° F.)		
(at sat'n)	(0.788)	(82.75)	(0.16881)	(0.759)	(82.98)	(0.16820)	(0.734)	(83.22)	(0.16810)	(0.716)	(83.44)	(0.16800)
50	0.808	84.17	0.17114	0.774	84.07	0.17036	0.744	83.99	0.16965	0.716	83.91	0.16896
60	0.827	85.65	.17400	0.794	85.56	.17326	0.763	85.48	.17255	0.734	85.40	.17185
70	0.847	87.14	.17684	0.814	87.06	.17612	0.782	86.98	.17541	0.752	86.90	.17471
80	0.867	88.64	.17966	0.833	88.57	.17894	0.801	88.49	.17824	0.770	88.41	.17753
90	0.886	90.15	.18244	0.852	90.08	.18172	0.819	90.01	.18102	0.788	89.93	.18033
100	0.906	91.68	0.18518	0.871	91.61	0.18446	0.837	91.54	0.18377	0.806	91.46	0.18309
110	0.925	93.22	.18789	0.890	93.16	.18718	0.856	93.08	.18651	0.824	93.00	.18583
120	0.945	94.77	.19059	0.908	94.71	.18989	0.874	94.63	.18921	0.842	94.55	.18854
130	0.964	96.33	.19325	0.927	96.27	.19255	0.892	96.19	.19188	0.860	96.11	.19122
140	0.983	97.90	.19590	0.945	97.84	.19520	0.910	97.77	.19453	0.877	97.68	.19387
150	1.002	99.48	0.19850	0.964	99.43	0.19782	0.928	99.36	0.19715	0.894	99.26	0.19648
160	1.021	101.07	.20109	0.982	101.03	.20043	0.946	100.96	.19975	0.912	100.86	.19908
170	1.040	102.68	.20365	1.001	102.64	.20299	0.964	102.57	.20232	0.929	102.47	.20166
180	1.059	104.30	.20621	1.019	104.25	.20554	0.981	104.19	.20487	0.946	104.09	.20423
190	1.078	105.93	.20873	1.037	105.88	.20806	0.999	105.83	.20739	0.963	105.72	.20676
200	1.097	107.58	0.21125	1.055	107.52	0.21057	1.016	107.48	0.20991	0.980	107.36	0.20927
210	1.116	109.23	.21374	1.073	109.17	.21305	1.034	109.14	.21241	0.997	109.02	.21177
220	1.134	110.89	.21620	1.091	110.84	.21553	1.051	110.81	.21487	1.014	110.70	.21424
230	1.153	112.56	.21865	1.109	112.51	.21797	1.068	112.49	.21731	1.031	112.39	.21669
240	1.172	114.26	.22110	1.127	114.20	.22042	1.086	114.18	.21977	1.048	114.10	.21914
250	1.190	115.96	0.22352	1.145	115.91	0.22283	1.103	115.88	0.22218	1.064	115.82	0.22155
260	1.208	117.67	.22591	1.163	117.63	.22523	1.120	117.59	.22458	1.081	117.55	.22396
270	1.227	119.40	.22829	1.181	119.37	.22762	1.138	119.31	.22698	1.098	119.29	.22635
280	1.245	121.14	.23065	1.199	121.11	.22999	1.155	121.05	.22934	1.114	121.04	.22871
290	1.263	122.90	.23299	1.216	122.86	.23233	1.172	122.80	.23169	1.130	122.80	.23105
300	1.281	124.66	0.23532	1.234	124.63	0.23467	1.189	124.57	0.23403	1.147	124.57	0.23340
310	1.298	126.42	.23763	1.251	126.40	.23699	1.206	126.36	.23635	1.164	126.35	.23574
320							1.223	128.17	.23867	1.180	128.14	.23806

TABLE 2-21. FREON 12: PROPERTIES OF SUPERHEATED VAPOR (Continued)

Temp. °F. t	Abs. Pressure 60 lb./in.² (Sat'n. Temp. 48.7° F.)			Abs. Pressure 70 lb./in.² (Sat'n. Temp. 57.9° F.)			Abs. Pressure 80 lb./in.² (Sat'n. Temp. 66.3° F.)			Abs. Pressure 90 lb./in.² (Sat'n. Temp. 73.9° F.)		
	v	H	S	v	H	S	v	H	S	v	H	S
(at sat'n)	(0.688)	(83.65)	(0.16791)	(0.594)	(84.61)	(0.16749)	(0.521)	(85.45)	(0.16716)	(0.465)	(86.21)	(0.16685)
50	0.690	83.83	0.16829									
60	0.708	85.33	17120	0.597	84.94	16810						
70	0.726	86.84	17407	0.612	86.44	17097	0.526	86.01	0.16819			
80	0.743	88.35	17689	0.628	87.96	17382	0.540	87.56	17108	0.473	87.18	0.16862
90	0.760	89.87	17968	0.643	89.49	17665	0.554	89.12	17394	0.486	88.74	17149
100	0.778	91.41	0.18246	0.658	91.03	0.17943	0.568	90.68	0.17675	0.499	90.31	0.17433
110	0.795	92.96	18519	0.673	92.59	18219	0.582	92.26	17954	0.511	91.89	17713
120	0.812	94.51	18789	0.689	94.16	18493	0.596	93.84	18229	0.523	93.48	17990
130	0.829	96.07	19056	0.704	95.75	18763	0.609	95.43	18500	0.535	95.08	18262
140	0.846	97.65	19323	0.719	97.34	19030	0.623	97.03	18771	0.547	96.69	18533
150	0.863	99.24	0.19585	0.733	98.94	0.19293	0.636	98.64	0.19035	0.559	98.31	0.18799
160	0.880	100.84	19846	0.748	100.54	19555	0.649	100.26	19298	0.571	99.94	19065
170	0.897	102.45	20104	0.763	102.16	19814	0.662	101.88	19558	0.584	101.58	19327
180	0.913	104.07	20360	0.777	103.80	20071	0.675	103.52	19817	0.596	103.23	19588
190	0.930	105.71	20613	0.792	105.45	20325	0.688	105.18	20073	0.607	104.89	19845
200	0.946	107.36	0.20865	0.806	107.10	0.20579	0.701	106.84	0.20328	0.619	106.56	0.20101
210	0.962	109.02	21113	0.820	108.76	20829	0.714	108.51	20580	0.630	108.24	20353
220	0.979	110.69	21361	0.835	110.43	21079	0.726	110.19	20828	0.642	109.93	20603
230	0.995	112.37	21607	0.849	112.13	21325	0.739	111.88	21076	0.653	111.63	20852
240	1.012	114.06	21853	0.863	113.83	21570	0.751	113.58	21321	0.665	113.35	21100
250	1.028	115.77	0.22094	0.878	115.55	0.21815	0.764	115.30	0.21566	0.676	115.08	0.21345
260	1.044	117.49	22334	0.892	117.28	22057	0.777	117.03	21809	0.688	116.82	21589
270	1.060	119.23	22573	0.906	119.02	22296	0.789	118.78	22049	0.699	118.57	21831
280	1.076	120.97	22810	0.923	120.76	22534	0.802	120.54	22289	0.710	120.33	22070
290	1.092	122.73	23045	0.934	122.52	22770	0.814	122.30	22525	0.721	122.10	22306
300	1.108	124.50	0.23280	0.948	124.29	0.23006	0.826	124.08	0.22760	0.732	123.88	0.22542
310	1.124	126.28	23513	0.961	126.07	23239	0.839	125.88	22995	0.743	125.67	22776
320	1.140	128.07	23745	0.975	127.88	23471	0.851	127.70	23229	0.754	127.48	23008
330				0.989	129.70	23702	0.864	129.52	23461	0.765	129.31	23240

Temp. °F.	Abs. Pressure 100 lb./in.² (Sat'n. Temp. 80.9° F.)			Abs. Pressure 110 lb./in.² (Sat'n. Temp. 87.3° F.)			Abs. Pressure 120 lb./in.² (Sat'n. Temp. 93.4° F.)			Abs. Pressure 130 lb./in.² (Sat'n. Temp. 99.1° F.)		
(at sat'n)	(0.419) (0.430)	(86.89) (88.32)	(0.16659) (0.16926)	(0.382) (0.385)	(87.50) (87.91)	(0.16635) (0.16711)	(0.350)	(88.05)	(0.16610)	(0.323)	(88.547)	(0.16589)
90	0.442	89.93	0.17210	0.396	89.51	0.17001	0.357	89.13	0.16803	0.324	88.69	0.16615
100	0.454	91.54	.17493	0.407	91.12	.17287	0.367	90.75	.17090	0.333	90.33	.16905
110	0.465	93.15	.17773	0.417	92.74	.17568	0.377	92.38	.17374	0.343	91.98	.17193
120	0.477	94.76	.18049	0.428	94.37	.17845	0.387	94.01	.17654	0.353	93.64	.17476
130	0.488	96.37	.18321	0.438	96.01	.18122	0.397	95.65	.17932	0.362	95.30	.17756
150	0.499	97.99	0.18590	0.449	97.66	0.18394	0.407	97.30	0.18207	0.371	96.97	0.18030
160	0.510	99.63	.18856	0.459	99.31	.18660	0.417	98.96	.18474	0.380	98.65	.18302
170	0.521	101.28	.19120	0.469	100.97	.18924	0.426	100.63	.18743	0.389	100.34	.18571
180	0.531	102.94	.19381	0.479	102.64	.19187	0.436	102.31	.19011	0.398	102.04	.18839
190	0.542	104.61	.19638	0.489	104.32	.19447	0.445	104.00	.19271	0.407	103.74	.19102
200	0.553	106.29	0.19894	0.499	106.01	0.19706	0.454	105.70	0.19529	0.416	105.45	0.19362
210	0.563	107.98	.20148	0.509	107.71	.19962	0.463	107.41	.19785	0.424	107.16	.19620
220	0.574	109.68	.20401	0.519	109.42	.20216	0.472	109.13	.20041	0.433	108.89	.19877
230	0.585	111.39	.20650	0.528	111.14	.20464	0.482	110.86	.20294	0.442	110.62	.20130
240	0.595	113.11	.20899	0.538	112.87	.20712	0.491	112.60	.20545	0.450	112.36	.20382
250	0.606	114.84	0.21145	0.548	114.61	0.20959	0.500	114.35	0.20792	0.458	114.11	0.20629
260	0.616	116.58	.21389	0.557	116.36	.21205	0.508	116.11	.21035	0.467	115.87	.20876
270	0.626	118.33	.21631	0.567	118.12	.21448	0.517	117.88	.21279	0.475	117.64	.21122
280	0.636	120.10	.21870	0.576	119.89	.21690	0.526	119.66	.21521	0.483	119.42	.21364
290	0.646	121.88	.22108	0.586	121.68	.21930	0.534	121.45	.21760	0.492	121.21	.21605
300	0.657	123.67	0.22347	0.595	123.48	0.22167	0.543	123.25	0.22000	0.500	123.01	0.21846
310	0.667	125.47	.22583	0.605	125.29	.22405	0.552	125.07	.22238	0.508	124.82	.22084
320	0.677	127.28	.22817	0.614	127.11	.22639	0.560	126.90	.22472	0.516	126.64	.22320
330	0.687	129.10	.23050	0.623	128.94	.22872	0.569	128.74	.22707	0.524	128.47	.22554
340	0.697	130.94	.23281	0.632	130.78	.23103	0.578	130.59	.22940	0.531	130.31	.22786
350	0.707	132.80	0.23510	0.641	132.63	0.23333	0.586	132.45	0.23171	0.539	132.17	0.23016
360	0.718	134.68	.23738	0.651	134.50	.23562	0.595	134.32	.23400	0.547	134.05	.23246
370										0.555	135.94	.23475

TABLE 2-21. FREON 12: PROPERTIES OF SUPERHEATED VAPOR (Concluded)

Temp. °F	Abs. Press. 140 lb./in.² (Sat'n. Temp. 104.5°F.)			Abs. Press. 160 lb./in.² (Sat'n. Temp. 114.5°F.)			Abs. Press. 180 lb./in.² (Sat'n. Temp. 123.7°F.)			Abs. Press. 200 lb./in.² (Sat'n. Temp. 132.1°F.)			Abs. Press. 220 lb./in.² (Sat'n. Temp. 139.9°F.)		
t	V	H	S	V	H	S	V	H	S	V	H	S	V	H	S
(at sat'n)	(0.298)	(88.99)	(0.16566)	(0.259)	(89.77)	(0.16522)	(0.228)	(90.38)	(0.16476)	(0.202)	(90.86)	(0.16424)	(0.181)	(91.50)	(0.16375)
100															
110	0.304	89.92	0.16725												
120	0.314	91.60	0.17021	0.264	90.68	0.16682									
130	0.323	93.28	0.17306	0.273	92.40	0.16977	0.233	91.47	0.16665						
140	0.332	94.96	0.17590	0.282	94.12	0.17269	0.241	93.23	0.16964	0.208	92.30	0.16661	0.181	91.52	0.16378
150	0.341	96.65	0.17868	0.290	95.84	0.17553	0.249	94.99	0.17254	0.216	94.10	0.16966	0.188	93.32	0.16685
160	0.350	98.34	0.18142	0.298	97.57	0.17832	0.257	96.75	0.17541	0.224	95.90	0.17262	0.195	95.13	0.16986
170	0.358	100.03	0.18412	0.306	99.31	0.18106	0.265	98.52	0.17823	0.231	97.70	0.17551	0.202	96.94	0.17282
180	0.366	101.72	0.18678	0.313	101.05	0.18377	0.272	100.29	0.18102	0.238	99.51	0.17838	0.209	98.75	0.17576
190	0.374	103.42	0.18941	0.321	102.80	0.18646	0.280	102.07	0.18377	0.245	101.32	0.18115	0.216	100.57	0.17861
200	0.383	105.14	0.19205	0.329	104.55	0.18913	0.287	103.85	0.18648	0.252	103.13	0.18388	0.223	102.39	0.18142
210	0.391	106.86	0.19466	0.336	106.31	0.19175	0.294	105.63	0.18912	0.258	104.94	0.18659	0.229	104.22	0.18420
220	0.399	108.59	0.19724	0.344	108.07	0.19435	0.301	107.42	0.19174	0.265	106.76	0.18927	0.236	106.05	0.18694
230	0.407	110.33	0.19976	0.351	109.83	0.19693	0.307	109.21	0.19433	0.272	108.58	0.19192	0.242	107.89	0.18962
240	0.415	112.09	0.20229	0.358	111.60	0.19949	0.314	111.01	0.19693	0.278	110.40	0.19455	0.248	109.74	0.19226
250	0.423	113.85	0.20479	0.366	113.38	0.20203	0.321	112.81	0.19947	0.284	112.23	0.19713	0.254	111.59	0.19487
260	0.431	115.63	0.20728	0.373	115.17	0.20453	0.327	114.62	0.20199	0.290	114.06	0.19967	0.259	113.44	0.19745
270	0.439	117.42	0.20974	0.380	116.97	0.20700	0.334	116.44	0.20449	0.296	115.89	0.20217	0.265	115.30	0.20001
280	0.447	119.22	0.21219	0.387	118.78	0.20946	0.340	118.26	0.20698	0.302	117.73	0.20467	0.271	117.16	0.20255
290	0.455	121.03	0.21461	0.394	120.60	0.21189	0.347	120.09	0.20944	0.308	119.58	0.20715	0.277	119.03	0.20504
300	0.462	122.85	0.21701	0.401	122.43	0.21432	0.353	121.92	0.21187	0.314	121.44	0.20961	0.282	120.91	0.20753
310	0.470	124.67	0.21939	0.408	124.27	0.21672	0.359	123.76	0.21428	0.320	123.31	0.21204	0.288	122.80	0.21002
320	0.477	126.50	0.22174	0.414	126.12	0.21909	0.365	125.61	0.21665	0.326	125.19	0.21445	0.293	124.70	0.21244
330	0.485	128.33	0.22411	0.421	127.98	0.22145	0.371	127.47	0.21904	0.331	127.08	0.21685	0.299	126.60	0.21485
340	0.492	130.17	0.22646	0.428	129.85	0.22381	0.377	129.34	0.22140	0.337	128.98	0.21923	0.304	128.51	0.21724
350	0.500	132.02	0.22880	0.435	131.73	0.22616	0.383	131.23	0.22374	0.343	130.89	0.22159	0.309	130.42	0.21960
360	0.507	133.89	0.23109	0.442	133.63	0.22849	0.390	133.13	0.22608	0.348	132.81	0.22392	0.314	132.34	0.22195
370	0.515	135.78	0.23336	0.448	135.55	0.23079	0.396	135.05	0.22840	0.354	134.74	0.22624	0.320	134.27	0.22430
380							0.402	136.98	0.23072	0.360	136.68	0.22856	0.325	136.21	0.22665
390							0.408	138.91	0.23301	0.365	138.63	0.23085	0.330	138.16	0.22895
400							0.414	140.85	0.23529	0.370	140.59	0.23314	0.335	140.12	0.23124

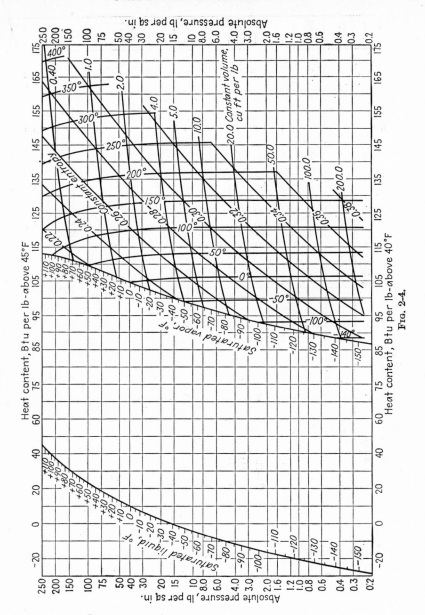

Fig. 2-4.

TABLE 2-22.   FREON 22: PROPERTIES OF LIQUID AND SATURATED VAPOR*

Temp. °F.	Absolute Pressure #/sq. in.	Volume cu. ft./lb.		Density #/cu. ft.		Heat Content Btu/#			Entropy Btu/# °F.		Temp. °F.
		Liquid	Vapor	Liquid	Vapor	Liquid	Latent	Vapor	Liquid	Vapor	
—155	0.19901	0.0102	188.1	97.67	.005316	—29.07	115.85	86.78	—0.0808	0.2996	—155
—150	0.2605	0.0103	146.1	97.33	.006847	—27.79	115.15	87.36	—0.0767	0.2952	—150
—145	0.3375	0.0103	114.5	96.99	.008733	—26.52	114.46	87.94	—0.0727	0.2912	—145
—140	0.4332	0.0103	90.61	96.63	.01104	—25.25	113.78	88.53	—0.0687	0.2874	—140
—135	0.5511	0.0104	72.33	96.27	.01383	—23.99	113.10	89.11	—0.0647	0.2837	—135
—130	0.6949	0.0104	58.21	95.91	.01718	—22.73	112.43	89.70	—0.0609	0.2803	—130
—125	0.8692	0.0105	47.23	95.53	.02118	—21.47	111.76	90.29	—0.0571	0.2770	—125
—120	1.079	0.0105	38.60	95.15	.02591	—20.22	111.10	90.88	—0.0534	0.2738	—120
—115	1.329	0.0106	31.77	94.76	.03147	—18.98	110.45	91.47	—0.0497	0.2708	—115
—110	1.626	0.0106	26.33	94.37	.03798	—17.73	109.80	92.07	—0.0461	0.2680	—110
—105	1.976	0.0106	21.96	93.97	.04554	—16.48	109.15	92.67	—0.0425	0.2653	—105
—100	2.386	0.0107	18.43	93.56	.05427	—15.23	108.50	93.27	—0.0390	0.2627	—100
—95	2.865	0.0107	15.54	93.14	.06433	—13.98	107.85	93.87	—0.0356	0.2602	—95
—90	3.417	0.0108	13.20	92.72	.07578	—12.73	107.20	94.47	—0.0322	0.2579	—90
—85	4.055	0.0108	11.26	92.29	.08884	—11.47	106.55	95.08	—0.0288	0.2556	—85
—80	4.787	0.01090	9.650	91.85	0.1036	—10.22	105.90	95.68	—0.0255	0.2535	—80
—78	5.100	0.01091	9.086	91.67	0.1101	—9.72	105.64	95.92	—0.0242	0.2526	—78
—76	5.430	0.01093	8.561	91.49	0.1168	—9.21	105.37	96.16	—0.0229	0.2518	—76
—74	5.79	0.01095	8.072	91.31	0.1239	—8.70	105.10	96.40	—0.0216	0.2510	—74
—72	6.17	0.01097	7.616	91.13	0.1313	—8.20	104.84	96.64	—0.0203	0.2502	—72
—70	6.57	0.01100	7.192	90.95	0.1391	—7.69	104.57	96.88	—0.0190	0.2494	—70
—68	6.99	0.01102	6.795	90.77	0.1472	—7.19	104.31	97.12	—0.0177	0.2487	—68
—66	7.40	0.01104	6.426	90.58	0.1556	—6.68	104.04	97.36	—0.0164	0.2479	—66
—64	7.86	0.01106	6.079	90.39	0.1645	—6.17	103.77	97.60	—0.0151	0.2472	—64
—62	8.35	0.01109	5.755	90.21	0.1738	—5.67	103.51	97.84	—0.0138	0.2465	—62

Temp											Temp
−60	0.2458	−0.0126	98.08	103.24	−5.16	0.1834	90.03	5.452	0.01111	8.86	−60
−58	0.2451	−0.0113	98.32	102.97	−4.65	0.1936	89.84	5.166	0.01113	9.39	−58
−56	0.2444	−0.0100	98.56	102.69	−4.13	0.2041	89.65	4.900	0.01115	9.94	−56
−54	0.2438	−0.0087	98.80	102.41	−3.61	0.2151	89.46	4.650	0.01118	10.51	−54
−52	0.2431	−0.0075	99.04	102.13	−3.09	0.2265	89.27	4.415	0.01120	11.11	−52
−50	0.2425	−0.0062	99.28	101.86	−2.58	0.2386	89.08	4.192	0.01123	11.74	−50
−48	0.2418	−0.0050	99.52	101.58	−2.06	0.2509	88.88	3.986	0.01125	12.40	−48
−46	0.2412	−0.0037	99.76	101.30	−1.54	0.2636	88.68	3.793	0.01128	13.09	−46
−44	0.2406	−0.0025	100.00	101.02	−1.02	0.2769	88.49	3.611	0.01130	13.80	−44
−42	0.2400	−0.0012	100.23	100.74	−0.51	0.2907	88.30	3.440	0.01133	14.54	−42
−40	0.2394	0.0000	100.46	100.46	0.00	0.3050	88.10	3.279	0.01135	15.31	−40
−38	0.2389	0.0013	100.70	100.17	0.53	0.3199	87.90	3.126	0.01138	16.12	−38
−36	0.2383	0.0025	100.93	99.88	1.05	0.3355	87.70	2.981	0.01140	16.97	−36
−34	0.2377	0.0037	101.17	99.59	1.58	0.3517	87.50	2.844	0.01143	17.85	−34
−32	0.2372	0.0050	101.40	99.30	2.10	0.3686	87.29	2.713	0.01146	18.77	−32
−30	0.2367	0.0062	101.63	99.01	2.62	0.3862	87.09	2.590	0.01148	19.72	−30
−28	0.2361	0.0074	101.86	98.71	3.15	0.4043	86.89	2.474	0.01151	20.71	−28
−26	0.2356	0.0086	102.10	98.41	3.69	0.4229	86.69	2.365	0.01154	21.73	−26
−24	0.2351	0.0099	102.33	98.11	4.22	0.4421	86.48	2.262	0.01156	22.79	−24
−22	0.2346	0.0111	102.56	97.81	4.75	0.4619	86.27	2.165	0.01159	23.88	−22
−20	0.2341	0.0123	102.79	97.51	5.28	0.4822	86.06	2.074	0.01162	25.01	−20
−18	0.2336	0.0135	103.02	97.20	5.82	0.5032	85.85	1.987	0.01165	26.18	−18
−16	0.2331	0.0147	103.25	96.89	6.40	0.5249	85.64	1.905	0.01168	27.39	−16
−14	0.2326	0.0159	103.48	96.58	6.90	0.5474	85.43	1.827	0.01171	28.64	−14
−12	0.2321	0.0170	103.70	96.27	7.43	0.5707	85.21	1.752	0.01174	29.94	−12
−10	0.2316	0.0182	103.92	95.96	7.96	0.5948	84.99	1.681	0.01177	31.29	−10
−8	0.2312	0.0194	104.14	95.65	8.49	0.6198	84.78	1.613	0.01180	32.69	−8
−6	0.2307	0.0205	104.36	95.34	9.02	0.6456	84.56	1.549	0.01183	34.14	−6
−4	0.2302	0.0217	104.58	95.03	9.55	0.6723	84.34	1.488	0.01186	35.64	−4
−2	0.2298	0.0228	104.80	94.71	10.09	0.6997	84.12	1.429	0.01189	37.19	−2

* Courtesy Kinetic Chemicals, Inc, Wilmington, Del. See Fig. 2-4.

TABLE 2-22. FREON 22: PROPERTIES OF LIQUID AND SATURATED VAPOR (Concluded)

Temp. °F.	Absolute Pressure #/sq. in.	Volume cu. ft./lb.		Density #/cu. ft.		Heat Content Btu/#			Entropy Btu/# °F.		Temp. °F.
		Liquid	Vapor	Liquid	Vapor	Liquid	Latent	Vapor	Liquid	Vapor	
0	38.79	0.01192	1.373	83.90	0.7282	10.63	94.39	105.02	0.0240	0.2293	0
2	40.43	0.01195	1.320	83.68	0.7574	11.17	94.07	105.24	0.0251	0.2289	2
4	42.14	0.01198	1.270	83.45	0.7877	11.70	93.75	105.45	0.0262	0.2285	4
5	43.02	0.01200	1.246	83.34	0.8034	11.97	93.59	105.56	0.0268	0.2283	5
6	43.91	0.01201	1.221	83.23	0.8191	12.23	93.43	105.66	0.0274	0.2280	6
8	45.74	0.01205	1.175	83.01	0.8514	12.76	93.11	105.87	0.0285	0.2276	8
10	47.63	0.01208	1.130	82.78	0.8847	13.29	92.79	106.08	0.0296	0.2272	10
12	49.58	0.01211	1.088	82.55	0.9191	13.82	92.47	106.29	0.0307	0.2268	12
14	51.59	0.01215	1.048	82.32	0.9545	14.36	92.14	106.50	0.0319	0.2264	14
16	53.66	0.01218	1.009	82.09	0.9911	14.90	91.81	106.71	0.0330	0.2260	16
18	55.79	0.01222	0.9721	81.86	1.029	15.44	91.48	106.92	0.0341	0.2257	18
20	57.98	0.01225	0.9369	81.63	1.067	15.98	91.15	107.13	0.0352	0.2253	20
22	60.23	0.01229	0.9032	81.39	1.107	16.52	90.81	107.33	0.0364	0.2249	22
24	62.55	0.01232	0.8707	81.16	1.149	17.06	90.47	107.53	0.0375	0.2246	24
26	64.94	0.01236	0.8398	80.92	1.191	17.61	90.12	107.73	0.0379	0.2242	26
28	67.40	0.01239	0.8100	80.69	1.235	18.17	89.76	107.93	0.0398	0.2239	28
30	69.93	0.01243	0.7816	80.45	1.280	18.74	89.39	108.13	0.0409	0.2235	30
32	72.53	0.01247	0.7543	80.21	1.326	19.32	89.01	108.33	0.0421	0.2232	32
34	75.21	0.01250	0.7283	79.97	1.373	19.90	88.62	108.52	0.0433	0.2228	34
36	77.97	0.01254	0.7032	79.73	1.422	20.49	88.22	108.71	0.0445	0.2225	36
38	80.81	0.01258	0.6791	79.49	1.473	21.09	87.81	108.90	0.0457	0.2222	38
40	83.72	0.01262	0.6559	79.25	1.525	21.70	87.39	109.09	0.0469	0.2218	40
42	86.69	0.01266	0.6339	79.00	1.578	22.29	86.98	109.27	0.0481	0.2215	42
44	89.74	0.01270	0.6126	78.76	1.632	22.90	86.55	109.45	0.0493	0.2211	44
46	92.88	0.01274	0.5922	78.51	1.689	23.50	86.13	109.63	0.0505	0.2208	46
48	96.10	0.01278	0.5726	78.26	1.747	24.11	85.69	109.80	0.0516	0.2205	48
50	99.40	0.01282	0.5537	78.02	1.806	24.73	85.25	109.98	0.0528	0.2201	50
52	102.8	0.01286	0.5355	77.77	1.868	25.34	84.80	110.14	0.0540	0.2198	52
54	106.2	0.01290	0.5184	77.51	1.929	25.95	84.35	110.30	0.0552	0.2194	54
56	109.8	0.01294	0.5014	77.26	1.995	26.58	83.89	110.47	0.0564	0.2191	56
58	113.5	0.01299	0.4849	77.01	2.062	27.22	83.41	110.63	0.0576	0.2188	58

60	0.2185	0.0588	110.78	82.95	27.83	2.130	76.75	0.4695	0.01303	117.2	60
62	0.2181	0.0600	110.93	82.47	28.46	2.200	76.50	0.4546	0.01307	121.0	62
64	0.2178	0.0612	111.08	81.99	29.09	2.271	76.24	0.4403	0.01312	124.9	64
66	0.2175	0.0624	111.22	81.50	29.72	2.346	75.98	0.4264	0.01316	128.9	66
68	0.2172	0.0636	111.35	81.00	30.35	2.422	75.72	0.4129	0.01320	133.0	68
70	0.2168	0.0648	111.49	80.50	30.99	2.500	75.46	0.4000	0.01325	137.2	70
72	0.2165	0.0661	111.63	79.98	31.65	2.581	75.20	0.3875	0.01330	141.5	72
74	0.2162	0.0673	111.75	79.46	32.29	2.664	74.94	0.3754	0.01334	145.9	74
76	0.2158	0.0684	111.88	78.94	32.94	2.749	74.68	0.3638	0.01339	150.4	76
78	0.2155	0.0696	112.01	78.40	33.61	2.836	74.41	0.3526	0.01344	155.0	78
80	0.2151	0.0708	112.13	77.86	34.27	2.926	74.15	0.3417	0.01349	159.7	80
82	0.2148	0.0720	112.24	77.32	34.92	3.019	73.89	0.3313	0.01353	164.5	82
84	0.2144	0.0732	112.36	76.76	35.60	3.113	73.63	0.3212	0.01358	169.4	84
86	0.2140	0.0744	112.47	76.19	36.28	3.213	73.36	0.3113	0.01363	174.5	86
88	0.2137	0.0756	112.57	75.63	36.94	3.313	73.09	0.3019	0.01368	179.6	88
90	0.2133	0.0768	112.67	75.06	37.61	3.415	72.81	0.2928	0.01374	184.8	90
92	0.2130	0.0780	112.76	74.48	38.28	3.520	72.53	0.2841	0.01379	190.1	92
94	0.2126	0.0792	112.85	73.88	38.97	3.630	72.24	0.2755	0.01384	195.6	94
96	0.2122	0.0803	112.93	73.28	39.65	3.742	71.95	0.2672	0.01390	201.2	96
98	0.2119	0.0815	113.00	72.69	40.32	3.855	71.65	0.2594	0.01396	206.8	98
100	0.2115	0.0827	113.06	72.08	40.98	3.973	71.35	0.2517	0.01402	212.6	100
102	0.2111	0.0839	113.12	71.47	41.65	4.094	71.05	0.2443	0.01408	218.5	102
104	0.2107	0.0851	113.16	70.84	42.32	4.220	70.74	0.2370	0.01414	224.6	104
106	0.2104	0.0862	113.20	70.22	42.98	4.347	70.42	0.2301	0.01420	230.7	106
108	0.2100	0.0874	113.24	69.58	43.66	4.479	70.11	0.2233	0.01426	237.0	108
110	0.2096	0.0886	113.29	68.94	44.35	4.614	69.78	0.2167	0.01433	243.4	110
112	0.2093	0.0898	113.34	68.30	45.04	4.752	69.45	0.2104	0.01440	249.9	112
114	0.2089	0.0909	113.38	67.64	45.74	4.896	69.12	0.2043	0.01447	256.6	114
116	0.2085	0.0921	113.42	66.98	46.44	5.043	68.78	0.1983	0.01454	263.4	116
118	0.2081	0.0933	113.46	66.32	47.14	5.192	68.44	0.1926	0.01461	270.3	118
120	0.2078	0.0945	113.52	65.67	47.85	5.345	68.10	0.1871	0.01469	277.3	120

TABLE 2-23. FREON 22: PROPERTIES OF SUPERHEATED VAPOR

Temp. °F.	Abs. Pressure 25 lb./in.² (Sat'n. Temp. −150.9°F.)			Abs. Pressure .30 lb./in.² (Sat'n. Temp. −147.4°F.)			Abs. Pressure .35 lb./in.² (Sat'n. Temp. −144.3°F.)			Abs. Pressure 40 lb./in.² (Sat'n. Temp. −141.7°F.)		
t	v	H	s	v	H	s	v	H	s	v	H	s
(at sat'n.)	(151.8)	(87.26)	(0.2960)	(127.9)	(87.66)	(0.2932)	(110.7)	(88.02)	(0.2907)	(97.62)	(88.33)	(0.2887)
−150	152.19	87.36	.2962	130.91	88.53	.2958						
−140	157.12	88.53	.2999	135.01	89.72	.2995	112.19	88.53	.2923	98.15	88.53	.2892
−130	162.04	89.72	.3036	139.12	90.92	.3031	115.71	89.72	.2959	101.23	89.71	.2929
−120	166.96	90.93	.3072	143.22	92.14	.3066	119.23	90.92	.2995	104.31	90.92	.2965
−110	171.89	92.14	.3107	147.33	93.37	.3101	122.75	92.14	.3031	107.39	92.14	.3000
−100	176.81	93.38	.3142	151.43	94.62	.3135	126.26	93.37	.3065	110.47	93.37	.3035
−90	181.74	94.62	.3176	155.53	95.88	.3168	129.78	94.62	.3100	113.55	94.62	.3069
−80	186.66	95.89	.3210	159.64	97.16	.3201	133.30	95.88	.3133	116.62	95.88	.3103
−70	191.59	97.16	.3243	163.74	98.45	.3234	136.82	97.16	.3166	119.70	97.16	.3136
−60	196.51	98.46	.3276	167.84	99.76	.3266	140.33	98.45	.3199	122.78	98.45	.3168
−50	201.43	99.76	.3308	171.95	101.08	.3298	143.85	99.76	.3231	125.86	99.75	.3201
−40	206.35	101.08	.3340	176.05	102.42	.3330	147.37	101.08	.3263	128.94	101.08	.3233
−30	211.28	102.42	.3371	180.15	103.77	.3361	150.89	102.41	.3295	132.01	102.41	.3264
−20	216.20	103.77	.3403	184.25	105.13	.3392	154.40	103.77	.3326	135.09	103.76	.3295
−10	221.12	105.14	.3433	188.36	106.51	.3422	157.92	105.13	.3357	138.17	105.13	.3326
0	226.04	106.52	.3464	192.46	107.91	.3452	161.44	106.51	.3387	141.25	106.51	.3357
10	230.97	107.91	.3494	196.56	109.32	.3482	164.96	107.91	.3417	144.33	107.91	.3387
20	235.89	109.32	.3524	200.66	110.75	.3512	168.47	109.32	.3447	147.40	109.32	.3417
30	240.81	110.75	.3553	204.76	112.18	.3541	171.99	110.74	.3476	150.48	110.74	.3446
40	245.73	112.19	.3582	208.87	113.64	.3569	175.50	112.18	.3506	153.56	112.18	.3475
50	250.66	113.64	.3611	212.97	115.11	.3598	179.02	113.64	.3534	156.63	113.64	.3504
60	255.58	115.11	.3639	217.07	116.59	.3626	182.54	115.11	.3563	159.71	115.10	.3532
70	260.50	116.59	.3668	221.17	118.09	.3654	186.05	116.59	.3591	162.79	116.59	.3561
80	265.42	118.09	.3696	225.28	119.60	.3682	189.57	118.09	.3619	165.87	118.09	.3589
90	270.34	119.61	.3724	229.38	121.13	.3710	193.09	119.60	.3647	168.94	119.60	.3617
100	275.27	121.13	.3751	233.48	122.68	.3737	196.60	121.13	.3675	172.02	121.13	.3644
110	280.19	122.68	.3779	237.58	124.23	.3764	200.12	122.68	.3702	175.10	122.67	.3672
120	285.11	124.24	.3806	241.68	125.81	.3791	203.63	124.23	.3729	178.17	124.23	.3699
130	290.03	125.81	.3833	245.78	127.40	.3818	207.15	125.81	.3756	181.25	125.80	.3726
140	294.95	127.40	.3859	249.89	129.00	.3844	210.66	127.39	.3783	184.33	127.39	.3752
150	299.87	129.00	.3886	253.99	130.62	.3871	214.18	129.00	.3809	187.40	129.00	.3779
160	......	......	......				217.70	130.61	.3835	190.48	130.61	.3805

Temp. °F.	Abs. Pressure .45 lb./in.² (Sat'n. Temp. −139.3°F.)			Abs. Pressure .50 lb./in.² (Sat'n. Temp. −137.2°F.)			Abs. Pressure .55 lb./in.² (Sat'n. Temp. −135.0°F.)			Abs. Pressure .60 lb./in.² (Sat'n. Temp. −133.3°F.)		
t	v	H	s	v	H	s	v	H	s	v	H	s
(at sat'n.)	(87.42)	(88.61)	(0.2868)	(79.18)	(88.86)	(0.2853)	(72.47)	(89.10)	(0.2838)	(66.77)	(89.31)	(0.2825)
−130	89.97	89.71	.2902	80.96	89.71	.2878	73.59	89.71	.2856	67.44	89.70	.2837
−120	92.70	90.92	.2938	83.42	90.91	.2914	75.83	90.91	.2892	69.50	90.91	.2873
−110	95.44	92.13	.2974	85.89	92.13	.2949	78.07	92.13	.2928	71.55	92.13	.2908
−100	98.18	93.37	.3008	88.35	93.36	.2984	80.31	93.36	.2962	73.61	93.36	.2943
−90	100.92	94.61	.3042	90.81	94.61	.3018	82.55	94.61	.2997	75.66	94.61	.2977
−80	103.65	95.88	.3076	93.28	95.87	.3052	84.79	95.87	.3031	77.71	95.87	.3010
−70	106.39	97.15	.3109	95.74	97.15	.3085	87.03	97.15	.3063	79.77	97.15	.3043
−60	109.13	98.45	.3142	98.21	98.44	.3118	89.27	98.44	.3096	81.32	98.44	.3076
−50	111.86	99.75	.3174	100.67	99.75	.3150	91.51	99.75	.3128	83.88	99.75	.3108
−40	114.60	101.07	.3206	103.13	101.07	.3182	93.75	101.07	.3160	85.93	101.07	.3140
−30	117.34	102.41	.3237	105.60	102.41	.3213	95.99	102.41	.3192	87.98	102.40	.3172
−20	120.07	103.76	.3269	108.06	103.76	.3245	98.23	103.76	.3223	90.03	103.76	.3203
−10	122.81	105.13	.3299	110.52	105.13	.3275	100.46	105.12	.3254	92.09	105.12	.3234
0	125.54	106.51	.3330	112.98	106.51	.3306	102.70	106.50	.3284	94.14	106.50	.3264
10	128.28	107.90	.3360	115.45	107.90	.3336	104.94	107.90	.3314	96.19	107.90	.3294
20	131.02	109.31	.3390	117.91	109.31	.3366	107.18	109.31	.3344	98.24	109.31	.3324
30	133.75	110.74	.3419	120.37	110.74	.3395	109.42	110.74	.3373	100.30	110.73	.3354
40	136.49	112.18	.3448	122.83	112.18	.3424	111.66	112.18	.3403	102.35	112.17	.3383
50	139.22	113.63	.3477	125.29	113.63	.3453	113.90	113.63	.3431	104.40	113.63	.3412
60	141.96	115.10	.3506	127.76	115.10	.3482	116.14	115.10	.3460	106.45	115.10	.3440
70	144.69	116.59	.3534	130.22	116.59	.3510	118.37	116.58	.3488	108.50	116.58	.3468
80	147.43	118.09	.3562	132.68	118.09	.3538	120.61	118.08	.3516	110.55	118.08	.3496
90	150.16	119.60	.3590	135.14	119.60	.3566	122.85	119.60	.3544	112.61	119.60	.3524
100	152.90	121.13	.3617	137.60	121.13	.3593	125.09	121.13	.3572	114.66	121.12	.3552
110	155.63	122.67	.3645	140.07	122.67	.3621	127.33	122.67	.3599	116.71	122.67	.3579
120	158.37	124.23	.3672	142.53	124.23	.3648	129.56	124.23	.3626	118.76	124.23	.3606
130	161.10	125.80	.3699	144.99	125.80	.3675	131.80	125.80	.3653	120.81	125.80	.3633
140	163.84	127.39	.3725	147.45	127.39	.3701	134.04	127.39	.3680	122.87	127.39	.3660
150	166.57	128.99	.3752	149.91	128.99	.3728	136.28	128.99	.3706	124.92	128.99	.3686
160	169.31	130.61	.3778	152.37	130.61	.3754	138.52	130.61	.3732	126.97	130.61	.3713
170	172.04	132.24	.3804	154.83	132.24	.3780	140.75	132.24	.3759	129.02	132.24	.3739

TABLE 2-23. FREON 22: PROPERTIES OF SUPERHEATED VAPOR (Continued)

Temp. °F.	Abs. Pressure .65 lb./in.² (Sat'n. Temp. −131.6°F.)			Abs. Pressure .70 lb./in.² (Sat'n. Temp. −129.9°F.)			Abs. Pressure .75 lb./in.² (Sat'n. Temp. −128.4°F.)			Abs. Pressure .80 lb./in.² (Sat'n. Temp. −127.0°F.)		
t	v	H	s	v	H	s	v	H	s	v	H	s
(at sat'n.)	(61.94)	(89.52)	(0.2813)	(57.81)	(89.72)	(0.2802)	(54.19)	(89.89)	(0.2792)	(51.01)	(90.06)	(0.2783)
−130	62.25	89.70	.2818	.....	.....	.....	.....	.....	.....	.....	.....	.....
−120	64.14	90.90	.2854	59.55	90.90	.2837	55.58	90.90	.2822	52.09	90.90	.2807
−110	66.04	92.12	.2890	61.31	92.12	.2873	57.22	92.12	.2857	53.64	92.11	.2842
−100	67.94	93.36	.2924	63.08	93.35	.2907	58.86	93.35	.2892	55.18	93.35	.2877
−90	69.83	94.60	.2958	64.84	94.60	.2942	60.51	94.60	.2926	56.72	94.60	.2911
−80	71.73	95.87	.2992	66.60	95.87	.2975	62.15	95.86	.2959	58.26	95.86	.2945
−70	73.62	97.14	.3025	68.36	97.14	.3005	63.79	97.14	.2992	59.80	97.14	.2978
−60	75.52	98.44	.3058	70.12	98.44	.3041	65.44	98.43	.3025	61.34	98.43	.3010
−50	77.42	99.74	.3090	71.88	99.74	.3073	67.08	99.74	.3057	62.88	99.74	.3043
−40	79.31	101.07	.3122	73.64	101.06	.3105	68.73	101.06	.3089	64.42	101.06	.3075
−30	81.21	102.40	.3154	75.40	102.40	.3137	70.37	102.40	.3121	65.96	102.40	.3106
−20	83.10	103.75	.3185	77.16	103.75	.3168	72.01	103.75	.3152	67.50	103.75	.3137
−10	85.00	105.12	.3216	78.92	105.12	.3199	73.65	105.12	.3183	69.04	105.11	.3168
0	86.89	106.50	.3246	80.68	106.50	.3229	75.30	106.50	.3213	70.58	106.50	.3199
10	88.79	107.90	.3276	82.44	107.89	.3259	76.94	107.89	.3244	72.12	107.89	.3229
20	90.68	109.31	.3306	84.20	109.31	.3289	78.58	109.30	.3273	73.66	109.30	.3259
30	92.58	110.73	.3335	85.96	110.73	.3318	80.22	110.73	.3303	75.20	110.73	.3288
40	94.47	112.17	.3364	87.72	112.17	.3348	81.86	112.17	.3332	76.74	112.17	.3317
50	96.36	113.63	.3393	89.48	113.63	.3376	83.51	113.62	.3361	78.28	113.62	.3346
60	98.26	115.10	.3422	91.23	115.09	.3405	85.15	115.09	.3389	79.82	115.09	.3374
70	100.15	116.58	.3450	92.99	116.58	.3433	86.79	116.58	.3417	81.36	116.58	.3403
80	102.05	118.08	.3478	94.75	118.08	.3461	88.43	118.08	.3446	82.90	118.08	.3431
90	103.94	119.59	.3506	96.51	119.59	.3489	90.07	119.59	.3473	84.44	119.59	.3459
100	105.84	121.12	.3534	98.27	121.12	.3517	91.72	121.12	.3501	85.98	121.12	.3486
110	107.73	122.67	.3561	100.03	122.67	.3544	93.36	122.66	.3528	87.52	122.66	.3514
120	109.62	124.22	.3588	101.79	124.22	.3571	95.00	124.22	.3555	89.06	124.22	.3541
130	111.52	125.80	.3615	103.55	125.80	.3598	96.64	125.80	.3582	90.60	125.79	.3568
140	113.41	127.39	.3642	105.31	127.38	.3625	98.28	127.38	.3609	92.14	127.38	.3594
150	115.30	128.99	.3668	107.06	128.99	.3651	99.92	128.99	.3636	93.68	128.98	.3621
160	117.20	130.61	.3694	108.82	130.60	.3678	101.56	130.60	.3662	95.21	130.60	.3647
170	119.09	132.24	.3721	110.58	132.24	.3704	103.21	132.24	.3688	96.75	132.23	.3673
180				112.34	133.88	.3730	104.85	133.88	.3714	98.29	133.88	.3699

Temp. °F. t	Abs. Pressure .90 lb./in.² (Sat'n. Temp. −124.3°F.)			Abs. Pressure 1.00 lb./in.² (Sat'n. Temp. −121.9°F.)			Abs. Pressure 1.25 lb./in.² (Sat'n. Temp. −116.9°F.)			Abs. Pressure 1.50 lb./in.² (Sat'n. Temp. −112.1°F.)		
	v	H	s	v	H	s	v	H	s	v	H	s
(at sat'n.)	(45.70)	(90.38)	(0.2765)	(41.42)	(90.66)	(0.2750)	(33.63)	(91.28)	(0.2718)	(28.38)	(91.82)	(0.2692)
−120	46.29	90.89	.2780	41.65	90.88	.2756						
−110	47.66	92.11	.2815	42.89	92.10	.2791	34.29	92.09	.2740	28.55	92.08	.2699
−100	49.03	93.34	.2850	44.12	93.34	.2826	35.27	93.33	.2775	29.38	93.31	.2733
−90	50.41	94.59	.2884	45.35	94.59	.2860	36.26	94.58	.2809	30.20	94.56	.2767
−80	51.78	95.86	.2918	46.59	95.85	.2894	37.25	95.84	.2843	31.02	95.83	.2801
−70	53.15	97.13	.2951	47.82	97.13	.2927	38.24	97.12	.2876	31.85	97.11	.2834
−60	54.52	98.43	.2984	49.05	98.42	.2960	39.22	98.41	.2909	32.67	98.40	.2867
−50	55.89	99.73	.3016	50.29	99.73	.2992	40.21	99.72	.2941	33.49	99.71	.2899
−40	57.26	101.06	.3048	51.52	101.05	.3024	41.20	101.04	.2973	34.32	101.03	.2931
−30	58.63	102.39	.3079	52.75	102.39	.3055	42.19	102.38	.3004	35.14	102.37	.2963
−20	59.99	103.74	.3111	53.99	103.74	.3087	43.17	103.73	.3036	35.96	103.72	.2994
−10	61.36	105.11	.3141	55.22	105.11	.3117	44.16	105.10	.3066	36.79	105.09	.3025
0	62.73	106.49	.3172	56.45	106.49	.3148	45.15	106.48	.3097	37.61	106.47	.3055
10	64.10	107.89	.3202	57.68	107.88	.3178	46.13	107.87	.3127	38.43	107.86	.3085
20	65.47	109.30	.3232	58.92	109.29	.3208	47.12	109.29	.3157	39.25	109.28	.3115
30	66.84	110.72	.3261	60.15	110.72	.3237	48.10	110.71	.3186	40.08	110.70	.3145
40	68.21	112.16	.3290	61.38	112.16	.3266	49.09	112.15	.3215	40.90	112.14	.3174
50	69.58	113.62	.3319	62.61	113.62	.3295	50.08	113.61	.3244	41.72	113.60	.3203
60	70.95	115.09	.3348	63.84	115.08	.3324	51.06	115.07	.3273	42.54	115.06	.3231
70	72.31	116.57	.3376	65.08	116.57	.3352	52.05	116.56	.3301	43.36	116.55	.3259
80	73.68	118.07	.3404	66.31	118.07	.3380	53.03	118.06	.3329	44.18	118.05	.3287
90	75.05	119.59	.3432	67.54	119.58	.3408	54.02	119.58	.3357	45.01	119.57	.3315
100	76.42	121.12	.3459	68.77	121.11	.3435	55.01	121.10	.3384	45.83	121.10	.3343
110	77.79	122.66	.3487	70.00	122.66	.3463	55.99	122.65	.3412	46.65	122.64	.3370
120	79.16	124.22	.3514	71.24	124.21	.3490	56.98	124.21	.3439	47.47	124.20	.3397
130	80.53	125.79	.3541	72.47	125.79	.3517	57.96	125.78	.3466	48.29	125.77	.3424
140	81.89	127.38	.3567	73.70	127.38	.3543	58.95	127.37	.3493	49.12	127.36	.3451
150	83.26	128.99	.3594	74.93	128.99	.3570	59.93	128.97	.3519	49.94	128.97	.3478
160	84.63	130.60	.3620	76.16	130.60	.3596	60.92	130.59	.3545	50.76	130.58	.3504
170	86.00	132.23	.3646	77.39	132.23	.3622	61.90	132.22	.3571	51.58	132.22	.3530
180	87.37	133.88	.3672	78.62	133.88	.3648	62.89	133.87	.3597	52.40	133.86	.3556
190	......	......	......	......	......	......	63.88	135.53	.3623	53.22	135.53	.3582

TABLE 2-23. FREON 22: PROPERTIES OF SUPERHEATED VAPOR (Continued)

Temp. °F.	Abs. Pressure 1.75 lb./in.² (Sat'n. Temp. −108.2°F.)			Abs. Pressure 2.0 lb./in.² (Sat'n. Temp. −104.7°F.)			Abs. Pressure 2.5 lb./in.² (Sat'n. Temp. −98.8°F.)			Abs. Pressure 3.0 lb./in.² (Sat'n. Temp. −93.8°F.)		
t	v	H	s	v	H	s	v	H	s	v	H	s
(at sat'n.)	(24.58)	(92.28)	(0.2670)	(21.71)	(92.72)	(0.2651)	(17.64)	(93.41)	(0.2621)	(14.89)	(94.02)	(0.2597)
−100	25.16	93.30	.2698	22.00	93.29	.2667						
−90	25.87	94.55	.2732	22.62	94.54	.2702	18.08	94.51	.2650	15.05	94.49	.2609
−80	26.58	95.82	.2766	23.21	95.81	.2735	18.57	95.78	.2684	15.46	95.76	.2642
−70	27.28	97.10	.2799	23.86	97.08	.2768	19.07	97.06	.2717	15.87	97.04	.2676
−60	27.99	98.39	.2832	24.48	98.38	.2801	19.56	98.36	.2750	16.29	98.34	.2708
−50	28.70	99.70	.2864	25.10	99.69	.2833	20.06	99.67	.2782	16.70	99.65	.2741
−40	29.40	101.02	.2896	25.72	101.01	.2865	20.55	100.99	.2814	17.11	100.97	.2773
−30	30.11	102.36	.2927	26.33	102.35	.2897	21.05	102.33	.2846	17.53	102.31	.2804
−20	30.81	103.71	.2959	26.95	103.70	.2928	21.54	103.68	.2877	17.94	103.66	.2835
−10	31.52	105.08	.2990	27.57	105.07	.2959	22.04	105.05	.2908	18.35	105.03	.2866
0	32.22	106.46	.3020	28.19	106.45	.2990	22.53	106.43	.2959	18.76	106.41	.2897
10	32.93	107.85	.3050	28.80	107.85	.3020	23.03	107.83	.2969	19.18	107.81	.2927
20	33.63	109.27	.3080	29.42	109.26	.3049	23.52	109.24	.2998	19.59	109.22	.2957
30	34.34	110.69	.3109	30.04	110.68	.3079	24.02	110.67	.3028	20.00	110.65	.2986
40	35.04	112.13	.3139	30.66	112.13	.3108	24.51	112.11	.3057	20.41	112.09	.3015
50	35.75	113.59	.3167	31.27	113.58	.3137	25.00	113.57	.3086	20.83	113.55	.3044
60	36.45	115.06	.3196	31.89	115.05	.3165	25.50	115.04	.3114	21.24	115.02	.3073
70	37.16	116.55	.3224	32.51	116.54	.3194	25.99	116.52	.3143	21.65	116.51	.3101
80	37.86	118.05	.3252	33.12	118.04	.3222	26.49	118.02	.3171	22.06	118.01	.3129
90	38.57	119.56	.3280	33.74	119.55	.3250	26.98	119.54	.3199	22.47	119.52	.3157
100	39.27	121.09	.3308	34.36	121.08	.3277	27.47	121.07	.3226	22.88	121.05	.3185
110	39.98	122.63	.3335	34.97	122.63	.3305	27.97	122.61	.3254	23.30	122.60	.3212
120	40.68	124.19	.3362	35.59	124.19	.3332	28.46	124.17	.3281	23.71	124.16	.3239
130	41.39	125.77	.3389	36.21	125.76	.3359	28.95	125.75	.3308	24.12	125.73	.3266
140	42.09	127.36	.3416	36.82	127.35	.3385	29.45	127.34	.3334	24.53	127.32	.3293
150	42.80	128.96	.3442	37.44	128.95	.3412	29.94	128.94	.3361	24.94	128.93	.3319
160	43.50	130.58	.3469	38.06	130.57	.3438	30.44	130.56	.3387	25.35	130.54	.3346
170	44.20	132.21	.3495	38.67	132.20	.3464	30.93	132.19	.3413	25.77	132.18	.3372
180	44.91	133.86	.3521	39.29	133.85	.3490	31.42	133.84	.3439	26.18	133.83	.3398
190	45.61	135.52	.3547	39.91	135.51	.3516	31.91	135.50	.3465	26.59	135.49	.3424
200	46.32	137.20	.3572	40.52	137.19	.3542	32.41	137.18	.3491	27.10	137.17	.3449
210							32.90	138.87	.3516	27.41	138.86	.3475

Temp. °F. t	Abs. Pressure 3.5 lb./in.² (Sat'n. Temp. —89.4°F.) v	H	s	Abs. Pressure 4.0 lb./in.² (Sat'n. Temp. —85.4°F.) v	H	s	Abs. Pressure 4.5 lb./in.² (Sat'n. Temp. —82.0°F.) v	H	s	Abs. Pressure 5.0 lb./in.² (Sat'n. Temp. —78.7°F.) v	H	s
(at sat'n.)	(12.90)	(94.55)	(0.2576)	(11.40)	(95.03)	(0.2558)	(10.22)	(95.46)	(0.2543)	(9.266)	(95.83)	(0.2529)
—80	13.24	95.74	.2607	11.57	95.72	.2576	10.27	95.69	.2549			
—70	13.59	97.02	.2640	11.88	97.00	.2609	10.55	96.97	.2582	9.483	96.95	.2558
—60	13.95	98.31	.2673	12.19	98.29	.2642	10.83	98.27	.2615	9.733	98.25	.2591
—50	14.30	99.62	.2705	12.50	99.60	.2674	11.10	99.58	.2647	9.983	99.56	.2623
—40	14.66	100.95	.2737	12.81	100.93	.2706	11.38	100.91	.2679	10.232	100.89	.2655
—30	15.01	102.29	.2769	13.12	102.27	.2738	11.66	102.25	.2711	10.481	102.23	.2687
—20	15.37	103.64	.2800	13.43	103.62	.2769	11.93	103.60	.2742	10.729	103.58	.2718
—10	15.72	105.01	.2831	13.74	104.99	.2800	12.21	104.98	.2773	10.978	104.96	.2749
0	16.07	106.40	.2861	14.05	106.38	.2831	12.48	106.36	.2804	11.226	106.34	.2780
10	16.43	107.80	.2892	14.36	107.78	.2861	12.76	107.76	.2834	11.475	107.74	.2810
20	16.78	109.21	.2921	14.67	109.19	.2891	13.04	109.17	.2864	11.723	109.16	.2840
30	17.13	110.63	.2951	14.98	110.62	.2920	13.31	110.60	.2893	11.972	110.59	.2869
40	17.49	112.07	.2980	15.29	112.06	.2950	13.59	112.05	.2922	12.220	112.03	.2898
50	17.84	113.53	.3009	15.60	113.52	.2978	13.86	113.50	.2951	12.468	113.49	.2927
60	18.19	115.00	.3037	15.91	114.99	.3007	14.14	114.96	.2980	12.715	114.96	.2956
70	18.55	116.49	.3066	16.22	116.48	.3035	14.41	116.46	.3008	12.963	116.45	.2984
80	18.90	117.99	.3094	16.53	117.98	.3063	14.69	117.97	.3036	13.211	117.95	.3012
90	19.25	119.51	.3122	16.84	119.50	.3091	14.96	119.48	.3064	13.460	119.47	.3040
100	19.61	121.04	.3149	17.15	121.03	.3119	15.24	121.01	.3092	13.707	121.00	.3068
110	19.96	122.58	.3177	17.46	122.57	.3146	15.51	122.56	.3119	13.955	122.55	.3095
120	20.31	124.14	.3204	17.77	124.13	.3173	15.79	124.12	.3146	14.202	124.11	.3122
130	20.67	125.72	.3231	18.08	125.70	.3200	16.06	125.69	.3173	14.450	125.68	.3149
140	21.02	127.31	.3258	18.39	127.29	.3227	16.34	127.28	.3200	14.697	127.27	.3176
150	21.37	128.91	.3284	18.69	128.90	.3254	16.61	128.89	.3227	14.945	128.88	.3202
160	21.73	130.53	.3310	19.00	130.52	.3280	16.89	130.51	.3253	15.192	130.49	.3229
170	22.08	132.17	.3337	19.31	132.15	.3306	17.16	132.14	.3279	15.440	132.13	.3255
180	22.43	133.81	.3363	19.62	133.80	.3332	17.44	133.79	.3305	15.687	133.78	.3281
190	22.78	135.48	.3388	19.93	135.46	.3358	17.71	135.45	.3331	15.931	135.44	.3307
200	23.14	137.15	.3414	20.24	137.14	.3383	17.98	137.13	.3357	16.181	137.12	.3332
210	23.49	138.85	.3439	20.55	138.84	.3409	18.26	138.82	.3382	16.429	138.81	.3358
220	23.84	140.56	.3465	20.86	140.54	.3434	18.53	140.53	.3407	16.676	140.52	.3383
230										16.923	142.24	.3408

TABLE 2-23. FREON 22: PROPERTIES OF SUPERHEATED VAPOR (Continued)

Temp. °F.	Abs. Pressure 6 lb./in.² (Sat'n. Temp. −73.0°F.)			Abs. Pressure 7 lb./in.² (Sat'n. Temp. −68.0°F.)			Abs. Pressure 8 lb./in.² (Sat'n. Temp. −63.5°F.)			Abs. Pressure 9 lb./in.² (Sat'n. Temp. −58.5°F.)		
t	v	H	s	v	H	s	v	H	s	v	H	s
(at sat'n.)	(7.823)	(96.52)	(0.2506)	(6.781)	(97.12)	(0.2487)	(5.991)	(97.66)	(0.2471)	(5.370)	(98.14)	(0.2456)
−70	7.886	96.91	.2516	......	......	......	......	......	......	......	......	......
−60	8.095	98.20	.2549	6.924	98.16	.2513	6.046	98.12	.2482	......	......	......
−50	8.303	99.52	.2581	7.103	99.48	.2545	6.204	99.44	.2514	5.503	99.39	.2487
−40	8.511	100.85	.2613	7.282	100.80	.2577	6.361	100.76	.2546	5.643	100.72	.2519
−30	8.719	102.19	.2645	7.461	102.15	.2609	6.517	102.10	.2578	5.783	102.06	.2551
−20	8.927	103.54	.2676	7.640	103.51	.2640	6.673	103.47	.2610	5.923	103.43	.2582
−10	9.135	104.92	.2707	7.813	104.88	.2671	6.830	104.84	.2641	6.062	104.81	.2613
0	9.342	106.31	.2738	7.996	106.27	.2702	6.986	106.23	.2671	6.201	106.19	.2644
10	9.549	107.71	.2768	8.174	107.67	.2732	7.143	107.63	.2701	6.341	107.60	.2674
20	9.757	109.12	.2798	8.352	109.09	.2762	7.299	109.05	.2731	6.479	109.02	.2704
30	9.964	110.55	.2827	8.530	110.52	.2792	7.455	110.48	.2761	6.613	110.45	.2734
40	10.171	112.00	.2856	8.708	111.96	.2821	7.611	111.93	.2790	6.757	111.90	.2763
50	10.378	113.46	.2885	8.886	113.42	.2850	7.767	113.39	.2819	6.896	113.36	.2792
60	10.585	114.93	.2914	9.064	114.90	.2878	7.922	114.87	.2848	7.035	114.83	.2820
70	10.792	116.42	.2942	9.241	116.39	.2907	8.073	116.36	.2876	7.173	116.32	.2849
80	10.999	117.92	.2970	9.419	117.89	.2935	8.234	117.86	.2904	7.312	117.83	.2877
90	11.206	119.44	.2998	9.597	119.41	.2963	8.389	119.38	.2932	7.450	119.35	.2905
100	11.413	120.97	.3026	9.774	120.94	.2990	8.545	120.91	.2960	7.589	120.88	.2933
110	11.620	122.52	.3053	9.952	122.49	.3018	8.700	122.46	.2987	7.727	122.43	.2960
120	11.826	124.08	.3080	10.129	124.05	.3045	8.856	124.02	.3014	7.865	124.00	.2987
130	12.033	125.66	.3107	10.306	125.63	.3072	9.011	125.60	.3041	8.004	125.57	.3014
140	12.239	127.25	.3134	10.483	127.22	.3099	9.166	127.19	.3068	8.142	127.17	.3041
150	12.446	128.85	.3161	10.660	128.82	.3125	9.321	128.80	.3095	8.280	128.77	.3068
160	12.653	130.47	.3187	10.837	130.45	.3152	9.477	130.42	.3121	8.418	130.39	.3094
170	12.859	132.11	.3213	11.014	132.08	.3178	9.632	132.06	.3147	8.556	132.03	.3120
180	13.065	133.75	.3239	11.192	133.73	.3204	9.787	133.71	.3173	8.694	133.68	.3146
190	13.271	135.41	.3265	11.369	135.40	.3230	9.942	135.37	.3199	8.832	135.35	.3172
200	13.477	137.09	.3291	11.545	137.08	.3255	10.097	137.05	.3225	8.970	137.03	.3198
210	13.683	138.79	.3316	11.722	138.77	.3281	10.252	138.75	.3250	9.108	138.72	.3223
220	13.889	140.50	.3341	11.899	140.47	.3306	10.407	140.45	.3276	9.245	140.43	.3249
230	14.096	142.22	.3366	12.076	142.20	.3331	10.562	142.18	.3301	9.383	142.15	.3274
240				12.253	143.94	.3356	10.717	143.91	.3326	9.521	143.89	.3299
250										9.659	145.65	.3324

Temp. °F. t	Abs. Pressure 10 lb./in.² (Sat'n. Temp. −55.8°F.)			Abs. Pressure 11 lb./in.² (Sat'n. Temp. −52.4°F.)			Abs. Pressure 12 lb./in.² (Sat'n. Temp. −49.2°F.)			Abs. Pressure 14 lb./in.² (Sat'n. Temp. −43.5°F.)		
	v	H	s	v	H	s	v	H	s	v	H	s
(at sat'n.)	(4.870)	(98.58)	(0.2444)	(4.458)	(98.99)	(0.2432)	(4.112)	(99.37)	(0.2422)	(3.562)	(100.05)	(0.2404)
−50	4.943	99.35	.2462	4.485	99.31	.2440						
−40	5.069	100.68	.2494	4.600	100.64	.2472	4.209	100.60	.2452	3.595	100.51	.2415
−30	5.195	102.02	.2526	4.715	101.98	.2504	4.315	101.94	.2484	3.685	101.86	.2447
−20	5.321	103.39	.2558	4.830	103.35	.2535	4.420	103.31	.2515	3.776	103.23	.2479
−10	5.447	104.77	.2589	4.944	104.73	.2567	4.525	104.69	.2546	3.867	104.62	.2510
0	5.573	106.16	.2619	5.059	106.12	.2597	4.630	106.08	.2577	3.957	106.01	.2541
10	5.699	107.56	.2650	5.173	107.53	.2628	4.735	107.49	.2607	4.048	107.42	.2571
20	5.824	108.98	.2680	5.288	108.95	.2658	4.840	108.91	.2637	4.138	108.84	.2601
30	5.950	110.40	.2709	5.402	110.38	.2687	4.945	110.35	.2667	4.228	110.28	.2631
40	6.075	111.86	.2739	5.516	111.83	.2716	5.050	111.79	.2696	4.318	111.73	.2660
50	6.200	113.32	.2767	5.630	113.29	.2745	5.155	113.26	.2725	4.408	113.19	.2689
60	6.325	114.80	.2796	5.743	114.77	.2774	5.260	114.74	.2754	4.499	114.67	.2718
70	6.450	116.29	.2824	5.857	116.26	.2802	5.364	116.23	.2782	4.588	116.17	.2746
80	6.575	117.80	.2853	5.971	117.77	.2831	5.468	117.74	.2810	4.673	117.68	.2775
90	6.700	119.32	.2881	6.085	119.29	.2859	5.573	119.26	.2838	4.768	119.20	.2803
100	6.824	120.85	.2908	6.199	120.82	.2886	5.677	120.80	.2866	4.857	120.74	.2830
110	6.949	122.40	.2936	6.312	122.37	.2914	5.781	122.35	.2894	4.947	122.29	.2858
120	7.073	123.97	.2963	6.425	123.94	.2941	5.885	123.91	.2921	5.036	123.86	.2885
130	7.198	125.55	.2990	6.539	125.52	.2968	5.989	125.49	.2948	5.126	125.44	.2912
140	7.322	127.14	.3017	6.652	127.11	.2995	6.093	127.08	.2975	5.215	127.03	.2939
150	7.447	128.74	.3043	6.766	128.72	.3021	6.197	128.69	.3001	5.304	128.64	.2966
160	7.571	130.37	.3070	6.879	130.34	.3048	6.301	130.32	.3028	5.394	130.27	.2992
170	7.696	132.01	.3096	6.992	131.98	.3074	6.405	131.96	.3054	5.483	131.91	.3018
180	7.820	133.66	.3122	7.105	133.63	.3100	6.509	133.61	.3080	5.573	133.56	.3044
190	7.945	135.32	.3148	7.218	135.30	.3126	6.613	135.27	.3106	5.661	135.23	.3070
200	8.069	137.00	.3173	7.331	136.98	.3152	6.717	136.96	.3132	5.750	136.91	.3096
210	8.193	138.70	.3199	7.444	138.68	.3177	6.820	138.65	.3157	5.840	138.61	.3121
220	8.317	140.41	.3224	7.557	140.39	.3202	6.924	140.36	.3182	5.929	140.32	.3147
230	8.441	142.13	.3250	7.670	142.11	.3228	7.028	142.09	.3208	6.018	142.05	.3172
240	8.565	143.87	.3275	7.783	143.85	.3253	7.131	143.83	.3233	6.107	143.79	.3197
250	8.689	145.63	.3300	7.896	145.60	.3278	7.234	145.58	.3258	6.196	145.54	.3222
260							7.338	147.35	.3282	6.285	147.31	.3247

TABLE 2-23.   FREON 22: PROPERTIES OF SUPERHEATED VAPOR (Continued)

Temp. °F. t	Abs. Pressure 16 lb./in.² (Sat'n. Temp. −38.3°F.) v	H	s	Abs. Pressure 18 lb./in.² (Sat'n. Temp. −33.7°F.) v	H	s	Abs. Pressure 20 lb./in.² (Sat'n. Temp. −29.4°F.) v	H	s	Abs. Pressure 25 lb./in.² (Sat'n. Temp. −20.0°F.) v	H	s
(at sat'n.)	(3.147)	(100.63)	(0.2390)	(2.820)	(101.19)	(0.2376)	(2.556)	(101.70)	(0.2365)	(2.074)	(102.79)	(0.2341)
−30	3.213	101.78	.2416	......	......	......	......	......	......	......	......	......
−20	3.293	103.16	.2447	2.846	101.70	.2388	2.616	103.00	.2394	......	......	......
−10	3.373	104.54	.2479	2.917	103.08	.2420	2.681	104.38	.2426	2.127	104.19	.2372
0	3.452	105.93	.2509	2.988	104.46	.2451	2.745	105.78	.2457	2.179	105.59	.2403
10	3.532	107.34	.2540	3.059	105.86	.2482	2.809	107.20	.2487	2.231	107.01	.2434
20	3.611	108.77	.2570	3.130	107.27	.2512	2.873	108.63	.2517	2.283	108.45	.2464
30	3.690	110.21	.2600	3.201	108.70	.2542	2.937	110.07	.2547	2.335	109.89	.2494
40	3.769	111.66	.2629	3.272	110.14	.2572	3.001	111.52	.2577	2.386	111.35	.2524
50	3.848	113.13	.2658	3.343	111.59	.2601	3.065	113.00	.2606	2.437	112.83	.2553
60	3.928	114.61	.2687	3.413	113.06	.2630	3.128	114.48	.2634	2.489	114.32	.2582
70	4.006	116.11	.2715	3.484	114.55	.2659	3.192	115.98	.2663	2.540	115.82	.2610
80	4.085	117.62	.2744	3.554	116.04	.2688	3.255	117.49	.2691	2.591	117.34	.2639
90	4.164	119.14	.2772	3.624	117.56	.2716	3.319	119.02	.2719	2.643	118.87	.2667
100	4.243	120.68	.2799	3.694	119.08	.2744	3.382	120.56	.2747·	2.693	120.42	.2695
110	4.321	122.23	.2827	3.764	120.62	.2772	3.445	122.12	.2775	2.744	121.98	.2722
120	4.399	123.80	.2854	3.834	122.18	.2799	3.508	123.69	.2802	2.795	123.55	.2750
130	4.478	125.38	.2881	3.904	123.74	.2827	3.571	125.27	.2829	2.846	125.14	.2777
140	4.557	126.98	.2908	3.975	125.33	.2854	3.635	126.87	.2856	2.897	126.74	.2804
150	4.635	128.59	.2935	4.044	126.92	.2881	3.698	128.49	.2883	2.947	128.36	.2831
160	4.713	130.21	.2961	4.114	128.54	.2907	3.761	130.11	.2909	2.998	129.99	.2857
170	4.792	131.86	.2987	4.184	130.16	.2934	3.824	131.76	.2936	3.049	131.63	.2883
180	4.870	133.51	.3014	4.254	131.81	.2960	3.886	133.41	.2962	3.099	133.29	.2910
190	4.948	135.18	.3039	4.324	133.46	.2986	3.949	135.08	.2988	3.150	134.96	.2936
200	5.026	136.86	.3065	4.393	135.13	.3012	4.012	136.77	.3013	3.200	136.65	.2961
210	5.104	138.56	.3091	4.463	136.82	.3038	4.074	138.47	.3039	3.251	138.36	.2987
220	5.182	140.27	.3116	4.532	138.52	.3063	4.137	140.19	.3064	3.301	140.07	.3012
230	5.260	142.00	.3141	4.602	140.23	.3089	4.200	141.91	.3090	3.352	141.80	.3038
240	5.338	143.74	.3166	4.671	141.96	.3114	4.263	143.66	.3115	3.402	143.55	.3063
250	5.416	145.50	.3191	4.740	143.70	.3139	4.325	145.42	.3140	3.452	145.31	.3088
260	5.494	147.27	.3216	4.810	145.46	.3164	4.388	147.19	.3165	3.503	147.08	.3113
270	5.572	149.05	.3241	4.880	147.23	.3189	4.450	148.98	.3189	3.553	148.88	.3138
280	......	......	......	4.949	149.02	.3214	4.512	150.78	.3214	3.603	150.68	.3162
290	......	......	......	......	......	......	......	......	......	3.653	152.50	.3187

Temp. °F.	Abs. Pressure 30 lb./in.² (Sat'n. Temp. −11.9°F.)			Abs. Pressure 35 lb./in.² (Sat'n. Temp. −4.9°F.)			Abs. Pressure 40 lb./in.² (Sat'n. Temp. 1.5°F.)			Abs. Pressure 45 lb./in.² (Sat'n. Temp. 7.2°F.)		
t	v	H	s	v	H	s	v	H	s	v	H	s
(at sat'n.)	(1.749)	(103.71)	(0.2322)	(1.513)	(104.49)	(0.2306)	(1.334)	(105.17)	(0.2293)	(1.193)	(105.81)	(0.2281)
−10	1.758	103.98	.2328	......	......	......	......	......	......	......	......	......
0	1.802	105.39	.2359	1.532	105.19	.2321	......	......	......	......	......	......
10	1.845	106.82	.2390	1.570	106.62	.2352	1.363	106.41	.2319	1.202	106.22	.2290
20	1.889	108.26	.2420	1.608	108.07	.2383	1.396	107.87	.2350	1.232	107.68	.2321
30	1.933	109.71	.2450	1.645	109.53	.2413	1.430	109.34	.2380	1.262	109.16	.2351
40	1.976	111.18	.2480	1.683	111.00	.2443	1.463	110.82	.2410	1.292	110.65	.2381
50	2.019	112.66	.2509	1.720	112.49	.2472	1.496	112.31	.2439	1.322	112.15	.2411
60	2.063	114.15	.2538	1.758	113.99	.2501	1.529	113.81	.2469	1.351	113.64	.2440
70	2.106	115.66	.2567	1.795	115.50	.2530	1.562	115.33	.2498	1.381	115.16	.2469
80	2.149	117.18	.2595	1.832	117.02	.2559	1.595	116.86	.2526	1.410	116.71	.2498
90	2.192	118.72	.2624	1.869	118.56	.2587	1.628	118.40	.2555	1.440	118.26	.2526
100	2.235	120.27	.2652	1.906	120.12	.2615	1.660	119.96	.2583	1.469	119.81	.2554
110	2.277	121.83	.2679	1.943	121.68	.2643	1.693	121.53	.2610	1.498	121.38	.2582
120	2.320	123.41	.2707	1.980	123.26	.2670	1.726	123.12	.2638	1.527	122.97	.2610
130	2.362	125.00	.2734	2.017	124.86	.2697	1.758	124.72	.2665	1.556	124.57	.2637
140	2.405	126.61	.2761	2.054	126.47	.2724	1.790	126.33	.2693	1.585	126.19	.2664
150	2.448	128.22	.2788	2.091	128.09	.2751	1.823	127.96	.2719	1.614	127.82	.2691
160	2.490	129.86	.2814	2.127	129.73	.2778	1.855	129.60	.2746	1.643	129.47	.2718
170	2.533	131.51	.2841	2.164	131.38	.2804	1.887	131.25	.2773	1.672	131.12	.2745
180	2.575	133.17	.2867	2.200	133.04	.2830	1.919	132.92	.2799	1.701	132.79	.2771
190	2.617	134.84	.2893	2.237	134.72	.2857	1.951	134.60	.2825	1.730	134.48	.2797
200	2.659	136.54	.2919	2.273	136.42	.2882	1.983	136.30	.2851	1.758	136.18	.2823
210	2.702	138.24	.2944	2.310	138.12	.2908	2.016	138.01	.2877	1.787	137.89	.2849
220	2.744	139.96	.2970	2.346	139.83	.2934	2.047	139.73	.2902	1.815	139.62	.2875
230	2.786	141.69	.2995	2.382	141.58	.2959	2.079	141.47	.2928	1.844	141.35	.2900
240	2.829	143.44	.3020	2.419	143.33	.2984	2.111	143.22	.2953	1.872	143.11	.2925
250	2.871	145.20	.3045	2.455	145.10	.3009	2.143	144.99	.2978	1.902	144.87	.2950
260	2.913	146.98	.3070	2.491	146.88	.3034	2.175	146.77	.3003	1.931	146.66	.2975
270	2.955	148.77	.3095	2.527	148.67	.3059	2.207	148.57	.3028	1.959	148.46	.3000
280	2.997	150.58	.3120	2.563	150.48	.3084	2.239	150.38	.3052	1.987	150.28	.3025
290	3.039	152.40	.3144	2.600	152.30	.3108	2.270	152.20	.3077	2.016	152.11	.3049
300	......	......	......	2.636	154.14	.3132	2.302	154.04	.3101	2.044	153.94	.3074
310	......	......	......	......	......	......	2.334	155.89	.3125	2.072	155.80	.3098

TABLE 2-23. FREON 22: PROPERTIES OF SUPERHEATED VAPOR (Continued)

Temp. °F.	Abs. Pressure 50 lb./in.² (Sat'n. Temp. 12.4°F.)			Abs. Pressure 55 lb./in.² (Sat'n. Temp. 17.2°F.)			Abs. Pressure 60 lb./in.² (Sat'n. Temp. 21.8°F.)			Abs. Pressure 65 lb./in.² (Sat'n. Temp. 26.0°F.)		
t	v	H	s.	v	H	s	v	H	s	v	H	s
(at sat'n.)	(1.080)	(106.36)	(0.2271)	(.9851)	(106.85)	(0.2261)	(.9061)	(107.32)	(0.2253)	(.8398)	(107.73)	(0.2242)
20	1.100	107.48	.2294	.9922	107.27	.2270	.9255	108.56	.2278	.8480	108.36	.2257
30	1.128	108.96	.2325	1.0176	108.76	.2300	.9491	110.07	.2308	.8700	109.88	.2288
40	1.155	110.46	.2355	1.0425	110.27	.2331						
50	1.182	111.96	.2384	1.0675	111.78	.2360	.9721	111.59	.2338	.8917	111.39	.2318
60	1.209	113.47	.2414	1.0921	113.28	.2390	.9950	113.10	.2368	.9130	112.91	.2347
70	1.236	114.99	.2443	1.1168	114.82	.2419	1.0180	114.64	.2397	.9343	114.46	.2377
80	1.262	116.54	.2472	1.1414	116.37	.2448	1.0406	116.20	.2426	.9557	116.02	.2406
90	1.289	118.10	.2500	1.1659	117.93	.2477	1.0634	117.77	.2455	.9763	117.60	.2435
100	1.316	119.66	.2528	1.1902	119.50	.2505	1.0858	119.35	.2483	.9973	119.18	.2463
110	1.342	121.23	.2556	1.2146	121.08	.2533	1.1082	120.92	.2511	1.0183	120.77	.2491
120	1.369	122.83	.2584	1.2386	122.68	.2561	1.1305	122.53	.2539	1.0390	122.38	.2519
130	1.395	124.43	.2612	1.2627	124.29	.2588	1.1529	124.14	.2567	1.0598	124.00	.2547
140	1.421	126.05	.2639	1.2870	125.91	.2616	1.1751	125.77	.2594	1.0804	125.63	.2574
150	1.448	127.68	.2666	1.3110	127.54	.2643	1.1974	127.41	.2621	1.1010	127.27	.2602
160	1.474	129.33	.2693	1.3349	129.20	.2670	1.2193	129.06	.2648	1.1217	128.93	.2629
170	1.500	130.99	.2719	1.3590	130.86	.2696	1.2415	130.73	.2675	1.1421	130.60	.2655
180	1.526	132.67	.2746	1.3827	132.54	.2723	1.2634	132.41	.2702	1.1627	132.28	.2682
190	1.552	134.35	.2772	1.4065	134.23	.2749	1.2853	134.10	.2728	1.1829	133.98	.2708
200	1.578	136.05	.2798	1.4301	135.93	.2775	1.3071	135.81	.2754	1.2031	135.68	.2734
210	1.604	137.77	.2824	1.4539	137.65	.2801	1.3290	137.53	.2780	1.2234	137.41	.2760
220	1.630	139.50	.2849	1.4774	139.38	.2827	1.3509	139.26	.2805	1.2437	139.15	.2786
230	1.655	141.24	.2875	1.5011	141.12	.2852	1.3726	141.01	.2831	1.2639	140.89	.2812
240	1.681	143.00	.2900	1.5246	142.88	.2877	1.3943	142.77	.2856	1.2841	142.66	.2837
250	1.707	144.76	.2925	1.5481	144.66	.2902	1.4159	144.55	.2882	1.3041	144.43	.2862
260	1.732	146.55	.2950	1.5716	146.44	.2927	1.4375	146.33	.2907	1.3240	146.23	.2887
270	1.758	148.35	.2975	1.5950	148.25	.2952	1.4591	148.14	.2932	1.3441	148.04	.2912
280	1.784	150.18	.3000	1.6184	150.07	.2977	1.4806	149.97	.2956	1.3641	149.87	.2937
290	1.810	152.01	.3024	1.6417	151.91	.3002	1.5021	151.81	.2981	1.3840	151.71	.2962
300	1.835	153.85	.3049	1.6651	153.75	.3026	1.5235	153.65	.3005	1.4038	153.55	.2986
310	1.861	155.70	.3073	1.6883	155.61	.3051	1.5451	155.51	.3030	1.4237	155.41	.3011
320	1.886	157.58	.3097	1.7116	157.48	.3075	1.5665	157.39	.3054	1.4436	157.29	.3035
330							1.5879	159.27	.3078	1.4634	159.18	.3059

Temp. °F.	Abs. Pressure 70 lb./in.² (Sat'n. Temp. 30.0°F.)			Abs. Pressure 75 lb./in.² (Sat'n. Temp. 33.8°F.)			Abs. Pressure 80 lb./in.² (Sat'n. Temp. 37.4°F.)			Abs. Pressure 90 lb./in.² (Sat'n. Temp. 44.2°F.)		
t	v	H	s	v	H	s	v	H	s	v	H	s
(at sat'n.)	(.7816)	(108.13)	(0.2235)	(.7301)	(108.31)	(0.2231)	(.6856)	(108.86)	(0.2224)	(.6109)	(109.48)	(0.2212)
40	.8023	109.67	.2268	.7421	109.47	.2249	.6904	109.26	.2232			
50	.8224	111.19	.2298	.7615	111.00	.2280	.7087	110.80	.2263	.6207	110.39	.2230
60	.8424	112.71	.2328	.7807	112.52	.2310	.7269	112.32	.2293	.6372	111.92	.2261
70	.8625	114.27	.2358	.7995	114.09	.2340	.7446	113.90	.2323	.6535	113.51	.2291
80	.8823	115.84	.2387	.8182	115.67	.2369	.7625	115.48	.2352	.6697	115.12	.2321
90	.9019	117.43	.2416	.8368	117.26	.2398	.7801	117.09	.2381	.6858	116.73	.2350
100	.9216	119.02	.2444	.8553	118.86	.2427	.7978	118.69	.2410	.7018	118.35	.2379
110	.9411	120.61	.2473	.8739	120.45	.2455	.8151	120.29	.2439	.7175	119.96	.2408
120	.9605	122.23	.2501	.8923	122.07	.2483	.8327	121.91	.2467	.7334	121.59	.2436
130	.9800	123.85	.2529	.9107	123.70	.2511	.8500	123.55	.2495	.7489	123.23	.2464
140	.9991	125.48	.2556	.9289	125.34	.2539	.8673	125.19	.2522	.7645	124.89	.2492
150	1.0187	127.12	.2583	.9470	126.99	.2566	.8844	126.84	.2550	.7800	126.55	.2520
160	1.0379	128.79	.2610	.9650	128.65	.2593	.9014	128.51	.2577	.7954	128.23	.2547
170	1.0569	130.47	.2637	.9831	130.33	.2620	.9184	130.19	.2604	.8108	129.92	.2574
180	1.0762	132.15	.2664	1.0012	132.02	.2647	.9356	131.89	.2630	.8262	131.62	.2601
190	1.0951	133.85	.2690	1.0188	133.72	.2673	.9524	133.59	.2657	.8411	133.34	.2627
200	1.1139	135.56	.2716	1.0366	135.44	.2699	.9689	135.31	.2683	.8561	135.06	.2654
210	1.1330	137.29	.2742	1.0544	137.17	.2725	.9857	137.04	.2709	.8711	136.80	.2680
220	1.1519	139.03	.2768	1.0722	138.91	.2751	1.0025	138.79	.2735	.8863	138.55	.2706
230	1.1707	140.78	.2794	1.0898	140.66	.2777	1.0192	140.54	.2761	.9013	140.31	.2732
240	1.1894	142.54	.2819	1.1075	142.43	.2802	1.0358	142.32	.2787	.9163	142.08	.2757
250	1.2082	144.32	.2844	1.1250	144.21	.2828	1.0524	144.10	.2812	.9312	143.87	.2783
260	1.2268	146.12	.2870	1.1426	146.01	.2853	1.0690	145.90	.2837	.9460	145.67	.2808
270	1.2456	147.93	.2895	1.1601	147.82	.2878	1.0854	147.72	.2862	.9608	147.50	.2833
280	1.2642	149.76	.2919	1.1776	149.66	.2903	1.1019	149.55	.2887	.9756	149.34	.2858
290	1.2829	151.60	.2944	1.1949	151.50	.2927	1.1183	151.40	.2912	.9902	151.19	.2883
300	1.3013	153.45	.2969	1.2122	153.35	.2952	1.1343	153.25	.2936	1.0048	153.05	.2908
310	1.3198	155.31	.2993	1.2296	155.22	.2976	1.1507	155.12	.2961	1.0194	154.92	.2932
320	1.3384	157.20	.3017	1.2481	157.10	.3001	1.1671	157.00	.2985	1.0341	156.81	.2957
330	1.3569	159.09	.3041	1.2655	158.99	.3025	1.1834	158.90	.3009	1.0487	158.71	.2981
340	1.3753	160.99	.3066	1.2829	160.90	.3049	1.1996	160.80	.3033	1.0633	160.62	.3005
350										1.0779	162.54	.3029

TABLE 2-23. FREON 22: PROPERTIES OF SUPERHEATED VAPOR (Continued)

Temp. °F. t	Abs. Pressure 100 lb./in.² (Sat'n. Temp. 50.4°F.)			Abs. Pressure 110 lb./in.² (Sat'n. Temp. 56.1°F.)			Abs. Pressure 120 lb./in.² (Sat'n. Temp. 61.5°F.)			Abs. Pressure 130 lb./in.² (Sat'n. Temp. 66.5°F.)		
	v	H	s	v	H	s	v	H	s	v	H	s
(at sat'n)	(.5505)	(110.03)	(0.2202)	(.5005)	(110.50)	(0.2192)	(.4586)	(110.91)	(0.2183)	(.4228)	(111.27)	(0.2178)
60	.5651	111.51	.2232	.5061	111.10	.2204						
70	.5802	113.11	.2262	.5202	112.70	.2235	.4698	112.28	.2210	.4272	111.84	.2187
80	.5953	114.74	.2292	.5343	114.35	.2266	.4833	113.95	.2241	.4398	113.53	.2217
90	.6101	116.37	.2322	.5480	115.99	.2296	.4961	115.60	.2271	.4520	115.20	.2248
100	.6249	118.00	.2351	.5617	117.64	.2325	.5089	117.27	.2301	.4641	116.88	.2278
110	.6394	119.62	.2380	.5753	119.27	.2354	.5215	118.91	.2330	.4761	118.54	.2307
120	.6539	121.26	.2408	.5886	120.93	.2383	.5343	120.58	.2359	.4879	120.23	.2337
130	.6682	122.92	.2437	.6020	122.59	.2411	.5466	122.26	.2388	.4996	121.92	.2365
140	.6824	124.58	.2465	.6151	124.27	.2440	.5589	123.94	.2416	.5112	123.61	.2394
150	.6965	126.25	.2492	.6281	125.94	.2467	.5711	125.63	.2444	.5227	125.31	.2422
160	.7107	127.94	.2520	.6412	127.64	.2495	.5832	127.34	.2472	.5341	127.03	.2450
170	.7246	129.64	.2547	.6541	129.35	.2522	.5952	129.06	.2499	.5454	128.76	.2478
180	.7386	131.35	.2574	.6669	131.07	.2549	.6072	130.79	.2526	.5566	130.50	.2505
190	.7523	133.07	.2601	.6796	132.80	.2576	.6190	132.53	.2553	.5677	132.25	.2532
200	.7660	134.80	.2627	.6922	134.54	.2603	.6307	134.27	.2580	.5786	134.01	.2559
210	.7796	136.55	.2654	.7048	136.29	.2629	.6424	136.03	.2607	.5895	135.77	.2586
220	.7933	138.30	.2680	.7174	138.05	.2655	.6541	137.80	.2633	.6005	137.55	.2612
230	.8071	140.07	.2706	.7299	139.82	.2681	.6657	139.58	.2659	.6114	139.33	.2638
240	.8206	141.85	.2731	.7424	141.61	.2707	.6772	141.37	.2685	.6221	141.13	.2664
250	.8343	143.64	.2757	.7550	143.40	.2733	.6888	143.17	.2711	.6330	142.94	.2690
260	.8477	145.45	.2782	.7673	145.22	.2758	.7003	144.99	.2736	.6437	144.76	.2716
270	.8612	147.28	.2807	.7796	147.06	.2784	.7118	146.84	.2762	.6543	146.61	.2741
280	.8746	149.13	.2832	.7919	148.91	.2809	.7231	148.69	.2787	.6649	148.48	.2766
290	.8879	150.98	.2857	.8041	150.77	.2834	.7344	150.59	.2812	.6754	150.34	.2791
300	.9011	152.84	.2882	.8162	152.64	.2858	.7456	152.43	.2837	.6859	152.22	.2816
310	.9144	154.72	.2906	.8284	154.52	.2883	.7569	154.32	.2861	.6965	154.12	.2841
320	.9277	156.62	.2931	.8406	156.42	.2907	.7681	156.22	.2886	.7069	156.03	.2866
330	.9410	158.52	.2955	.8529	158.33	.2932	.7793	158.14	.2910	.7174	157.94	.2890
340	.9541	160.43	.2979	.8650	160.25	.2956	.7906	160.06	.2934	.7277	159.87	.2914
350	.9674	162.36	.3003	.8771	162.18	.2980	.8018	162.00	.2959	.7381	161.81	.2939
360	.9806	164.31	.3027	.8891	164.13	.3004	.8129	163.95	.2983	.7485	163.77	.2963
370							.8240	165.92	.3007	.7588	165.74	.2987

Temp. °F. t	Abs. Pressure 140 lb./in.² (Sat'n. Temp. 71.3°F.) v (.3919)	H (111.60)	s (0.2167)	Abs. Pressure 150 lb./in.² (Sat'n. Temp. 75.8°F.) v (.3648)	H (111.89)	s (0.2160)	Abs. Pressure 160 lb./in.² (Sat'n. Temp. 80.1°F.) v (.3411)	H (112.06)	s (0.2152)	Abs. Pressure 180 lb./in.² (Sat'n. Temp. 88.2°F.) v (.3012)	H (112.60)	s (0.2138)
(at sat'n.) 80	.4022	113.08	.2195	.3695	112.61	.2173						
90	.4141	114.79	.2226	.3810	114.35	.2205	.3518	113.90	.2184	.3031	112.93	.2145
100	.4257	116.48	.2256	.3922	116.07	.2235	.3627	115.64	.2215	.3135	114.73	.2177
110	.4369	118.16	.2286	.4030	117.77	.2265	.3733	117.36	.2246	.3236	116.51	.2208
120	.4483	119.86	.2315	.4139	119.49	.2296	.3838	119.10	.2276	.3331	118.29	.2239
130	.4593	121.57	.2344	.4245	121.21	.2325	.3939	120.84	.2306	.3427	120.07	.2269
140	.4704	123.27	.2373	.4349	122.93	.2354	.4039	122.58	.2335	.3520	121.85	.2299
150	.4812	124.99	.2402	.4453	124.66	.2382	.4138	124.33	.2364	.3611	123.63	.2329
160	.4921	126.72	.2430	.4556	126.40	.2411	.4236	126.08	.2392	.3701	125.41	.2358
170	.5027	128.46	.2458	.4657	128.15	.2439	.4332	127.84	.2420	.3791	127.19	.2386
180	.5132	130.20	.2485	.4757	129.91	.2466	.4429	129.60	.2448	.3879	128.98	.2415
190	.5236	131.96	.2512	.4856	131.67	.2494	.4522	131.38	.2476	.3966	130.78	.2443
200	.5340	133.73	.2539	.4953	133.45	.2521	.4615	133.17	.2503	.4051	132.59	.2470
210	.5444	135.50	.2566	.5051	135.24	.2548	.4709	134.96	.2530	.4137	134.41	.2498
220	.5546	137.29	.2593	.5149	137.03	.2574	.4801	136.76	.2557	.4221	136.23	.2525
230	.5649	139.08	.2619	.5245	138.83	.2601	.4892	138.57	.2583	.4303	138.06	.2551
240	.5749	140.89	.2645	.5341	140.64	.2624	.4933	140.40	.2610	.4386	139.90	.2578
250	.5850	142.70	.2671	.5436	142.47	.2653	.5073	142.23	.2636	.4468	141.75	.2604
260	.5951	144.54	.2697	.5530	144.31	.2679	.5162	144.08	.2662	.4550	143.61	.2630
270	.6051	146.39	.2722	.5625	146.17	.2704	.5251	145.94	.2687	.4630	145.49	.2656
280	.6150	148.26	.2747	.5718	148.04	.2730	.5340	147.82	.2713	.4711	147.38	.2682
290	.6248	150.13	.2773	.5811	149.92	.2755	.5428	149.70	.2738	.4791	149.27	.2707
300	.6347	152.02	.2798	.5903	151.81	.2780	.5516	151.60	.2763	.4870	151.17	.2732
310	.6446	153.91	.2822	.5997	153.71	.2805	.5604	153.51	.2788	.4951	153.09	.2757
320	.6544	155.83	.2847	.6090	155.63	.2829	.5692	155.43	.2813	.5029	155.03	.2782
330	.6641	157.75	.2871	.6181	157.56	.2854	.5777	157.36	.2838	.5106	156.97	.2807
340	.6739	159.68	.2896	.6278	159.49	.2878	.5864	159.31	.2862	.5184	158.92	.2832
350	.6835	161.63	.2920	.6364	161.45	.2903	.5950	161.26	.2886	.5263	160.89	.2856
360	.6933	163.59	.2944	.6454	163.41	.2927	.6036	163.23	.2911	.5340	162.87	.2881
370	.7029	165.57	.2968	.6545	165.39	.2951	.6121	165.21	.2935	.5417	164.86	.2905
380	.7125	167.56	.2992	.6635	167.39	.2975	.6207	167.22	.2959	.5493	166.87	.2929
390							.6292	169.22	.2982	.5570	168.87	.2953

TABLE 2-23.   FREON 22: PROPERTIES OF SUPERHEATED VAPOR (Concluded)

Temp. °F. t	Abs. Pressure 200 lb./in.² (Sat'n. Temp. 95.6°F.)			Abs. Pressure 220 lb./in.² (Sat'n. Temp. 102.5°F.)			Abs. Pressure 240 lb./in.² (Sat'n. Temp. 108.9°F.)			Abs. Pressure 260 lb./in.² (Sat'n. Temp. 115.0°F.)		
	v	H	s	v	H	s	v	H	s	v	H	s
(at sat'n.)	(.2690)	(112.93)	(0.2124)	(.2425)	(113.17)	(0.2112)	(.2202)	(113.28)	(0.2099)	(.2013)	(113.42)	(0.2084)
100	.2734	113.75	.2139									
110	.2829	115.61	.2172	.2498	114.62	.2138						
120	.2922	117.42	.2204	.2586	116.49	.2171	.2207	113.51	.2103	.2066	114.45	.2106
130	.3013	119.25	.2236	.2674	118.37	.2203	.2305	115.48	.2137	.2147	116.47	.2141
140	.3102	121.06	.2266	.2759	120.23	.2235	.2388	117.43	.2171	.2227	118.45	.2174
150	.3189	122.89	.2296	.2843	122.11	.2265	.2471	119.36	.2204	.2303	120.44	.2207
160	.3274	124.71	.2326	.2923	123.96	.2295	.2551	121.29	.2236	.2379	122.36	.2238
170	.3358	126.52	.2355	.3004	125.81	.2325	.2629	123.18	.2266	.2454	124.29	.2270
180	.3439	128.34	.2384	.3079	127.66	.2354	.2705	125.06	.2297	.2526	126.22	.2300
190	.3521	130.17	.2412	.3155	129.52	.2383	.2779	126.95	.2327	.2596	128.16	.2330
200	.3599	132.00	.2440	.3229	131.39	.2411	.2851	128.85	.2356	.2663	130.10	.2359
210	.3679	133.84	.2467	.3304	133.25	.2439	.2922	130.76	.2385	.2728	132.01	.2388
220	.3756	135.68	.2495	.3377	135.12	.2467	.2992	132.64	.2413	.2793	133.92	.2416
230	.3834	137.53	.2522	.3450	136.99	.2494	.3061	134.53	.2441	.2857	135.84	.2444
240	.3909	139.39	.2548	.3519	138.87	.2521	.3128	136.42	.2469	.2921	137.76	.2472
250	.3985	141.26	.2575	.3590	140.76	.2548	.3196	138.32	.2496	.2984	139.70	.2499
260	.4060	143.13	.2601	.3660	142.64	.2575	.3262	140.24	.2523	.3045	141.62	.2526
270	.4134	145.02	.2627	.3729	144.55	.2601	.3326	142.14	.2550	.3107	143.56	.2553
280	.4209	146.92	.2653	.3798	146.46	.2627	.3392	144.06	.2576	.3168	145.51	.2580
290	.4281	148.83	.2679	.3866	148.38	.2653	.3456	145.99	.2603	.3229	147.46	.2606
300	.4351	150.75	.2704	.3933	150.31	.2678	.3520	147.93	.2629	.3287	149.43	.2632
310	.4428	152.68	.2729	.4001	152.25	.2704	.3582	149.87	.2654	.3346	151.39	.2658
320	.4499	154.62	.2754	.4067	154.21	.2729	.3645	151.82	.2680	.3404	153.37	.2683
330	.4572	156.57	.2779	.4133	156.17	.2754	.3707	153.79	.2705	.3462	155.36	.2709
340	.4642	158.54	.2804	.4199	158.15	.2779	.3769	155.77	.2731	.3520	157.36	.2734
350	.4713	160.51	.2829	.4264	160.13	.2804	.3830	157.75	.2755	.3577	159.36	.2759
360	.4784	162.50	.2853	.4330	162.13	.2828	.3892	159.75	.2780	.3633	161.38	.2783
370	.4855	164.50	.2877	.4394	164.14	.2852	.3952	161.75	.2805	.3690	163.41	.2808
380	.4924	166.51	.2902	.4459	166.16	.2877	.4012	163.77	.2829	.3746	165.46	.2832
390	.4994	168.53	.2926	.4524	168.19	.2901	.4072	165.81	.2854	.3802	167.51	.2857
400	.5064	170.57	.2949	.4588	170.24	.2925	.4132	167.85	.2878	.3858	169.57	.2881
410				.4652	172.31	.2949	.4192	169.90	.2902	.3913	171.66	.2905
420							.4251	171.98	.2926	.3968	173.77	.2929

Table 2-24 appears on pages 118–121.

TABLE 2-24. FREON 113: PROPERTIES OF SATURATED VAPOR*

Temp. °F t	Abs. Pressure lb./in.² p	Volume Liquid ft.³/lb. v_f	Volume Vapor ft.³/lb. v_g	Density Liquid lb./ft.³ 1/v_f	Density Vapor lb./ft.³ 1/v_g	Heat Content from −40° Liquid Btu./lb. h_f	Heat Content from −40° Latent Btu./lb. h	Heat Content from −40° Vapor Btu./lb. h_g	Entropy from −40° Liquid Btu./lb.°F. s_f	Entropy from −40° Vapor Btu./lb.°F. s_g	Temp. °F t
−30	0.2987	0.00947	82.26	105.64	0.01216	1.97	72.68	74.65	0.0047	0.1738	−30
−28	.3214	.00948	76.81	105.50	.01302	2.36	72.57	74.93	.0056	.1737	−28
−26	.3458	.00949	71.71	105.37	.01395	2.76	72.45	75.21	.0065	.1736	−26
−24	.3718	.00950	66.99	105.23	.01493	3.16	72.33	75.49	.0074	.1735	−24
−22	.3995	.00952	62.63	105.09	.01597	3.56	72.21	75.77	.0083	.1733	−22
−20	0.4288	0.00953	58.61	104.96	0.01706	3.96	72.09	76.05	0.0092	0.1732	−20
−18	.4600	.00954	54.88	104.82	.01822	4.36	71.98	76.34	.0101	.1731	−18
−16	.4931	.00955	51.42	104.68	.01945	4.76	71.86	76.62	.0110	.1730	−16
−14	.5280	.00957	48.23	104.54	.02074	5.16	71.74	76.90	.0119	.1729	−14
−12	.5652	.00958	45.25	104.40	.02210	5.56	71.62	77.18	.0128	.1729	−12
−10	0.6046	0.00959	42.48	104.26	0.02354	5.96	71.51	77.47	0.0137	0.1728	−10
−8	.6462	.00960	39.92	104.12	.02505	6.36	71.39	77.75	.0146	.1727	−8
−6	.6902	.00962	37.54	103.98	.02664	6.76	71.27	78.03	.0155	.1726	−6
−4	.7369	.00963	35.31	103.84	.02832	7.17	71.15	78.32	.0164	.1726	−4
−2	.7860	.00964	33.24	103.70	.03009	7.57	71.03	78.60	.0173	.1725	−2
0	0.8377	0.00966	31.31	103.56	0.03194	7.98	70.92	78.89	0.0182	0.1725	0
2	.8924	.00967	29.52	103.41	.03388	8.38	70.80	79.18	.0190	.1724	2
4	.9503	.00968	27.84	103.27	.03592	8.78	70.68	79.46	.0199	.1724	4
5†	0.9802	.00969	27.04	103.20	.03698	8.98	70.62	79.60	.0203	.1723	5†
6	1.011	.00970	26.27	103.13	.03806	9.19	70.56	79.75	.0208	.1723	6
8	1.075	.00971	24.81	102.98	.04031	9.59	70.44	80.03	.0216	.1723	8
10	1.142	0.00972	23.45	102.84	0.04265	10.00	70.32	80.32	0.0225	0.1723	10
12	1.213	.00974	22.17	102.69	.04511	10.41	70.20	80.61	.0234	.1722	12
14	1.288	.00975	20.97	102.55	.04769	10.81	70.08	80.89	.0242	.1722	14
16	1.366	.00977	19.84	102.40	.05040	11.22	69.96	81.18	.0251	.1722	16
18	1.448	.00978	18.79	102.25	.05322	11.62	69.84	81.46	.0259	.1722	18

20	0.1722	0.0268	81.75	69.72	12.03	0.05616	102.10	17.81	0.00979	1.534	20
22	.1721	.0276	82.04	69.60	12.44	.05922	101.96	16.89	.00981	1.624	22
24	.1721	.0285	82.33	69.48	12.85	.06243	101.81	16.02	.00982	1.719	24
26	.1722	.0293	82.62	69.36	13.26	.06579	101.66	15.20	.00984	1.818	26
28	.1722	.0302	82.91	69.24	13.67	.06929	101.51	14.43	.00985	1.922	28
30	0.1722	0.0310	83.20	69.12	14.08	0.07294	101.36	13.71	0.00987	2.031	30
32	.1722	.0318	83.49	69.00	14.49	.07675	101.21	13.03	.00988	2.145	32
34	.1722	.0327	83.78	68.87	14.91	.08071	101.06	12.39	.00990	2.264	34
36	.1722	.0335	84.07	68.75	15.32	.08483	100.91	11.79	.00991	2.388	36
38	.1722	.0343	84.36	68.62	15.74	.08913	100.76	11.22	.00993	2.519	38
40	0.1723	0.0352	84.65	68.50	16.16	0.09361	100.60	10.68	0.00994	2.655	40
42	.1723	.0360	84.94	68.37	16.57	.09826	100.45	10.18	.00996	2.797	42
44	.1723	.0368	85.24	68.25	16.99	.1031	100.30	9.703	.00997	2.944	44
46	.1724	.0377	85.53	68.12	17.41	.1081	100.14	9.253	.00999	3.098	46
48	.1724	.0385	85.82	68.00	17.82	.1133	99.99	8.830	.01000	3.258	48
50	0.1725	0.0393	86.11	67.87	18.24	0.1187	99.83	8.426	0.01002	3.427	50
52	.1726	.0401	86.40	67.74	18.66	.1243	99.68	8.044	.01003	3.602	52
54	.1726	.0410	86.69	67.61	19.08	.1302	99.52	7.682	.01005	3.784	54
56	.1727	.0418	86.98	67.48	19.50	.1362	99.37	7.342	.01006	3.973	56
58	.1727	.0426	87.28	67.35	19.93	.1425	99.21	7.018	.01008	4.170	58
60	0.1728	0.0434	87.57	67.22	20.35	0.1490	99.05	6.713	0.01010	4.374	60
62	.1729	.0442	87.86	67.09	20.77	.1557	98.89	6.424	.01011	4.586	62
64	.1729	.0450	88.15	66.96	21.19	.1626	98.73	6.149	.01013	4.807	64
66	.1730	.0459	88.45	66.83	21.62	.1698	98.58	5.889	.01015	5.036	66
68	.1731	.0467	88.74	66.69	22.05	.1773	98.42	5.640	.01016	5.275	68
70	0.1731	0.0475	89.04	66.56	22.48	0.1851	98.26	5.404	0.01018	5.523	70
72	.1732	.0483	89.33	66.43	22.90	.1931	98.10	5.180	.01019	5.780	72
74	.1733	.0491	89.62	66.29	23.33	.2012	97.93	4.971	.01021	6.042	74
76	.1734	.0499	89.92	66.16	23.76	.2097	97.77	4.769	.01023	6.320	76
78	.1735	.0507	90.21	66.02	24.19	.2186	97.61	4.574	.01025	6.607	78

* Courtesy Kinetic Chemicals, Inc., Wilmington, Del.

TABLE 2-24. FREON 113: PROPERTIES OF SATURATED VAPOR (Concluded)

Temp. °F. t	Abs. Pressure lb./in.² p	Volume Liquid ft.³/lb. v_f	Volume Vapor ft.³/lb. v_g	Density Liquid lb./ft.³ 1/v_f	Density Vapor lb./ft.³ 1/v_g	Heat Content from —40° Liquid Btu./lb. h_f	Heat Content from —40° Latent Btu./lb. h	Heat Content from —40° Vapor Btu./lb. h_g	Entropy from —40° Liquid Btu./lb.°F s_f	Entropy from —40° Vapor Btu./lb.°F s_g	Temp. °F. t
80	6.902	0.01026	4.392	97.45	0.2277	24.63	65.88	90.51	0.0515	0.1736	80
82	7.208	.01028	4.218	97.28	.2371	25.06	65.74	90.80	.0523	.1737	82
84	7.527	.01030	4.051	97.12	.2468	25.49	65.60	91.09	.0531	.1738	84
86†	7.856	.01031	3.893	96.96	.2569	25.93	65.46	91.39	.0539	.1739	86†
88	8.194	.01033	3.742	96.79	.2672	26.36	65.32	91.68	.0547	.1740	88
90	8.545	0.01035	3.600	96.63	0.2778	26.80	65.18	91.98	0.0555	0.1741	90
92	8.908	.01037	3.463	96.46	.2888	27.24	65.04	92.28	.0563	.1742	92
94	9.281	.01039	3.333	96.30	.3001	27.67	64.90	92.57	.0571	.1743	94
96	9.668	.01040	3.208	96.13	.3117	28.11	64.75	92.86	.0578	.1744	96
98	10.07	.01042	3.089	95.96	.3237	28.55	64.60	93.15	.0586	.1745	98
100	10.48	0.01044	2.976	95.79	0.3360	28.99	64.46	93.45	0.0594	0.1746	100
102	10.91	.01046	2.867	95.63	.3488	29.44	64.31	93.75	.0602	.1747	102
104	11.35	.01048	2.762	95.46	.3620	29.89	64.16	94.05	.0610	.1748	104
106	11.81	.01050	2.662	95.29	.3756	30.33	64.01	94.34	.0618	.1750	106
108	12.28	.01051	2.567	95.12	.3896	30.78	63.86	94.64	.0626	.1751	108
110	12.76	0.01053	2.477	94.95	0.4038	31.22	63.71	94.93	0.0634	0.1752	110
112	13.25	.01055	2.391	94.78	.4182	31.67	63.56	95.23	.0641	.1753	112
114	13.76	.01057	2.308	94.61	.4333	32.12	63.40	95.52	.0649	.1755	114
116	14.29	.01059	2.228	94.43	.4489	32.57	63.25	95.82	.0657	.1756	116
118	14.84	.01061	2.151	94.26	.4649	33.03	63.09	96.12	.0665	.1757	118
120	15.40	0.01063	2.078	94.09	0.4813	33.48	62.93	96.41	0.0673	0.1758	120
122	15.97	.01065	2.008	93.92	.4981	33.93	62.78	96.71	.0680	.1760	122
124	16.56	.01067	1.941	93.74	.5153	34.38	62.62	97.00	.0688	.1761	124
126	17.17	.01069	1.876	93.57	.5330	34.83	62.46	97.29	.0696	.1763	126
128	17.80	.01071	1.814	93.39	.5514	35.29	62.30	97.59	.0704	.1764	128

Temp.											Temp.
130	18.45	0.01073	1.754	93.22	0.5702	35.75	62.14	97.89	0.0712	0.1765	130
132	19.11	.01075	1.697	93.04	.5894	36.21	61.97	98.18	.0719	.1767	132
134	19.79	.01077	1.642	92.86	.6091	36.67	61.80	98.47	.0727	.1768	134
136	20.48	.01079	1.590	92.69	.6290	37.13	61.64	98.77	.0735	.1770	136
138	21.19	.01081	1.540	92.51	.6494	37.59	61.48	99.06	.0742	.1771	138
140	21.93	0.01083	1.491	92.33	0.6707	38.05	61.31	99.36	0.0750	0.1773	140
142	22.69	.01085	1.444	92.15	.6926	38.52	61.13	99.65	.0758	.1774	142
144	23.47	.01087	1.399	91.98	.7150	38.98	60.96	99.94	.0765	.1775	144
146	24.27	.01089	1.355	91.80	.7379	39.45	60.79	100.24	.0773	.1777	146
148	25.09	.01092	1.313	91.62	.7615	39.92	60.61	100.53	.0781	.1778	148
150	25.93	0.01094	1.273	91.44	0.7856	40.38	60.44	100.82	0.0789	0.1780	150
152	26.79	.01096	1.234	91.25	.8102	40.85	60.27	101.11	.0796	.1782	152
154	27.67	.01098	1.197	91.07	.8353	41.32	60.09	101.41	.0804	.1783	154
156	28.56	.01100	1.162	90.89	.8608	41.79	59.91	101.70	.0812	.1785	156
158	29.48	.01102	1.128	90.71	.8869	42.26	59.73	101.99	.0819	.1786	158
160	30.44	0.01105	1.094	90.53	0.9141	42.74	59.55	102.29	0.0827	0.1788	160
170	35.53	.01116	0.9442	89.60	1.059	45.12	58.62	103.74	.0865	.1796	170
180	41.22	.01128	.8193	88.67	1.221	47.53	57.66	105.19	.0903	.1804	180
190	47.60	.01140	.7134	87.72	1.402	49.97	56.66	106.63	.0940	.1813	190
200	54.66	.01153	.6241	86.76	1.602	52.45	55.62	108.07	.0978	.1821	200
210	62.50	.01166	.5477	85.79	1.826	54.96	54.54	109.50	.1015	.1830	210
220	71.07	0.01179	0.4827	84.80	2.072	57.49	53.43	110.92	0.1052	0.1839	220

† Standard ton temperatures.

TABLE 2-25. FREON 113: PROPERTIES OF SUPERHEATED VAPOR

Temp. °F	Abs. Pressure 0.3 lb./in.² (Sat'n. Temp. -29.9° F.)			Abs. Pressure 0.4 lb./in.² (Sat'n. Temp. -22.0° F.)			Abs. Pressure 0.5 lb./in.² (Sat'n. Temp. -15.6° F.)			Abs. Pressure 0.6 lb./in.² (Sat'n. Temp. -10.2° F.)		
t	V	H	s	V	H	s	V	H	s	V	H	s
(At sat'n.)	(81.95)	(74.66)	(0.1738)	(62.55)	(75.77)	(0.1733)	(50.79)	(76.68)	(0.1730)	(42.81)	(77.44)	(0.1728)
-20	83.83	76.06	0.1770	62.82	76.05	0.1740	....	....	....	....	....	....
-10	85.74	77.48	.1802	64.25	77.47	.1772	51.43	77.47	0.1748	42.83	77.47	0.1729
0	87.65	78.91	0.1834	65.68	78.90	0.1803	52.58	78.90	0.1779	43.79	78.90	0.1760
10	89.55	80.35	.1865	67.11	80.34	.1834	53.72	80.34	.1810	44.74	80.34	.1791
20	91.46	81.80	.1895	68.63	81.80	.1865	54.87	81.79	.1841	45.70	81.79	.1822
30	93.37	83.26	.1925	70.06	83.26	.1895	56.01	83.26	.1871	46.65	83.25	.1852
40	95.27	84.74	.1955	71.49	84.74	.1925	57.16	84.73	.1901	47.61	84.73	.1882
50	97.18	86.23	0.1985	72.92	86.22	0.1954	58.31	86.22	0.1931	48.56	86.22	0.1911
60	99.09	87.73	.2014	74.35	87.72	.1983	59.47	87.72	.1960	49.52	87.72	.1940
70	101.0	89.24	.2043	75.79	89.23	.2012	60.63	89.23	.1989	50.47	89.23	.1969
80	102.9	90.76	.2071	77.22	90.76	.2041	61.78	90.75	.2017	51.43	90.75	.1998
90	104.8	92.29	.2099	78.65	92.29	.2069	62.93	92.28	.2045	52.38	92.28	.2026
100	106.7	93.83	0.2127	80.08	93.83	0.2097	64.07	93.83	0.2073	53.34	93.82	0.2054
110	108.6	95.40	.2155	81.51	95.39	.2124	65.21	95.39	.2101	54.31	95.39	.2081
120	110.5	96.97	.2182	82.94	96.96	.2152	66.36	96.96	.2128	55.27	96.96	.2109
130	112.4	98.55	.2209	84.37	98.54	.2179	67.51	98.54	.2155	56.22	98.54	.2136
140	114.3	100.14	.2236	85.80	100.13	.2206	68.65	100.13	.2182	57.18	100.13	.2162
150	116.3	101.74	0.2262	87.23	101.74	0.2232	69.80	101.73	0.2208	58.13	101.73	0.2189
160	118.2	103.36	.2289	88.66	103.35	.2258	70.94	103.35	.2234	59.09	103.34	.2215
170	120.1	104.98	.2315	90.10	104.98	.2284	72.09	104.98	.2260	60.04	104.97	.2241
180	122.0	106.62	.2341	91.53	106.62	.2310	73.23	106.61	.2286	60.99	106.61	.2267
190	124.0	108.27	.2366	92.96	108.27	.2336	74.38	108.26	.2312	61.95	108.26	.2293
200	125.9	109.93	0.2392	94.39	109.93	0.2361	75.52	109.92	0.2337	62.90	109.92	0.2318
210	127.8	111.61	.2417	95.82	111.61	.2386	76.67	111.60	.2363	63.85	111.60	.2343
220	129.7	113.30	.2442	97.25	113.30	.2411	77.81	113.29	.2388	64.81	113.29	.2368
230	131.6	115.00	.2467	98.68	114.99	.2436	78.96	114.99	.2412	65.76	114.99	.2393
240	133.6	116.71	.2491	100.1	116.70	.2461	80.10	116.70	.2437	66.71	116.70	.2418
250	135.5	118.42	0.2516	101.5	118.42	0.2485	81.25	118.42	0.2461	67.67	118.41	0.2442
260	137.4	120.15	.2540	103.0	120.15	.2509	82.39	120.15	.2486	68.62	120.14	.2466
270	139.3	121.89	.2564	104.4	121.88	.2533	83.54	121.88	.2510	69.57	121.87	.2490
280	141.2	123.64	.2588	105.9	123.63	.2557	84.68	123.63	.2533	70.53	123.62	.2514
290	....	....	....	....	....	....	85.83	125.40	0.2557	71.48	125.39	0.2538

Temp. ° F.	Abs. Pressure 0.7 lb./in.² (Sat'n. Temp. −5.6° F.)			Abs. Pressure 0.8 lb./in.² (Sat'n. Temp. −1.5° F.)			Abs. Pressure 0.9 lb./in.² (Sat'n. Temp. +2.3° F.)			Abs. Pressure 1.0 lb./in.² (Sat'n. Temp. 5.6° F.)		
(At sat'n.)	(37.05)	(78.10)	(0.1726)	(32.71)	(78.68)	(0.1725)	(29.30)	(79.22)	(0.1724)	(26.54)	(79.69)	(0.1723)
0	37.49	78.90	0.1743	32.81	78.89	0.1729	....	....	....	....	....	(0.1723)
10	38.32	80.34	.1774	33.53	80.33	.1760	29.79	80.33	0.1748	26.79	80.32	0.1737
20	39.15	81.79	.1805	34.25	81.78	.1791	30.43	81.78	.1779	27.38	81.78	.1768
30	39.98	83.25	.1835	34.97	83.25	.1821	31.07	83.24	.1809	27.96	83.24	.1798
40	40.80	84.72	.1865	35.69	84.72	.1851	31.71	84.72	.1839	28.53	84.71	.1828
50	41.62	86.21	0.1895	36.41	86.21	0.1881	32.35	86.20	0.1868	29.10	86.20	0.1857
60	42.43	87.71	.1924	37.13	87.71	.1910	32.99	87.70	.1897	29.67	87.70	.1886
70	43.25	89.22	.1953	37.85	89.22	.1939	33.63	89.21	.1926	30.25	89.21	.1915
80	44.07	90.74	.1981	38.57	90.74	.1967	34.27	90.73	.1955	30.82	90.73	.1943
90	44.89	92.28	.2009	39.29	92.27	.1995	34.91	92.27	.1983	31.39	92.27	.1972
100	45.71	93.82	0.2037	40.01	93.82	0.2023	35.55	93.81	0.2011	31.97	93.81	0.2000
110	46.53	95.38	.2065	40.72	95.38	.2051	36.19	95.37	.2038	32.56	95.37	.2027
120	47.35	96.95	.2092	41.44	96.95	.2078	36.83	96.94	.2066	33.14	96.94	.2054
130	48.18	98.53	.2119	42.16	98.53	.2105	37.47	98.52	.2093	33.71	98.52	.2081
140	49.00	100.12	.2146	42.88	100.12	.2132	38.11	100.12	.2119	34.28	100.11	.2108
150	49.83	101.73	0.2172	43.60	101.72	0.2158	38.75	101.72	0.2146	34.85	101.72	0.2135
160	50.65	103.34	.2199	44.32	103.34	.2185	39.39	103.33	.2172	35.42	103.33	.2161
170	51.47	104.97	.2225	45.04	104.96	.2211	40.03	104.96	.2198	35.99	104.96	.2187
180	52.29	106.61	.2251	45.75	106.60	.2236	40.67	106.60	.2224	36.57	106.60	.2213
190	53.10	108.26	.2276	46.47	108.25	.2262	41.31	108.25	.2249	37.15	108.25	.2238
200	53.92	109.92	0.2302	47.18	109.91	0.2288	41.94	109.91	0.2275	37.73	109.91	0.2264
210	54.74	111.60	.2327	47.90	111.59	.2313	42.57	111.59	.2300	38.30	111.59	.2289
220	55.56	113.29	.2352	48.61	113.28	.2338	43.21	113.28	.2325	38.88	113.28	.2314
230	56.37	114.98	.2377	49.33	114.98	.2363	43.84	114.98	.2350	39.46	114.97	.2339
240	57.19	116.69	.2401	50.04	116.69	.2387	44.48	116.69	.2375	40.03	116.68	.2363
250	58.01	118.41	0.2426	50.76	118.41	0.2412	45.12	118.40	0.2399	40.60	118.40	0.2388
260	58.83	120.14	.2450	51.47	120.13	.2436	45.75	120.13	.2423	41.18	120.13	.2412
270	59.64	121.87	.2474	52.19	121.86	.2460	46.39	121.86	.2447	41.75	121.86	.2436
280	60.46	123.62	.2498	52.90	123.61	.2484	47.02	123.61	.2471	42.32	123.62	.2460
290	61.28	125.39	.2522	53.62	125.38	.2507	47.66	125.38	.2495	42.89	125.38	.2484
300	62.10	127.18	0.2545	54.34	127.17	0.2531	48.30	127.17	0.2518	43.46	127.16	0.2507
310	.....	.....	.....	.....	.....	.....	48.93	128.97	0.2542	44.04	128.96	0.2531

TABLE 2-25. FREON 113: PROPERTIES OF SUPERHEATED VAPOR (Continued)

Temp. °F. (t)	Abs. Pressure 1.1 lb./in.² (Sat'n. Temp. 8.7° F.)			Abs. Pressure 1.2 lb./in.² (Sat'n. Temp. 11.6° F.)			Abs. Pressure 1.3 lb./in.² (Sat'n. Temp. 14.3° F.)			Abs. Pressure 1.4 lb./in.² (Sat'n. Temp. 16.8° F.)		
	V	H	S	V	H	S	V	H	S	V	H	S
(At sat'n.)	(24.29)	(80.13)	(0.1723)	(22.40)	(80.55)	(0.1722)	(20.79)	(80.93)	(0.1722)	(19.40)	(81.30)	(0.1722)
10	24.35	80.32	0.1726									
20	24.87	81.77	.1757	22.80	81.77	0.1748	21.03	81.76	0.1740	19.52	81.76	0.1731
30	25.39	83.24	.1787	23.28	83.23	.1778	21.47	83.23	.1770	19.93	83.23	.1762
40	25.91	84.71	.1817	23.75	84.71	.1808	21.91	84.70	.1800	20.35	84.70	.1792
50	26.43	86.20	.1847	24.23	86.19	.1837	22.36	86.19	.1829	20.76	86.19	.1821
60	26.96	87.70	.1876	24.71	87.69	.1866	22.80	87.69	.1858	21.17	87.69	.1850
70	27.49	89.21	.1905	25.19	89.20	.1895	23.24	89.20	.1887	21.58	89.20	.1879
80	28.01	90.73	.1933	25.67	90.72	.1924	23.68	90.72	.1915	21.99	90.72	.1907
90	28.53	92.26	.1961	26.15	92.26	.1952	24.13	92.26	.1944	22.40	92.25	.1935
100	29.05	93.81	.1989	26.63	93.80	.1980	24.58	93.80	.1971	22.81	93.80	.1963
110	29.57	95.37	.2017	27.11	95.36	.2007	25.02	95.36	.1999	23.22	95.36	.1991
120	30.09	96.94	.2044	27.59	96.93	.2035	25.46	96.93	.2026	23.63	96.93	.2018
130	30.62	98.52	.2071	28.07	98.51	.2062	25.90	98.51	.2053	24.04	98.51	.2045
140	31.15	100.11	.2098	28.55	100.10	.2089	26.34	100.10	.2080	24.45	100.10	.2072
150	31.68	101.71	.2124	29.03	101.71	.2115	26.78	101.70	.2106	24.86	101.70	.2099
160	32.20	103.33	.2151	29.51	103.32	.2141	27.23	103.32	.2133	25.27	103.32	.2125
170	32.72	104.95	.2177	29.99	104.95	.2167	27.68	104.95	.2159	25.68	104.94	.2151
180	33.24	106.59	.2202	30.47	106.59	.2193	28.12	106.59	.2185	26.10	106.58	.2177
190	33.76	108.24	.2228	30.95	108.24	.2219	28.56	108.24	.2211	26.52	108.23	.2202
200	34.28	109.90	.2253	31.43	109.90	.2244	29.00	109.90	.2236	26.93	109.89	.2228
210	34.80	111.58	.2279	31.91	111.58	.2270	29.44	111.58	.2261	27.34	111.57	.2253
220	35.32	113.27	.2304	32.39	113.27	.2295	29.88	113.27	.2286	27.75	113.26	.2278
230	35.85	114.97	.2329	32.87	114.97	.2319	30.32	114.96	.2311	28.16	114.96	.2303
240	36.37	116.68	.2353	33.35	116.68	.2344	30.76	116.67	.2335	28.57	116.67	.2328
250	36.90	118.40	.2378	33.83	118.39	.2368	31.20	118.39	.2360	28.98	118.39	.2352
260	37.43	120.13	.2402	34.31	120.12	.2393	31.64	120.12	.2384	29.39	120.12	.2376
270	37.95	121.86	.2426	34.79	121.86	.2417	32.08	121.86	.2408	29.80	121.85	.2400
280	38.47	123.61	.2450	35.26	123.61	.2441	32.53	123.61	.2432	30.21	123.60	.2424
290	38.99	125.38	.2474	35.74	125.38	.2464	32.98	125.37	.2456	30.62	125.37	.2448
300	39.51	127.16	.2497	36.22	127.16	.2488	33.43	127.16	.2479	31.03	127.16	.2471
310	40.03	128.96	.2521	36.69	128.96	.2511	33.88	128.96	.2503	31.44	128.95	.2495
320				37.17	130.76	.2535	34.32	130.76	.2526	31.85	130.75	0.2518

Temp. °F.	Abs. Pressure 1.6 lb./in.² (Sat'n. Temp. 21.5° F.)			Abs. Pressure 1.8 lb./in.² (Sat'n. Temp. 25.6° F.)			Abs. Pressure 2.0 lb./in.² (Sat'n. Temp. 29.4° F.)			Abs. Pressure 2.2 lb./in.² (Sat'n. Temp. 32.9° F.)		
(At sat'n.)	(17.13)	(81.97)	(0.1721)	(15.35)	(82.57)	(0.1722)	(13.91)	(83.12)	(0.1722)	(12.74)	(83.62)	(0.1722)
30	17.43	83.22	0.1747	15.49	83.21	0.1735	13.92	83.20	0.1724	.....	.....	.....
40	17.79	84.69	.1777	15.81	84.68	.1765	14.21	84.68	.1753	12.92	84.67	0.1743
50	18.15	86.18	0.1807	16.13	86.17	0.1794	14.50	86.16	0.1783	13.18	86.16	0.1773
60	18.51	87.68	.1836	16.45	87.67	.1823	14.79	87.66	.1812	13.44	87.66	.1802
70	18.87	89.19	.1865	16.77	89.18	.1852	15.08	89.17	.1841	13.70	89.17	.1831
80	19.23	90.71	.1893	17.09	90.70	.1881	15.37	90.69	.1869	13.96	90.69	.1859
90	19.59	92.24	.1921	17.41	92.24	.1909	15.66	92.23	.1898	14.22	92.22	.1887
100	19.95	93.79	0.1949	17.73	93.78	0.1937	15.95	93.77	0.1926	14.48	93.77	0.1915
110	20.31	95.35	.1977	18.05	95.34	.1964	16.24	95.33	.1953	14.75	95.33	.1943
120	20.67	96.92	.2004	18.37	96.91	.1992	16.53	96.90	.1980	15.02	96.90	.1970
130	21.03	98.50	.2031	18.69	98.49	.2019	16.82	98.49	.2007	15.28	98.49	.1997
140	21.39	100.09	.2058	19.01	100.08	.2045	17.11	100.09	.2034	15.54	100.08	.2024
150	21.75	101.69	0.2084	19.33	101.69	0.2072	17.39	101.69	0.2061	15.81	101.68	0.2051
160	22.11	103.31	.2111	19.65	103.31	.2098	17.68	103.31	.2087	16.07	103.30	.2077
170	22.47	104.94	.2137	19.97	104.93	.2124	17.96	104.93	.2113	16.33	104.93	.2103
180	22.83	106.58	.2163	20.29	106.57	.2150	18.25	106.57	.2139	16.59	106.56	.2129
190	23.19	108.22	.2188	20.61	108.22	.2176	18.54	108.22	.2164	16.85	108.21	.2154
200	23.55	109.89	0.2214	20.93	109.88	0.2201	18.83	109.88	0.2190	17.11	109.88	0.2180
210	23.91	111.57	.2239	21.25	111.56	.2226	19.12	111.56	.2215	17.38	111.55	.2205
220	24.27	113.26	.2264	21.57	113.25	.2251	19.40	113.24	.2240	17.64	113.24	.2230
230	24.63	114.95	.2289	21.89	114.95	.2276	19.69	114.94	.2265	17.90	114.93	.2255
240	24.99	116.66	.2313	22.21	116.66	.2301	19.97	116.65	.2290	18.16	116.64	.2279
250	25.35	118.38	0.2338	22.53	118.38	0.2325	20.26	118.37	0.2314	18.42	118.36	0.2304
260	25.71	120.11	.2362	22.85	120.11	.2349	20.55	120.09	.2338	18.68	120.09	.2328
270	26.07	121.85	.2386	23.17	121.84	.2373	20.84	121.84	.2362	18.94	121.83	.2352
280	26.43	123.60	.2410	23.49	123.59	.2397	21.13	123.59	.2386	19.20	123.58	.2376
290	26.78	125.37	.2434	23.81	125.36	.2421	21.42	125.35	.2409	19.47	125.35	.2400
300	27.14	127.16	0.2457	24.12	127.15	0.2445	21.71	127.15	0.2433	19.74	127.14	0.2423
310	27.50	128.95	.2481	24.44	128.94	.2468	22.00	128.94	.2457	20.00	128.93	.2447
320	27.86	130.75	.2504	24.76	130.74	.2491	22.28	130.74	.2480	20.26	130.73	.2470
330	28.23	132.56	.2527	25.08	132.56	.2514	22.57	132.55	.2503	20.52	132.55	.2493
340										20.78	134.37	0.2516

TABLE 2-25. FREON 113: PROPERTIES OF SUPERHEATED VAPOR (Continued)

Temp. °F, t	Abs. Pressure 2.4 lb./in.² (Sat'n. Temp. 36.2° F.)			Abs. Pressure 2.6 lb./in.² (Sat'n. Temp. 39.2° F.)			Abs. Pressure 2.8 lb./in.² (Sat'n. Temp. 42.0° F.)			Abs. Pressure 3.0 lb./in.² (Sat'n. Temp. 44.7° F.)		
	v	H	s	v	H	s	v	H	s	v	H	s
(At sat'n.)	(11.74)	(84.10)	(0.1722)	(10.89)	(84.53)	(0.1723)	(10.17)	(84.94)	(0.1723)	(9.537)	(85.34)	(0.1723)
40	11.84	84.66	0.1734	10.91	84.65	0.1725						
50	12.08	86.15	0.1763	11.13	86.14	0.1755	10.33	86.13	0.1747	9.637	86.12	0.1739
60	12.32	87.65	.1792	11.35	87.64	.1784	10.54	87.63	.1776	9.831	87.62	.1769
70	12.56	89.16	.1821	11.58	89.15	.1813	10.75	89.14	.1805	10.02	89.13	.1797
80	12.80	90.68	.1850	11.80	90.67	.1841	10.95	90.66	.1833	10.22	90.66	.1826
90	13.04	92.21	.1878	12.02	92.21	.1869	11.16	92.20	.1861	10.41	92.19	.1854
100	13.28	93.76	0.1906	12.24	93.75	0.1897	11.37	93.74	0.1889	10.60	93.74	0.1882
110	13.52	95.32	.1934	12.47	95.31	.1925	11.58	95.30	.1917	10.80	95.30	.1910
120	13.76	96.89	.1961	12.69	96.88	.1952	11.79	96.87	.1944	10.99	96.87	.1937
130	14.00	98.48	.1988	12.91	98.47	.1979	11.99	98.46	.1971	11.18	98.46	.1964
140	14.24	100.07	.2015	13.13	100.06	.2006	12.20	100.06	.1998	11.38	100.05	.1991
150	14.48	101.68	0.2041	13.36	101.67	0.2033	12.40	101.66	0.2025	11.57	101.65	0.2017
160	14.72	103.29	.2068	13.58	103.28	.2059	12.61	103.28	.2051	11.76	103.27	.2044
170	14.96	104.92	.2094	13.80	104.91	.2085	12.82	104.90	.2077	11.95	104.90	.2070
180	15.20	106.56	.2120	14.02	106.55	.2111	13.02	106.54	.2103	12.15	106.54	.2095
190	15.44	108.21	.2145	14.25	108.20	.2137	13.23	108.19	.2129	12.34	108.19	.2121
200	15.68	109.87	0.2171	14.47	109.86	0.2162	13.44	109.86	0.2154	12.53	109.85	0.2147
210	15.93	111.54	.2196	14.69	111.54	.2187	13.65	111.54	.2179	12.72	111.53	.2172
220	16.17	113.23	.2221	14.91	113.22	.2212	13.85	113.23	.2204	12.92	113.22	.2197
230	16.41	114.93	.2246	15.13	114.92	.2237	14.05	114.92	.2229	13.11	114.92	.2222
240	16.65	116.64	.2270	15.35	116.63	.2262	14.26	116.63	.2254	13.30	116.63	.2246
250	16.89	118.35	0.2295	15.58	118.35	0.2286	14.46	118.35	0.2278	13.49	118.35	0.2271
260	17.13	120.08	.2319	15.80	120.08	.2310	14.67	120.08	.2302	13.68	120.08	.2295
270	17.37	121.82	.2343	16.02	121.82	.2334	14.88	121.82	.2326	13.87	121.82	.2319
280	17.61	123.58	.2367	16.24	123.57	.2358	15.09	123.57	.2350	14.06	123.57	.2343
290	17.85	125.35	.2391	16.46	125.34	.2382	15.29	125.34	.2374	14.26	125.33	.2367
300	18.09	127.14	0.2414	16.68	127.13	0.2406	15.50	127.13	0.2398	14.46	127.11	0.2390
310	18.33	128.93	.2437	16.90	128.92	.2429	15.70	128.92	.2421	14.65	128.91	.2414
320	18.57	130.73	.2461	17.12	130.72	.2452	15.90	130.73	.2444	14.84	130.71	.2437
330	18.81	132.54	.2484	17.34	132.54	.2475	16.11	132.54	.2467	15.03	132.52	.2460
340	19.05	134.36	.2507	17.56	134.36	.2498	16.31	134.36	.2490	15.22	134.35	.2483
350							16.52	136.20	0.2513	15.41	136.19	0.2505

Temp. °F	Abs. Pressure 3.2 lb./in.² (Sat'n. Temp. 47.3° F.)			Abs. Pressure 3.4 lb./in.² (Sat'n. Temp. 49.7° F.)			Abs. Pressure 3.6 lb./in.² (Sat'n. Temp. 52.0° F.)			Abs. Pressure 3.8 lb./in.² (Sat'n. Temp. 54.2° F.)		
At sat'n	(8.983)	(85.71)	(0.1124)	(8.489)	(86.06)	(0.1725)	(8.047)	(86.40)	(0.1725)	(7.653)	(86.72)	(0.1726)
50	9.030	86.12	0.1733	8.493	86.11	0.1726						
60	9.209	87.62	.1762	8.665	87.61	.1755	8.177	87.60	0.1749			
70	9.391	89.13	.1791	8.837	89.12	.1784	8.338	89.11	.1778	7.742	87.59	0.1743
80	9.573	90.65	.1819	9.009	90.64	.1813	8.499	90.63	.1806	7.895	89.10	.1772
90	9.755	92.18	.1847	9.181	92.18	.1841	8.659	92.17	.1834	8.048	90.62	.1800
100	9.938	93.73	0.1875	9.353	93.72	0.1869	8.819	93.71	0.1862	8.201	92.16	.1829
110	10.12	95.29	.1903	9.525	95.28	.1896	8.980	95.27	.1890	8.354	93.71	0.1857
120	10.30	96.86	.1930	9.697	96.85	.1924	9.141	96.84	.1917	8.506	95.27	.1884
130	10.48	98.45	.1957	9.869	98.44	.1951	9.305	98.43	.1944	8.659	96.84	.1911
140	10.66	100.04	.1984	10.03	100.03	.1977	9.466	100.03	.1971	8.812	98.43	.1938
150	10.84	101.65	0.2010	10.20	101.64	0.2004	9.627	101.63	0.1998	8.965	100.02	.1965
160	11.02	103.26	.2037	10.37	103.26	.2030	9.788	103.25	.2024	9.118	101.62	0.1992
170	11.20	104.89	.2063	10.54	104.89	.2056	9.948	104.88	.2050	9.271	103.24	.2018
180	11.38	106.54	.2089	10.71	106.53	.2082	10.11	106.53	.2076	9.423	104.87	.2044
190	11.56	108.19	.2114	10.88	108.18	.2108	10.27	108.18	.2102	9.576	106.52	.2070
200	11.74	109.85	0.2140	11.05	109.85	0.2133	10.43	109.84	0.2127	9.729	108.17	.2096
210	11.92	111.53	.2165	11.22	111.52	.2159	10.59	111.51	.2153	9.882	109.83	0.2121
220	12.10	113.21	.2190	11.39	113.21	.2184	10.75	113.20	.2178	10.03	111.51	.2147
230	12.28	114.91	.2215	11.56	114.90	.2208	10.91	114.90	.2202	10.19	113.19	.2172
240	12.47	116.62	.2240	11.73	116.61	.2233	11.07	116.61	.2227	10.34	114.89	.2196
250	12.65	118.34	0.2264	11.90	118.33	0.2257	11.23	118.32	0.2252	10.49	116.60	.2221
260	12.83	120.06	.2288	12.07	120.05	.2282	11.40	120.05	.2276	10.64	118.32	0.2245
270	13.01	121.80	.2312	12.24	121.79	.2306	11.56	121.79	.2300	10.79	120.04	.2270
280	13.19	123.55	.2336	12.41	123.55	.2330	11.72	123.54	.2324	10.95	121.78	.2294
290	13.37	125.32	.2360	12.58	125.32	.2353	11.88	125.31	.2347	11.10	123.53	.2318
300	13.56	127.11	0.2383	12.75	127.11	0.2377	12.04	127.10	0.2371	11.25	125.30	.2341
310	13.74	128.90	.2407	12.92	128.90	.2400	12.20	128.89	.2394	11.40	127.09	0.2365
320	13.92	130.70	.2430	13.09	130.70	.2423	12.36	130.69	.2417	11.55	128.89	.2388
330	14.09	132.52	.2453	13.26	132.51	.2446	12.52	132.51	.2441	11.70	130.69	.2412
340	14.27	134.34	.2476	13.43	134.34	.2469	12.68	134.33	.2464	11.85	132.50	.2435
350	14.45	136.18	0.2499	13.60	136.18	0.2492	12.84	136.17	0.2486	12.00	134.33	.2458
360							13.00	138.02	.2509	12.15	136.17	0.2481
										12.31	138.01	.2503

TABLE 2-25. FREON 113: PROPERTIES OF SUPERHEATED VAPOR (Continued)

Temp. °F. t	Abs. Pressure 4.0 lb./in.² (Sat'n. Temp. 56.3° F.)			Abs. Pressure 4.5 lb./in.² (Sat'n. Temp. 61.2° F.)			Abs. Pressure 5.0 lb./in.² (Sat'n. Temp. 65.7° F.)			Abs. Pressure 5.5 lb./in.² (Sat'n. Temp. 69.8° F.)		
	v	H	s	v	H	s	v	H	s	v	H	s
(At sat'n.)	(7.297)	(87.03)	(0.1727)	(6.542)	(87.74)	(0.1728)	(5.930)	(88.41)	(0.1730)	(5.426)	(89.01)	(0.1731)
60	7.351	87.58	0.1738	....	....	....	....	....	....	....	....	....
70	7.497	89.10	.1767	6.657	89.08	0.1754	5.979	89.06	0.1742	5.428	89.04	0.1732
80	7.642	90.62	.1795	6.786	90.60	.1782	6.096	90.58	.1771	5.533	90.56	.1761
90	7.787	92.15	.1823	6.915	92.13	.1810	6.213	92.12	.1799	5.638	92.10	.1789
100	7.932	93.70	0.1851	7.044	93.68	0.1838	6.329	93.67	0.1827	5.743	93.64	0.1817
110	8.077	95.26	.1879	7.173	95.24	.1866	6.445	95.22	.1855	5.849	95.20	.1844
120	8.222	96.83	.1906	7.302	96.81	.1893	6.562	96.79	.1882	5.955	96.77	.1872
130	8.367	98.42	.1933	7.431	98.40	.1920	6.678	98.38	.1909	6.061	98.36	.1899
140	8.522	100.01	.1960	7.560	99.99	.1947	6.795	99.98	.1936	6.168	99.96	.1925
150	8.667	101.62	0.1986	7.689	101.60	0.1974	6.912	101.58	0.1962	6.274	101.57	0.1952
160	8.812	103.23	.2013	7.818	103.22	.2000	7.029	103.20	.1989	6.380	103.19	.1978
170	8.957	104.86	.2039	7.947	104.85	.2026	7.146	104.83	.2015	6.485	104.82	.2004
180	9.102	106.51	.2065	8.076	106.49	.2052	7.263	106.48	.2041	6.589	106.47	.2030
190	9.247	108.16	.2091	8.205	108.14	.2078	7.380	108.13	.2066	6.695	108.12	.2056
200	9.387	109.82	0.2116	8.334	109.81	0.2103	7.497	109.80	0.2092	6.801	109.78	0.2081
210	9.532	111.50	.2141	8.463	111.49	.2128	7.614	111.48	.2117	6.907	111.46	.2107
220	9.677	113.19	.2166	8.592	113.18	.2153	7.731	113.16	.2142	7.013	113.15	.2132
230	9.822	114.88	.2191	8.721	114.88	.2178	7.848	114.86	.2167	7.120	114.84	.2157
240	9.967	116.59	.2216	8.850	116.59	.2203	7.965	116.57	.2192	7.226	116.55	.2181
250	10.11	118.31	0.2240	8.979	118.31	0.2228	8.082	118.29	0.2216	7.332	118.27	0.2206
260	10.25	120.04	.2264	9.108	120.03	.2252	8.199	120.02	.2240	7.438	120.00	.2230
270	10.40	121.78	.2288	9.237	121.77	.2276	8.316	121.76	.2264	7.544	121.74	.2254
280	10.54	123.53	.2312	9.366	123.52	.2300	8.422	123.51	.2288	7.651	123.49	.2278
290	10.69	125.30	.2336	9.495	125.29	.2323	8.538	125.28	.2312	7.758	125.26	.2302
300	10.83	127.09	0.2359	9.624	127.08	0.2347	8.654	127.07	0.2336	7.864	127.05	0.2325
310	10.97	128.88	.2383	9.753	128.88	.2370	8.771	128.86	.2359	7.970	128.85	.2349
320	11.12	130.68	.2406	9.882	130.68	.2394	8.887	130.67	.2383	8.077	130.65	.2372
330	11.26	132.50	.2429	10.01	132.49	.2417	9.003	132.48	.2406	8.182	132.47	.2395
340	11.40	134.32	.2452	10.14	134.32	.2440	9.120	134.31	.2429	8.287	134.29	.2418
350	11.54	136.16	0.2475	10.27	136.16	0.2463	9.236	136.14	0.2451	8.392	136.13	0.2441
360	11.69	138.01	.2498	10.39	138.00	.2485	9.352	137.99	.2474	8.497	137.98	.2464
370	....	....	.....	10.52	139.86	0.2508	9.468	139.85	.2497	8.602	139.84	0.2486

Temp. °F. (At. sat'n.)	Abs. Pressure 6.0 lb./in.² (Sat'n. Temp. 73.7° F.)			Abs. Pressure 6.5 lb./in.² (Sat'n. Temp. 77.3° F.)			Abs. Pressure 7.0 lb./in.² (Sat'n. Temp. 80.6° F.)			Abs. Pressure 7.5 lb./in.² (Sat'n. Temp. 83.8° F.)		
	(5.004)	(89.58)	(0.1733)	(4.646)	(90.10)	(0.1735)	(4.336)	(90.60)	(0.1736)	(4.061)	(91.06)	(0.1738)
80	5.066	90.54	0.1751	4.671	90.52	0.1743	....	....	....	....	....	....
90	5.163	92.08	.1779	4.762	92.06	.1771	4.414	92.05	0.1763	4.111	92.03	0.1755
100	5.260	93.62	0.1807	4.853	93.60	0.1799	4.498	93.60	0.1791	4.190	93.58	0.1783
110	5.357	95.18	.1835	4.944	95.16	.1827	4.581	95.16	.1818	4.269	95.14	.1811
120	5.454	96.76	.1862	5.035	96.74	.1854	4.666	96.73	.1845	4.348	96.71	.1838
130	5.551	98.35	.1889	5.125	98.33	.1881	4.749	98.32	.1872	4.427	98.30	.1865
140	5.649	99.95	.1916	5.215	99.93	.1908	4.834	99.91	.1899	4.507	99.90	.1892
150	5.746	101.56	0.1943	5.305	101.54	0.1934	4.919	101.52	0.1926	4.585	101.50	0.1919
160	5.843	103.17	.1969	5.394	103.16	.1961	5.003	103.14	.1952	4.663	103.12	.1945
170	5.940	104.80	.1995	5.484	104.79	.1987	5.086	104.77	.1978	4.741	104.75	.1971
180	6.037	106.45	.2021	5.573	106.43	.2013	5.169	106.42	.2004	4.819	106.40	.1997
190	6.134	108.10	.2047	5.663	108.09	.2038	5.253	108.07	.2030	4.897	108.05	.2023
200	6.233	109.77	0.2072	5.752	109.75	0.2064	5.337	109.73	0.2056	4.975	109.72	0.2048
210	6.330	111.44	.2097	5.841	111.43	.2089	5.420	111.41	.2081	5.053	111.39	.2073
220	6.427	113.13	.2122	5.930	113.11	.2114	5.504	113.10	.2106	5.131	113.08	.2098
230	6.525	114.83	.2147	6.021	114.81	.2139	5.587	114.80	.2131	5.209	114.78	.2123
240	6.622	116.54	.2172	6.110	116.52	.2164	5.671	116.50	.2156	5.286	116.49	.2148
250	6.719	118.26	0.2197	6.200	118.24	0.2188	5.755	118.22	0.2180	5.365	118.21	0.2173
260	6.816	119.99	.2221	6.290	119.97	.2212	5.838	119.95	.2204	5.444	119.94	.2197
270	6.913	121.73	.2245	6.381	121.71	.2236	5.921	121.69	.2228	5.523	121.68	.2221
280	7.011	123.48	.2269	6.470	123.46	.2260	6.004	123.45	.2252	5.602	123.44	.2245
290	7.108	125.25	.2293	6.558	125.23	.2284	6.087	125.22	.2276	5.680	125.21	.2269
300	7.205	127.04	0.2316	6.647	127.02	0.2308	6.170	127.01	0.2300	5.757	127.00	0.2292
310	7.302	128.84	.2340	6.737	128.82	.2331	6.254	128.81	.2323	5.834	128.80	.2316
320	7.398	130.64	.2363	6.827	130.63	.2354	6.337	130.61	.2346	5.911	130.60	.2339
330	7.495	132.46	.2386	6.917	132.44	.2377	6.420	132.43	.2370	5.988	132.42	.2362
340	7.591	134.28	.2409	7.008	134.27	.2400	6.504	134.26	.2393	6.064	134.24	.2385
350	7.687	136.12	0.2432	7.097	136.11	0.2423	6.587	136.09	0.2415	6.142	136.08	0.2408
360	7.784	137.97	.2455	7.186	137.96	.2446	6.670	137.94	.2438	6.221	137.93	.2431
370	7.880	139.83	.2477	7.274	139.82	.2469	6.752	139.80	.2461	6.299	139.79	.2453
380	7.975	141.70	.2500	7.362	141.69	.2491	6.834	141.68	.2483	6.378	141.67	.2476
390	....	....	....	....	....	....	6.916	143.57	0.2506	6.457	143.56	0.2498

TABLE 2-25. FREON 113: PROPERTIES OF SUPERHEATED VAPOR (Continued)

Temp. °F, t	Abs. Pressure 8.0 lb./in.² (Sat'n. Temp. 86.9° F.)			Abs. Pressure 9.0 lb./in.² (Sat'n. Temp. 92.5° F.)			Abs. Pressure 10.0 lb./in.² (Sat'n. Temp. 97.6° F.)			Abs. Pressure 11 lb./in.² (Sat'n. Temp. 102.4° F.)		
	V	H	s	V	H	s	V	H	s	V	H	s
(At sat'n.)	(3.828)	(91.52)	(0.1739)	(3.431)	(92.35)	(0.1742)	(3.110)	(93.11)	(0.1745)	(2.845)	(93.81)	(0.1747)
90	3.850	92.01	0.1748	....	....	....	....	....	....	....	....	....
100	3.924	93.56	.1776	3.481	93.52	0.1763	3.124	93.48	0.1751	....	....	....
110	3.999	95.12	.1804	3.547	95.08	.1791	3.183	95.04	.1779	2.887	95.01	0.1769
120	4.073	96.69	.1831	3.613	96.66	.1819	3.242	96.62	.1806	2.941	96.58	.1796
130	4.147	98.28	.1858	3.679	98.25	.1846	3.301	98.21	.1834	2.995	98.17	.1823
140	4.221	99.88	.1885	3.745	99.84	.1872	3.361	99.81	.1860	3.049	99.77	.1850
150	4.295	101.48	0.1912	3.810	101.45	0.1899	3.420	101.41	0.1887	3.103	101.38	0.1877
160	4.369	103.10	.1938	3.874	103.07	.1925	3.480	103.03	.1914	3.157	103.00	.1903
170	4.442	104.74	.1964	3.940	104.70	.1951	3.539	104.66	.1940	3.211	104.63	.1929
180	4.515	106.38	.1990	4.004	106.34	.1977	3.599	106.31	.1966	3.265	106.28	.1955
190	4.588	108.04	.2016	4.070	108.00	.2003	3.658	107.96	.1991	3.319	107.93	.1981
200	4.661	109.71	0.2041	4.135	109.67	0.2028	3.716	109.63	0.2017	3.373	109.60	0.2006
210	4.734	111.38	.2066	4.199	111.35	.2054	3.774	111.32	.2042	3.426	111.28	.2032
220	4.807	113.07	.2091	4.265	113.04	.2079	3.832	113.01	.2067	3.480	112.97	.2057
230	4.880	114.77	.2116	4.330	114.74	.2104	3.891	114.71	.2092	3.533	114.67	.2082
240	4.952	116.48	.2141	4.395	116.45	.2129	3.950	116.42	.2117	3.586	116.38	.2106
250	5.024	118.20	0.2166	4.460	118.17	0.2153	4.010	118.14	0.2141	3.639	118.10	0.2131
260	5.096	119.93	.2190	4.525	119.91	.2177	4.068	119.87	.2166	3.692	119.84	.2155
270	5.168	121.67	.2214	4.590	121.64	.2201	4.126	121.61	.2190	3.745	121.58	.2179
280	5.240	123.42	.2238	4.656	123.40	.2225	4.185	123.37	.2214	3.798	123.34	.2203
290	5.313	125.19	.2261	4.721	125.17	.2249	4.243	125.15	.2237	3.852	125.12	.2227
300	5.387	126.98	0.2285	4.787	126.96	0.2273	4.302	126.94	0.2261	3.906	126.91	0.2250
310	5.460	128.78	.2309	4.852	128.76	.2296	4.360	128.74	.2285	3.960	128.71	.2274
320	5.533	130.58	.2332	4.918	130.57	.2319	4.419	130.54	.2308	4.014	130.51	.2298
330	5.607	132.40	.2355	4.983	132.39	.2343	4.477	132.36	.2331	4.068	132.33	.2321
340	5.682	134.23	.2378	5.048	134.21	.2366	4.537	134.19	.2354	4.122	134.16	.2344
350	5.756	136.07	0.2401	5.112	136.05	0.2388	4.596	136.03	0.2377	4.175	136.00	0.2367
360	5.830	137.92	.2424	5.178	137.90	.2411	4.656	137.88	.2400	4.229	137.85	.2389
370	5.904	139.78	.2447	5.243	139.76	.2434	4.714	139.74	.2422	4.283	139.71	.2412
380	5.975	141.66	.2470	5.307	141.64	.2456	4.772	141.62	.2445	4.336	141.59	.2434
390	6.047	143.55	0.2492	5.372	143.52	.2479	4.829	143.50	.2467	4.389	143.48	.2457
400	....	....	....	5.436	145.41	0.2501	4.887	145.39	.2489	4.441	145.37	0.2479
410	....	....	....	....	....	....	....	....	....	4.493	147.28	0.2501

Temp. °F.	Abs. Pressure 12 lb./in.² (Sat'n. Temp. 106.8° F.)			Abs. Pressure 13 lb./in.² (Sat'n. Temp. 111.0° F.)			Abs. Pressure 14 lb./in.² (Sat'n. Temp. 114.9° F.)			Abs. Pressure 16 lb./in.² (Sat'n. Temp. 122.1° F.)		
(At sat'n.)	(2.624)	(94.46)	(0.1750)	(2.435)	(95.08)	(0.1753)	(2.271)	(95.66)	(0.1755)	(2.004)	(96.72)	(0.1760)
110	2.640	94.97	0.1759	.....	.....	.....	2.291	96.47	0.1770	.....	.....	.....
120	2.689	96.55	.1786	2.477	96.51	0.1778	2.334	98.06	.1797	.....	.....	.....
130	2.738	98.14	.1813	2.522	98.10	.1805	2.377	99.66	.1823	2.034	97.99	0.1782
140	2.788	99.73	.1840	2.567	99.70	.1832	2.421	101.27	0.1850	2.072	99.59	.1809
150	2.838	101.34	0.1867	2.613	101.31	0.1858	2.465	102.90	.1876	2.110	101.20	0.1835
160	2.888	102.97	.1894	2.659	102.94	.1885	2.508	104.53	.1902	2.148	102.83	.1862
170	2.938	104.60	.1920	2.704	104.57	.1911	2.550	106.18	.1928	2.186	104.46	.1888
180	2.987	106.25	.1946	2.749	106.21	.1937	2.593	107.84	.1954	2.224	106.11	.1914
190	3.037	107.90	.1972	2.795	107.87	.1963	2.635	109.51	0.1980	2.262	107.77	.1940
200	3.086	109.57	0.1997	2.841	109.54	0.1988	2.678	111.20	.2005	2.299	109.44	0.1965
210	3.135	111.26	.2022	2.887	111.23	.2013	2.720	112.89	.2030	2.336	111.13	.1991
220	3.184	112.95	.2047	2.933	112.92	.2039	2.763	114.59	.2055	2.374	112.83	.2016
230	3.234	114.65	.2072	2.979	114.62	.2064	2.806	116.30	.2080	2.411	114.53	.2041
240	3.283	116.36	.2097	3.025	116.33	.2088	2.848	118.02	0.2105	2.448	116.24	.2065
250	3.332	118.08	0.2121	3.071	118.05	0.2113	2.890	119.76	.2129	2.486	117.96	0.2090
260	3.382	119.81	.2146	3.117	119.79	.2137	2.932	121.50	.2153	2.523	119.70	.2114
270	3.431	121.55	.2170	3.162	121.53	.2162	2.975	123.26	.2177	2.560	121.45	.2138
280	3.479	123.31	.2194	3.208	123.29	.2186	3.018	125.04	.2201	2.596	123.21	.2162
290	3.528	125.09	.2218	3.254	125.07	.2209	3.060	126.84	0.2225	2.633	124.99	.2186
300	3.578	126.88	0.2241	3.300	126.86	0.2232	3.103	128.64	.2248	2.671	126.78	0.2210
310	3.627	128.68	.2265	3.345	128.66	.2256	3.145	130.44	.2271	2.709	128.58	.2233
320	3.676	130.49	.2288	3.391	130.47	.2279	3.187	132.26	.2294	2.746	130.39	.2257
330	3.725	132.31	.2311	3.436	132.29	.2302	3.229	134.09	.2317	2.783	132.21	.2280
340	3.774	134.14	.2334	3.481	134.12	.2325	3.271	135.94	0.2340	2.820	134.04	.2303
350	3.823	135.98	0.2357	3.526	135.96	0.2348	3.313	137.79	.2363	2.857	135.88	0.2326
360	3.872	137.83	.2380	3.572	137.81	.2371	3.355	139.65	.2386	2.895	137.74	.2349
370	3.922	139.69	.2402	3.617	139.68	.2394	3.397	141.52	.2408	2.932	139.60	.2371
380	3.972	141.57	.2425	3.662	141.56	.2416	3.439	143.41	.2430	2.968	141.47	.2394
390	4.021	143.45	.2447	3.707	143.44	.2439	3.481	145.31	0.2453	3.005	143.36	.2416
400	4.069	145.34	0.2469	3.752	145.33	0.2461	3.522	147.22	.2475	3.042	145.26	0.2438
410	4.117	147.25	.2491	3.797	147.24	.2483	3.562	149.14	.2497	3.079	147.17	.2460
420	.....	.....	.....	3.841	149.16	.2505	.....	.....	.....	3.115	149.10	.2482
430	.....	.....	.....	.....	.....	.....	.....	.....	.....	3.152	151.03	.2504

Table 2-25. Freon 113: Properties of Superheated Vapor (Concluded)

Temp. °F. t	Abs. Pressure 18 lb./in.² (Sat'n. Temp. 128.6° F.)			Abs. Pressure 20 lb./in.² (Sat'n. Temp. 134.6° F.)			Abs. Pressure 25 lb./in.² (Sat'n. Temp. 147.8° F.)			Abs. Pressure 30 lb./in.² (Sat'n. Temp. 159.1° F.)		
	v	h	s	v	h	s	v	h	s	v	h	s
(At sat'n.)	(1.795)	(97.68)	(0.1764)	(1.625)	(98.56)	(0.1769)	(1.317)	(100.30)	(0.1778)	(1.109)	(102.15)	(0.1787)
130	1.799	97.91	0.1769	1.640	99.43	0.1783	.....	.....	.....	.....	.....	.....
140	1.833	99.51	.1795	1.672	101.05	0.1810	.....	.....	.....	.....	.....	.....
150	1.867	101.12	.1822	1.703	102.68	.1836	1.322	100.87	0.1784	1.111	102.31	0.1790
160	1.901	102.75	.1848	1.734	104.32	.1862	1.348	102.50	.1811	1.132	103.96	.1816
170	1.935	104.39	.1875	1.765	105.97	.1888	1.373	104.14	.1837	1.153	105.62	.1842
180	1.968	106.04	.1901	1.796	107.64	.1914	1.398	105.80	.1863	1.173	107.29	.1868
190	2.002	107.71	.1926	1.827	109.32	0.1940	1.423	107.47	.1889	1.194	108.97	0.1894
200	2.036	109.39	0.1952	1.857	111.01	.1966	1.448	109.15	0.1915	1.215	110.67	.1919
210	2.069	111.08	.1977	1.887	112.70	.1991	1.472	110.84	.1940	1.236	112.37	.1945
220	2.103	112.77	.2003	1.917	114.40	.2016	1.497	112.54	.1966	1.257	114.08	.1970
230	2.136	114.47	.2028	1.947	116.12	.2041	1.522	114.25	.1991	1.278	115.80	.1995
240	2.169	116.18	.2052	1.977	117.84	0.2065	1.546	115.96	.2015	1.299	117.53	0.2019
250	2.203	117.90	0.2077	2.007	119.58	.2090	1.571	117.69	0.2040	1.320	119.28	.2044
260	2.236	119.64	.2101	2.037	121.33	.2114	1.595	119.44	.2064	1.341	121.03	.2068
270	2.269	121.39	.2125	2.068	123.09	.2138	1.619	121.19	.2089	1.362	122.80	.2092
280	2.303	123.15	.2149	2.098	124.87	.2162	1.643	122.95	.2113	1.382	124.59	.2116
290	2.336	124.92	.2173	2.128	126.67	0.2185	1.667	124.73	.2137	1.402	126.39	0.2140
300	2.370	126.72	0.2197	2.158	128.47	.2209	1.691	126.53	0.2160	1.422	128.20	.2163
310	2.403	128.53	.2220	2.187	130.28	.2232	1.716	128.34	.2184	1.442	130.02	.2187
320	2.436	130.34	.2244	2.217	132.10	.2255	1.741	130.16	.2207	1.462	131.85	.2210
330	2.469	132.16	.2267	2.247	133.94	.2278	1.765	131.98	.2231	1.483	133.69	.2233
340	2.502	133.99	.2290	2.277	135.78	0.2301	1.789	133.82	.2254	1.503	135.54	0.2256
350	2.535	135.83	0.2313	2.308	137.64	.2324	1.813	135.66	0.2277	1.524	137.40	.2279
360	2.569	137.69	.2336	2.338	139.50	.2347	1.838	137.52	.2300	1.545	139.27	.2302
370	2.602	139.55	.2358	2.368	141.38	.2369	1.862	139.39	.2322	1.565	141.15	.2324
380	2.635	141.43	.2381	2.398	143.27	.2392	1.886	141.26	.2345	1.585	143.05	.2347
390	2.667	143.32	.2403	2.427	145.17	0.2414	1.910	143.15	.2367	1.604	144.95	0.2369
400	2.700	145.22	0.2425	2.456	147.08	.2436	1.933	145.05	0.2389	1.624	146.86	.2391
410	2.733	147.13	.2447	2.485	149.01	.2458	1.957	146.97	.2411	1.645	148.79	.2413
420	2.765	149.05	.2469	2.515	150.94	.2480	1.981	148.90	.2433	1.665	150.73	.2435
430	2.797	150.99	.2491	2.544	152.89	.2501	2.005	150.83	.2455	1.685	152.68	.2457
440	.....	.....	.....	.....	.....	.....	2.029	152.78	.2477	1.706	154.65	0.2479
450	.....	.....	.....	.....	.....	.....	2.052	154.74	0.2498	1.726	156.62	0.2500
460	.....	.....	.....	.....	.....	.....	.....	.....	.....	.....	.....	.....

Temp. °F.	Abs. Pressure 35 lb./in.² (Sat'n. Temp. 169.0° F.)			Abs. Pressure 40 lb./in.² (Sat'n. Temp. 177.9° F.)			Abs. Pressure 50 lb./in.² (Sat'n. Temp. 193.5° F.)			Abs. Pressure 60 lb./in.² (Sat'n. Temp. 206.9° F.)		
(At sat'n.)	(0.9580)	(103.60)	(0.1795)	(0.8435)	(104.90)	(0.1802)	(0.6809)	(107.14)	(0.1816)	(0.5705)	(109.06)	(0.1827)
170	0.9594	103.77	0.1797									
180	0.9780	105.43	.1824	0.8462	105.26	0.1808						
190	0.9963	107.10	.1850	.8627	106.94	.1834						
200	1.015	108.79	0.1876	0.8791	108.62	0.1860	0.6899	108.27	0.1833			
210	1.033	110.49	.1901	.8953	110.32	.1885	.7031	109.97	.1858	0.5738	109.60	0.1835
220	1.051	112.20	.1927	.9114	112.03	.1911	.7163	111.69	.1884	.5853	111.31	.1861
230	1.069	113.91	.1952	.9274	113.74	.1936	.7296	113.41	.1909	.5968	113.04	.1886
240	1.088	115.63	.1977	.9435	115.47	.1961	.7430	115.14	.1934	.6082	114.78	.1912
250	1.106	117.37	0.2002	0.9596	117.21	0.1986	0.7562	116.90	0.1959	0.6193	116.54	0.1937
260	1.124	119.12	.2026	.9756	118.97	.2010	.7693	118.67	.1984	.6303	118.32	.1961
270	1.142	120.88	.2051	0.9915	120.74	.2035	.7821	120.45	.2008	.6413	120.11	.1986
280	1.160	122.66	.2075	1.008	122.52	.2059	.7950	122.23	.2033	.6525	121.91	.2010
290	1.177	124.45	.2099	1.023	124.31	.2083	.8079	124.03	.2057	.6639	123.72	.2035
300	1.195	126.26	0.2122	1.038	126.12	0.2107	0.8207	125.84	0.2081	0.6751	125.53	0.2059
310	1.212	128.07	.2146	1.054	127.94	.2131	.8335	127.66	.2104	.6860	127.36	.2083
320	1.230	129.89	.2169	1.070	129.76	.2154	.8463	129.48	.2128	.6969	129.19	.2106
330	1.248	131.72	.2193	1.085	131.59	.2178	.8591	131.31	.2152	.7079	131.03	.2130
340	1.266	133.56	.2216	1.101	133.44	.2201	.8716	133.16	.2175	.7188	132.89	.2153
350	1.284	135.41	0.2239	1.117	135.29	0.2224	0.8844	135.02	0.2198	0.7296	134.75	0.2176
360	1.302	137.27	.2262	1.133	137.16	.2247	.8973	136.89	.2221	.7403	136.63	.2199
370	1.319	139.15	.2285	1.148	139.03	.2269	.9101	138.77	.2244	.7510	138.52	.2222
380	1.336	141.03	.2307	1.164	140.91	.2292	.9228	140.67	.2266	.7619	140.42	.2245
390	1.353	142.93	.2329	1.179	142.81	.2314	.9354	142.57	.2289	.7725	142.33	.2267
400	1.370	144.83	0.2352	1.194	144.72	0.2337	0.9480	144.48	0.2311	0.7831	144.24	0.2290
410	1.388	146.75	.2374	1.210	146.64	.2359	.9605	146.41	.2333	.7937	146.16	.2312
420	1.405	148.68	.2396	1.225	148.57	.2381	.9728	148.35	.2356	.8043	148.10	.2334
430	1.422	150.62	.2418	1.240	150.51	.2403	.9851	150.30	.2378	.8151	150.06	.2356
440	1.439	152.58	.2440	1.256	152.47	.2425	.9974	152.25	.2400	.8257	152.02	.2378
450	1.457	154.54	0.2461	1.271	154.44	0.2447	1.010	154.22	0.2421	0.8362	154.00	0.2400
460	1.474	156.52	.2483	1.286	156.41	.2468	1.023	156.21	.2443	.8466	155.98	.2422
470	1.491	158.51	0.2505	1.302	158.40	.2490	1.036	158.20	.2464	.8570	157.98	.2443
480				1.317	160.40	0.2511	1.048	160.20	.2486	.8675	159.98	.2465
490							1.060	162.22	.2507	.8776	162.00	.2486
500							1.072	164.24	0.2528	0.8880	164.03	0.2508
510										0.8987	166.07	0.2529

TABLE 2-26. METHYL CHLORIDE: PROPERTIES OF SATURATED VAPOR*

Temp °F.	Abs. Pressure lb./in.²	Volume Liquid ft.³/lb.	Volume Vapor ft.³/lb.	Density Liquid lb./ft.³	Density Vapor lb./ft.³	Heat Content from —40° Liquid Btu./lb.	Heat Content from —40° Latent Btu./lb.	Heat Content from —40° Vapor Btu./lb.	Entropy from —10° Liquid Btu./lb.°F	Entropy from —10° Vapor Btu./lb.°F	Temp. °F.
-80	1.953	0.01493	41.08	66.98	0.02434	-13.888	198.64	184.75	-0.0351	0.4882	-80
-70	2.751	.01508	29.84	66.31	.03351	-10.521	196.77	186.25	-.0261	.4790	-70
-60	3.799	.01523	22.09	65.66	.04527	- 7.039	194.78	187.74	-.0172	.4703	-60
-50	5.155	.01538	16.64	65.02	.06010	- 3.532	192.72	189.19	-.0085	.4620	-50
-40	6.878	0.01553	12.72	64.39	0.07861	0.000	190.66	190.66	0.0000	0.4544	-40
-38	7.272	.01556	12.08	64.27	.08278	.713	190.23	190.95	.0017	.4529	-38
-36	7.684	.01559	11.48	64.14	.08712	1.426	189.81	191.23	.0034	.4515	-36
-34	8.115	.01562	10.91	64.02	.09166	2.138	189.38	191.51	.0051	.4500	-34
-32	8.566	.01565	10.38	63.90	.09639	2.850	188.95	191.80	.0067	.4486	-32
-30	9.036	0.01568	9.873	63.78	0.1013	3.562	188.52	192.08	0.0084	0.4472	-30
-28	9.526	.01571	9.399	63.65	.1064	4.277	188.09	192.37	.0100	.4458	-28
-26	10.04	.01574	8.953	63.53	.1117	4.993	187.65	192.65	.0117	.4445	-26
-24	10.57	.01577	8.533	63.41	.1172	5.711	187.22	192.93	.0133	.4431	-24
-22	11.13	.01580	8.136	63.29	.1229	6.427	186.78	193.21	.0150	.4418	-22
-20	11.71	0.01583	7.761	63.17	0.1289	7.146	186.34	193.49	0.0166	0.4405	-20
-18	12.31	.01586	7.408	63.86	.1350	7.863	185.90	193.76	.0183	.4393	-18
-16	12.93	.01589	7.074	62.93	.1414	8.584	185.46	194.04	.0199	.4380	-16
-14	13.58	.01592	6.758	62.81	.1480	9.307	185.01	194.32	.0215	.4367	-14
-12	14.26	.01595	6.459	62.70	.1548	10.03	184.56	194.59	.0232	.4355	-12
-10	14.96	0.01598	6.176	62.58	0.1619	10.75	184.11	194.87	0.0247	0.4343	-10
-8	15.69	.01601	5.908	62.46	.1693	11.48	183.66	195.14	.0263	.4331	-8
-6	16.45	.01604	5.654	62.34	.1769	12.20	183.21	195.42	.0279	.4319	-6
-4	17.24	.01607	5.413	62.23	.1847	12.93	182.76	195.69	.0295	.4307	-4
-2	18.05	.01610	5.185	62.11	.1929	13.66	182.30	195.96	.0311	.4296	-2

Temp											Temp
0	0.4284	0.0327	196.23	181.85	14.39	0.2013	62.00	4.969	0.01613	18.90	0
2	.4273	.0343	196.51	181.39	15.12	.2100	61.88	4.763	.01616	19.77	2
4	.4262	.0359	196.78	180.93	15.85	.2189	61.77	4.568	.01619	20.68	4
5	.4257	.0367	196.92	180.70	16.21	.2237	61.65	4.471	.01622	21.15	5
6	.4251	.0375	197.05	180.47	16.58	.2284	61.54	4.379	.01625	21.62	6
8	.4240	.0390	197.31	180.01	17.31	.2378	61.43	4.206	.01628	22.59	8
10	0.4229	0.0406	197.58	179.53	18.04	0.2477	61.31	4.038	0.01631	23.60	10
12	.4218	.0422	197.83	179.06	18.77	.2579	61.20	3.878	.01634	24.64	12
14	.4208	.0437	198.09	178.58	19.51	.2684	61.09	3.726	.01637	25.72	14
16	.4198	.0453	198.34	178.10	20.25	.2792	60.98	3.581	.01640	26.83	16
18	.4187	.0468	198.59	177.61	20.98	.2904	60.83	3.443	.01644	27.97	18
20	0.4177	0.0484	198.84	177.11	21.73	0.3019	60.72	3.312	0.01647	29.16	20
22	.4166	.0499	199.08	176.61	22.47	.3138	60.61	3.186	.01650	30.38	22
24	.4156	.0514	199.32	176.11	23.21	.3261	60.46	3.067	.01654	31.64	24
26	.4146	.0530	199.56	175.61	23.95	.3388	60.31	2.952	.01658	32.95	26
28	.4136	.0545	199.79	175.10	24.70	.3517	60.17	2.843	.01662	34.29	28
30	0.4126	0.0560	200.03	174.59	25.44	0.3650	60.06	2.739	0.01665	35.68	30
32	.4117	.0575	200.26	174.08	26.18	.3787	59.92	2.640	.01669	37.11	32
34	.4107	.0590	200.49	173.56	26.93	.3928	59.77	2.546	.01673	38.58	34
36	.4098	.0605	200.72	173.05	27.67	.4073	59.63	2.455	.01677	40.09	36
38	.4088	.0621	200.95	172.53	28.42	.4222	59.49	2.369	.01681	41.65	38
40	0.4079	0.0636	201.17	172.00	29.17	0.4375	59.38	2.286	0.01684	43.25	40
42	.4070	.0651	201.40	171.48	29.92	.4532	59.24	2.206	.01688	44.91	42
44	.4061	.0665	201.62	170.95	30.67	.4694	59.10	2.130	.01692	46.61	44
46	.4052	.0680	201.84	170.42	31.42	.4861	58.96	2.057	.01696	48.35	46
48	.4043	.0695	202.06	169.89	32.17	.5033	58.82	1.987	.01700	50.15	48

*Courtesy E. I. du Pont de Nemours and Co. The R and H Chemicals Department, Wilmington, Del. See Fig. 2-5.

TABLE 2-26.   METHYL CHLORIDE: PROPERTIES OF SATURATED VAPOR (Concluded)

Temp. °F.	Abs. Pressure lb./in.²	Volume Liquid ft.³/lb.	Volume Vapor ft.³/lb.	Density Liquid lb./ft.³	Density Vapor lb./ft.³	Heat Content from −40° Liquid Btu./lb.	Heat Content from −40° Latent Btu./lb.	Heat Content from −40° Vapor Btu./lb.	Entropy from −40° Liquid Btu./lb.°F.	Entropy from −40° Vapor Btu./lb.°F.	Temp. °F.
50	51.99	0.01704	1.920	58.69	0.5208	32.93	169.35	202.28	0.0710	0.4034	50
52	53.88	.01708	1.856	58.55	.5388	33.68	168.81	202.49	.0725	.4025	52
54	55.83	.01712	1.794	58.41	.5573	34.44	168.27	202.71	.0740	.4017	54
56	57.83	.01716	1.735	58.28	.5763	35.19	167.72	202.91	.0754	.4008	56
58	59.88	.01720	1.679	58.14	.5958	35.95	167.18	203.13	.0769	.3999	58
60	62.00	0.01724	1.624	58.00	0.6158	36.71	166.62	203.33	0.0784	0.3991	60
62	64.17	.01728	1.572	57.87	.6362	37.47	166.07	203.54	.0798	.3983	62
64	66.39	.01732	1.522	57.74	.6572	38.23	165.51	203.74	.0813	.3974	64
66	68.67	.01736	1.473	57.60	.6788	39.00	164.95	203.95	.0827	.3966	66
68	71.01	.01740	1.427	57.47	.7008	39.76	164.39	204.15	.0842	.3958	68
70	73.41	0.01744	1.382	57.34	0.7234	40.52	163.82	204.34	0.0856	0.3950	70
72	75.86	.01748	1.339	57.21	.7467	41.29	163.24	204.53	.0870	.3941	72
74	78.37	.01752	1.298	57.08	.7704	42.06	162.66	204.72	.0885	.3933	74
76	80.94	.01756	1.258	56.95	.7948	42.82	162.08	204.90	.0899	.3925	76
78	83.57	.01760	1.220	56.82	.8196	43.59	161.50	205.09	.0913	.3918	78
80	86.26	0.01764	1.183	56.69	0.8451	44.36	160.91	205.27	0.0928	0.3910	80
82	89.01	.01768	1.148	56.56	.8710	45.13	160.32	205.45	.0942	.3902	82
84	91.82	.01773	1.114	56.40	.8979	45.90	159.72	205.62	.0956	.3894	84
86	94.70	.01778	1.081	56.24	.9253	46.67	159.13	205.80	.0970	.3887	86
88	97.64	.01782	1.049	56.12	.9531	47.44	158.52	205.96	.0984	.3879	88
90	100.6	0.01786	1.018	55.99	0.9819	48.21	157.92	206.13	0.0998	0.3872	90
92	103.7	.01791	.9889	55.83	1.011	48.99	157.31	206.30	.1012	.3865	92
94	106.9	.01796	.9603	55.68	1.041	49.77	156.69	206.46	.1026	.3857	94
96	110.1	.01800	.9333	55.56	1.072	50.54	156.08	206.62	.1041	.3850	96
98	113.4	.01804	.9069	55.43	1.103	51.32	155.46	206.78	.1055	.3843	98

100	0.3836	0.1069	206.94	154.85	52.09	1.135	55.31	.8814	0.01808	116.7	100
102	.3828	.1082	207.09	154.22	52.87	1.167	55.15	.8568	.01813	120.1	102
104	.3822	.1096	207.25	153.60	53.65	1.200	55.01	.8331	.01818	123.6	104
106	.3815	.1110	207.40	152.97	54.43	1.234	54.85	.8105	.01823	127.2	106
108	.3808	.1124	207.55	152.33	55.22	1.268	54.70	.7884	.01828	130.8	108
110	0.3801	0.1138	207.70	151.70	56.00	1.303	54.55	.7672	0.01833	134.5	110
112	.3794	.1151	207.84	151.06	56.78	1.339	54.41	.7466	.01838	138.3	112
114	.3787	.1165	207.98	150.41	57.57	1.376	54.26	.7268	.01843	142.2	114
116	.3781	.1179	208.13	149.77	58.36	1.414	54.11	.7075	.01848	146.1	116
118	.3774	.1193	208.26	149.11	59.15	1.452	53.97	.6889	.01853	150.1	118
120	0.3768	0.1206	208.39	148.46	59.93	1.490	53.79	.6710	0.01859	154.2	120
122	.3762	.1220	208.53	147.80	60.73	1.530	53.62	.6534	.01865	158.4	122
124	.3755	.1234	208.65	147.14	61.51	1.571	53.48	.6367	.01870	162.6	124
126	.3749	.1247	208.78	146.47	62.31	1.613	53.33	.6201	.01875	167.0	126
128	.3742	.1261	208.90	145.80	63.10	1.655	53.16	.6043	.01881	171.4	128
130	0.3736	0.1274	209.02	145.13	63.89	1.698	52.99	.5889	0.01887	175.9	130
132	.3730	.1288	209.14	144.45	64.69	1.742	52.83	.5741	.01893	180.4	132
134	.3723	.1301	209.25	143.77	65.48	1.787	52.69	.5596	.01898	185.1	134
136	.3717	.1314	209.37	143.09	66.28	1.833	52.52	.5455	.01904	189.8	136
138	.3711	.1328	209.48	142.40	67.08	1.880	52.38	.5320	.01909	194.7	138
140	0.3705	0.1341	209.58	141.71	67.87	1.927	52.22	.5189	0.01915	199.6	140
150	0.3674	0.1407	210.10	138.23	71.87	2.181	51.41	.4586	0.01945	225.4	150
160	0.3646	0.1473	210.56	134.66	75.90	2.457	50.56	.4070	0.01978	253.5	160
170	0.3618	0.1538	210.93	130.96	79.97	2.768	49.63	.3613	0.02015	283.9	170

TABLE 2-27. METHYL CHLORIDE: PROPERTIES OF SUPERHEATED VAPOR

Temp. °F. t	Abs. Pressure, 6 lbs./in.² (Sat'n Temp., −41.8° F.)			Abs. Pressure, 7 lbs./in.² (Sat'n Temp., −39.4° F.)			Abs. Pressure, 8 lbs./in.² (Sat'n Temp., −34.5° F.)			Abs. Pressure, 9 lbs./in.² (Sat'n Temp., −30.2° F.)			Temp. °F. t
(At sat'n)	v (14.45)	H (189.96)	s (.4580)	v (12.52)	H (190.75)	s (.4539)	v (11.06)	H (191.41)	s (.4504)	v (9.911)	H (192.07)	s (.4473)	(At sat'n)
−40	14.62	190.77	.4599	.....	.....	.....	.....	.....	.....	.....	.....	.....	−40
−30	14.99	192.52	.4640	12.80	192.34	.4578	11.17	192.17	.4523	9.911	192.10	.4475	−30
−20	15.36	194.27	.4681	13.12	194.12	.4618	11.46	193.97	.4563	10.16	193.82	.4515	−20
−10	15.72	196.06	.4721	13.43	195.92	.4658	11.74	195.78	.4603	10.41	195.64	.4556	−10
0	16.09	197.84	.4760	13.74	197.71	.4698	12.01	197.58	.4643	10.66	197.45	.4595	0
10	16.45	199.66	.4799	14.06	199.54	.4737	12.29	199.42	.4682	10.91	199.30	.4635	10
20	16.82	201.48	.4838	14.37	201.37	.4776	12.57	201.26	.4721	11.15	201.15	.4673	20
30	17.18	203.34	.4876	14.69	203.23	.4814	12.84	203.12	.4760	11.39	203.02	.4712	30
40	17.55	205.19	.4914	15.00	205.09	.4852	13.11	204.97	.4798	11.63	204.88	.4750	40
50	17.91	207.10	.4952	15.31	207.00	.4890	13.39	206.90	.4836	11.88	206.80	.4788	50
60	18.27	209.01	.4989	15.63	208.92	.4927	13.66	208.82	.4873	12.12	208.72	.4825	60
65	18.45	209.98	.5007	15.78	209.88	.4945	13.79	209.79	.4891	12.24	209.69	.4843	65
70	18.63	210.95	.5025	15.94	210.85	.4964	13.93	210.76	.4910	12.36	210.67	.4862	70
80	18.99	212.88	.5061	16.25	212.79	.5000	14.21	212.70	.4946	12.61	212.62	.4899	80
90	19.35	214.85	.5097	16.56	214.77	.5036	14.48	214.68	.4982	12.85	214.60	.4935	90
100	19.71	216.82	.5133	16.86	216.74	.5072	14.75	216.66	.5018	13.09	216.58	.4971	100
110	20.07	218.83	.5169	17.17	218.76	.5108	15.02	218.68	.5054	13.33	218.60	.5007	110
120	20.42	220.84	.5204	17.48	220.77	.5143	15.29	220.70	.5089	13.58	220.62	.5042	120
130	20.78	222.89	.5239	17.79	222.82	.5178	15.56	222.75	.5124	13.82	222.68	.5077	130
140	21.14	224.94	.5274	18.11	224.87	.5212	15.83	224.81	.5159	14.06	224.74	.5112	140
150	21.50	227.03	.5308	18.42	226.96	.5247	16.10	226.90	.5193	14.30	226.83	.5146	150
160	21.86	229.11	.5342	18.73	229.05	.5281	16.37	228.99	.5227	14.54	228.93	.5181	160
170	22.21	231.24	.5376	19.04	231.18	.5315	16.64	231.12	.5261	14.79	231.06	.5215	170
180	22.57	233.36	.5410	19.35	233.30	.5348	16.91	233.25	.5295	15.03	233.19	.5248	180
190	22.93	235.52	.5443	19.65	235.47	.5382	17.18	235.41	.5329	15.27	235.36	.5282	190
200	23.29	237.69	.5476	19.96	237.63	.5415	17.45	237.58	.5362	15.51	237.53	.5315	200
210	23.64	239.89	.5510	20.26	239.83	.5448	17.72	239.78	.5395	15.75	239.73	.5348	210
220	24.00	242.00	.5542	20.58	242.04	.5481	17.99	241.99	.5428	15.99	241.94	.5381	220
230	24.35	244.34	.5575	20.88	244.30	.5514	18.26	244.25	.5460	16.23	244.20	.5414	230
240	24.71	246.60	.5607	21.19	246.55	.5546	18.52	246.51	.5493	16.47	246.46	.5446	240
250	25.06	248.88	.5640	21.49	248.83	.5578	18.79	248.79	.5525	16.71	248.74	.5479	250
260	25.42	251.15	.5672	21.79	251.11	.5610	19.06	251.06	.5557	16.95	251.02	.5511	260
270	.....	.....	.....	22.10	253.44	.5642	19.33	253.40	.5589	17.19	253.36	.5543	270

Temp. °F	Abs. Pressure, 10 lbs./in.² (Sat'n. Temp. −26.1° F.)			Abs. Pressure, 11 lbs./in.² (Sat'n. Temp. −22.5° F.)			Abs. Pressure, 12 lbs./in.² (Sat'n. Temp. −19.0° F.)			Abs. Pressure, 13 lbs./in.° (Sat'n. Temp. −15.8° F.)			Temp. °F
(At sat'n.)	(8.993)	(192.64)	(.4446)	(8.224)	(193.16)	(.4421)	(7.587)	(193.64)	(.4399)	(7.042)	(194.10)	(.4379)	(At sat'n.)
−20	9.124	193.67	.4471	8.271	193.52	.4431							−20
−10	9.346	195.50	.4512	8.473	195.36	.4472	7.752	195.21	.4436	7.143	195.08	.4403	−10
0	9.567	197.32	.4552	8.675	197.19	.4512	7.943	197.06	.4476	7.317	196.93	.4443	0
10	9.788	199.18	.4591	8.877	199.06	.4552	8.131	198.94	.4516	7.489	198.82	.4483	10
20	10.01	201.04	.4630	9.079	200.93	.4591	8.318	200.82	.4555	7.661	200.71	.4522	20
30	10.23	202.91	.4669	9.281	202.81	.4630	8.503	202.70	.4594	7.831	202.60	.4561	30
40	10.45	204.78	.4707	9.483	204.68	.4668	8.688	204.58	.4632	8.001	204.48	.4599	40
50	10.67	206.70	.4745	9.685	206.60	.4706	8.873	206.51	.4670	8.171	206.41	.4637	50
60	10.89	208.62	.4782	9.887	208.53	.4744	9.056	208.43	.4708	8.341	208.34	.4675	60
65	11.00	209.60	.4800	9.988	209.50	.4762	9.147	209.41	.4726	8.426	209.32	.4693	65
70	11.11	210.58	.4819	10.09	210.48	.4781	9.239	210.39	.4745	8.511	210.30	.4712	70
80	11.33	212.53	.4856	10.29	212.44	.4818	9.422	212.35	.4782	8.681	212.27	.4749	80
90	11.55	214.51	.4892	10.49	214.43	.4854	9.605	214.34	.4818	8.851	214.26	.4786	90
100	11.77	216.50	.4928	10.70	216.42	.4890	9.788	216.34	.4855	9.021	216.26	.4822	100
110	11.99	218.52	.4964	10.89	218.44	.4926	9.971	218.37	.4890	9.191	218.29	.4858	110
120	12.21	220.54	.5000	11.09	220.47	.4961	10.15	220.40	.4926	9.361	220.32	.4894	120
130	12.43	222.61	.5035	11.29	222.54	.4996	10.34	222.47	.4961	9.531	222.40	.4929	130
140	12.65	224.67	.5069	11.49	224.61	.5031	10.52	224.54	.4996	9.699	224.47	.4964	140
150	12.86	226.77	.5104	11.69	226.70	.5065	10.70	226.64	.5030	9.867	226.57	.4998	150
160	13.08	228.86	.5138	11.88	228.80	.5100	10.88	228.74	.5065	10.04	228.68	.5032	160
170	13.30	231.00	.5172	12.08	230.94	.5134	11.06	230.88	.5099	10.20	230.82	.5066	170
180	13.52	233.13	.5206	12.28	233.07	.5168	11.24	233.02	.5133	10.37	232.96	.5100	180
190	13.74	235.30	.5240	12.47	235.25	.5201	11.42	235.19	.5166	10.54	235.14	.5134	190
200	13.95	237.47	.5273	12.67	237.42	.5235	11.60	237.37	.5200	10.70	237.31	.5168	200
210	14.17	239.68	.5306	12.87	239.63	.5268	11.78	239.58	.5233	10.87	239.53	.5201	210
220	14.38	241.89	.5339	13.07	241.84	.5301	11.96	241.79	.5266	11.04	241.74	.5234	220
230	14.60	244.15	.5372	13.26	244.11	.5334	12.15	244.06	.5299	11.21	244.01	.5267	230
240	14.81	246.42	.5405	13.46	246.37	.5367	12.33	246.33	.5332	11.37	246.28	.5300	240
250	15.03	248.70	.5437	13.66	248.65	.5399	12.51	248.61	.5364	11.54	248.57	.5332	250
260	15.24	250.98	.5469	13.85	250.94	.5431	12.69	250.90	.5396	11.71	250.85	.5364	260
270	15.46	253.32	.5501	14.05	253.28	.5463	12.87	253.24	.5428	11.87	253.19	.5396	270
280	15.67	255.66	.5532	14.25	255.62	.5495	13.05	255.38	.5460	12.04	255.53	.5428	280
290							13.23	257.98	.5491	12.21	257.93	.5459	290

TABLE 2-27. METHYL CHLORIDE: PROPERTIES OF SUPERHEATED VAPOR (Continued)

Temp. °F. t	Abs. Pressure, 11 lbs./in.² (Sat'n. Temp., −12.8° F.)			Abs. Pressure, 15 lbs./in.² (Sat'n. Temp., −9.9° F.)			Abs. Pressure, 16 lbs./in.² (Sat'n. Temp., −7.2° F.)			Abs. Pressure, 18 lbs./in.² (Sat'n. Temp., −2.1° F.)			Temp. °F. t
	v	H	s	v	H	s	v	H	s	v	H	s	
(At sat'n.)	(6.570)	(194.51)	(.4359)	(6.161)	(194.91)	(.4342)	(5.804)	(195.28)	(.4326)	(5.200)	(195.97)	(.4296)	(At sat'n.)
−10	6.614	194.92	.4371	....	....	....	....	....	....	....	....	....	−10
0	6.777	196.80	.4412	6.313	196.67	.4383	5.907	196.54	.4355	5.227	196.27	.4305	0
10	6.940	198.70	.4452	6.464	198.58	.4423	6.050	198.45	.4396	5.355	198.20	.4345	10
20	7.102	200.60	.4491	6.618	200.48	.4462	6.192	200.37	.4435	5.482	200.12	.4385	20
30	7.262	202.49	.4530	6.766	202.38	.4501	6.333	202.27	.4474	5.608	202.04	.4425	30
40	7.422	204.38	.4569	6.916	204.28	.4540	6.473	204.18	.4513	5.734	203.96	.4464	40
50	7.581	206.31	.4607	7.067	206.21	.4578	6.613	206.10	.4552	5.859	205.91	.4502	50
60	7.740	208.24	.4645	7.215	208.14	.4616	6.753	208.05	.4589	5.984	207.86	.4541	60
65	7.819	209.22	.4663	7.289	209.13	.4635	6.823	209.04	.4608	6.046	208.85	.4559	65
70	7.899	210.21	.4682	7.363	210.12	.4654	6.893	210.03	.4627	6.109	209.84	.4578	70
80	8.057	212.18	.4719	7.511	212.09	.4691	7.033	212.00	.4664	6.234	211.83	.4616	80
90	8.215	214.18	.4756	7.659	214.09	.4727	7.173	214.01	.4701	6.359	213.84	.4652	90
100	8.373	216.19	.4792	7.806	216.09	.4764	7.311	216.01	.4737	6.483	215.85	.4689	100
110	8.531	218.21	.4828	7.953	218.13	.4800	7.449	218.06	.4773	6.607	217.90	.4725	110
120	8.688	220.25	.4863	8.100	220.17	.4835	7.587	220.10	.4809	6.730	219.95	.4761	120
130	8.845	222.32	.4899	8.247	222.25	.4871	7.725	222.18	.4844	6.853	222.04	.4796	130
140	9.002	224.40	.4934	8.394	224.33	.4906	7.863	224.26	.4879	6.976	224.13	.4831	140
150	9.159	226.51	.4968	8.540	226.44	.4940	8.001	226.38	.4914	7.098	226.25	.4866	150
160	9.314	228.61	.5003	8.686	228.55	.4975	8.137	228.49	.4949	7.220	228.37	.4901	160
170	9.469	230.76	.5037	8.832	230.70	.5009	8.273	230.64	.4983	7.342	230.52	.4935	170
180	9.624	232.90	.5071	8.978	232.85	.5043	8.409	232.79	.5017	7.464	232.67	.4969	180
190	9.779	235.08	.5105	9.124	235.03	.5077	8.545	234.97	.5051	7.586	234.86	.5003	190
200	9.934	237.26	.5138	9.268	237.21	.5110	8.681	237.15	.5084	7.707	237.05	.5037	200
210	10.09	239.48	.5172	9.412	239.43	.5144	8.817	239.38	.5118	7.828	239.27	.5070	210
220	10.24	241.69	.5205	9.556	241.64	.5177	8.953	241.60	.5151	7.949	241.50	.5104	220
230	10.40	243.97	.5237	9.700	243.92	.5210	9.089	243.87	.5184	8.070	243.78	.5136	230
240	10.55	246.24	.5270	9.844	246.19	.5242	9.225	246.14	.5216	8.191	246.05	.5169	240
250	10.71	248.52	.5302	9.988	248.48	.5275	9.361	248.43	.5249	8.312	248.35	.5202	250
260	10.86	250.81	.5334	10.13	250.77	.5307	9.497	250.73	.5281	8.433	250.64	.5234	260
270	11.01	253.15	.5366	10.28	253.11	.5339	9.632	253.07	.5313	8.554	252.98	.5266	270
280	11.17	255.49	.5398	10.42	255.45	.5371	9.767	255.40	.5345	8.675	255.32	.5298	280
290	11.32	257.83	.5430	10.56	257.80	.5403	9.902	257.76	.5377	8.796	257.68	.5330	290
300	....	....	....	10.71	260.16	.5434	10.04	260.12	.5409	8.917	260.04	.5362	300

Temp. °F	Abs. Pressure, 20 lbs./in.² (Sat'n. Temp., 2.5° F.)			Abs. Pressure, 22 lbs./in.² (Sat'n. Temp., 6.8° F.)			Abs. Pressure, 24 lbs./in.² (Sat'n. Temp., 10.8° F.)			Abs. Pressure, 26 lbs./in.² (Sat'n. Temp., 14.5° F.)			Temp. °F
(At sat'n.)	(4.710)	(196.58)	(.4270)	(4.310)	(197.13)	(.4216)	(3.973)	(197.67)	(.4224)	(3.686)	(198.14)	(.4204)	(At sat'n.)
10	4.801	197.95	.4300	4.346	197.76	.4259	....	....	....	....	....	....	10
20	4.917	199.90	.4341	4.452	199.65	.4299	4.063	199.41	.4262	3.737	199.15	.4227	20
30	5.032	201.82	.4380	4.557	201.59	.4340	4.161	201.35	.4301	3.828	201.11	.4267	30
40	5.146	203.75	.4420	4.661	203.52	.4379	4.259	203.30	.4341	3.918	203.07	.4307	40
50	5.260	205.71	.4458	4.765	205.50	.4418	4.356	205.29	.4380	4.008	205.08	.4346	50
60	5.373	207.56	.4496	4.868	207.47	.4457	4.452	207.28	.4419	4.097	207.09	.4385	60
65	5.429	208.66	.4515	4.919	208.47	.4476	4.499	208.28	.4438	4.141	208.10	.4404	65
70	5.486	209.66	.4534	4.971	209.47	.4495	4.547	209.29	.4457	4.186	209.11	.4423	70
80	5.599	211.65	.4572	5.074	211.48	.4533	4.642	211.29	.4495	4.274	211.12	.4461	80
90	5.711	213.67	.4608	5.177	213.50	.4570	4.737	213.33	.4532	4.362	213.16	.4499	90
100	5.823	215.69	.4645	5.279	215.53	.4607	4.831	215.37	.4569	4.449	215.20	.4536	100
110	5.935	217.75	.4681	5.381	217.59	.4643	4.925	217.44	.4606	4.536	217.28	.4573	110
120	6.046	219.80	.4717	5.483	219.65	.4679	5.019	219.50	.4642	4.623	219.36	.4609	120
130	6.157	221.90	.4753	5.585	221.75	.4714	5.112	221.61	.4678	4.710	221.47	.4645	130
140	6.268	223.99	.4788	5.687	223.85	.4749	5.205	223.71	.4713	4.797	223.57	.4680	140
150	6.379	226.12	.4823	5.789	225.98	.4784	5.298	225.85	.4748	4.883	225.72	.4715	150
160	6.489	228.24	.4858	5.891	228.11	.4819	5.390	227.99	.4782	4.969	227.86	.4750	160
170	6.599	230.40	.4892	5.992	230.28	.4853	5.482	230.16	.4818	5.055	230.04	.4785	170
180	6.709	232.56	.4927	6.094	232.44	.4888	5.574	232.32	.4852	5.141	232.21	.4819	180
190	6.819	234.75	.4961	6.193	234.64	.4922	5.666	234.53	.4886	5.227	234.41	.4853	190
200	6.929	236.94	.4994	6.293	236.84	.4956	5.758	236.73	.4920	5.312	236.62	.4887	200
210	7.038	239.17	.5028	6.393	239.07	.4989	5.849	238.97	.4954	5.397	238.86	.4921	210
220	7.147	241.40	.5061	6.493	241.30	.5022	5.940	241.20	.4987	5.482	241.10	.4955	220
230	7.256	243.68	.5094	6.593	243.59	.5055	6.031	243.49	.5020	5.567	243.39	.4988	230
240	7.365	245.96	.5127	6.693	245.87	.5088	6.122	245.78	.5053	5.652	245.69	.5021	240
250	7.474	248.26	.5159	6.792	248.17	.5121	6.213	248.08	.5086	5.736	247.99	.5053	250
260	7.583	250.55	.5192	6.891	250.47	.5153	6.304	250.39	.5118	5.820	250.30	.5086	260
270	7.692	252.89	.5224	6.990	252.81	.5185	6.393	252.72	.5150	5.904	252.64	.5118	270
280	7.801	255.23	.5256	7.088	255.15	.5217	6.486	255.06	.5182	5.988	254.98	.5150	280
290	7.910	257.60	.5287	7.186	257.52	.5249	6.577	257.43	.5214	6.072	257.36	.5182	290
300	8.019	259.96	.5319	7.284	259.88	.5280	6.668	259.80	.5245	6.155	259.73	.5213	300
310	8.128	262.36	.5350	7.382	262.29	.5312	6.759	262.21	.5277	6.238	262.14	.5245	310
320	....	....	....	....	....	....	6.850	264.62	.5308	6.321	264.55	.5276	320

TABLE 2-27. METHYL CHLORIDE: PROPERTIES OF SUPERHEATED VAPOR (Continued)

Temp. °F	Abs. Pressure, 28 lbs./in.² (Sat'n. Temp. 18.0° F.)			Abs. Pressure, 30 lbs./in.² (Sat'n. Temp. 21.4° F.)			Abs. Pressure, 32 lbs./in.² (Sat'n. Temp. 24.5° F.)			Abs. Pressure, 34 lbs./in.² (Sat'n. Temp. 27.6° F.)			Temp. °F
t	v	H	s	v	H	s	v	H	s	v	H	s	t
(At sat'n.)	(3.439)	(198.59)	(.4186)	(3.224)	(199.00)	(.4169)	(3.034)	(199.39)	(.4153)	(2.866)	(199.76)	(.4137)	(At sat'n.)
20	3.455	198.89	.4194										20
30	3.541	200.87	.4235	3.292	200.62	.4205	3.075	200.38	.4176	2.883	200.12	.4149	30
40	3.626	202.84	.4275	3.373	202.62	.4245	3.151	202.38	.4216	2.955	202.17	.4190	40
50	3.710	204.87	.4314	3.453	204.66	.4284	3.226	204.44	.4256	3.026	204.22	.4230	50
60	3.794	206.90	.4353	3.532	206.70	.4324	3.300	206.50	.4295	3.097	206.30	.4269	60
65	3.835	207.91	.4372	3.571	207.71	.4343	3.337	207.52	.4314	3.132	207.32	.4288	65
70	3.877	208.92	.4392	3.610	208.73	.4362	3.374	208.54	.4334	3.167	208.35	.4308	70
80	3.960	210.95	.4430	3.687	210.77	.4400	3.447	210.58	.4372	3.236	210.40	.4346	80
90	4.042	212.99	.4467	3.764	212.82	.4438	3.520	212.64	.4410	3.305	212.47	.4384	90
100	4.124	215.04	.4504	3.840	214.87	.4475	3.592	214.70	.4447	3.373	214.54	.4421	100
110	4.206	217.12	.4541	3.916	216.96	.4512	3.664	216.81	.4485	3.441	216.65	.4459	110
120	4.287	219.21	.4578	3.992	219.06	.4548	3.736	218.91	.4521	3.509	218.76	.4495	120
130	4.368	221.32	.4614	4.067	221.18	.4585	3.807	221.03	.4558	3.577	220.89	.4532	130
140	4.449	223.44	.4649	4.142	223.30	.4620	3.878	223.16	.4593	3.644	223.02	.4568	140
150	4.529	225.59	.4685	4.217	225.45	.4656	3.949	225.32	.4629	3.711	225.18	.4604	150
160	4.609	227.73	.4720	4.292	227.61	.4691	4.020	227.48	.4664	3.778	227.35	.4639	160
170	4.689	229.91	.4755	4.367	229.79	.4726	4.090	229.67	.4699	3.845	229.55	.4674	170
180	4.768	232.09	.4789	4.442	231.97	.4761	4.160	231.86	.4734	3.911	231.74	.4709	180
190	4.847	234.30	.4823	4.517	234.19	.4795	4.230	234.08	.4768	3.977	233.96	.4743	190
200	4.926	236.51	.4857	4.591	236.40	.4829	4.300	236.30	.4802	4.043	236.19	.4777	200
210	5.005	238.76	.4891	4.665	238.65	.4862	4.370	238.55	.4836	4.109	238.45	.4811	210
220	5.084	241.00	.4924	4.739	240.90	.4896	4.439	240.80	.4870	4.174	240.70	.4845	220
230	5.163	243.30	.4957	4.813	243.20	.4929	4.508	243.11	.4903	4.239	243.01	.4878	230
240	5.241	245.59	.4990	4.887	245.50	.4962	4.577	245.41	.4936	4.304	245.32	.4911	240
250	5.319	247.90	.5023	4.961	247.82	.4995	4.646	247.73	.4969	4.369	247.64	.4944	250
260	5.397	250.21	.5056	5.034	250.13	.5028	4.715	250.04	.5002	4.434	249.96	.4977	260
270	5.475	252.56	.5088	5.107	252.48	.5060	4.784	252.39	.5034	4.498	252.31	.5009	270
280	5.553	254.90	.5120	5.180	254.82	.5092	4.852	254.74	.5066	4.562	254.66	.5041	280
290	5.631	257.28	.5152	5.253	257.20	.5124	4.920	257.13	.5098	4.626	257.05	.5073	290
300	5.709	259.66	.5184	5.326	259.58	.5156	4.988	259.51	.5130	4.690	259.43	.5105	300
310	5.787	262.07	.5215	5.399	262.00	.5187	5.056	261.92	.5161	4.754	261.85	.5137	310
320	5.865	264.48	.5246	5.472	264.41	.5218	5.124	264.34	.5192	4.818	264.27	.5168	320
330	.....	.....	.....	5.545	266.85	.5249	5.192	266.79	.5223	4.882	266.72	.5199	330

Temp. °F.	Abs. Pressure, 36 lbs./in.² (Sat'n. Temp., 30.5° F.)			Abs. Pressure, 38 lbs./in.² (Sat'n. Temp., 33.2° F.)			Abs. Pressure, 40 lbs./in.² (Sat'n. Temp., 35.9° F.)			Abs. Pressure, 45 lbs./in.² (Sat'n. Temp., 42.1° F.)			Temp. °F.
(At sat'n.)	(2.717)	(200.10)	(.4123)	(2.582)	(200.43)	(.4110)	(2.461)	(200.73)	(.4097)	(2.201)	(201.45)	(.4069)	(At sat'n.)
40	2.781	201.89	.4162	2.625	201.63	.4138	2.485	201.38	.4115	.....	.....	.....	40
50	2.849	203.99	.4203	2.690	203.76	.4179	2.547	203.54	.4156	2.244	202.99	.4102	50
60	2.916	206.10	.4243	2.754	205.90	.4219	2.608	205.69	.4196	2.300	205.08	.4143	60
65	2.949	207.13	.4262	2.785	206.93	.4239	2.638	206.73	.4216	2.327	206.15	.4163	65
70	2.982	208.16	.4282	2.817	207.96	.4259	2.668	207.77	.4236	2.355	207.22	.4183	70
80	3.048	210.21	.4321	2.880	210.03	.4297	2.729	209.84	.4275	2.410	209.37	.4222	80
90	3.113	212.29	.4359	2.942	212.11	.4336	2.788	211.94	.4313	2.464	211.49	.4261	90
100	3.178	214.37	.4397	3.004	214.20	.4373	2.847	214.03	.4351	2.518	213.61	.4299	100
110	3.243	216.49	.4434	3.066	216.33	.4411	2.906	216.17	.4389	2.571	215.77	.4337	110
120	3.307	218.61	.4471	3.127	218.46	.4448	2.964	218.32	.4426	2.624	217.92	.4375	120
130	3.371	220.75	.4508	3.188	220.60	.4484	3.022	220.46	.4463	2.676	220.08	.4412	130
140	3.435	222.88	.4544	3.249	222.74	.4521	3.080	222.60	.4499	2.728	222.24	.4448	140
150	3.499	225.05	.4579	3.310	224.92	.4557	3.188	224.78	.4535	2.780	224.44	.4484	150
160	3.562	227.22	.4615	3.370	227.09	.4592	3.195	226.96	.4570	2.831	226.64	.4520	160
170	3.625	229.42	.4650	3.430	229.30	.4627	3.252	229.18	.4606	2.882	228.87	.4556	170
180	3.688	231.62	.4685	3.490	231.50	.4662	3.309	231.38	.4641	2.933	231.09	.4591	180
190	3.751	233.85	.4719	3.550	233.74	.4697	3.366	233.62	.4675	2.984	233.34	.4626	190
200	3.813	236.08	.4754	3.609	235.97	.4731	3.423	235.86	.4710	3.034	235.59	.4661	200
210	3.875	238.34	.4788	3.668	238.24	.4765	3.479	238.13	.4744	3.084	237.87	.4695	210
220	3.937	240.60	.4821	3.727	240.50	.4799	3.535	240.40	.4778	3.134	240.15	.4729	220
230	3.999	242.92	.4855	3.786	242.82	.4832	3.591	242.72	.4811	3.184	242.48	.4763	230
240	4.061	245.23	.4888	3.844	245.14	.4866	3.647	245.04	.4845	3.234	244.81	.4796	240
250	4.122	247.55	.4921	3.902	247.46	.4899	3.703	247.37	.4878	3.284	247.15	.4829	250
260	4.183	249.87	.4953	3.960	249.79	.4931	3.759	249.70	.4910	3.334	249.48	.4862	260
270	4.244	252.23	.4986	4.018	252.15	.4964	3.814	252.06	.4943	3.384	251.85	.4895	270
280	4.305	254.58	.5018	4.076	254.50	.4996	3.869	254.42	.4975	3.433	254.22	.4927	280
290	4.366	256.97	.5050	4.134	256.89	.5028	3.924	256.82	.5007	3.482	256.62	.4959	290
300	4.427	259.36	.5082	4.192	259.28	.5060	3.979	259.21	.5039	3.531	259.02	.4991	300
310	4.488	261.78	.5114	4.250	261.71	.5092	4.034	261.64	.5071	3.580	261.45	.5023	310
320	4.549	264.20	.5145	4.308	264.13	.5123	4.089	264.06	.5102	3.629	263.88	.5054	320
330	4.610	266.67	.5176	4.366	266.60	.5154	4.144	266.53	.5133	3.678	266.36	.5085	330
340	4.671	269.14	.5207	4.424	269.07	.5185	4.199	269.00	.5164	3.727	268.83	.5116	340
350	.....	.....	.....	.....	.....	.....	.....	.....	.....	3.776	271.34	.5147	350

TABLE 2-27. METHYL CHLORIDE: PROPERTIES OF SUPERHEATED VAPOR (Continued)

Temp. °F t	Abs. Pressure, 50 lbs./in.² (Sat'n. Temp., 47.8° F.)			Abs. Pressure, 55 lbs./in.² (Sat'n. Temp., 53.1° F.)			Abs. Pressure, 60 lbs./in.² (Sat'n. Temp., 58.1° F.)			Abs. Pressure, 65 lbs./in.² (Sat'n. Temp., 62.7° F.)			Temp. °F t
(At sat'n.)	v	H	s	v	H	s	v	H	s	v	H	s	(At sat'n.)
	(1.992)	(202.09)	(.4013)	(1.820)	(202.66)	(.4019)	(1.676)	(203.17)	(.3998)	(1.552)	(203.65)	(.3978)	
50	2.003	202.55	.4053										50
60	2.054	204.65	.4094	1.852	204.11	.4049	1.684	203.49	.4008				60
65	2.079	205.71	.4114	1.875	205.18	.4069	1.705	204.60	.4028	1.561	204.13	.3988	65
70	2.104	206.77	.4134	1.898	206.26	.4090	1.727	205.71	.4049	1.581	205.17	.4010	70
80	2.154	208.89	.4174	1.944	208.40	.4130	1.770	207.92	.4089	1.622	207.43	.4051	80
90	2.203	211.03	.4213	1.989	210.57	.4170	1.812	210.11	.4129	1.662	209.64	.4092	90
100	2.252	213.18	.4252	2.034	212.74	.4209	1.854	212.30	.4169	1.701	211.86	.4131	100
110	2.300	215.35	.4290	2.079	214.92	.4248	1.895	214.50	.4208	1.740	214.08	.4171	110
120	2.348	217.52	.4328	2.123	217.11	.4286	1.936	216.69	.4246	1.778	216.31	.4210	120
130	2.396	219.70	.4366	2.167	219.32	.4323	1.977	218.93	.4284	1.816	218.55	.4248	130
140	2.443	221.88	.4402	2.211	221.52	.4361	2.017	221.16	.4322	1.854	220.80	.4286	140
150	2.490	224.10	.4439	2.254	223.76	.4397	2.057	223.41	.4359	1.891	223.06	.4323	150
160	2.537	226.32	.4475	2.297	225.99	.4434	2.097	225.66	.4396	1.928	225.33	.4360	160
170	2.584	228.55	.4511	2.340	228.24	.4470	2.137	227.92	.4432	1.965	227.61	.4397	170
180	2.630	230.79	.4546	2.383	230.49	.4505	2.176	230.19	.4468	2.002	229.88	.4433	180
190	2.676	233.05	.4581	2.425	232.77	.4541	2.215	232.48	.4503	2.038	232.19	.4468	190
200	2.722	235.32	.4616	2.467	235.04	.4576	2.254	234.77	.4538	2.074	234.49	.4504	200
210	2.768	237.61	.4650	2.509	237.35	.4610	2.293	237.08	.4573	2.110	236.82	.4539	210
220	2.813	239.90	.4684	2.551	239.65	.4644	2.331	239.40	.4608	2.146	239.14	.4573	220
230	2.858	242.24	.4718	2.593	242.00	.4678	2.369	241.75	.4642	2.182	241.51	.4608	230
240	2.903	244.58	.4752	2.634	244.35	.4712	2.407	244.11	.4676	2.217	243.88	.4642	240
250	2.948	246.92	.4785	2.675	246.70	.4746	2.445	246.47	.4709	2.252	246.25	.4675	250
260	2.993	249.27	.4818	2.716	249.05	.4779	2.483	248.83	.4742	2.287	248.62	.4709	260
270	3.038	251.65	.4851	2.757	251.43	.4811	2.521	251.22	.4775	2.322	251.01	.4742	270
280	3.083	254.02	.4884	2.798	253.82	.4844	2.559	253.61	.4808	2.357	253.41	.4774	280
290	3.128	256.43	.4916	2.839	256.23	.4876	2.597	256.03	.4840	2.392	255.84	.4807	290
300	3.173	258.83	.4948	2.880	258.65	.4908	2.634	258.46	.4872	2.427	258.27	.4839	300
310	3.217	261.27	.4980	2.921	261.09	.4940	2.671	260.91	.4904	2.462	260.72	.4871	310
320	3.261	263.71	.5011	2.962	263.53	.4972	2.708	263.35	.4936	2.497	263.18	.4903	320
330	3.305	266.18	.5043	3.002	266.01	.5003	2.745	265.83	.4967	2.531	265.66	.4934	330
340	3.349	268.65	.5074	3.042	268.48	.5034	2.782	268.31	.4999	2.565	268.15	.4965	340
350	3.393	271.17	.5105	3.082	270.99	.5065	2.819	270.82	.5030	2.599	270.66	.4996	350
360				3.122	273.49	.5096	2.856	273.33	.5061	2.633	273.18	.5027	360
370										2.667	275.72	.5058	370

Temp. °F.	Abs. Pressure, 70 lbs./in.² (Sat'n. Temp., 67.1° F.)			Abs. Pressure, 75 lbs./in.² (Sat'n. Temp., 71.3° F.)			Abs. Pressure, 80 lbs./in.² (Sat'n. Temp., 75.3° F.)			Abs. Pressure, 90 lbs./in.² (Sat'n. Temp., 82.7° F.)			Temp. °F.
(At sat'n.)	(1.446)	(204.08)	(.3960)	(1.354)	(204.48)	(.3943)	(1.272)	(204.84)	(.3927)	(1.136)	(205.32)	(.3898)	(At sat'n.)
70	1.458	204.72	.3974	.....	.....	.....	.....	.....	.....	.....	.....	.....	70
80	1.496	206.93	.4015	1.385	206.40	.3981	1.289	205.85	.3949	.....	.....	.....	80
90	1.533	209.17	.4056	1.420	208.68	.4022	1.323	208.17	.3991	1.158	207.18	.3931	90
100	1.570	211.41	.4096	1.455	210.96	.4063	1.356	210.50	.4032	1.189	209.57	.3973	100
110	1.606	213.64	.4136	1.490	213.20	.4103	1.389	212.76	.4073	1.220	211.87	.4015	110
120	1.642	215.86	.4175	1.524	215.44	.4143	1.421	215.02	.4113	1.250	214.18	.4055	120
130	1.678	218.14	.4214	1.558	217.75	.4182	1.453	217.35	.4152	1.279	216.55	.4096	130
140	1.713	220.43	.4253	1.592	220.05	.4221	1.485	219.68	.4191	1.308	218.92	.4135	140
150	1.748	222.71	.4290	1.625	222.36	.4259	1.516	222.00	.4229	1.336	221.28	.4174	150
160	1.783	224.99	.4327	1.658	224.66	.4296	1.547	224.32	.4267	1.364	223.64	.4212	160
170	1.818	227.28	.4364	1.691	226.97	.4333	1.578	226.64	.4304	1.392	225.99	.4250	170
180	1.852	229.57	.4400	1.723	229.27	.4370	1.608	228.96	.4341	1.419	228.34	.4287	180
190	1.886	231.89	.4436	1.755	231.60	.4406	1.638	231.30	.4377	1.446	230.71	.4324	190
200	1.920	234.21	.4471	1.787	233.93	.4441	1.668	233.65	.4413	1.473	233.08	.4360	200
210	1.954	236.55	.4506	1.819	236.28	.4476	1.698	236.01	.4448	1.500	235.46	.4396	210
220	1.987	238.89	.4541	1.850	238.63	.4511	1.728	238.37	.4483	1.527	237.85	.4431	220
230	2.021	241.26	.4576	1.881	241.02	.4546	1.758	240.77	.4518	1.554	240.27	.4466	230
240	2.053	243.64	.4610	1.912	243.40	.4580	1.788	243.16	.4552	1.581	242.68	.4501	240
250	2.086	246.02	.4644	1.943	245.79	.4614	1.817	245.56	.4586	1.607	245.10	.4536	250
260	2.119	248.39	.4677	1.974	248.17	.4648	1.846	247.95	.4620	1.633	247.51	.4569	260
270	2.152	250.80	.4710	2.005	250.59	.4681	1.875	250.37	.4654	1.659	249.94	.4603	270
280	2.185	253.20	.4743	2.035	253.00	.4714	1.904	252.79	.4687	1.685	252.38	.4636	280
290	2.218	255.64	.4776	2.065	255.44	.4747	1.933	255.24	.4720	1.711	254.84	.4669	290
300	2.250	258.08	.4808	2.095	257.89	.4779	1.961	257.69	.4752	1.737	257.31	.4702	300
310	2.282	260.54	.4840	2.125	260.35	.4811	1.989	260.17	.4784	1.763	259.80	.4734	310
320	2.314	263.00	.4872	2.155	262.82	.4843	2.017	262.64	.4816	1.788	262.29	.4767	320
330	2.346	265.49	.4904	2.185	265.32	.4875	2.045	265.14	.4848	1.813	264.80	.4798	330
340	2.378	267.98	.4935	2.215	267.81	.4906	2.073	267.64	.4879	1.838	267.31	.4830	340
350	2.410	270.50	.4966	2.245	270.34	.4938	2.101	270.17	.4911	1.863	269.85	.4862	350
360	2.442	273.02	.4997	2.275	272.86	.4969	2.129	272.70	.4942	1.888	272.39	.4893	360
370	2.474	275.57	.5028	2.305	275.44	.5000	2.157	275.28	.4973	1.913	274.97	.4924	370
380	.....	.....	.....	2.335	278.02	.5030	2.185	277.86	.5004	1.938	277.55	.4955	380
390	.....	.....	.....	.....	.....	.....	.....	.....	.....	1.963	280.18	.4985	390

TABLE 2-27. METHYL CHLORIDE: PROPERTIES OF SUPERHEATED VAPOR (Continued)

Temp. °F t	Abs. Pressure, 100 lbs./in.² (Sat'n. Temp., 89.6° F.)			Abs. Pressure, 110 lbs./in.² (Sat'n. Temp., 95.9° F.)			Abs. Pressure, 120 lbs./in.² (Sat'n. Temp., 101.9° F.)			Abs. Pressure, 130 lbs./in.² (Sat'n. Temp., 107.5° F.)			Temp. °F t
	V	H	S	V	H	S	V	H	S	V	H	S	
(At sat'n.) 90	(1.025)	(206.11)	(.3872)	(.934)	(206.63)	(.3849)	(.858)	(207.10)	(.3827)	(.793)	(207.53)	(.3809)	(At sat'n.) 90
100	1.026	206.21	.3877	.946	207.54	.3870	.....	.....	.....	.....	.....	.....	100
110	1.055	208.58	.3920	.972	210.01	.3913	.878	209.12	.3867	.799	208.16	.3824	110
120	1.083	210.96	.3962	.998	212.47	.3955	.903	211.61	.3910	.823	210.71	.3867	120
130	1.111	213.33	.4003	1.023	214.92	.3996	.927	214.09	.3952	.846	213.23	.3909	130
140	1.138	215.74	.4044	1.048	217.37	.4037	.951	216.57	.3993	.868	215.76	.3951	140
150	1.165	218.15	.4084	1.072	219.80	.4077	.974	219.04	.4034	.890	218.27	.3992	150
160	1.191	220.55	.4124	1.096	222.24	.4116	.996	221.51	.4074	.911	220.78	.4033	160
170	1.217	222.94	.4163	1.120	224.65	.4155	1.019	223.97	.4113	.933	223.27	.4073	170
180	1.243	225.33	.4201	1.143	227.07	.4194	1.041	226.42	.4152	.953	225.76	.4112	180
190	1.268	227.71	.4239	1.166	229.49	.4231	1.062	228.88	.4190	.973	228.25	.4151	190
200	1.293	230.10	.4276	1.189	231.92	.4268	1.083	231.33	.4228	.993	230.73	.4189	200
210	1.318	232.50	.4312	1.212	234.36	.4305	1.104	233.79	.4265	1.013	233.22	.4227	210
220	1.343	234.91	.4349	1.235	236.79	.4341	1.125	236.25	.4301	1.033	235.71	.4264	220
230	1.367	237.32	.4384	1.257	239.25	.4377	1.146	238.74	.4337	1.052	238.22	.4301	230
240	1.391	239.76	.4420	1.279	241.71	.4412	1.167	241.22	.4373	1.071	240.72	.4336	240
250	1.415	242.20	.4455	1.301	244.16	.4447	1.187	243.69	.4408	1.090	243.21	.4372	250
260	1.439	244.63	.4489	1.323	246.61	.4481	1.207	246.16	.4443	1.109	245.70	.4407	260
270	1.463	247.06	.4523	1.345	249.08	.4516	1.227	248.64	.4477	1.128	248.20	.4441	270
280	1.487	249.51	.4557	1.367	251.54	.4549	1.247	251.12	.4511	1.147	250.70	.4475	280
290	1.511	251.96	.4591	1.389	254.04	.4583	1.267	253.64	.4545	1.166	253.23	.4509	290
300	1.534	254.44	.4624	1.410	256.54	.4616	1.287	256.15	.4578	1.184	255.75	.4543	300
310	1.557	256.92	.4657	1.431	259.05	.4648	1.307	258.67	.4611	1.202	258.29	.4576	310
320	1.580	259.43	.4689	1.452	261.56	.4681	1.327	261.20	.4643	1.220	260.83	.4608	320
330	1.603	261.93	.4722	1.473	264.10	.4713	1.346	263.75	.4676	1.238	263.39	.4641	330
340	1.626	264.45	.4754	1.494	266.63	.4745	1.365	266.29	.4708	1.256	265.95	.4673	340
350	1.649	266.97	.4786	1.515	269.19	.4777	1.384	268.87	.4740	1.274	268.54	.4705	350
360	1.672	269.52	.4817	1.536	271.75	.4808	1.403	271.44	.4771	1.292	271.12	.4737	360
370	1.695	272.07	.4849	1.557	274.35	.4840	1.422	274.03	.4803	1.310	273.72	.4769	370
380	1.717	274.66	.4880	1.578	276.94	.4871	1.441	276.63	.4834	1.328	276.33	.4800	380
390	1.739	277.25	.4911	1.598	279.55	.4902	1.460	279.25	.4865	1.345	278.96	.4831	390
400	1.761	279.87	.4942	1.618	282.16	.4932	1.479	281.87	.4896	1.362	281.59	.4862	400
410	.....	.....	.....	.....	.....	.....	1.498	284.52	.4926	1.379	284.24	.4893	410

Temp. °F.	Abs. Pressure, 140 lbs./in.² (Sat'n. Temp., 112.9° F.)			Abs. Pressure, 150 lbs./in.² (Sat'n. Temp., 117.9° F.)			Abs. Pressure, 160 lbs./in.² (Sat'n. Temp., 122.8° F.)			Abs. Pressure, 180 lbs./in.² (Sat'n. Temp., 131.9° F.)			Temp. °F.
(At sat'n.)	(.738)	(207.91)	(.3790)	(.680)	(208.27)	(.3775)	(.617)	(208.50)	(.3757)	(.573)	(209.15)	(.3728)	(At sat'n.)
120	.754	209.70	.3825	.694	208.68	.3785							120
130	.776	212.32	.3868	.714	211.39	.3830	.661	210.54	.3793				130
140	.796	214.94	.3911	.735	214.09	.3874	.681	213.24	.3837	.590	211.42	.3768	140
150	.818	217.48	.3954	.755	216.68	.3917	.700	215.87	.3881	.608	214.17	.3814	150
160	.838	220.03	.3995	.774	219.27	.3959	.719	218.50	.3924	.626	216.92	.3858	160
170	.858	222.56	.4036	.793	221.84	.4000	.737	221.11	.3966	.642	219.62	.3902	170
180	.877	225.09	.4076	.812	224.41	.4041	.754	223.73	.4007	.658	222.32	.3944	180
190	.896	227.61	.4115	.830	226.97	.4081	.772	226.31	.4048	.675	224.98	.3986	190
200	.915	230.13	.4154	.848	229.52	.4120	.789	228.90	.4087	.691	227.64	.4027	200
210	.934	232.65	.4192	.866	232.07	.4158	.806	231.48	.4126	.706	230.28	.4067	210
220	.953	235.17	.4229	.883	234.61	.4196	.823	234.05	.4164	.722	232.92	.4106	220
230	.971	237.70	.4266	.901	237.17	.4233	.839	236.63	.4202	.737	235.55	.4145	230
240	.989	240.23	.4302	.917	239.72	.4270	.855	239.21	.4239	.752	238.17	.4182	240
250	1.007	242.73	.4338	.935	242.25	.4306	.872	241.76	.4275	.766	240.77	.4219	250
260	1.024	245.24	.4373	.952	244.77	.4341	.888	244.30	.4311	.781	243.36	.4255	260
270	1.042	247.76	.4407	.968	247.31	.4376	.903	246.86	.4346	.795	245.95	.4291	270
280	1.060	250.28	.4442	.984	249.85	.4411	.919	249.42	.4381	.809	248.54	.4326	280
290	1.077	252.82	.4476	1.000	252.40	.4445	.934	251.99	.4415	.823	251.15	.4361	290
300	1.094	255.36	.4510	1.017	254.96	.4479	.950	254.56	.4449	.837	253.75	.4395	300
310	1.111	257.91	.4543	1.033	257.53	.4512	.965	257.14	.4483	.851	256.36	.4429	310
320	1.128	260.46	.4576	1.049	260.10	.4545	.980	259.72	.4516	.865	258.97	.4463	320
330	1.145	263.04	.4609	1.065	262.68	.4578	.995	262.32	.4549	.878	261.60	.4496	330
340	1.162	265.61	.4641	1.081	265.27	.4610	1.010	264.92	.4582	.892	264.22	.4529	340
350	1.179	268.21	.4673	1.097	267.87	.4643	1.025	267.54	.4614	.906	266.86	.4562	350
360	1.196	270.80	.4705	1.113	270.48	.4675	1.040	270.15	.4647	.919	269.50	.4595	360
370	1.213	273.41	.4737	1.129	273.10	.4707	1.055	272.78	.4679	.933	272.15	.4627	370
380	1.230	276.02	.4768	1.145	275.72	.4738	1.070	275.42	.4710	.946	274.80	.4659	380
390	1.247	278.66	.4799	1.161	278.37	.4770	1.085	278.07	.4742	.959	277.48	.4691	390
400	1.264	281.30	.4830	1.176	281.02	.4801	1.100	280.73	.4773	.972	280.15	.4722	400
410	1.280	284.01	.4861	1.191	283.73	.4832	1.114	283.44	.4805	.985	282.88	.4753	410
420	1.296	286.71	.4892	1.206	286.43	.4863	1.128	286.16	.4836	.999	285.60	.4784	420
430							1.142	288.93	.4866	1.011	288.33	.4815	430
440										1.024	291.05	.4845	440

TABLE 2-27. METHYL CHLORIDE: PROPERTIES OF SUPERHEATED VAPOR (Concluded)

Temp. °F. t (At sat'n.)	Abs. Pressure, 200 lbs./in.² (Sat'n. Temp., 140.3° F.)			Abs. Pressure, 220 lbs./in.² (Sat'n. Temp., 148.0° F.)			Abs. Pressure, 240 lbs./in.² (Sat'n. Temp., 155.3° F.)			Abs. Pressure, 260 lbs./in.² (Sat'n. Temp., 162.3° F.)			Temp. °F. t (At sat'n.)
	v	H	s	v	H	s	v	H	s	v	H	s	
	(.517)	(209.60)	(.3702)	(.469)	(209.98)	(.3678)	(.430)	(210.32)	(.3657)	(.396)	(210.62)	(.3637)	
150	.533	212.41	.3749	.472	210.58	.3690	.....	.....	.....	.....	.....	.....	150
160	.551	215.30	.3796	.489	213.60	.3739	.437	211.75	.3683	.....	.....	.....	160
170	.566	218.09	.3842	.504	216.49	.3785	.451	214.79	.3732	.406	213.04	.3679	170
180	.582	220.87	.3886	.519	219.38	.3831	.466	217.82	.3779	.421	216.18	.3728	180
190	.597	223.61	.3929	.533	222.20	.3875	.480	220.73	.3824	.434	219.20	.3775	190
200	.612	226.35	.3971	.547	225.02	.3918	.493	223.64	.3868	.447	222.22	.3820	200
210	.626	229.05	.4012	.561	227.79	.3960	.506	226.49	.3911	.459	225.15	.3865	210
220	.641	231.75	.4052	.574	230.56	.4001	.519	229.33	.3953	.471	228.08	.3908	220
230	.654	234.43	.4091	.587	233.30	.4041	.531	232.13	.3994	.483	230.95	.3950	230
240	.668	237.12	.4129	.600	236.03	.4080	.543	234.93	.4034	.495	233.81	.3991	240
250	.682	239.75	.4167	.613	238.72	.4118	.555	237.67	.4073	.506	236.60	.4031	250
260	.695	242.39	.4204	.625	241.40	.4156	.566	240.40	.4111	.517	239.38	.4070	260
270	.708	245.02	.4240	.632	244.07	.4193	.578	243.11	.4149	.528	242.14	.4108	270
280	.721	247.65	.4276	.650	246.74	.4230	.590	245.82	.4186	.539	244.90	.4145	280
290	.734	250.29	.4311	.662	249.42	.4265	.601	248.54	.4222	.549	247.66	.4182	290
300	.747	252.93	.4346	.674	252.10	.4301	.612	251.26	.4258	.560	250.41	.4218	300
310	.760	255.58	.4380	.685	254.78	.4336	.623	253.97	.4293	.570	253.15	.4254	310
320	.772	258.21	.4414	.697	257.45	.4370	.634	256.67	.4328	.581	255.89	.4289	320
330	.785	260.86	.4448	.708	260.12	.4404	.645	259.37	.4363	.591	258.62	.4324	330
340	.797	263.51	.4481	.720	262.80	.4438	.655	262.08	.4397	.601	261.35	.4359	340
350	.810	266.17	.4515	.731	265.48	.4471	.666	264.79	.4430	.611	264.09	.4393	350
360	.822	268.84	.4547	.743	268.17	.4504	.677	267.50	.4464	.621	266.82	.4426	360
370	.834	271.51	.4580	.754	270.87	.4537	.687	270.22	.4497	.631	269.56	.4460	370
380	.847	274.19	.4612	.765	273.56	.4569	.697	272.94	.4529	.640	272.31	.4493	380
390	.859	276.88	.4644	.776	276.28	.4601	.708	275.67	.4562	.650	275.05	.4525	390
400	.870	279.59	.4676	.787	278.99	.4633	.718	278.40	.4594	.659	277.80	.4558	400
410	.883	282.31	.4707	.798	281.74	.4665	.729	281.17	.4626	.669	280.60	.4590	410
420	.895	285.05	.4738	.810	284.50	.4696	.739	283.94	.4658	.679	283.39	.4621	420
430	.906	287.79	.4769	.820	287.25	.4727	.748	286.71	.4689	.688	286.17	.4653	430
440	.918	290.52	.4800	.831	290.00	.4758	.758	289.48	.4720	.697	288.96	.4684	440

TABLE 2-28. SATURATED SULFUR DIOXIDE (SO₂)

Temp., °F.	Abs. Pressure lb./sq. in.	Volume		Enthalpy from −40°		Entropy from −40°		
		Liquid, cu. ft./lb.	Vapor, cu. ft./lb.	Liquid, Btu./lb.	Vapor, Btu./lb.	Liquid	Evap.	Vapor
−40	3.136	0.01044	22.42	0.00	178.61	0.00000	0.42562	0.42562
−30	4.331	0.01053	16.56	2.93	179.90	0.00674	0.41190	0.41864
−20	5.883	0.01063	12.42	5.98	181.07	0.01366	0.39826	0.41192
−10	7.863	0.01072	9.44	9.16	182.13	0.02075	0.38469	0.40544
0	10.35	0.01082	7.280	12.44	183.07	0.02795	0.37122	0.39917
2	10.91	0.01084	6.923	13.12	183.25	0.02941	0.36853	0.39794
4	11.50	0.01086	6.584	13.78	183.41	0.03084	0.46586	0.39670
5†	11.81	0.01087	6.421	14.11	183.49	0.03155	0.36454	0.39609
6	12.12	0.01088	6.266	14.45	183.57	0.03228	0.36319	0.39547
8	12.75	0.01090	5.967	15.13	183.73	0.03373	0.36053	0.39426
10	13.42	0.01092	5.682	15.80	183.87	0.03519	0.35787	0.39306
11	13.77	0.01093	5.548	16.14	183.94	0.03592	0.35654	0.39246
12	14.12	0.01094	5.417	16.48	184.01	0.03664	0.35521	0.39185
13	14.48	0.01095	5.289	16.81	184.07	0.03737	0.35388	0.39125
14	14.84	0.01096	5.164	17.15	184.14	0.03808	0.35257	0.39065
15	15.21	0.01097	5.042	17.49	184.21	0.03880	0.35125	0.39005
16	15.59	0.01098	4.926	17.84	184.28	0.03953	0.34993	0.38946
17	15.98	0.01099	4.812	18.18	184.34	0.04026	0.34861	0.38887
18	16.37	0.01100	4.701	18.52	184.40	0.04098	0.34729	0.38827
19	16.77	0.01101	4.593	18.86	184.46	0.04169	0.34598	0.38767
20	17.18	0.01102	4.487	19.20	184.52	0.04241	0.34466	0.38707
21	17.60	0.01104	4.386	19.55	184.58	0.04313	0.34335	0.38648
22	18.03	0.01105	4.287	19.90	184.64	0.04385	0.34204	0.38589
23	18.46	0.01106	4.190	20.24	184.69	0.04457	0.34073	0.38530
24	18.89	0.01107	4.096	20.58	184.74	0.04528	0.33943	0.38471
25	19.34	0.01108	3.994	20.92	184.79	0.04600	0.33812	0.38412
26	19.80	0.01109	3.915	21.26	184.84	0.04671	0.33683	0.38354
27	20.26	0.01110	3.829	21.61	134.89	0.04743	0.33553	0.38296
28	20.73	0.01112	3.744	21.96	184.94	0.04814	0.33422	0.38236
29	21.21	0.01113	3.662	22.30	184.98	0.04886	0.33292	0.38178
30	21.70	0.01114	3.581	22.64	185.02	0.04956	0.33163	0.38119
31	22.20	0.01115	3.503	22.98	185.06	0.05027	0.33034	0.38061
32	22.71	0.01116	3.437	23.33	185.10	0.05099	0.32904	0.38003
33	23.23	0.01118	3.355	23.68	185.14	0.05171	0.32774	0.37945
34	23.75	0.01119	3.283	24.03	185.18	0.05242	0.32645	0.37887
35	24.28	0.01120	3.212	24.38	185.22	0.05312	0.32517	0.37829
40	27.10	0.01126	2.887	26.12	185.37	0.05668	0.31873	0.37541
45	30.15	0.01132	2.601	27.86	185.48	0.06020	0.31234	0.37254
50	33.45	0.01138	2.348	29.61	185.56	0.06370	0.30599	0.36969
55	37.05	0.01144	2.124	31.36	185.60	0.06715	0.29971	0.36686
60	40.93	0.01150	1.926	33.10	185.59	0.07060	0.29345	0.36405
65	45.13	0.01156	1.749	34.84	185.54	0.07401	0.28724	0.36125
70	49.62	0.01163	1.590	36.58	185.46	0.07736	0.28110	0.35846
75	54.47	0.01169	1.448	38.32	185.34	0.08070	0.27498	0.35568
80	59.68	0.01176	1.321	40.05	185.17	0.08399	0.26897	0.35296
81	60.77	0.01177	1.297	40.39	185.13	0.08462	0.26772	0.35234
82	61.88	0.01179	1.274	40.73	185.09	0.08525	0.26652	0.35177
83	63.01	0.01180	1.253	41.08	185.05	0.08589	0.26532	0.35121
84	64.14	0.01181	1.229	41.43	185.01	0.08653	0.26412	0.35065
85	65.28	0.01183	1.207	41.78	184.97	0.08718	0.26291	0.35009
86†	66.45	0.01184	1.185	42.12	184.92	0.08783	0.26171	0.34954
87	67.64	0.01185	1.164	42.46	184.87	0.08847	0.26052	0.34899
88	68.84	0.01187	1.144	42.80	184.82	0.08910	0.25993	0.34843
89	70.04	0.01188	1.124	43.15	184.77	0.08974	0.25813	0.34787
90	71.25	0.01190	1.104	43.50	184.72	0.09038	0.25693	0.34731
95	77.60	0.01196	1.011	45.20	184.43	0.09349	0.25103	0.34452
100	84.52	0.01204	0.9262	46.90	184.10	0.09657	0.24516	0.34173
110	99.76	0.01219	0.7804	50.26	183.31	0.10254	0.23357	0.33611
120	120.93	0.01236	0.6598	53.58	182.36	0.10829	0.22217	0.33046
140	158.61	0.01272	0.4758	60.04	179.94	0.11893	0.19990	0.31883

TABLE 2-29. SUPERHEATED SULFUR DIOXIDE (SO₂)

Temp., °F.	Abs. pressure 10 lb./sq. in. (Sat'n. temp. −1.34°F.)			Abs. pressure 15 lb./sq. in. (Sat'n. temp. 14.43°F.)			Abs. pressure 20 lb./sq. in. (Sat'n. temp. 26.44°F.)			Abs. pressure 25 lb./sq. in. (Sat'n. temp. 36.33°F.)		
t	v	h	s	v	h	s	v	h	s	v	h	s
(at sat'n)	(7.52)	(182.95)	(0.4000)	(5.110)	(184.17)	(0.39001)	(3.878)	(184.86)	(0.38329)	(3.123)	(185.26)	(0.37754)
20	7.939	186.7	0.40802	5.192	185.4	0.39270						
30	8.030	188.4	.41159	5.333	187.3	.39672						
40	8.316	190.1	.41505	5.470	189.2	.40054	4.035	187.8	0.38959	3.181	186.1	0.37927
50	8.500	191.8	.41837	5.604	191.0	.40424	4.145	189.8	.39346	3.273	188.4	.38372
60	8.681	193.5	.42161	5.734	192.8	.40777	4.251	191.8	.39719	3.363	190.6	.38795
70	8.860	195.2	0.42480	5.862	195.6	0.41116	4.354	193.7	0.40080	3.451	192.7	0.39198
80	9.038	196.9	.42795	5.988	196.4	.41443	4.454	195.6	.40429	3.536	194.7	.39582
90	9.214	198.6	.43104	6.112	198.2	.41765	4.552	197.5	.40758	3.618	196.7	.39945
100	9.389	200.3	.43407	6.233	199.9	.42076	4.648	199.3	.41093	3.696	198.6	.40291
110	9.563	202.0	.43705	6.353	210.6	.42383	4.742	201.1	.41415	3.772	200.5	.40625
120	9.736	203.7	0.43997	6.471	203.3	0.42682	4.834	202.9	0.41726	3.848	202.4	0.40049
130	9.908	205.4	.44283	6.588	205.6	.42976	4.925	204.7	.42027	3.923	204.2	.41261
140	10.08	207.1	.44565	6.705	206.7	.43264	5.015	206.5	.42322	3.998	206.0	.41568
150	10.25	208.8	.44842	6.821	208.4	.43548	5.104	208.2	.42613	4.073	207.8	.41866
160	10.42	210.5	.45116	6.937	210.1	.43825	5.193	209.9	.42898	4.145	209.6	.42158
170	10.59	212.2	0.45296	7.052	211.8	0.44097	5.281	211.6	0.43176	4.216	211.4	0.42439
180	10.76	213.8	.45651	7.167	213.5	.44366	5.369	213.3	.43449	4.287	213.2	.42717
190	10.93	215.4	.45913	7.282	215.2	.44630	5.456	215.0	.43716	4.358	215.0	.42988
200	11.10	217.0	.46171	7.396	216.9	.44889	5.542	216.7	.43977	4.428	216.7	.43253
210							5.629	218.4	.44234	4.498	218.4	.43413

Temp., °F.	Abs. pressure 40 lb./sq. in. (Sat'n. temp. 58.83°F.)			Abs. pressure 50 lb./sq. in. (Sat'n. temp. 70.40°F.)			Abs. pressure 60 lb./sq. in. (Sat'n. temp. 80.29°F.)			Abs. pressure 70 lb./sq. in. (Sat'n. temp. 88.97°F.)		
(at sat'n)	(1.970)	(185.60)	(0.36470)	(1.577)	(185.45)	(0.35826)	(1.3144)	(185.16)	(0.35272)	(1.125)	(184.77)	(0.3478)
100	2.246	196.1	0.38415	1.650	193.9	0.37369	1.448	191.4	0.36403	1.181	187.6	0.3544
110	2.304	198.3	0.38810	1.825	196.4	0.37815	1.500	194.3	0.36906	1.228	191.6	0.3602t
120	2.360	200.4	.39183	1.872	198.8	.38234	1.548	197.0	.37375	1.272	194.8	.3654t
130	2.413	202.5	.39541	1.917	201.1	.38627	1.590	199.5	.37810	1.313	197.6	.3702t
140	2.465	204.6	.39881	1.961	203.3	.38998	1.629	201.9	.38217	1.352	200.3	.3747t
150	2.515	206.5	.40209	2.003	205.4	.39353	1.669	204.2	.38603	1.389	202.9	.3789t
160	2.565	208.5	0.40525	2.044	207.5	0.39691	1.708	206.5	0.38963	1.424	205.3	0.38291
170	2.614	210.4	.40831	2.084	209.6	.40015	1.744	208.6	.39310	1.457	207.6	.38662
180	2.662	212.3	.41127	2.123	211.6	.40327	1.778	210.7	.39639	1.489	209.9	.39014
190	2.709	214.2	.41416	2.161	213.4	.40628	1.808	212.8	.39956	1.521	212.0	.39348
200	2.755	216.0	.41694	2.199	215.4	.40919	1.842	214.8	.40260	1.551	214.1	.39670
210	2.800	217.9	0.41966	2.237	217.3	0.41200	1.874	216.8	0.40554	1.580	216.1	0.39978
220	2.845	219.7	.42233	2.274	219.2	.41477	1.907	218.7	.40839	1.608	218.1	.40275
230	2.889	221.5	.42494	2.311	221.1	.41748	1.939	220.7	.41118	1.636	220.1	.40564
240	2.933	223.3	.42751	2.347	223.0	.42015	1.970	222.6	.41391	1.664	222.1	.40845
250	2.977	225.1	.43007	2.383	224.9	.42275	2.000	224.5	.41657	1.691	224.1	.41120
260	3.021	227.0	0.43262	2.418	226.7	0.42535	2.032	226.4	0.41917	1.718	226.0	0.41389

Temp., °F.	Abs. pressure 80 lb./sq. in. (Sat'n. temp. 96.88°F.)			Abs. pressure 100 lb./sq. in. (Sat'n. temp. 110.15°F.)			Abs. pressure 120 lb./sq. in. (Sat'n. temp. 121.52°F.)			Abs. pressure 140 lb./sq. in (Sat'n. temp. 131.64°F.)		
(at sat'n)	(0.9800)	(184.33)	(0.34357)	(0.7786)	(183.50)	(0.33603)	(0.6430)	(182.19)	(0.33954)	(0.5431)	(181.04)	(0.32388)
140	1.163	198.6	0.35528	0.8928	194.6	0.35528	0.7085	190.1	0.34264	0.5734	185.1	0.33089
150	1.199	201.3	0.37270	0.9255	197.9	0.36061	0.7403	193.9	0.34904	0.6035	189.7	0.33777
160	1.232	203.9	.37692	0.9561	200.9	.36558	0.7700	197.4	.35484	0.6345	193.6	.34442
170	1.263	206.4	.38093	0.9848	203.7	.37000	0.7972	200.6	.36012	0.6613	196.3	.35041
180	1.292	208.7	.38461	1.012	206.4	.37431	0.8228	203.7	.36494	0.6861	200.8	.35588
190	1.320	211.0	.38813	1.038	209.0	.37829	0.8470	206.7	.36936	0.7092	204.0	.36088
200	1.347	213.3	0.39150	1.062	211.5	0.38203	0.8699	209.4	0.37348	0.7309	207.1	0.36548
210	1.374	215.5	.39471	1.086	213.8	.38556	0.8916	212.0	.37737	0.7513	210.0	.36976
220	1.400	217.5	.39780	1.109	216.1	.38892	0.9124	214.5	.38104	0.7707	212.7	.37379
230	1.426	219.6	.40079	1.131	218.4	.39214	0.9324	217.0	.38451	0.7892	215.4	.37758
240	1.451	221.6	.40369	1.152	220.5	.39524	0.9515	219.3	.38788	0.8070	217.9	.38118

CHAPTER 3

REFRIGERATION CYCLES

Refrigeration is that branch of engineering which deals with the pumping of heat from a substance of lower temperature to a substance of higher temperature. It is possible to do this by many methods. This book will deal with the commonly used compression types of refrigerating systems. Compression-type systems may be single- or multiple-stage. A *single-stage system* is one in which the refrigerant is pumped from one temperature level to another by a single compression process. A *multiple-stage system* is one in which the refrigerant is pumped from one temperature level to another by two or more compression processes, with intercooling of the refrigerant between the compression processes. Because of its simplicity, the single-stage system is usually used for maintaining temperatures down to 0°F. Below this temperature it is economical to use a multiple-stage system because of the lower power required.

THE SINGLE-STAGE REFRIGERATING SYSTEM

A simple single-stage refrigerating system may consist of an evaporator, a compressor, a condenser, and an expansion valve, with the necessary refrigerant, piping controls, and power equipment to drive the compressor. Such a system is shown diagrammatically in Fig. 3-1. It may also have several evaporators, compressors, condensers, or expansion valves, provided that the compressors are pumping in parallel with each other to a single system of condensers. We will study the function of these various parts separately.

The Evaporator. The evaporator is the container, or coil, within which the refrigerant boils and, by the boiling action, takes in heat. Since the boiling point is a function of refrigerant pressure, at low pressure the boiling temperature will be low, and at high pressure the boiling temperature will be high. The temperature of the refrigerant in the evaporator is called the *evaporating temperature*, and the corresponding pressure is called the *evaporating pressure*. The evaporating temperature must be lower than the space or substance to be cooled in order that heat will flow through the walls of the evaporator into the refrigerant. An evaporator may be called a *coil*, a *chilling unit*, a *blower unit*, a *brine* *cooler,* a *water cooler,* etc.   The vapor that is formed in the evaporator is carried to the compressor by means of a pipe called *the suction line.*

The Compressor.   The compressor is the machine that pumps the heat-laden refrigerant vapor from the evaporator to the condenser.   It maintains the pressure low in the evaporator so that the refrigerant will boil at a low temperature, and, at the same time, it maintains the pressure in the condenser sufficiently high that the refrigerant will condense at the temperature maintained there.   The compressor may be the recipro-

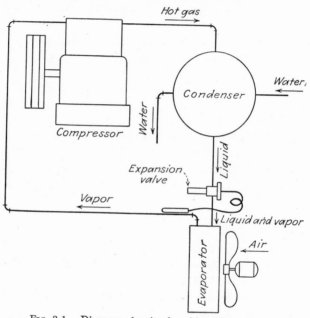

Fig. 3-1.   Diagram of a simple refrigerating system.

cating, rotary, or centrifugal type.   The compressed gas flows to the condenser from the compressor through the *discharge line.*

The Condenser.   The condenser is the heat exchanger in which the refrigerant condenses.   Heat flows from the compressed gas to the cooling medium and condenses during the process.   The pressure at which the gas condenses is a function of the temperature maintained within the condenser.   The cooling medium used may be air, water, or a combination of the two.   The pressure at which the gas condenses is called the *condensing pressure,* and the corresponding temperature is called the *condensing temperature.*   The condensed refrigerant travels from the condenser to the expansion valve through the *liquid line.*

The Expansion Valve. The expansion valve regulates the flow of liquid refrigerant to the evaporator so that the evaporator is maintained nearly full of liquid refrigerant, but so that liquid refrigerant does not enter the suction line. Upon leaving the expansion valve, the liquid enters the evaporator, and the cycle starts anew.

SINGLE-STAGE REFRIGERATING CYCLES

A refrigerating cycle is the complete course of operation of the refrigerant, from a starting point in a refrigerating system, through the system, and back to the starting point, in terms of processes. Before studying refrigerating cycles, let us first review the terms involved.

Change of State. When the condition of a substance is changed, owing to the addition or subtraction of energy, the substance is said to have undergone a change of state. A change of state may take place without a change of phase. A change of state of a fluid is known as a *process*. Quantities that determine the state of a substance are called *properties*. The main properties involved in refrigeration are pressure, volume, temperature, enthalpy, and entropy.

Pressure. Pressure is the force per unit of area exerted on the walls of a container. If the pressure is measured above absolute zero pressure, it is called *absolute pressure*. A perfect vacuum has zero pressure on the absolute scale. If the pressure is measured above atmospheric pressure, it is called *gauge pressure*. Since atmospheric pressure varies, gauge pressure is not a true pressure, but, rather, the pressure difference between that in the container and the atmospheric pressure. Throughout this text absolute pressures will be used unless it is specifically stated otherwise. The atmospheric pressure at sea level is 14.7 psi. Absolute pressure in pounds per square foot is designated P, and absolute pressure in pounds per square inch is designated p.

Saturated Liquids and Vapors, Subcooled Liquids, and Superheated Vapors. A saturated liquid, or vapor, is one at its boiling point. Thus, if water is boiling at normal atmospheric pressure, there will be saturated liquid and saturated vapor at 212°F. A subcooled liquid is one that has been cooled below its boiling point. Tap water is a subcooled liquid. A superheated vapor is one that has been heated above its boiling point. If steam at normal atmospheric pressure were heated to 250°F, it would be superheated 38°F.

Enthalpy. Enthalpy is the energy content of a fluid. Mathematically, it is defined as follows:

$$h = u + \frac{Pv}{J} \qquad (3\text{-}1)$$

where h = enthalpy, Btu/lb

u = internal energy, Btu/lb*

P = absolute pressure, psf

v = specific volume, cu ft/lb

In refrigerating tables, h is the energy content in Btu/lb above that of the saturated liquid at $-40°F$.

Change of Entropy.   Change of entropy is the amount of heat added to, or removed, from a fluid, divided by its absolute temperature.   This definition can be given as follows:

$$dS = \frac{dQ}{T} \tag{3-2}$$

where dS = change of entropy,

dQ = transferred heat[1]

T = absolute temperature

In refrigerating tables, entropy is designated s and is the transferred heat required to change 1 lb of the refrigerant from a saturated liquid at $-40°F$ to its existing state, divided by the absolute temperature in degrees Rankine.

Refrigerating Processes.   The common processes met in a refrigerating cycle are at constant temperature (isothermal), constant pressure (isobaric), and constant entropy (adiabatic).   Since there is no change of entropy in the adiabatic process, $dS = 0$, but $dS = dQ/T$, and since T always has a positive value, dQ must equal zero.   An adiabatic process is, therefore, one in which no heat is transferred.   In all the other processes, heat is transferred.

The Simple Saturated Refrigerating Cycle.   The refrigerating cycle in which the liquid refrigerant leaves the condenser in a saturated condition and the vapor leaves the evaporator in a saturated condition is called the simple saturated refrigerating cycle.   Figure 3-2 shows this cycle on temperature-entropy coordinates for a Freon 12 system in which the condensing pressure is 130 psi and the evaporating temperature is 20°F.   Figure 3-3 shows this same cycle on pressure-enthalpy coordinates.

In discussing this cycle we will start with the state of the liquid refrigerant leaving the condenser.   The properties are as follows:

$t = 99.1°F,$ $p = 130$ psi

$s = 0.06277$ Btu/(lb)(°R), $h = 30.94$ Btu/lb

This point is designated a on the diagrams.

---

* See Appendix 2.

[1] See Appendix 3.

The process *ab* is called the *throttling process*. In this process the refrigerant is cooled down to the evaporating temperature by the flashing into vapor of a small portion of the refrigerant immediately after passing through the expansion valve. If the throttling process may be assumed to be without gain or loss of heat through the walls of the pipe or valve and without the performance of external work, then both enthalpy and entropy will be constant during the process. Therefore, the properties at point *b* are

$$t = 20°F, \qquad\qquad p = 35.75 \text{ psi}$$
$$s = 0.06277 \text{ Btu/(lb)(°R)}, \qquad h = 30.94 \text{ Btu/lb}$$

The process *bc* is called the *evaporating process;* it is both isobaric and isothermal. Heat is absorbed in the evaporator by the evaporation of the refrigerant. The condition of the refrigerant at point *c* is saturated vapor; therefore its properties are

$$t = 20°F, \qquad\qquad p = 35.75 \text{ psi}$$
$$s = 0.16949 \text{ Btu/(lb)(°R)}, \qquad h = 80.49 \text{ Btu/lb}$$

The process *cd* is the compression process. In a modern compressor the process is so rapid that there can be little heat transfer between the compressed gas and the cylinder walls; therefore the process may be considered adiabatic. With adiabatic compression, the entropy after compression will be the same as before compression; however, since work is done on the gas, it will be superheated, and its enthalpy and temperature will change. These properties may be determined as follows: Turn to the superheated table corresponding to the condensing pressure. The entropy will be the same as that for point *c*. Read the other properties corresponding to this entropy.

Use of the Temperature-entropy and Pressure-enthalpy diagrams. If one understands the various processes of the refrigerating cycle as represented in Figs. 3-2 and 3-3, he may readily compute the refrigerating capacity, displacement, power required, and heat to be removed by the condenser in a refrigerating system. In the discussion of these cycles, the enthalpy at points *a*, *b*, *c*, *d*, and *e* will be designated h_a, h_b, h_c, h_d, and h_e.

In the throttling process *ab*, the liquid refrigerant at the condensing temperature is cooled down to the evaporating temperature by rapid expansion of a portion of the liquid refrigerant immediately after passing through the expansion valve. Since the process takes place without heat transfer into or from the system, the process is adiabatic and $s_a = s_b$. Since no work is done on, or by, the system, the heat content at *a* will equal the heat content at b, and hence $h_a = h_b$. No refrigeration is accomplished during this process.

The refrigeration effect takes place in the evaporator with the evaporation of refrigerant at its evaporating temperature. This is represented by the process bc. At point c the refrigerant has completely evaporated,

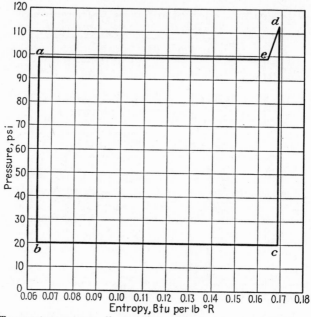

Fig. 3-2. Temperature-entropy diagram for a Freon system operating at 130 psi condensing pressure and 20°F evaporating temperature.

and heat has been taken in during the process. The refrigerating effect per pound of refrigerant is, therefore,

$$q_1 = h_c - h_b \tag{3-3}$$

where q_1 is the absorbed heat per pound of refrigerant evaporated. But $h_a = h_b$; therefore

$$q_1 = h_c - h_a \tag{3-4}$$

Now, if Q_1 is the total heat taken in by evaporator in Btu per minute, then the weight w of refrigerant passing through the expansion valve per minute is

$$w = \frac{Q_1}{q_1} \tag{3-5}$$

The actual displacement of the compressor will be

$$V_a = w v_g \qquad (3\text{-}6)$$

where V_a = actual displacement, cu ft/min
v_g = specific volume, cu ft/lb

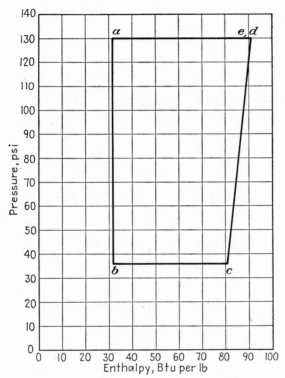

Fig. 3-3. Pressure-enthalpy diagram for a Freon 12 system with a 130-psi condensing pressure and a 20°F evaporating temperature.

The compression process *cd* takes place within the compressor. Since the time of compression is short, and since the temperature difference between the refrigerant and the cylinder is not great, there is little heat flow in the process. The process is, therefore, nearly adiabatic. In the ideal cycle, we shall consider it strictly adiabatic. Since the process is considered strictly adiabatic, the entropy after compression will be the same as the entropy before compression. The enthalpy, however, increases, since mechanical work is done on the gas. The heat of compression is the difference of enthalpies before and after compression; that is,

$$q_2 = h_d - h_c \qquad (3\text{-}7)$$

where q_2 is the heat of compression in Btu per pound of refrigerant pumped.

The total heat of compression per minute for a system is

$$Q_2 = w(h_d - h_c) \tag{3-8}$$

where Q_2 is the heat of compression in Btu/min.

The total work per minute will be 778 $w(h_d - h_c)$, and the horsepower of a 100 per cent efficient system will be

$$\text{Horsepower} = \frac{w(h_d - h_c)}{42.42} \tag{3-9}$$

Usually, both processes, dc and ea, take place in the condenser; that is, the hot gas from the compressor is cooled down to the evaporating temperature and condensed within the condenser. The heat removed per pound of refrigerant is, therefore,

$$q_3 = h_d - h_a \tag{3-10}$$

The total heat removed per minute by the condenser will be

$$Q_3 = w(h_d - h_a) \tag{3-11}$$

where Q_3 is the total heat removed by the condenser in Btu/min.

From the first law of thermodynamics, the heat removed by the condenser should be the heat taken in by the evaporator, plus the heat of compression; that is,

$$Q_3 = Q_1 + Q_2 \tag{3-12}$$

In working problems involving refrigeration cycles, Eqs. (3-11) and (3-12) will give the same answer, if the calculations are done correctly.

Coefficient of Performance. The coefficient of performance of a refrigerating system is defined as the refrigerating capacity of a system divided by the energy supplied to the compressor. For any refrigerating system

Coefficient of performance =

$$\frac{\text{heat absorbed from the refrigerated space}}{\text{energy supplied to the compressor}} \tag{3-13}$$

For the simple refrigerating cycle, this may be stated as follows:

$$\text{Coefficient of performance} = \frac{h_c - h_b}{h_d - h_c} \tag{3-14}$$

For other refrigerating cycles that will be discussed subsequently, there will be considerable deviation from this formula. The selection of the particular cycle will depend upon many factors, such as initial cost of the equipment, operating cost, and complexity.

The Effect of Subcooling the Liquid with a Water-cooled Subcooler. In the simple saturated refrigerating cycle, the liquid refrigerant during the throttling process is cooled down to the evaporating temperature by the flashing into vapor of a portion of refrigerant at the expansion valve.

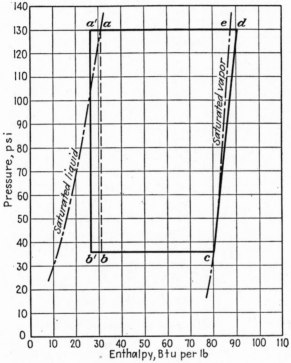

Fig. 3-4. Pressure-enthalpy diagram of a Freon 12 system operating at 130 psi condensing pressure and 20°F evaporating temperature with the liquid cooled to 80°F by water.

The flash gas produced thus can provide no further refrigerating effect. Any heat removed from the liquid will reduce the amount of flash gas and increase the capacity of the system. The increase in capacity will be exactly the same as the amount of heat that is removed from the liquid refrigerant. The subcooler generally used for this purpose is the double-tube type with the water tube inside and the liquid-refrigerant tube outside, with the water flowing counter to the refrigerant. With such a heat interchanger, the liquid refrigerant can be cooled to within a few degrees of the entering water temperature. Figure 3-4 shows the simple saturated refrigerating cycle with liquid subcooling for a Freon 12 system working at 130 psi condensing pressure and 20°F evaporating temperature, with the liquid subcooled to 80°F. The letters a, b, c, d, and e designate the simple saturated cycle, and the letters a', b', c, d and e designate the same cycle with the liquid subcooled to 80°F. The increase in capacity is $h_b - h_{b'}$, which is the same as $h_a - h_{a'}$.

$$h_a - h_{a'} = 30.94 - 26.28 = 4.66 \text{ Btu/lb}$$

The percentage increase in capacity is

$$\frac{(100)(4.66)}{80.49 - 30.94} = 9.4 \text{ per cent}$$

Since there has been no increase in power used, the capacity per unit of power is increased 9.4 per cent.

The increase in capacity per unit of power can also be analyzed by comparing the coefficients of performance. The coefficient of performance with the liquid subcooled cycle is

$$\frac{h_c - h_{a'}}{h_d - h_c} = \frac{80.49 - 26.28}{90.58 - 80.49} = 5.37$$

The coefficient of performance with the simple saturated cycle is

$$\frac{h_c - h_a}{h_d - h_c} = \frac{80.49 - 30.94}{90.58 - 80.49} = 4.91$$

The ratio of the capacities per unit of power is the ratio of the coefficients of performance, which is $5.37/4.91 = 1.094$. The increase in capacity is, therefore, 9.4 per cent.

The Effect of Superheating the Vapor Leaving the Evaporator. Superheating of the vapor leaving the evaporator may occur under one or more of the following conditions:

1. Heating of the vapor within the evaporator due to the adjustment of the expansion valve

2. Heating of the vapor within the suction line outside the cooled space

3. Heating of the vapor after leaving the evaporator, in a coil or piping located within the cooled space

When the amount of refrigerant in the evaporator of a system is controlled by a thermostatic expansion valve, it is customary to adjust the valve so that the vapor will leave the evaporator superheated 10°F above its saturated condition. This is necessary to prevent liquid refrigerant from flooding back to the compressor during starting, or during sudden changes of load. Liquid refrigerant passing back to the compressor will cause "slugging," which may result in serious damage to the compressor. When the expansion valve is adjusted in this manner, a portion of the coil will be completely filled with vapor rather than with a mixture of liquid and vapor. The heat transfer per degree of temperature difference is not as great with vapor as it is with liquid or a mixture of liquid and vapor. The suction temperature will therefore have to be lowered in order that the evaporator may take in the required amount of heat. With the lowered suction temperature, both the capacity and coefficient of performance of the system will be reduced from their values in the simple saturated cycle.

When heat is transferred through the suction line outside the cooled space, the vapor is expanded and hence has a higher specific volume. The compressor will therefore pump a smaller weight of gas, and its capacity will be reduced. The power per unit of refrigeration will be increased, and hence the coefficient of performance will be reduced.

When the vapor is heated after leaving the evaporator by heat transferred through a coil other than the evaporator, or through piping located within the refrigerated space, the refrigerating capacity is increased owing to absorbed heat. To offset this increased capacity, the heated vapor returns to the compressor in an expanded condition; hence the compressor pumps a smaller weight of gas. With the gas superheated in this manner, the capacity of the system is always slightly greater than it is with the simple saturated cycle; however, the increase may be so so small that it is negligible. The increase in capacity is more noticeable with refrigerants of high molecular weight than those of low molecular weight.

Figure 3-5 shows a comparison of the superheated cycle with the simple saturated cycle for a Freon 12 system operating at 130 psi condensing pressure and 35.75 psi evaporating pressure, with the vapor heated to 30°F by a coil or piping within the refrigerated space. The letters a, b, c, d, and e designate the saturated cycle, and the letters a, b, c', d', and e designate the superheated cycle. The ratio of the refrigerating effect per pound with the superheated cycle to that with the saturated cycle is

$$\frac{h_{c'} - h_a}{h_c - h_a} = \frac{81.89 - 30.94}{80.49 - 30.94} = 1.03$$

The increase in capacity per pound of refrigerant pumped is therefore 3 per cent. The vapor, however, is expanded because of the heat absorbed. The specific volume of the vapor varies directly as the absolute temperature; therefore, the weight of the refrigerant pumped varies inversely as the absolute temperature.   The ratio of the weight of gas pumped to the weight pumped with the saturated cycle is

$$\frac{460 + 20}{460 + 30} = 0.98$$

Taking both factors into consideration, the ratio of the capacity of a system using the superheated cycle to the capacity using the saturated

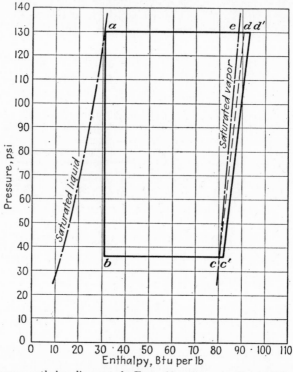

Fig. 3-5.   Pressure-enthalpy diagram of a Freon 12 system operating at 130 psi condensing pressure and 20°F evaporating temperature with the vapor heated to 30°F.

cycle is $0.98 \times 1.03 = 1.01$.   The net increase in capacity is therefore 1 per cent.

The coefficient of performance with the superheated cycle is

$$\frac{h_{c'} - h_a}{h_{d'} - h_{c'}} = \frac{81.89 - 30.94}{92.25 - 81.89} = 4.91$$

The coefficient of performance with the saturated cycle is

$$\frac{h_c - h_a}{h_d - h_c} = \frac{80.49 - 30.94}{90.58 - 80.49} = 4.91$$

The coefficient of performance is affected so slightly that it is negligible in this case. With greater superheating of the vapor, the coefficient of performance will be slightly lower with the superheated cycle than with the saturated cycle.

The Effect of Subcooling the Liquid by Superheating the Vapor. In order to prevent the suction line from sweating without the use of insulation, the suction line is often run inside the liquid line. At other times, a heat exchanger is used for the same purpose. With this arrangement, the refrigerating effect per pound is increased, owing to the subcooling of the refrigerant. The number of pounds of refrigerant pumped is reduced because of the superheating of the vapor. The net effect is the same as when the vapor is superheated by means of a coil located in the refrigerated space through which the vapor passes after it has left the evaporator. The capacity of the system is slightly increased, and the coefficient of performance is negligibly reduced.

In order to study this condition, let us consider a Freon 12 system operating at 130 psi condensing pressure and 35.75 psi evaporating pressure, with the vapor heated to 60°F in the process of cooling the liquid refrigerant. Figure 3-6 shows this cycle on pressure-enthalpy coordinates. The letters a, b, c, d, and e indicate the simple saturated cycle. The increase in capacity using the heat exchanger is due to the reduction of the amount of flash gas. The increase in refrigerating effect per pound of refrigerant handled is $h_b - h_{b'}$. But by the first law of thermodynamics,

$$h_b - h_{b'} = h_{c'} - h_c$$

The refrigerating effect per pound is therefore $h_{c'} - h_a$.

The ratio of the refrigerating effect per pound for the cycle under consideration to that for the saturated cycle is

$$\frac{h_{c'} - h_a}{h_c - h_a} = \frac{86.27 - 30.94}{80.49 - 30.94} = 1.11$$

The increase in capacity per pound of refrigerant handled is therefore 11 per cent. This increase is offset by the smaller weight of refrigerant pumped. The specific volume varies directly as the absolute temperature; therefore the volume of refrigerant pumped varies inversely as the absolute temperature. The ratio of the refrigerant pumped to the weight pumped with the simple saturated cycle is therefore

$$\frac{460 + 20}{460 + 60} = 0.925$$

The net effect on the capacity, considering both factors, is $0.925 \times 1.11 = 1.03$. The net increase in capacity is therefore 3.0 per cent.

The coefficient of performance with this cycle is

$$\frac{h_{c'} - h_a}{h_{d'} - h_{c'}} = \frac{86.27 - 30.94}{97.51 - 86.27} = 4.91$$

The coefficient of performance with the saturated cycle is 4.91. The change in the coefficient of performance is so slight that it is negligible.

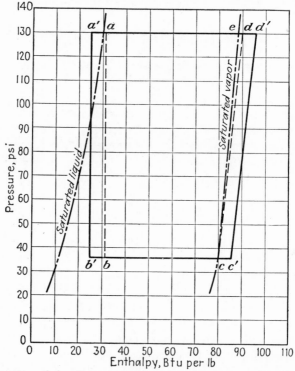

Fig. 3-6.   Pressure-enthalpy diagram of a Freon 12 system operating at 130 psi condensing pressure and 20°F evaporating temperature with the liquid subcooled by superheating the vapor.

The Effect of Friction in the Evaporator.

If resistance to flow of refrigerant occurs in the evaporator, the evaporating temperature and pressure will be less at the compressor end of the coil than at the expansion-valve end of the coil. The average temperature must be the same if the size of the coil and the cooling load are fixed. The suction pressure will be lowered, the capacity of the system will be reduced, and the coefficient of performance will be decreased.

In order to study this condition, let us examine a Freon 12 system operating on a simple saturated cycle at 130 psi condensing pressure and with saturated evaporating temperature of 24°F and 16°F at the two ends of the coil. This difference of evaporating temperatures would result from 5.50 psi pressure drop through the coil. We will compare this system with one that operates on a simple saturated cycle at 130 psi condensing pressure and 20°F evaporating temperature with no friction in the evaporator. The average refrigerating effects per pound are very nearly the same in the two cases; therefore the ratio of the capacities will be the ratios of the densities at the compressor ends of the coils.

$$\frac{d'}{d} = \frac{0.8288}{0.8921} = 0.928$$

The reduction in capacity of the system is therefore 7.2 per cent.

Let us now compare the coefficients of performance. Let $h_{c'}$ and $h_{d'}$ be the enthalpies before and after compression, starting with 16°F saturated vapor, and let h_c and h_d be the enthalpies before and after compression, starting with 20°F saturated vapor. Since the average refrigerating effects per pound of refrigerant are very nearly the same, the ratio of the coefficients of performance will be the inverse ratio of the heats of compression.

$$\frac{h_d - h_c}{h_{d'} - h_{c'}} = \frac{90.58 - 80.49}{90.94 - 80.05} = 0.926$$

The capacity of the system per unit of power consumed is therefore reduced 7.4 per cent by the friction in the coil.

The Effect of Friction in the Suction line. If we assume that the suction line is perfectly insulated, friction will cause a drop in pressure, and the resulting expansion will be adiabatic. For adiabatic expansion pv^γ is a constant,[1] where γ is the ratio c_p/c_v. With expanded vapor, the weight pumped will be reduced, and hence the capacity of the system will be reduced. In order to analyze the importance of this factor, let us examine a Freon 12 system operating at 130 psi condensing pressure and 20°F saturated suction temperature, with a pressure drop of 5 psi in the suction line. The specific volume of the expanded vapor will be

$$v_2{}^\gamma = \frac{p_1 v_1{}^\gamma}{p_2} = \frac{(35.75)(1.121)^{1.16}}{30.75} = 1.276$$

The ratio of the expanded gas pumped to the amount that would be pumped with a frictionless suction line will be the inverse of the specific-

[1] See Appendix 4.

volume ratios, or 1.121/1.276 = 87.8 per cent.   The reduction in capacity is therefore 12.2 per cent.

The power per unit of refrigeration can best be compared by use of the formula[1]

$$W = \frac{P_2 V_2 - P_1 V_1}{1 - \gamma}$$

where W = work, ft-lb

P_2 = pressure, psi, before compression

V_2 = volume before compression

The volume after compression may be computed by the formula[2]

$$P_1 V_1{}^\gamma = P_2 V_2{}^\gamma$$

When values for pressure and volume are substituted for the example under consideration, a 5-psi pressure drop in the suction line results in 11 per cent increase in power per unit of refrigeration.

The Effect of Friction in the Discharge Line.   Friction in the discharge line changes the volume of gas pumped only to the extent that the volumetric efficiency of the compressor is changed.   For pressure drops of less than 5 psi, this may be considered negligible.   The refrigerating effect per pound of refrigerant pumped is not changed, since the evaporating and condensing temperatures are not affected.   The effect on the required power is the same as if the condensing pressure were increased. To analyze this condition, let us consider a Freon 12 system operating on the simple saturated cycle at 130 psi condensing pressure and 20°F evaporating temperature, with a 5-psi pressure drop in the discharge line.   The heat of compression is the same as that of a system operating at 135 psi condensing pressure, or $90.89 - 80.49 = 10.40$ Btu/lb.   The heat of compression of the same system with a frictionless discharge pipe is $90.39 - 80.49 = 9.90$ Btu/lb.   The increase in power required is 5.05 per cent.

The Effect of Friction in the Liquid Line.   Friction in the liquid line reduces the pressure, which causes a portion of the liquid to flash into vapor unless the liquid has been subcooled.   Flashing of the liquid into vapor cools the liquid refrigerant down to the saturation temperature corresponding to the reduced pressure.   If the liquid line is below the temperature of the surrounding air, the heat transferred into the liquid line will increase, causing further flashing of the liquid into vapor.   The friction of a pipe containing liquid and vapor is greatly increased over that of a pipe containing only liquid; therefore the flashing of liquid into

---

[1] See Appendix 5.

[2] See Appendix 4.

vapor is cumulative and has a cumulative effect on the friction. Where appreciable flashing occurs in the liquid line, the expansion valve must be selected to operate on reduced pressures. The reduction in capacity if a properly sized expansion valve is used will be the amount of heat that is transferred into the liquid line.

The Effect of Friction in the Condenser. Friction in the condenser has the same effect as friction in the discharge line.

VOLUMETRIC EFFICIENCY

Volumetric efficiency, designated e, is the ratio of the gas pumped to the piston displacement of the compressor. Since volumetric efficiency comprises several factors, the term *total volumetric efficiency* will often be used to separate it from its components.

The Effect of Clearance. At the end of each discharge stroke, there will be a small portion of gas left in the cylinder due to its clearance. Since this gas has not passed through the discharge valve, the actual gas pumped will be less than the piston displacement. This factor is termed *apparent volumetric efficiency* and is designated e_c. While this factor reduces the capacity of the compressor, it increases the power required per unit of refrigeration only slightly. If the gas handled were a perfect gas, and if the compressor were frictionless, the power used in compressing the clearance gas would be given back to the system on the suction stroke, and there would be no loss of power. Actually, all refrigerants deviate considerably from being perfect gases, and friction is involved. Apparent volumetric efficiency has, therefore, a small but appreciable effect upon the power required per unit of capacity.

The Effect of Spring Tension of the Valves. Spring tension and friction of the gas through the suction valves will have the same effect as lowering the suction pressure. The capacity will be reduced, and the power required per unit of refrigeration will be increased. Spring tension on the discharge valves and friction through them will have the same effect as raising the discharge pressure. The capacity will be reduced, and the power will be increased. While spring tension is required to close the valves promptly, excessive spring tension on either suction or discharge valves will greatly reduce the capacity of the compressor and increase the power required per unit of refrigeration.

The Effect of Valve and Piston-ring Leakage. There is very little leakage past the rings on a compressor in good condition. The leakage past the valves is primarily due to the fact that the valves do not close instantaneously. If heavy valves were used on high-speed compressors, this factor would become quite large. For this reason all high-speed compressors have lightweight valves.

The Effect of Heating of the Vapor. Heat, other than the heat of compression, is added to the gas during the suction stroke and the beginning of the compression stroke by the heat conducted from the cylinder walls. This heat expands the vapor, making it less dense, and hence less weight of the refrigerant will be pumped. The capacity is thereby reduced, and the power per unit of capacity increased. Heat is also added to the vapor owing to the fact that refrigerants are not perfect gases, to turbulence of the gas within the cylinder, and to friction of the piston in the cylinder. It is difficult to separate these factors; hence they are all grouped together, and their effect upon the volumetric efficiency is termed *thermal volumetric efficiency.*

Total Volumetric Efficiency. The total volumetric efficiency is the ratio of the gas pumped to the piston displacement of the compressor. It is the product of the various volumetric efficiencies, or

$$e = e_c \times e_t \times ell_1 \times e_{st}$$

where e = total volumetric efficiency
e_c = volumetric efficiency due to clearance
e_t = thermal volumetric efficiency
ell_1 = volumetric efficiency due to leakage past rings and valves
e_{st} = volumetric efficiency due to spring tension on the valves

Application of Volumetric Efficiency. The actual displacement of a compressor is equal to the piston displacement times the volumetric efficiency.

$$V = V_p \times e$$

where V = volume of gas pumped
V_p = piston displacement
e = total volumetric efficiency

An approximation of the actual power required by a compressor operating on the simple saturated cycle can be obtained by dividing the power as computed by Eq. (3-9) by the volumetric efficiency and allowing about 10 per cent for friction. Equation (3-9) then becomes

$$\text{Horsepower} = \frac{1.1w(h_d - h_c)}{42.42e} \tag{3-15}$$

To obtain a more accurate determination, it would be necessary actually to test the compressor.[1]

[1] It has been pointed out previously that volumetric efficiency due to clearance has a slight, but appreciable, effect of the power required. For this reason, some authorities separate this factor from the others. If this is done, a greater factor for

Volumetric Efficiency as a Function of the Compression Ratio. The compression ratio of a refrigerating compressor is the ratio of the discharge pressure to the suction pressure.

The volumetric efficiency due to clearance can be shown mathematically to be a function of the compression ratio. It can also be easily explained why this is the case. If the compression ratio is small, the volume of the gas after compression will be nearly the same as it was before it was pumped; therefore nearly the entire displacement will pass through the discharging valve. If no compression occurred, the actual volume pumped would be the same as the piston displacement, regardless of clearance. In a reciprocating water pump, there is no change in volume during pumping, and the water pumped equals the piston displacement, regardless of what the clearance may be. Now let us consider the condition with a large compression ratio. The vapor after compression occupies only a small portion of the volume that it occupied before compression. Any space between the piston and the cylinder head, therefore, will hold a considerable weight of the gas. This gas does not pass through the discharge valve, and hence the actual gas pumped will be reduced by the amount that is compressed in the clearance volume. Therefore, the larger the compression ratio, the lower is the volumetric efficiency due to clearance.

Thermal volumetric efficiency cannot be shown rigorously by mathematics to be a function of the compression ratio, since the type of cooling of the head of the compressor would be involved. We can, however, explain why this is the case. If the compression ratio is small, there will be little work of compression, and hence little heat will be added to the gas. The head of the compressor, therefore, will be cool, and little heat will be conducted along the cylinder walls. With the cylinder walls cool, little heat will be added to the gas, and expansion due to heat conducted from the walls will be small. Now, let the compression ratio become great. The heat of compression will be great; the head of the compressor will become hot, and hence heat will be conducted along the cylinder walls. The hot cylinder walls will transmit heat to the incoming gas, expanding it and hence allowing less to enter the cylinder. The larger the compression ratio, therefore, the lower is the volumetric efficiency.

The volumetric efficiency due to spring tension on the valves and friction through them is not a direct function of the compression ratio. The volumetric efficiency due to leakage past the suction and dis-

---

friction should be added, since volumetric efficiency due to clearance does have some effect on the power required. Actually, the separation will change the answer only slightly, since volumetric efficiency due to clearance is usually a small part in the total volumetric efficiency.

charge valves during the closing process is a function of the compression ratio. The larger the compression ratio, the larger is the pressure difference across the valve and the larger is the proportion of the gas leaking to that which should be pumped. The larger the compression ratio, therefore, the lower the volumetric efficiency due to leakage.

Since the total volumetric efficiency is a product of the separate volumetric efficiencies, and since each of these except the volumetric efficiency due to spring tension is a function of the compression ratio, we will find the volumetric efficiency to be nearly constant for a given compression ratio, regardless of what the range may be. Following are typical volumetric efficiencies of compressors of 5 to 25 hp for various types of compressors, computed from several manufacturers' ratings.

TABLE 3-1. APPROXIMATE VOLUMETRIC EFFICIENCIES OF AMMONIA COMPRESSORS
FROM 5 TO 25 HP

R	e	R	e	R	e
3	80	7	67	11	58
4	76	8	64	12	56
5	73	9	62	13	54
6	70	10	60	14	52

TABLE 3-2. APPROXIMATE VOLUMETRIC EFFICIENCIES OF METHYL CHLORIDE COMPRESSORS FROM 5 TO 25 HP

R	e	R	e	R	e
1.5	84	4.0	73	6.5	63
2.0	82	4.5	71	7.0	62
2.5	80	5.0	69	7.5	61
3.0	77	5.5	67	8.0	59
3.5	75	6.0	65	8.5	58
				9.0	57

TABLE 3-3. APPROXIMATE VOLUMETRIC EFFICIENCIES OF FREON 12 COMPRESSORS
FROM 5 TO 25 HP

R	e	R	e	R	e
1.5	83	4.0	70	6.5	59
2.0	80	4.5	68	7.0	58
2.5	77	5.0	65	7.5	57
3.0	74	5.5	63	8.0	56
3.5	72	6.0	61	8.5	55
				9.0	54

Larger compressors may be expected to have slightly higher volumetric efficiencies, and smaller compressors may be expected to have slightly lower volumetric efficiencies.

MULTIPLE-COMPRESSION SINGLE-STAGE SYSTEMS

A refrigerating system can be arranged so that it will operate on several separate suction pressures without throttling the vapor from the

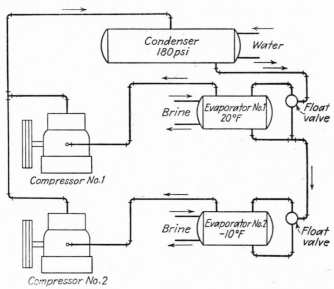

Fig. 3-7. Schematic diagram of a multiple-compression single-stage system.

higher to the lower pressures. This can be accomplished by a dual-effect compressor arranged so that the cylinder is first opened to the lower pressure. The low-pressure vapor enters the cylinder as the stroke progresses. Near the end of the stroke the valves from the higher pressure suction main are opened, and the higher pressure gas enters the cylinder, raising the pressure in it and closing the low-pressure intake valves. Usually a more suitable method is the use of several compressors. The discharge lines are connected to a discharge header, which delivers the hot gas to the condenser. The liquid for each succeeding lower temperature is taken from an accumulator or float valve used in connection with the evaporator for the next higher stage. Figure 3-7 shows such a system diagrammatically. Figure 3-8 shows the cycle on pressure-enthalpy coordinates. Since the liquid for the lower temperature evaporator is subcooled, there is a greater refrigerating effect per pound of refrigerant than if two single-stage systems were used.

Values for pressure and enthalpy at the various points for Fig. 3-8 are as follows:

Point	Pressure, psi	Enthalpy, Btu/lb
a_1	180	143.3
b_1	48.21	143.3
c_1	48.21	617.8
d_1	180	698.6
a_2	48.21	64.7
b_2	23.74	64.7
c_2	23.74	608.5
d_2	180	738.7

In order to study this system, let us compare it to two separate single-stage systems working at the same condensing and evaporating temperatures as the multiple-compression system.   Let us assume the following

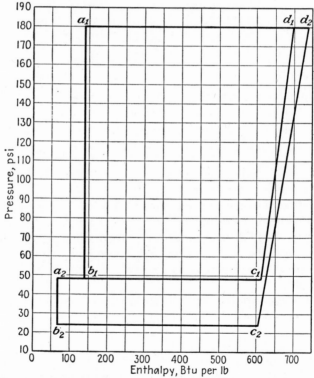

Fig. 3-8.   Pressure-enthalpy chart for a multiple-compression single-stage system using ammonia at a condensing pressure of 180 psi and evaporators at 20°F and −10°F.

operating conditions: 180 psi condensing pressure; in evaporator No. 1—20°F evaporating temperature, capacity 1 ton ime;[1] in evaporator No. 2—10°F, capacity 1 ton ime. We will compare these systems on the basis of piston displacement and required horsepower. In making these comparisons, we will assume that the vapor leaves the evaporators in a saturated condition; we will use volumetric efficiencies as given in Table 3-1, and we will compute the horsepower by Eq. (3-15).

The results are as follows:

Compressor	Piston displacement, cu ft/min	Horsepower
Multiple-compression single-stage system		
No. 1............................	3.71	1.34
No. 2............................	6.48	1.90
Total......................	10.19	3.24
Two separate single-stage systems		
No. 1............................	3.24	1.15
No. 2............................	7.58	2.22
Total......................	10.82	3.37

From the above comparison it will be seen that the multiple compression has 6.0 per cent less displacement and requires 4.0 per cent less horsepower than two separate single-stage systems.

MULTIPLE-STAGE REFRIGERATING SYSTEMS

With a simple single-stage system, as the difference between condensing and evaporating temperature widens, the refrigerating effect per pound of refrigerant and the volumetric efficiency decrease. A simple single-stage system operating on wide temperature differences must, therefore, have large displacement and will consume a large amount of power. To keep the displacement and power requirements at a minimum, multiple-stage systems are generally used for maintaining temperatures below 0°F.

Multiple-stage System with Vapor Cooling Between Stages. The most simple method of securing multiple-stage refrigeration is to cool the vapor to about 90°F, with water, between stages. Figure 3-9 shows a

---

[1] The refrigerating capacity of a system is often measured in tons ime (ice-melting equivalent). One ton ime is the rate of cooling offered by 1 ton of ice at 32°F melting in 1 day. It is 200 Btu/min, 12,000 Btu/hr, or 288,000 Btu/day.

system of this type.   Figure 3-10 shows this cycle on *p-h* coordinates. Values for pressure and enthalpy at the various points for Fig. 3-10 are as follows:

Point	Pressure, psi	Enthalpy, Btu/lb
a_1	180	143.3
b_1	50	143.3
c_1	50	618.2
d_1	180	696.7
a_2	50	66.5
b_2	10.41	66.5
c_2	10.41	597.6
d_2	50	688.5
c_2'	50	658.2
d_2'	180	750.1

In order to study this system, let us compare it to two single-stage systems working at the same condensing and evaporating temperatures as the two-stage system.   Let us assume the following operating conditions: 180 psi condensing pressure; in evaporator No. 1, 21.67°F evaporating temperature, capacity 1 ton ime; in evaporator No. 2, −40°F evapo-

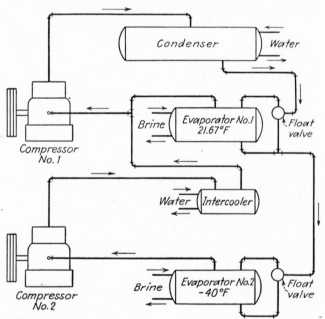

Fig. 3-9.   Schematic diagram of a two-stage refrigerating system with the vapor cooled between stages.

rating temperature, capacity 1 ton ime; discharge gas from compressor No. 2 cooled to 90°F, with water, in the two-stage system. The comparison will be on the basis of piston displacement and horsepower. Volumetric efficiencies as given in Table 3-1 will be used when possible.

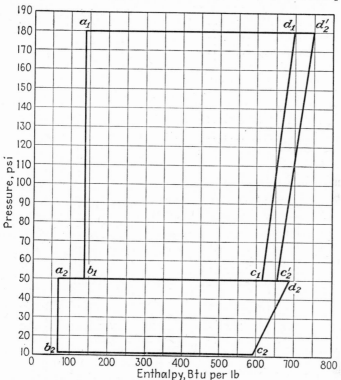

Fig. 3-10. Multiple-stage system with vapor cooled to 90°F between stages. Condensing pressure 180 psi, evaporators at 21.67°F and −40°F using ammonia.

For the compression ratio of 17.3, a volumetric efficiency of 50 per cent will be used. (Volumetric efficiencies are extremely variable at high compression ratios.)

The results are as shown in the table on page 176.

From the above comparison it will be seen that the two-stage system requires 22 per cent less displacement and 34 per cent less horsepower than two separate single-stage systems.

Multiple-stage System with Flash-type Intercooling between Stages. With this type of two-stage system, liquid refrigerant is injected into the discharge line of the lower temperature compressor, and the discharge gas is cooled down to the evaporating temperature of the higher temperature evaporator. This system is shown schematically in Fig. 3-11, and

Compressor	Piston displacement, cu ft/min	Horsepower
Two-stage system		
No. 1........................	6.78	2.42
No. 2........................	12.7	1.21
Total......................	19.48	3.63
Two single-stage systems		
No. 1........................	3.1	1.10
No. 2........................	21.9	4.41
Total......................	25.0	5.51

Fig. 3-12 shows the cycle on *p-h* coordinates.   Controls for injection will be discussed in a subsequent chapter.

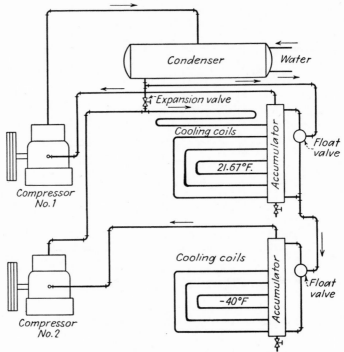

Fig. 3-11. Schematic diagram of a two-stage refrigerating system with flash-type intercooling.

Values for pressure and enthalpy at the various points for Fig. 3-12 are as follows:

Point	Pressure, psi	Enthalpy, Btu/lb
a_1	180	143.3
b_1	50	143.3
c_1	50	618.2
d_1	180	696.7
a_2	50	66.5
b_2	10.41	66.5
c_2	10.41	597.6
d_2	50	688.5

In order to study this system, let us compare it, as before, to two single-stage systems working at the same condensing temperatures and

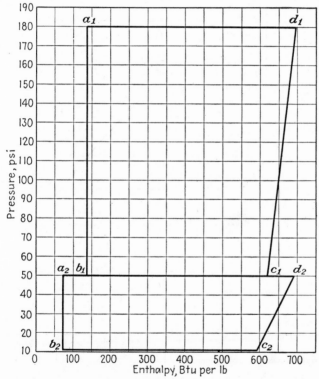

Fig. 3-12. Multiple-stage system with flash-type intercooling between stages. Condenser pressure 180 psi, evaporators at 21.67°F and −40°F using ammonia.

evaporating temperatures as the two-stage system. We will assume the following operating conditions: 180 psi condensing pressure; evaporator No. 1, 21.67°F evaporating temperature, 1 ton ime capacity; evaporator No. 2, −40°F evaporating temperature, 1 ton ime capacity. Volumetric efficiencies as given in Table 3-1 will be used when possible. For the compression ratio of 17.3, a volumetric efficiency of 50 per cent will be used. It will further be assumed that the entire energy input of com-

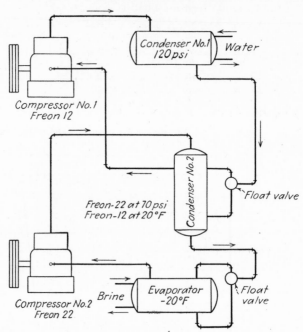

Fig. 3-13. Schematic diagram of a two-stage refrigerating system using a condenser between stages.

pressor No. 2 is carried over in the discharge gas to the higher temperature stage.

The results are as follows:

Compressor	Piston displacement, cu ft/min	Horsepower
Two-stage system		
No. 1	5.42	2.48
No. 2	12.70	1.21
Total	18.12	3.69
Two single-stage systems		
No. 1	3.10	1.10
No. 2	21.90	4.41
Total	25.00	5.51

From the above comparison it will be seen that the two-stage system with flash intercooling requires 27.5 per cent less displacement and 33.0 per cent less horsepower than two single-stage systems.

Multiple-compression System using a Condenser between Stages. The foregoing two-stage systems could only be used if a single refrigerant

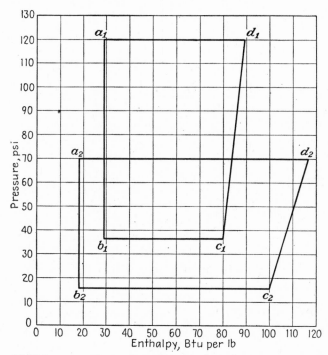

FIG. 3-14. Multiple-compression system using a condenser between stages. Upper stage: Freon 12, condensing pressure 120 psi, evaporator at 20°F. Lower stage: Freon 22, condensing pressure 70 psi, evaporator at −40°F.

were involved, and if this refrigerant were insoluble in oil. Ammonia would be nearly the only satisfactory refrigerant. If an oil-solvent refrigerant were used, it would be difficult to maintain proper oil levels in the two crankcases. Two refrigerants could not be used, since they would mix. In either of these two cases, a condenser should be used between stages. This condenser is usually a shell-and-tube interchanger using evaporating refrigerant from the higher temperature stage to condense the refrigerant of the lower temperature stage. Figure 3-13 shows such a system, and Fig. 3-14 shows its refrigerating cycle on *p-h* coordinates.

Values for pressure and enthalpy at the various points for Fig. 3-14 are as follows:

	Pressure, psi	Enthalpy, Btu/lb
a_1	120	29.53
b_1	35.75	29.53
c_1	35.75	80.49
d_1	120	89.95
a_2	70	18.74
b_2	15.31	18.74
c_2	15.31	100.46
d_2	70	116.22

In order to study this system, let us consider a two-stage system using Freon 12 in the higher temperature stage and Freon 22 in the lower temperature stage. We will assume conditions as follows: The Freon 12 stage will operate at 120 psi condensing pressure and 20°F evaporating temperature. The Freon 22 stage will operate at 70 psi condensing pressure and −40°F evaporating temperature. The system will have a capacity of 1 ton ime, all the heat being taken in at the lower temperature evaporator. We will compare the horsepower required by this system to that required by a single-stage Freon 22 system. A comparison of displacements would have no meaning, since two refrigerants of different pressure-volume characteristics are used in one system, while only one refrigerant is used in the other.

The results are as follows:

Freon 12 stage... 1.72 hp
Freon 22 stage... 1.41 hp
    Total... 3.13
Single stage... 4.45 hp

From the foregoing it will be seen that the two-stage system requires 29.6 per cent less power than the single-stage system.

Problems

1. Plot the simple saturated refrigerating cycle for a Freon 12 system operating at 120 psi condensing pressure and 0°F evaporating temperature on T-s and p-h coordinates.

2. Plot the simple saturated refrigerating cycle for an ammonia system operating at 180 psi condensing pressure and 0°F evaporating temperature on T-s and p-h coordinates.

3. What are the condensing temperatures and the temperatures after compression in Probs. 1 and 2? Why is the discharge temperature for ammonia higher than that for Freon 12?

4. Find the quantity of Freon 12 that must be pumped for a 50-ton-ime system operating at 120 psi condensing temperature and 0°F evaporating temperature.

5. Find the piston displacement and horsepower required for a 75-ton ammonia refrigerating system operating at 170 psi condensing pressure and 20°F evaporating temperature.

6. Find the piston displacement and horsepower required for a 75-ton single-stage ammonia refrigerating system operating at 170 psi condensing pressure and −20°F evaporating temperature.

7. A cold-storage plant requires a refrigerating capacity of 600,000 Btu/hr at 21.67°F evaporating temperature and 300,000 Btu/hr at −40°F evaporating temperature. The condensing temperature is to be 86.29°F. A multiple-compression single-stage ammonia system having two compressors is to be used. Find the horsepower and piston displacement required for each compressor.

8. If the installation described in Prob. 7 were to be refrigerated by a two-stage ammonia system using two compressors with the vapor cooled to 80°F between stages, what would be the piston displacement and horsepower required for each compressor?

9. If the installation described in Prob. 7 were to be refrigerated by a two-stage ammonia system using two compressors with flash-type intercooling, what would be the horsepower and piston displacement required for each compressor?

10. If the installation described in Prob. 7 were to be refrigerated by a two-stage ammonia system with two compressors, with the vapor between stages first cooled to 80°F with water, then further cooled down to the saturated condition by flash-type intercooling, what would be the horsepower and piston displacement required for each system?

11. If the installation described in Prob. 7 were to be refrigerated by a two-stage system using Freon 12 in the higher temperature stage and Freon 22 in the lower temperature stage, with a condensing pressure of 70 psi in the lower temperature stage, what would be the piston displacement and horsepower required by each compressor? (Assume volumetric efficiencies for Freon 22 as given in Table 3-2.)

CHAPTER 4

COMPRESSORS AND THEIR LUBRICATION

There are three types of compressors used on refrigerating systems. They are the reciprocating, the rotary, and the centrifugal types. Before studying the lubrication of these compressors, let us first examine their constructional details.

THE RECIPROCATING COMPRESSOR

The reciprocating compressor is most suited to pumping refrigerants requiring relatively small displacement and operating at relatively high

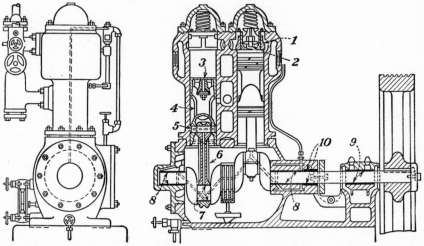

Fig. 4-1. Enclosed ammonia compressor. Parts: (1) safety head, (2) poppet-type discharge valve, (3) poppet-type suction valve, (4) trunk-type piston, (5) wrist pin, (6) connecting rod, (7) crankpin bearings, (8) main bearings, (9) outboard bearings, (10) shaft packing.

condensing pressure. Typical refrigerants used with this type of compressor are ammonia, Freon 12, methyl chloride, and sulfur dioxide. Because of the high pressures and small volumes involved, the refrigerant may be easily piped throughout the refrigerating plant. This characteristic has made the reciprocating compressor the most common type. The construction of reciprocating compressors will be given in detail. Figure 4-1 shows a section and elevation of an enclosed ammonia compressor.

Speed. The rotative speeds of modern reciprocating compressors are usually from 300 to 1,750 rpm with maximum piston speeds (at mid-stroke) not to exceed 600 fpm. The rotative speed at which a compressor may be satisfactorily operated depends on the valve action, length of piston stroke, balance, and the type of lubrication. Compressors may have high rotative speed without excessive piston speed, if the piston stroke is small in comparison to its bore and if it has many cylinders. Properly designed compressors having high rotative speeds may be equal in length of life and in performance to compressors having low rotative speeds. High-speed compressors have the advantage of lighter weight and smaller space requirements. The design tendency has therefore been toward higher rotative speeds.

Clearance. In all compressors, some volume of gas, v_c, remains in the cylinder when the exhaust valve closes. This volume of clearance gas at the discharge pressure p_2 expands at the beginning of the suction stroke until it has a volume v_d at the suction pressure p_1. If v is the actual volume pumped per stroke, then

$$v = v_p + v_c - v_d \qquad (4\text{-}1)$$

If v_c is given as a fractional part of the piston displacement, then

$$v = v_p + mv_p - v_d$$

But for adiabatic expansion $v_d = v_c(p_2/p_1)^{1/\gamma}$, where γ is the ratio of the specific heat at constant pressure to the specific heat at constant volume; therefore,

$$v = v_p + mv_p - mv_p \left(\frac{p_2}{p_1}\right)^{1/\gamma}$$

or

$$v = v_p \left[1 + m - m \left(\frac{p_2}{p_1}\right)^{1/\gamma} \right] \qquad (4\text{-}2)$$

The term $[1 + m - m \, (p_2/p_1)^{1/\gamma}]$ is called the *clearance factor*, or the *volumetric efficiency due to clearance*. It therefore becomes apparent that as the clearance becomes greater, the size of the compressor must be increased to have the required capacity.

The power required per unit of capacity is only slightly increased per unit of capacity with increased clearance. If the expansion and compression of the clearance gas were strictly adiabatic, and if the gas were a perfect gas, the work done by the gas during expansion would be the same as that done on the gas during compression. Actually, strict adiabatic expansion and compression are not achieved, and refrigerants deviate appreciably from perfect gases. Furthermore, losses due to friction occur. Increase in clearance, therefore, does increase slightly the power required per unit of capacity.

If quietness of operation is desired, appreciable clearance should be used to cushion the action of the valves. High-speed compressors usually have greater clearance than low-speed compressors.

The clearance for most compressors used in refrigeration work is about 0.020 in. The clearance for compressors used in air-conditioning work is usually greater. Poppet valves can be made with their surfaces flush with the head and with the top of the piston; the clearance volume is therefore quite small with this type of valve. Lightweight valves must be recessed; the clearance volume is therefore greater with this type of valve. This does not necessarily mean that the total volumetric efficiency will be greater with poppet valves than with lightweight valves. Other factors described in Chap. 3 and subsequently in this chapter may more than offset the effect of greater clearance.

Cylinders. From two to sixteen cylinders are generally used. Large double-acting compressors may have only one. The design tendency has been to increase the number of cylinders as the size of the compressor increases. By following this procedure, high rotative speeds may be used without having high piston speeds. High rotative speeds help in maintaining an oil film in the bearings. Using a short piston stroke also makes high rotative speeds possible without excessive piston speeds. Often the manufacturer uses the same cylinder size over a wide range of capacities. This is accomplished by increasing the number of cylinders as the capacity increases. Cylinders may be arranged in line, radially, in V formation, or in W formation.

Close-grained cast iron has proved to be the most satisfactory material for cylinders. It is easily machined and polished and is not subject to tempering or warping. Cylinders and heads may be air-cooled or water-cooled. The main purpose of cooling the cylinders and heads is to prevent excessive heating of the oil film on the cylinder walls. Slightly higher volumetric efficiency is also obtained when ample cooling of the cylinders and head is used.

Cylinders are usually removable, although sometimes the crankcase and cylinders are cast as a single unit. When the cylinders are not removable, they are usually equipped with replaceable sleeves, except on very small sizes.

Pistons and Rings. Three types of pistons are in common use. They are the automotive type, the automotive type with suction valves in the top, and the trunk type. The automotive types usually have two compression rings and one scraper ring. The trunk type is constructed as shown in Fig. 4-1, with the bottom portion at the wrist pin sealed from the crankcase. The suction vapor enters through the side of the cylinder. Two or three compression rings and two scraper rings are generally used. Fine-grained cast iron is the most suitable material for the piston and the piston rings. It is easily machined, is not subject to tempering or warping, and has good wearing qualities. Rings are usually butt-cut with a clearance between their ends of approximately 0.004 in./in. diameter of piston.

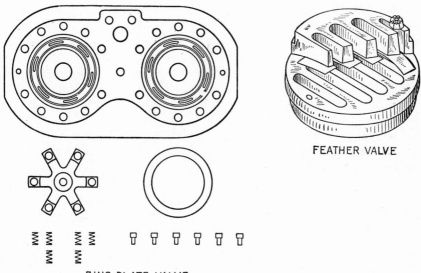

FEATHER VALVE

RING PLATE VALVE

FIG. 4-2. Lightweight valves.

Suction and Discharge Valves. The type and action of the valves are two of the most important factors in determining the rotational speed at which a compressor may be successfully operated. The ideal valve would meet the following requirements:

1. Largest possible restricted area
2. Light weight combined with low lift for quick action
3. Straight gas flow—no directional changes
4. Minimum clearance
5. Rugged
6. Tight seating

The two general types of valves are the poppet valve and the lightweight valve. Poppet valves are made of cast mild steel, and lightweight valves are constructed of thin Swedish steel.

Two types of lightweight valves and valve plates are shown in Fig. 4-2. The face of the suction poppet valve is flush with the top of the piston, and the face of the discharge poppet valve is flush with the bottom of the head. The valves are held in a normally closed position by a single weak spring on the stem of each valve. On the credit side, the poppet valve is rugged and tightly fitting, and provides a minimum clearance. On the debit side, the poppet valve has high inertia and cannot be constructed with large restricted area without having excessive lift. It is therefore a slow-speed valve and should not be used on compressors operating at greater than 400 rpm. Because of the slow action and limited area of the valve, compressors using it are equipped with a safety head held in place by strong springs. In case a slug of oil is pumped, the safety head lifts, preventing damage to the compressor.

Lightweight suction valves cannot be constructed with their faces flush with the top of the piston, nor can lightweight discharge valves be constructed with their faces flush with the bottom of the valve plate. Clearance is therefore greater with the lightweight valve than with the poppet valve. In spite of this, compressors using lightweight valves often have higher volumetric efficiencies than those using poppet valves because of the quicker action of the lightweight valve. Lightweight valves are usually held in a normally closed position by several small springs; however, they can be held in position by their own spring action. The valves often have such large restricted areas that safety heads are not necessary. The lift usually does not exceed 0.075 in. Gas velocities through the restricted areas of these valves usually do not exceed 5,000 fpm. Lightweight valves are used on compressors operating at 400 to 1,750 rpm.

Valve arrangement may be as follows:

1. Suction valves in the top of the piston with suction vapor entering through the crankcase; discharge valves in the head
2. Suction valves in the top of the piston with suction gas entering through the cylinder walls; discharge valves in the head
3. Suction and discharge valves in the head

Arrangements 1 and 3 use the automotive-type piston. Arrangement 2 uses the trunk-type piston.

Arrangement 1 is satisfactory for compressors of oil-solvent refrigerants using splash lubrication if the piston speed does not exceed 400 fpm. Higher speeds may cause excessive splash, resulting in slugging of the oil at the head of the compressor. This arrangement is also satisfactory at higher speeds with forced lubrication if the crankshaft is arranged high above the oil level so that excessive splash does not occur.

With oil-solvent refrigerants there is always a circulation of oil through the compressor. This oil may pass through the system and return to the crankcase or it may be removed by an oil trap in the discharge line and automatically returned to the crankcase. With non-oil-solvent refrigerants, such as ammonia, very little oil passes through the compressor discharge valves, and this oil does not readily return to the crankcase. The small amount of oil that passes is collected in a discharge-line oil trap. The oil is drained from the discharge-line oil trap and wasted. If valve arrangement 1 were used on ammonia, excessive oil would pass through the discharge valve and be wasted; hence, it is not used with this kind of compressor.

Valve arrangement 2 is used on all vertical enclosed compressors and a considerable number of other compressors above 5 hp. The trunk-type piston tends to keep the oil in the crankcase, and the only contact of the oil with the refrigerant is on the cylinder walls. There is no abrupt directional change of the gas flow through the compressor, and a maximum valve area is obtainable. With ammonia compressors, very little oil is carried through the discharge valve. When used with ammonia, poppet valves are generally used; rotative speeds are usually less than 400 rpm, and piston speeds are usually less than 400 fpm. When this arrangement is used with Freon 12 compressors, lightweight valves are used; rotative speeds may be up to 1,750 rpm, and piston speeds may be up to 600 fpm. With arrangement 3, the gas enters through valves in the head and leaves through valves in the head. The piston is of the automotive type with a solid top; the oil in the crankcase, therefore, does not come directly in contact with the refrigerant. Since both valves are in the head, the valve area is somewhat limited. This disadvantage may be overcome by making the cylinder bore greater than the length of the piston stroke. This arrangement has a slightly greater tendency to heat the incoming vapor than does arrangement 2, and directional changes of the flow of gas are involved. This valve arrangement is used on compressors of all sizes not requiring a water-cooled head. When used with lightweight valves, rotative speeds up to 900 rpm have been used. Piston speeds are usually moderate because of the necessity of having the cylinder bore greater than the length of the piston stroke.

Bearings. Crankpin bearings are usually tin-base babbit metal; however, bronze is sometimes used. Main bearings are usually of the sleeve type, using tin-base babbit or bronze. Roller and ball main bearings are also used. Thrust bearings must be provided to counteract the pressure acting on the shaft area at the stuffing box or shaft seal, and to prevent end play of the crankshaft. Thrust bearings are usually a part of the main bearings. Wrist-pin bushings are usually bronze or cast iron. The wrist pins themselves are casehardened steel. Roller and ball wrist-pin bearings have also been successfully used. Bearing pressures usually do not exceed the following: main bearings, 300 psi; crankpin bearing, 600 psi; wristpin bearings, 1,200 psi. These pressures are based on square inches of projected area. If properly machined and lubricated, the foregoing list of materials will stand many times the above-mentioned pressures. Refrigerant compressors, however, are designed for long life, and the above values are seldom exceeded.

Crankshafts. Crankshafts are constructed of nickel-chrome steel. All journals are accurately machined and polished. High-speed compressors require counterweights on the crankshaft. Counterweights are made of cast iron and fastened to the crank web by studs. To prevent movement of the counterweights on the crank, they are machined to fit over the cheeks, but are made a few thousandths of an inch smaller to give a light shrink fit. The counterweights are heated before assembling. Counterweights have the following functions:

1. To balance the inertia of the reciprocating parts
2. To obtain a dynamic balance
3. To reduce bearing pressures

In the first case, one-half the inertia force set up by the reciprocating parts may be neutralized by proper counterweights attached opposite the crankpin. In the second case, weights are added to offset unbalanced couples. A two-throw crankshaft with 180° between cranks, if accurately machined, is balanced statically but not dynamically. To obtain dynamic balance, suitable counterweights are required.

The third case applies to compressors in static and dynamic balance, such as all vertical compressors with three or more throws. In these compressors, the big ends of the connecting rods produce centrifugal force, which results in an increase of main-bearing pressure. These periodic centrifugal forces can be eliminated by counterbalancing each big connecting-rod end with a weight located opposite the crankpin and producing an equal moment. It is for this purpose that counterweights are used on multicylinder compressors intrinsically balanced.

Compressors using counterweights must take precautions to avoid slugging of oil due to excessive oil splash. To avoid slugging, both suction and discharge valves may be located in the head, the trunk-type piston may be used, or the crankshaft may be located high above the oil level and forced lubrication used.

Shaft Packing and Shaft Seals. Ammonia is easily held by various soft, as well as metallic, packings. These packings are graphited and are further lubricated by a slight leakage of oil from the crankcase.

The Freons and methyl chloride are difficult to hold, and shaft seals have been developed. These seals depend upon two polished metal surfaces, one of which rotates with the shaft, while the other is held stationary. Tension on the two metal surfaces is usually supplied by a spring. The effectiveness of the seal depends upon cleanliness of the working parts, proper lubrication, and the quality of the polished surfaces. A polished surface is one that has been ground at such high speeds that the surface is melted and floated. The irregularities of a well-polished surface are molecular in dimension and cannot be detected with the ordinary microscope. The maintenance of this polish depends upon clean working conditions and proper lubrication. On installation a shaft seal should be rinsed with carbon tetrachloride and, if necessary, wiped with a clean chamois. Cloth should not be used, since a small fiber may cause leakage. The seal faces should then be dipped in clean oil, or coated with a thin film of vaseline. The compressor should be designed so that the seal runs in a bath of oil at all times.

Capacity Regulation. The capacity of a reciprocating compressor may be regulated by cylinder by-passes, clearance pockets, or by speed regulation.

Cylinder by-passes are of several types: suction valves may be held open on some of the cylinders; a valve may be opened between cylinders whose crank bends are 180° apart; a by-pass may be arranged at the bottom half of the cylinder so that only its upper half is used; or a solenoid valve may be arranged to by-pass the discharge gas from some of the cylinders back to the suction line. With all these devices, the efficiency of the compressor is lowered. When working at half capacity, the compressor will consume about 70 per cent of the power it uses at full capacity, assuming that the suction and discharge pressure are held constant.

A clearance pocket is a pocket at the top of the cylinder opened automatically or manually. Its effect is the same as that of the cylinder by-pass. The power is reduced, but not in proportion to the capacity reduction.

Because of the lowered efficiency of compressors using cylinder by-passes or clearance pockets, the vapor will superheat more than it does normally upon compression. With Freon 12 the superheated temperature is not excessive, but with ammonia, provision must be made to inject liquid ammonia into the suction line automatically, after starting, to prevent the gas from becoming excessively superheated.

The capacity of a compressor may be satisfactorily regulated by a two-speed motor, provided that the slower speed is sufficiently high to maintain an oil film in the bearings. Two-speed three-phase induction motors are obtainable at 25 and 50 per cent speed reduction. Before this method is used, the minimum speed at which the compressor may be run should be carefully checked. With modern high-speed Freon 12 compressors, a 50 per cent speed reduction is usually all right if the high speed is the top speed allowed by the manufacturer. With large ammonia compressors, this method may not be satisfactory.

The most often used and usually the best method of securing capacity regulation is the use of multiple compressors in parallel. The disadvan-

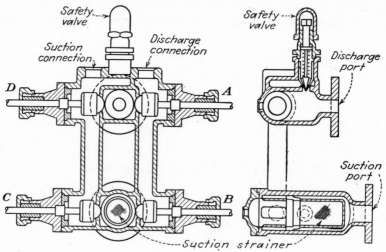

Fig. 4-3.   The valve manifold.

tages of this method are slightly higher first cost, a greater number of parts to the system, and larger space requirements.

Suction Scale Traps and Valve Manifold. All compressors except very small ones should be equipped with suction scale traps. For nearly all ammonia systems, and for some Freon 12 systems, the scale traps are a part of the valve manifold and are arranged as shown in Fig. 4-3. The valve manifold is arranged to unload the compressor completely for starting, and to cross-connect the suction and discharge lines so that the condenser may be pumped down and the refrigerant discharged into the evaporating coils. To unload the compressor, valves A, B, and C should be open. Closing of valve B will restore normal operation. To pump down the condenser, valves A and C should be closed and valves B and D should be open. The valve manifold is usually equipped with a spring-loaded relief valve to discharge the compressed gas into the suction pipe if the pressure becomes excessive, or if the discharge valves are accidentally left closed. The scale-trap screen is located at the suction inlet as shown. It can be removed for cleaning after the compressor has been pumped down and after all valves have been closed.

With Freon 12 systems having dry-expansion coils the cross connections are of little value, since the amount of refrigerant the evaporating coils will hold is small. For this reason most Freon 12 compressors are not equipped with a valve manifold. A scale trap for Freon 12 is shown in Fig. 4-4. An oil connection with a check valve is made to the crank-

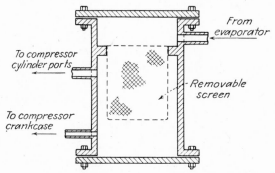

FIG. 4-4. Suction-scale trap for Freon compressor.

case. This type of scale trap has been termed a suction-line oil separator; however, it is not very effective in this respect. Oil does not separate readily from the refrigerant unless the refrigerant is highly superheated. Traps of this type do help, to a limited extent, in avoiding slugging.

ROTARY COMPRESSORS

The rotary compressor is most suited to pumping refrigerants having moderate or low condensing pressures. Suitable refrigerants are sulfur dioxide. Freon 21, and Freon 114. Rotary compressors are generally of

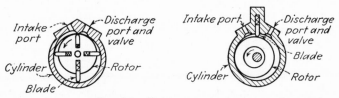

FIG. 4-5. Rotary compressors.

two types. In the blade type, the rotor shaft is concentric with the rotor and eccentric with the cylinder. In the other, the rotor shaft is eccentric with the rotor and concentric with the cylinder. Both types are shown in Fig. 4-5. The blade type is the more common. With it, the blades are held outward against the stator by centrifugal force, or by centrifugal force and spring action. Either type always includes a discharge valve, but a suction valve is not needed. With either, the action is positive, the volumetric efficiency is high, and a large displacement is obtainable with a moderate-sized compressor. Rotary compressors must be used with oil-solvent refrigerants in order that the blades and rotor be properly lubricated.

Rotary compressors require accurate machining and polishing of the parts. No gaskets can be used between the end plates and the cylinder, since the rotor must fit accurately between the end plates. The polish between these parts must be maintained in order that leaks will not occur. Because of the accurate fitting required, rotary compressors are not as easily overhauled as reciprocating compressors. They can be made in small sizes without manufacturing difficulties but are difficult to construct in larger sizes. They are particularly adaptable to household refrigerators.

THE CENTRIFUGAL COMPRESSOR

The centrifugal compressor is suitable for pumping refrigerants requiring large displacement and operating at low condensing pressures. It resembles in principle the multiple-stage centrifugal water pump.

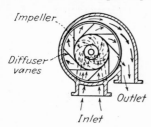

FIG. 4-6. Section of a centrifugal compressor.

Figure 4-6 shows a section of a centrifugal compressor. Pressure is produced largely by centrifugal action but partially by throwing action. The impeller blade is strongly backward curved so that the pressure produced will be largely by centrifugal action. The velocity pressure, due to the throwing action, is partially changed to static pressure by a set of stationary diffuser blades for each impeller. The available pressure produced by each impeller is the sum of the pressure produced by centrifugal action and the static pressure developed by the diffuser blades. Two to four impellers, in series, are generally used. The total pressure produced is the sum of the pressures produced by the separate impellers. The pressure produced is proportional to the density of the refrigerant and to the square of the velocity of the tip of the impeller blades.

Refrigerants. Since the pressure produced by a centrifugal compressor is proportional to the density of vapor of the refrigerant, only those refrigerants having high molecular weights are used. Compressors manufactured by the Carrier, Worthington, and York Corporations use Freon 11, $CFCl_3$ (molecular weight, 137.4). Compressors manufactured by the Trane Company use Freon 113, CCl_2FCClF_2, (molecular weight, 187.4). At atmospheric pressure Freon 11 has a boiling point of 74.7°F, and Freon 113 has a boiling point of 117.6°F. At a condensing temperature of 86°F, Freon 11 has a saturation pressure of 18.28 psi, and Freon 113 has a saturation pressure of 7.86. Compressors using Freon 11, therefore, operate at a condensing pressure above that of the atmosphere and an evaporating pressure below that of the atmosphere, while Freon 113 systems operate at a vacuum on both high and low sides. For multiple-stage systems involving centrifugal compressors and operating at very low temperatures, Freon 12 has been used in the lowest temperature stage with Freon 11 in the higher temperature stages. Systems of this type have been used to chill special brines down to −100°F. Other refrigerants that have been successfully used with centrifugal compression are dichloroethylene, $C_2H_2Cl_2$; trichloroethylene, C_2HCl_3; Carrene No. 1, CH_2Cl_2; ethyl bromide, C_2H_1Br; ethyl chloride, C_2H_5Cl; and water vapor, H_2O. Carrene No. 2 and Freon 11 are the same refrigerant.

Liquid Intercooling. Because centrifugal compressors have several sets of impellers, liquid intercooling is often obtained by installing an extra float valve with accumulator before the main float valve for the cooler. A separate suction line is run from the top of the accumulator to a position on the compressor between impellers. Both lower horsepower and smaller size of compressor result from this arrangement. This matter has been discussed in Chap. 3 under the caption Multiple-compression Single-stage systems.

Indirect Systems. With some systems, refrigerant is piped to the cooling coils located in the refrigerated space. This type of system is called a *direct-expansion system*. With other systems, brine is cooled in the evaporator and piped to the cooling coils in the refrigerated space. This type of system is called a *brine system*, or an *indirect system*. Because of the large volume of vapor required with refrigerants used with centrifugal compression, direct expansion is not practical. All centrifugal-compression systems are closely connected brine systems, with the suction line not more than a few feet long.

Centrifugal-compressor Sizes. With a given refrigerant, the pressure produced by a single impeller is proportional to the square of the tip speed of the impeller. The condensing pressure is a function of the condenser-water temperature and of the heat-transfer conditions in the condenser. This pressure may be obtained with an impeller having high rotative speed or large diameter; it may also be obtained by multiple impellers in series. The resulting combinations of these factors must be the same for small compressors as for large compressors. This makes small sizes very expensive. The smallest size is manufactured by the Trane Company and is a 35-hp. compressor. Other companies do not make centrifugal compressors of less than 100 hp.

Lubricating System. Nearly all centrifugal compressors have force-feed lubrication to the two main bearings and to the shaft seal. There are no other wearing parts. Since the suction side of the compressor operates on a vacuum, lubrication of the shaft seal can be maintained only with a positive oil pressure. About 30 to 40 psi gauge pressure is generally used. Trane compressors avoid shaft-seal difficulties by using motors sealed in the same enclosure as the compressor. In one respect this is a great advantage; however, it limits the type of power equipment that may be used to drive the compressor.

Purge System. Any leakage at the shaft seal is inward to the compressor. A slight leakage may occur even though the shaft seal is pressure lubricated. This air is noncondensable and collects in the condenser. The corrosive nature of the noncondensable gases in the presence of oil, refrigerant, and a slight trace of moisture, which may be present, makes it imperative that these noncondensable gases be removed quickly. Centrifugal refrigerating systems are, therefore, equipped with an automatic purging system. Automatic purgers will be discussed in a subsequent chapter.

Power Equipment. As has been previously stated, the pressure a centrifugal compressor will develop is proportional to the density of the gas. The suction vapor is most dense when starting the compressor. The condensing pressure is determined by the temperature of the condenser water and the heat-transfer characteristics of the condenser. Centrifugal compressors therefore tend to lower the suction pressure rapidly, and to use excessive power as they come up to full speed. If a steam turbine is used to drive the compressor, it should be brought up to speed gradually. If a synchronous motor is used, it should have high pull-in and pull-out torques. A 3,600-rpm synchronous motor with an 0.8 leading power factor has desirable characteristics for this service, and very attractive electric rates are obtainable when it is used. The three-phase slip-ring induction motor also has desirable starting characteristics. The Trane compressor uses a three-phase squirrel-cage induction motor.

One of the advantages of the centrifugal compressor is that it may be connected directly to a steam turbine. Steam turbines are economical when there is sufficient waste steam from any other process in the plant. They may be obtained to operate on steam at any pressure from several hundred pounds down to atmospheric pressure. The exhaust of the turbine is maintained at about 3 or 4 psi absolute by a steam condenser.

Capacity Regulation. The capacity of a system using a centrifugal compressor may be regulated by varying its speed if it is driven by a steam turbine or by a slip-ring motor. In case a synchronous motor is used, the capacity may be varied by a suction damper. The power used drops off rapidly as the suction damper is closed. The suction damper should be closed when starting the compressor.

LUBRICATION OF COMPRESSORS

If an oil film is maintained between two polished rubbing surfaces, and if this film is maintained free from abrasive and corrosive substances, there will be no wear of the rubbing parts. The problem of lubrication, then, is one of selecting the proper oil, keeping it at its proper viscosity, and maintaining it free from corrosive and abrasive substances.

Discharge-line Oil Separators. Oil that is put in the crankcase of compressors is for the purpose of lubricating compressors only. Oil that leaves the compressor and circulates through the system has no beneficial effect, but reduces the heat-transfer rate in the condenser and in the evaporator. Furthermore, excess oil in circulation may cause slugging at the head of the compressor.

The discharge-line oil separator for use with ammonia is, ordinarily, just a large vertical section of pipe with inlet and outlet connections at the top and a drain valve at the bottom. The discharge-line oil separator for Freon 12 and other oil-solvent refrigerants is equipped with a float valve at the bottom by which the oil is returned automatically to the crankcase of the compressor. Oil traps for oil-solvent refrigerants and ammonia are shown in Fig. 7-2.

Oil is not readily dissolved by ammonia; however, a small portion passes the pistons and discharge valves, largely by mechanical action. If the system is without a discharge-line oil separator, this oil will settle out at the bottom of the receiver, the condenser, the accumulator, or the evaporator. Oil is heavier than liquid ammonia, and settles out below it. Many ammonia systems do not have a discharge-line oil separator, but the receiver is arranged with a pocket or space below the liquid-line take-off from which the oil may be drained. The practice of omitting the discharge-line separator is questionable, since the oil film formed on the condenser tubes inhibits heat transfer materially. The discharge-line oil separator is very effective in removing the oil that escapes from the compressor; however, it should not be depended upon to remove all the oil. All receivers, accumulators, evaporators, and other vessels containing liquid ammonia should be equipped with a valve at the bottom by which the oil may be drained. With ammonia systems having the low-pressure side operating on a vacuum, moisture and air often enter at the shaft packing. Water is heavier than liquid ammonia and is drained off with the oil. The air is usually purged at the condenser by an automatic purger. Oil is drained out of the oil separator, or at the other drain valves, in a foaming condition. Care must be taken to shut the valve quickly when the foaming ceases.   Failure to do this will cause distress and danger.   Oil is replaced by pumping a vacuum on the crankcase, and drawing the oil in through a rubber-tube connection.   New, clean, dehydrated oil should be used.   Reclaiming the oil that has been drawn off is considered questionable practice.

With oil-solvent refrigerants such as methyl chloride and Freon 12, oil leaves the crankcase readily.   This oil will circulate through the system and return to the crankcase without the use of an oil separator if all pipes are properly sized and the coil is properly designed.

Oil circulating through the system lowers the rate of heat transfer in the condenser and in the evaporator.   Furthermore, excess oil in circulation may cause slugging at the head of the compressor.   The best practice, therefore, would demand the use of the discharge-line oil separator on all systems using oil-solvent refrigerants.

The amount of oil in circulation through a system using an oil-solvent refrigerant depends upon the oil level in the crankcase and the adjustment of the expansion valve.   If the expansion valve is adjusted for low superheat of the suction vapor, the oil does not separate readily from the vapor, and a solution of oil and refrigerant is returned to the crankcase.   This lowers the viscosity of the oil, causing a larger amount to be pumped. Excessively low viscosities and low oil level in the crankcase may result, and the rate of heat transfer in the condenser and evaporator may be greatly decreased.

Where the system is designed for great capacity reduction by the use of the cylinder by-pass, or by the use of multiple compressors, the expansion valves will be required to work under widely varying conditions. This will lead to inaccurate control of superheat, with varying amounts of oil in circulation and in the crankcase, unless the discharge-line oil separator is used.   Where the system is designed for capacity of reduction of 50 per cent or more without a corresponding reduction in the number of coils in operation, the discharge-line oil separator may be considered essential for good lubrication.

The discharge-line oil separators should be used on all systems using oil-solvent refrigerants operating at 0°F or below, for the following reasons:

1. The viscosity of the oil increases as the temperature decreases, causing a lowering of the heat-transfer rate in the evaporator.

2. Wax tends to separate at the expansion valve.

3. It is more difficult to maintain a constant superheat with a thermostatic expansion valve at low temperatures than at higher temperatures.

Oil Filters.   If a system is thoroughly cleaned when installed, evacuated to a nearly perfect vacuum before charging, and a suitable oil used, no corrosive or abrasive substances will form in the compressor. If, however, repair work is carelessly done and air, moisture, and grit are allowed to enter the system, corrosion and abrasion may occur, and sludge may form. A good oil filter will do nothing to avert corrosion, but it is insurance against abrasion and prevents clogging of the oil lines by sludge. Oil filters are not usually considered necessary, but they are a desirable feature to have on a force-feed oil system.

Viscosity of Oil. For proper lubrication, one of the most important properties of oil is its viscosity. Several units of viscosity are used. In the cgs system the unit of absolute viscosity is the poise and is measured in dynes per square centimeter, per centimeter per second, per centimeter of film thickness. The unit is quite large, so one-hundredth of it, the centipoise, is commonly used. The absolute viscosity in English units is measured in pounds per square inch, per inch per second, per inch of film thickness. If the viscosity in centipoise is designated Z, and the absolute viscosity in the English system is designated μ_0, then

$$\mu_0 = 1.45 \times 10^{-7} Z$$

In practice, viscosity is measured by instruments called *viscosimeters*, or *viscometers*. The viscosimeter used in this country is the Saybolt Universal. It measures the time in seconds required for 60 cc of a fluid to flow by gravity from a container of designated shape[1] through a metering tube 0.483 in. long and 0.0695 in. in diameter. For heavy oils, the Saybolt-Furol viscosimeter is used. It differs from the Saybolt Universal in that the tube diameter is 0.1240 in. The time of efflux of the Furol is approximately one-tenth that of the Universal. Since viscosity varies with temperature, the readings must be made at certain temperatures, usually at 100°F, or 210°F, or both. The viscosity of refrigeration lubricating oils is usually given in seconds Saybolt Universal at 100°F. This measurement is generally written as follows: Viscosity 300 at 100°F (SSU). The viscosity thus determined is called *specific viscosity*. In order to convert specific viscosity to absolute viscosity, another coefficient, called the *kinematic viscosity*, is introduced. Kinematic viscosity Z_k is the absolute viscosity Z in centipoises divided by the density. However, density in the cgs system has the same numerical value as specific gravity in the English system, so the latter may be used. If G is the specific gravity, then

$$Z_k = Z \div G$$

The specific gravity of most refrigeration lubricating oils is about 0.90.

[1] For further data refer to ASA Bulletin Z11.2-1944.

The relation between kinematic viscosity Z_k in centistokes and the specific viscosity τ_s in seconds Saybolt Universal is given by the following expression:

$$Z_k = 0.22\tau_s - \frac{180}{\tau_s}$$

Lubrication of Bearings.   Three phases of lubrication will be considered: starting, thin film, and thick film.   These phases are shown in Fig. 4-7.

When machinery stands at rest, the oil between the journal and the bearing will tend to be squeezed out, allowing the two metal surfaces to

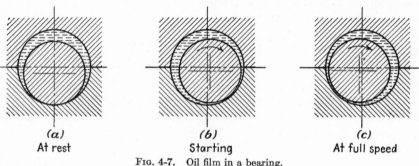

| *(a)* | *(b)* | *(c)* |
| At rest | Starting | At full speed |

FIG. 4-7.   Oil film in a bearing.

come more or less into contact as shown in part *a*, Fig. 4-7.   When the shaft starts to rotate, the friction of the journal against the bearing is high and a certain amount of abrasion will occur.

As the journal begins to rotate, it tends to roll toward the right side of the bearing as shown in part *b*, Fig. 4-7.   Because of molecular attraction, a thin wedge-shaped oil film is drawn between the two surfaces.   In this film lubrication there exists an unstable condition where the metal surfaces may touch from time to time.   Under certain conditions, such as very low rubbing speeds or high unit loads, thin-film lubrication may exist indefinitely.

As the surface velocity increases above that required for thin-film lubrication, enough oil pressure will develop to raise the shaft completely off the bearing and make it float on the lubricant.   Such lubrication is called *thick-film lubrication*.   The center of the shaft is transferred to the left as shown in part *c*, Fig. 4-7.   The rotating journal acts as a pump. The oil pressure increases with speed until it exceeds the bearing pressure, after which time the journal floats on a film of oil.   Since bearing pressures are often 500 psi and since the oil pressure developed must exceed this figure, it becomes apparent that the function of force-feed lubrication is merely to bring oil to the bearings.

The most important factors influencing the thickness of the oil film are the viscosity, the rotative speed, and the bearing pressure. These factors are combined in the expression Zn/P, called the *bearing number*, in which Z is the viscosity in centipoises, n is the rpm, and P is the average bearing pressure in pounds per square inch of projected area. For good lubrication the bearing number should exceed 20. Where this cannot be achieved, hardened bearing material such as copper-lead and bronze should be used. Because of the low rotative speeds of the wrist pins, wrist-pin bushings are usually inadequately lubricated. Wrist-pin bushings are therefore usually bronze or cast iron, while the wrist pins themselves are casehardened steel.

When oil-solvent refrigerants such as Freon 12 or methyl chloride are used, the oil becomes diluted with the refrigerant, and its viscocity often drops to one-half of what it was when installed. This factor should be taken into consideration when selecting the proper oil. A discharge-line oil trap will tend to keep the oil at its initial viscosity. The proper oil will be one whose viscosity is sufficient to maintain an oil film, but not so high that it will develop excessive friction. Modern compressors are usually designed to use oils of the following viscosities:

TABLE 4-1.

Refrigerant	Compressor type	Viscosity, SSU at 100°F
Freon group	Reciprocating Rotary Centrifugal	300–400 300–400 300
Methyl chloride	Reciprocating	200–300
Carrene	Centrifugal	300
Sulfur dioxide	Reciprocating Rotary	100–200 100–200
Ammonia	Reciprocating	150–300

Ammonia compressors operating at an evaporating temperature above −10°F usually use oil having a viscosity of 300 SSU at 100°F. For lower temperatures, the viscosity must be lowered in order that the pour point will be below the evaporating temperature. Household refrigerators using a capillary expansion tube should use oil of low viscosities, say, 100 to 200 SSU at 100°F, in order that the oil may pass through the tube.

Cloud Point. The cloud point of a petroleum oil is the temperature at which paraffin wax, or other solid substances, begin to separate from solution when the oil is chilled. It is a measure of the wax content of the oil. Low-temperature refrigerating equipment demands oils of low wax content to avoid clogging at the expansion valve. Good grades of napthene-base oils have no cloud test, as they contain no solid paraffin. Paraffin-base oils often have a cloud point 20°F above the pour point. In general paraffin-base oils should not be considered for low-temperature refrigeration lubrication.

Pour Point. The temperature at which oil ceases to flow under standardized test conditions is its pour point. It is desirable that a refrigerator-compressor oil have a pour point lower than the lowest temperature encountered in the system. With oil-solvent refrigerants, the pour point lowers with solution of refrigerant so that temperatures below the pour point of the oil can be maintained without the oil's setting.

Dielectric Strength. It is essential that moisture content in refrigerator-compressor oils be kept at an absolute minimum, especially where chlorinated refrigerants are concerned. With these refrigerants, an acidic condition may be set up that will cause corrosion, especially at the shaft seal and any control bellows that may be in the system. If copper coils or tubing are present in the system, metallic copper is deposited on the cylinder walls, pistons, valves, and bearings, resulting in excessive wear. Oils are generally hygroscopic and absorb moisture from the air readily. These small traces of water may be detected by testing its dielectric strength. In a test machine, a satisfactory refrigeration oil requires 25,000 volts to put a spark through it. When suitable oil has been purchased, it should be handled carefully. Exposure to the air will lower its dielectric strength quickly. Good practice demands that the oil be purchased in small sealed cans and that these cans be kept tightly sealed. Oil that has been exposed to the air for more than a few minutes should be discarded.

Stability of Oil. Stability against oxidation is of great importance in refrigeration lubricating oils, especially where chlorinated refrigerants are concerned. When the oil oxidizes, the acidity of the oil is increased and sludge is formed. Ammonia prevents the formation of acids, but the chlorinated refrigerants and sulfur dioxide do not. When an oil oxidizes, the original properties are changed. Carbon residue and viscosity are increased; the oil is no longer neutral and becomes corrosive in the presence of a small amount of water. Naphthene-base oils are less acidic in nature than paraffin-base oils.

CHAPTER 5

HEAT-TRANSFER EQUIPMENT

The advancement in knowledge of heat transfer in the last two decades has led to great advances in refrigeration. More than any other factor, it has reduced the size and cost of refrigerating equipment.

With condensers, evaporators, and other heat exchangers, heat is usually transferred through tubes and plates. Let us, therefore, consider the principles involved in heat transfer through tubes and plates before considering their application to various types of equipment.

Over-all Heat-transfer Coefficient U. When we considered walls in Chap. 1, the heat conducted per square feet per hour per degree Fahrenheit was given by Eq. (1-8), which will be restated here for convenience:

$$\frac{1}{U} = \frac{1}{f_o} + \frac{1}{f_i} + \frac{x_1}{k_1} + \frac{x_2}{k_2} + \cdots$$

Each of the terms in this equation represents a resistance to heat flow. The total resistance is the sum of the separate resistances offered by the films and layers. The formula applies to any plate surface. It also applies to tubes, but with one modification. The outside and inside areas differ, and therefore a correction must be made. Usually the over-all coefficient U is based upon the outside area. The inside surface film tends to offer greater resistance than does the outside film since there is a smaller area through which the heat must flow. The resistance for the inside film is therefore multiplied by A_o/A_i where A_o is the outside area and A_i is the inside area. In considering the resistance offered by the metal, one should make a correction A_o/A_m where A_m would be an area halfway between A_o and A_i for a plain tube. If hard water flows through the inside of the tube of a condenser, a scale will be formed that offers appreciable resistance to heat flow. The term indicating scale resistance should also be multiplied by A_o/A_i. If f_s is the scale conductance, Eq. (1-8) becomes

$$\frac{1}{U_o} = \frac{1}{f_o} + \frac{A_o}{A_i f_i} + \frac{A_o x_1}{A_m k_1} + \frac{A_o}{A_i f_s} \tag{5-1}$$

For a plain tube, the term indicating the resistance offered by the metal has such a small value that it affects U only in the third or fourth significant figure. This term is, therefore, usually ignored.

201

For a finned tube, most of the heat passes through the fin edgeways. The area A_m is then the sum of the cross-sectional areas of the fins, whose surface area is A_o. The distance x_1 should be taken as the mean distance through which the heat travels.

The Combined Convection and Conduction Film Coefficient for Fluids Flowing inside Tubes. Heat transfer by convection is a mixing process. A thin stationary film always adheres to the surface of the tube. In case the flow of the fluid in the tube is streamline, heat flows through this film largely by conduction. In case the flow is turbulent, portions of this film are continually disrupted and mixed with the balance of the fluid in the tube. The greater the turbulence, the greater will be the mixing action, and the thinner will be the film through which the heat is conducted. Heat transfer by convection then becomes related to fluid flow.

Experiments of Osborne Reynolds[1] in the latter part of the nineteenth century showed that the pattern of flow of a fluid in a tube was a function of a group of variables that form a dimensionless number. This number is called the *Reynolds number* and is designated Re.

$$\text{Re} = \frac{Dv\rho}{\mu} \tag{5-2}$$

where D = inside diameter of tube
v = velocity of fluid flow
ρ = density
μ = absolute viscosity

Any set of consistent units will give the same Reynolds number. The units generally used in this country are D in feet, v in feet per hour, ρ in pounds per cubic foot, and μ in pounds per hour per foot, hr or 2.42 centipoises.

When the Reynolds number is sufficiently small, the individual particles of fluid flow nearly in straight lines parallel to the axis of the pipe. This type of motion is termed *streamline, viscous,* or *laminar*. As Re increases to 2,100, eddies and vortexes form at the central portion of the pipe. Between 2,100 and 3,100 is a transition zone from streamline to turbulent flow. Above 3,100 the flow may be considered almost entirely turbulent. In the design of heat-transfer equipment Re should always be kept above 3,100.

The film conductance f has been studied by many investigators as functions of Re and of another dimensionless number $c_p\mu/k$, known as the

---

[1] REYNOLDS, O., "Scientific Papers of Osborne Reynolds," vol. 1, pp. 81–85, Cambridge University Press, London, 1901.

Prandtl number, which deals primarily with heat conduction. Nusselt showed by dimensional analysis that

$$\frac{f_i D}{k} = a \left(\frac{Dv\rho}{\mu}\right)^b \left(\frac{c_p\mu}{k}\right)^e \tag{5-3}$$

Evaluation of the constants a, b, and e by many investigators has led to the following equation,[1] which is generally used for fluids having viscosities not more than twice that of water and for Re exceeding 2,100.

$$f_i = 0.023 \frac{k}{D} \left(\frac{Dv\rho}{\mu}\right)^{0.8} \left(\frac{c_p\mu}{k}\right)^{0.4} \tag{5-4}$$

Any set of consistent units may be used. In the English system the following units are used: f in Btu/(sq ft)(°FTD), k in Btu/(hr)(sq ft) (°F per ft), D in ft, v in ft/hr, ρ in lb/cu ft, and μ in lb/(hr)(ft) or 2.42 × centipoises.

For liquids of high viscosity and for Reynolds numbers exceeding 10,000, the Colburn equation[2] gives better results.

$$f_i = 0.023 \frac{k}{D} \left(\frac{Dv\rho}{\mu}\right)^{0.8} \left(\frac{c_p\mu}{k}\right)^{0.33} \tag{5-5}$$

where all values should be considered at the mean temperature of the fluid.

For clean water flowing inside pipes, McAdams and Frost have shortened Eq. (5-4) to the following:

$$f_i = 207 \frac{(v/Z)^{0.8}}{d^{0.2}} \tag{5-6}$$

where v = water velocity, ft/sec
Z = water viscosity, centipoises
d = inside diameter of tube, in.

The Condensing-film Conductance for Fluids Condensing outside of Tubes. A vapor condensing in a film on a cooling surface flows under the influence of gravity but is retarded by the viscous forces of the fluid. The heat of condensation passes through the film from the condensing vapor to the wall. Even though the film is thin, it presents an appreci-

[1] McAdams, W. H., "Heat Transmission," 2d ed., p. 168, McGraw-Hill Book Company, Inc., New York, 1942.
[2] Colburn, A. P., *Trans. AICE*, vol. 29, pp. 174–210, 1933.

able resistance to heat flow.   By combining the laws of laminar flow and of heat conduction, Nusselt arrived at the following relation:

$$f_o = C \left(\frac{g\rho^2 l k^3}{L\mu \, \Delta t}\right)^{0.25} \tag{5-7}$$

where f_o = film conductance, Btu/(hr)(sq ft)(°FTD)

    g = gravitational constant, 418×10^6 ft/hr²

    l = latent heat of evaporation, Btu/lb

    L = height of a vertical wall or tube or the outer diameter of a horizontal tube on which condensation occurs

    C = constant, 0.943 for vertical walls or tubes, 0.725 for horizontal tubes

    Δt = temperature difference, °F, between the condensing vapor and the metal

The Combined Convection and Conduction Film Coefficient for Air Flowing to Plates not Condensing Moisture.   The film conductance of an air film on a smooth surface, parallel to the flow of air, with the flow of air moving at less than 35 mph, was found by Houghton and McDermott[1] to be

$$f_o = 1.4 + 0.281v \tag{5-8}$$

where v is measured in mph.   If we consider fins on tubes spaced about four to the inch, as is the case with finned cooling coils, several factors contribute to increasing the film conductance above that indicated by the formula.

Air moving even at low velocities is usually turbulent because of its low viscosity.   Its turbulence increases as the fins are placed closer together.   A very thin stationary film adheres to the fin.   The velocity between the fins is two or three times as great as the air velocity approaching or leaving the coil.   The tubes upon which the fins are mounted run transverse to the air flow.   This further increases the amount of turbulence of the air.   In case the tubes are staggered with respect to each other, the turbulence is still further increased.   These factors make it very difficult to predict the air-film conductances accurately.   A very conservative value will be obtained with Eq. (5-8) if the velocity is taken as the maximum velocity that may be expected between the fins.   Moisture that condenses on the fins will offer little additional resistance to the convected heat flow.   The total heat transferred is, therefore, the amount convected as computed by Eq. (5-8) plus the heat of condensation of the moisture that forms on the fins.

[1] HOUGHTON, F. C., and PAUL McDERMOTT, Wind Velocity Gradients near a Surface and Their Effect on Film Conductance, *Trans. ASHVE*, vol. 37, pp. 301–322, 1931.

The Combined Convection and Conduction Film Coefficient for Air Flowing Transversely across Pipes. The Colburn equation for the film coefficient of a fluid flowing normal to a bank of staggered tubes is

$$\frac{f_o D_o}{k} = 0.33 \left(\frac{c_p \mu}{k}\right)^{\frac{1}{3}} \left(\frac{D_o G}{\mu}\right)^{0.6} \tag{5-9}$$

where f_o = film coefficient, Btu/(sq ft)(hr)(°FTD)

D_o = outside diameter of the pipe, ft

k = thermal conductivity, Btu/(hr)(sq ft)(°FTD per ft)

c_p = specific heat

μ = absolute viscosity in the English system = 2.42 × centipoises

G = mass velocity

The mass velocity is the weight in pounds that passes per hour through 1 sq ft of free area between the tubes. For air at 32°F, this formula reduces to the following:

$$f_o = \frac{0.028 G^{0.6}}{D^{0.4}} \tag{5-10}$$

Equation (5-10) may be used over the entire range of temperatures used in cold-storage or quick-freezing work without appreciable error.

For staggered tubes having unobstructed gravity flow of air, the film coefficient is usually about 2 or 3 Btu/(sq ft)(hr)(°FTD). For forced circulation the rate increases rapidly; however, the space required for bare cooling coils is excessive unless a brine spray is used over the coils. The problem then becomes one of considering the temperature of the brine and the saturation efficiency of the spray.

The Film Conductance during Evaporation. A glance into a beaker of slowly boiling water shows the process of heat transfer by boiling. The usual type of boiling is nuclear boiling, that is, boiling that starts from nuclei and develops into gaseous bubbles. These bubbles originate on small natural roughnesses of the heating surface. The heat is transmitted from the solid surface to he liquid in contact with the solid surface by conduction and convection. At the bubble surface more liquid vaporizes, and the bubble grows until it breaks away from the surface. Experiments by M. Jakob[1] show that the temperature of the liquid is higher than that of the vapor, which must be the case in order that heat be transferred from the liquid to the bubble. The film becomes thinner, and hence the rate of heat transfer increases as the rate of boiling increases.

[1] JAKOB, M., Local Temperature Differences Occurring in Evaporation, Condensation and in Catalytic Reactions, in "Temperature—Its Measurement and Control in Science and Industry," American Institute of Physics, Reinhold Publishing Corporation, New York, 1941.

If the temperature difference between the metal and the liquid increases excessively, the liquid film is destroyed, in which case heat transfer must take place through vapor, and hence the heat-transfer rate will be very low. Everyone has seen the latter process take place when a drop of water falls on a hot stove. The droplet dances but does not evaporate very fast. Temperature differences used in refrigeration are not great enough to cause the latter type of heat transfer to take place.

The film between the bubbles and the metal surfaces has about the same thickness as a condensing film, if the bubbles are allowed to escape freely during evaporation. One would therefore expect the evaporating film to have about the same film conductance as the condensing film. This is essentially the case at small temperature differences between the metal and the fluid (less than 10°FTD). One important difference occurs. The conductance of the evaporating film increases with an increase in temperature difference, while the conductance of the condensing film decreases with an increase in temperature difference. No satisfactory formula has been developed for the film conductance during evaporation; however, if the refrigerant is pure and the vapor bubbles are allowed to escape freely, it is usually above the values given in Table 5-1. Lower values may be expected if the evaporation occurs in horizontal tubes without a slope or in small-diameter tubes, or if the vapor becomes pocketed. Forced circulation greatly increases the heat transfer in such cases. If the refrigerant is oil solvent and the compressor is not equipped with an oil separator on its discharge side, that portion of the refrigerant near the end of a long coil will have an excessive concentration of oil, in which case the film becomes essentially an oil film, and very little heat will flow. The author has observed conditions of this type in which the latter half of the coil could be eliminated without greatly affecting the total heat that it would transfer at a given temperature difference.

TABLE 5-1. SUGGESTED EVAPORATING-FILM CONDUCTANCES

Refrigerant	f, Btu/(sq ft)(hr)(°F)
Ammonia	1,200
Freon 12	350
Methyl chloride	500

Conductance of Scale Deposits. The amount of scale that will form in condenser tubes is a function of the type of water, the condensing temperature, and the velocity of the water. Water that contains calcium and magnesium compounds is said to be hard. Hard water is the chief offender in forming scale deposits, although water containing other semisoluble or colloidal matter may also form a scale. Many minerals are less soluble in water at high temperatures than they are at low temperatures. The temperature of the condenser tube is always hotter than that of the water; therefore the mineral deposits on the hot metal. The higher the temperature of the metal, the greater will be the tendency for scale to form. At high water velocities the water-film conductance is greater than at lower velocities; therefore the metal has a lower temperature at higher velocities and less scale will form. Table 5-2 gives values of f_s for temperatures below 125°F from Standards of Tubular Exchanger Manufacturers Association, 1941.[1]

TABLE 5-2. SCALE CONDUCTANCES
Btu/(sq ft)(hr)(°FTD)

Kind of water	Water velocity, fps	
	3 and less	Over 3
	f_s	
Distilled water..........................	2,000	2,000
Sea water............................	2,000	2,000
Treated boiler feed water.................	1,000	2,000
Treated make-up for cooling tower.........	1,000	1,000
City, well, Great Lakes..................	1,000	1,000
Brackish, clean river water..............	500	1,000
River water, muddy, silty...............	330	500
Hard (over 15 g/gal)...................	330	330
Chicago Sanitary Canal	130	170

Mean Temperature Difference. The discussion so far has been concerned with a constant temperature difference on the two sides of a heat-exchange surface. This condition does not always exist. In many cases both hot and cold fluids undergo a temperature change, so that the mean temperature difference must be used to compute the transferred heat. The fundamental equation of heat transfer then becomes

$$Q = UA \, \Delta t_m$$

Usually fluids in heat exchangers flow in opposite directions, in which case the flow is said to be *counterflow*. It is possible for them to flow in the same direction, in which case the flow is called *parallel flow*. Fortunately, the derived expression for mean temperature difference is the same in both cases. We will derive the expression assuming counterflow of the two fluids.

Let us consider a differential area of transmitting surface dA. As

[1] Tubular Exchanger Manufacturers Association, New York.

the cold fluid passes this area, its temperature changes a differential amount dt_c, due to the transfer of a differential quantity of heat dQ. Similarly, the hot fluid transmits the same quantity of heat, and its temperature changes a differential amount, $-dt_h$. The negative sign indicates that the temperature change is in the opposite direction to that of the cold fluid. The changes in temperature will be as follows:

$$dt_c = \frac{dQ}{w_c c_c} \quad \text{and} \quad dt_h = -\frac{dQ}{w_h c_h}$$

where the subscripts h and c indicate the respective properties of the hot and cold fluids. By subtraction,

$$dt_h - dt_c = -dQ\left(\frac{1}{w_h c_h} + \frac{1}{w_c c_c}\right)$$

Let us designate $\Delta t = t_h - t_c$. The change of the difference in temperature $d\,\Delta t$ across the section dA is equal to the change of the temperature of the hot fluid minus the change of temperature of the cold fluid; that is,

$$d\,\Delta t = dt_h - dt_c$$

Then

$$d\,\Delta t = -dQ\left(\frac{1}{w_h c_h} + \frac{1}{w_c c_c}\right)$$

but

$$dQ = U\,dA\,\Delta t$$

Then

$$d\,\Delta t = -U\,dA\,\Delta t\left(\frac{1}{w_h c_h} + \frac{1}{w_c c_c}\right)$$

or

$$\int_{\Delta t_1}^{\Delta t_2} \frac{d\,\Delta t}{\Delta t} = -U\left(\frac{1}{w_h c_h} + \frac{1}{w_c c_c}\right)\int_0^A dA$$

where subscripts 1 and 2 indicate the condition at any two sections of the interchanger.

$$\log_e \frac{\Delta t_2}{\Delta t_1} = -\log_e \frac{\Delta t_1}{\Delta t_2} = -\left(\frac{UA}{w_h c_h} + \frac{UA}{w_c c_c}\right) \tag{5-10a}$$

From $Q = UA\,\Delta t_m$ we have for counterflow

$$UA = \frac{Q}{\Delta t_m} = \frac{w_h c_h(t_{h_1} - t_{h_2})}{\Delta t_m} = -\frac{w_c c_c(t_{c_1} - t_{c_2})}{\Delta t_m}$$

The negative sign indicates that the heat lost by the hot fluid equals the heat gained by the cold fluid. By substituting the values of UA in Eq. (5-10a), we obtain

$$\log_e \frac{\Delta t_1}{\Delta t_2} = \frac{t_{h_1} - t_{h_2} - t_{c_1} + t_{c_2}}{\Delta t_m} = \frac{(t_{h_1} - t_{c_1}) - (t_{h_2} - t_{c_2})}{\Delta t_m} .$$

or

$$\Delta t_m = \frac{\Delta t_1 - \Delta t_2}{\log_e \dfrac{\Delta t_1}{\Delta t_2}}$$

Since the subscripts 1 and 2 indicate any two sections of the interchanger, the above formula may be written

$$\Delta t_m = \frac{\Delta t_g - \Delta t_1}{\log_e \dfrac{\Delta t_g}{\Delta t_1}} \tag{5-11}$$

where Δt_g indicates the greater temperature difference and Δt_1 indicates the lesser temperature difference.

The same formula will be obtained when considering parallel flow; however, very different numerical values for Δt_m will be obtained under the two conditions of flow.

Let us consider two interchangers, one using counterflow and the other using parallel flow. In these interchangers the hot fluid shall be cooled from 100° to 90°F, and the cold fluid shall be heated from 70° to 85°F. For counterflow

$$\Delta t_m = \frac{20 - 15}{\log_e \dfrac{20}{15}} = 17.5°\text{F}$$

For parallel flow

$$\Delta t_m = \frac{30 - 5}{\log_e \dfrac{30}{5}} = 14.0°\text{F}$$

In all cases, counterflow gives a greater mean temperature difference than parallel flow; it is therefore used whenever possible.

HEAT TRANSFER IN A WATER OR BRINE SPRAY CHAMBER

In refrigerating applications, heat is often transferred from air to a chilled water or brine spray. In this case, the heat transfer cannot be determined from the film coefficient, the area of the surface, and the temperature difference, since the moisture content of the air is modified and the area of the water surface cannot be determined.

If air is passed through water, it will evaporate a portion of the water, provided that the vapor tension of the water surface is greater than the vapor pressure in the air. This will occur if the water temperature is above the dew-point temperature of the air. If the water is below the dew-point temperature of the air, its vapor tension will be less than the vapor pressure in the air, and moisture will be extracted from the air. In either case, if the air passes through the water for sufficient distance, it will become saturated, and the temperature of the leaving air will be the same as the water at that point.

The action of air with sodium chloride brine is almost the same as with water. Sodium chloride brine is not hygroscopic, and its vapor tension differs only slightly from that of pure water. Calcium chloride brine is highly hygroscopic and should not be used in a spray unless low humidities are required. Hereafter, when the term *brine* is used in connection with spray equipment, it will mean sodium chloride brine, unless specifically stated otherwise.

Saturation Efficiency of a Spray Chamber. With water or brine spray equipment, it is not practical to pass the air for sufficient distance through the spray to saturate it completely. The saturation efficiency is therefore considered. The saturation efficiency of spray chamber is the temperature range through which the air is cooled divided by the temperature range through which it would be cooled if it left the chamber at the same temperature as the leaving water, or

$$e = \frac{t_i - t_o}{t_i - t_w} \tag{5-12}$$

where e = saturation efficiency
t_i = temperature of incoming air
t_o = temperature of outgoing air
t_w = temperature of leaving water

If a tall vertical spray chamber is used with the water spraying downward and the air flowing upward, as is the case with forced-draft cooling towers, t_w may be taken as the water temperature at the top of the tower. Values for saturation efficiencies will be discussed in connection with the constructional details of the spray chambers.

Condition of the Air Leaving a Spray Chamber. The condition of the air leaving a spray chamber can be determined from the psychrometric chart as follows: Draw a line between the point representing the condition of the entering air and a point on the saturation curve at the temperature of the leaving water. If the spray chamber had a saturation efficiency of 100 per cent, the air would leave at the temperature of the point on the saturation curve. For lower efficiencies, measure the distance between the two points; multiply this distance by the saturation efficiency; and measure the resulting distance from the point representing the incoming air. The point thus determined represents the condition of the outgoing air.

Saturation Efficiency of a Finned Cooling Coil. A finned coil cooling air will condense moisture from the atmosphere if its temperature is below the dew point of the air passing through it. After a film of moisture has condensed on the coil, heat no longer transfers directly to the metal, but to the water film. Heat transfer is then the same as in a spray chamber. Owing to the close spacing of fins, the staggered tubes, and the high velocity between the fins, air flows in a highly turbulent manner through the coil, and fairly high saturation efficiencies are obtainable. Saturation efficiency for a finned cooling coil is termed its *contact factor*.

Transferred Heat. The heat taken from the air equals the heat added to the water. This may be stated by the following equation:

$$Q = w_l c_l (t_{l_o} - t_{l_i}) = w_a (h_i - h_o) \qquad (5\text{-}13)$$

where Q = transferred heat, Btu
w_1 = weight of liquid
c_l = specific heat of liquid
t_{l_o} = temperature of outgoing liquid
t_{l_i} = temperature of incoming liquid
w_a = weight of air
h_i = enthalpy of incoming air
h_o = enthalpy of outgoing air

Heat Transfer in a Cooled Tower. A cooling tower is a special case of a water spray chamber, and the principles applying to a water spray chamber will also apply to a cooling tower. There is one additional equation, however, that must be considered. If no heat were added to the water and air were continuously passed through it, the water would come to the wet-bulb temperature of the air. If heat is added to the water, the temperature of the outgoing water will be somewhat higher than the wet-bulb temperature of the air, depending on the quantity of air, the droplet size in the spray, and the spray density. These factors determine the efficiency of the cooling tower. The efficiency of a cooling tower is defined as the temperature range through which the water is cooled divided by the temperature range through which it would be cooled if it were cooled to the wet-bulb temperature of the incoming air.

$$e = \frac{t_i - t_o}{t_i - t'} \qquad (5\text{-}14)$$

where e = cooling-tower efficiency
t_i and t_o = incoming and outgoing temperatures of water
t' = wet-bulb temperature of incoming air

A given cooling tower with fixed air and water quantities will have nearly constant efficiency for the range of air and water temperatures used in refrigeration work. Efficiencies of cooling towers will be discussed with their constructional details later in this chapter.

CONDENSERS

Condensers may use air, water, or a combination of the two as a cooling medium. With evaporative condensers water is sprayed over the condensing coil while air is drawn through it. Air-cooled condensers are generally used on systems requiring less than 2 hp. Water-cooled condensers are used on systems of all sizes above 1 hp. Evaporative condensers are used on systems between 5 and 25 hp.

The condensing temperature of a refrigerating system is a function of the following factors:

1. Type of cooling medium
2. Quantity of cooling medium
3. Temperature of cooling medium
4. Amount of condenser surface
5. Velocity of the cooling medium
6. Condition of the heat-transfer surface
7. Type of refrigerant
8. Purity of the refrigerant

These factors will be discussed in detail.

Type of Cooling Medium.   Air-cooled condensers are usually designed for condensing temperatures 30 to 40°F above the temperature of the entering air. Water-cooled condensers are usually designed for condensing temperatures 12 to 25°F above the entering water. In localities where the maximum air temperature is 100°F, water is often available at 75°F. With these conditions, the condensing temperature with air-cooled condensers will be about 130 or 140°F, while the condensing temperature with water-cooled condensers will be about 87 to 100°F. The heat-transfer rate with dirty water or salt water is not as good as with clean water. This fact should be taken into consideration in the design of the system, but often it is not. Higher condensing temperatures can therefore be expected where the water is not clean or pure.

Quantity of Cooling Medium.   The air quantity with air-cooled condensers is about 800 to 1,000 cfm/ton ime of the system. Air is blown or drawn through the condenser by a propeller-type fan attached to the shaft of the electric motor. The temperature rise of the air through the condenser is about 15 to 20°F. The water quantity with water-cooled condensers will vary from 1.5 to 4 gpm/ton, depending on whether the water is taken from the city main, a well, or a cooling tower. When using water from a city main, it is usually economical to use about 1.5 gpm/ton, in which case the rise of water temperature through the condenser will be about 20°F, and the condensing temperature will be about 25 or 30°F above the temperature of the water entering the condenser. When using water from a well, it is usually economical to use about 2 or 3 gpm/ton, depending on the height from which the water must be lifted and on the distance of the well from the condenser. With 3 gpm/ton, the rise in temperature of the water through the condenser will be about 10°F, and the condensing temperature will be about 15°F above the temperature of the water entering the condenser. With an atmospheric cooling tower, it is economical to use about 3 or 4 gpm/ton, depending on the distance of the cooling tower from the condenser. The smaller water quantity is used when the required piping is extensive. When 4 gpm/ton is used, the rise in temperature of the water through the condenser is about 7.5°F, and the condensing temperature is about 12°F above the entering water temperature. Because of the higher cooling efficiency of the forced-draft, or induced-draft, cooling tower, less water is used than with the atmospheric cooling tower. The water quantity is usually about 2 or 2.5 gpm/ton, and the air quantity is usually about 300 to 400 cfm/ton. The condensing temperature is usually about 20 to 25°F above the temperature of the water entering the condenser. Evaporative condensers use about the same air and water quantities as the forced-draft cooling tower. In the former the condensing temperature is usually about 25 to 30°F above the wet-bulb temperature of the incoming air.

Amount of Condensing Surface. The greater the amount of heat-transfer surface, all other factors being equal, the smaller will be the spread between the condensing temperature and the temperature of the cooling medium. Water-cooled condensers having bare tubes usually have between 6 and 10 sq ft of condensing surface per ton of refrigeration.

Velocity of the Cooling Medium. The heat-transfer rate through a condenser tube increases with an increase in velocity of the cooling medium. With air-cooled condensers, the face velocity (average velocity) is about 800 to 1,000 fpm. With water-cooled condensers, suitable velocities are 4 to 6 fps for 1-in. tubes and 6 to 8 fps for 2-in. tubes. The velocity should not exceed 8 fps except for clean water from a city main, because of the danger of erosion of the tubes.

Condition of the Condenser Surface. The most common cause of high condensing temperatures is an accumulation of dirt, sludge, scale, etc., on the heat-transfer surface. All dirt and sludge should be brushed from air-cooled condensers regularly. Copper-coil water-cooled condensers may be cleaned with hydrochloric or commercial muriatic acid pumped through the coil continuously until all foaming ceases. In case the water comes from a cooling tower, the condenser should be flushed thoroughly before resuming operation, and a small amount of sodium hydroxide put in the cooling-tower tank so that the water is just barely alkaline. Finned-coil evaporative condensers have not proved satisfactory except in soft-water districts. The coils cannot be readily cleaned. They may be kept from scaling by using a scale-solvent material such as sodium hexametaphosphate in the water, or by connecting a small tube to the discharge side of the pump and continuously wasting a portion of the water. The latter method will keep the mineral content from building up in the water. It is usually the more convenient method, and less corrosion is involved. Evaporative condensers should be constructed with bare condenser tubes that are accessible through removable inspection plates so that the tubes can be easily cleaned.

Type of Refrigerant. The condensing-film conductance increases with an increase of density, latent heat, and thermal conductivity and decreases with an increase in viscosity. These properties vary greatly with the various refrigerants, and hence the rate of heat transfer will vary greatly. The amount of condensing surface must be much greater for the chlorinated refrigerants than for ammonia.

Purity of the Refrigerant. If there is an excess of oil in the refrigerant, the oil will form a film on the condensing surface and impede the flow of heat. This factor is noticeable with the chlorinated refrigerants. A discharge-line oil separator will tend to keep the heat-transfer rate at a maximum.

If there is air present in a system, it will collect in the condenser, and some of it will adhere to the tubes, insulating them from the refrigerant. The heat-transfer rate is thus decreased, and the condensing temperature will rise. Systems in which the evaporator operates on a vacuum do not completely avoid the leakage of air. These systems should be equipped with an automatic purger to evacuate the air.

Owing to carelessness of operation or repair, air may enter a system whose evaporator operates above atmospheric pressure. These systems do not require an automatic purger, and hence purging must be done manually. The following procedure may be followed. Shut off the compressor, but maintain a flow of water through the condenser for a few minutes. Shut valves on both sides of the condenser. Open purge valve on top of condenser until the pressure in it has dropped nearly to atmospheric pressure. If the condenser is used also as a receiver, the pressure will not drop. In such cases, the operator must use his judgment as to the amount to discharge. A good deal of refrigerant will be wasted in the process. All gases have high diffusion rates and do not separate readily.

Shell-and-tube Condensers. The shell-and-tube condenser is the most common and usually the most satisfactory of all types of condensers. Figure 5-1 shows the various parts of this type of condenser. The heads are removable so that the tubes may be easily cleaned. Baffles in the heads send the entire water quantity back and forth across the condenser several times. The number of times that the water crosses any transverse section of the condenser is called the *number of passes* of the con-

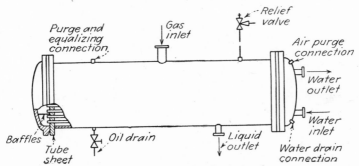

FIG. 5-1. Horizontal shell-and-tube condenser.

denser. The water velocity is determined by the water quantity and the number of passes. The tubes are constructed of steel or copper and are usually rolled or expanded into the tube sheets. Steel tubes may be electrically welded. The tube sheets must be at least $1\frac{1}{4}$ in. thick to stand the stress of being rolled in. The shell thickness should be in accordance with the American Standard Safety Code for Mechanical Refrigeration.[1] It should be designed for a working pressure of 250 psi gauge for ammonia or 225 psi gauge for Freon 12. The condenser should be equipped with all connections shown in Fig. 5-1. Bare steel tubes are used in ammonia condensers. Freon 12 condensers use either bare steel tubes or copper tubes with a low fin. Since the condensing-film conductance with ammonia is very high (about 1500 Btu/(sq ft)(°F)), fins are superfluous. The condensing-film conductance with Freon 12 is about 350 Btu/(sq ft)(hr)(°F). This is usually lower than the water-film conductance; therefore fins are desirable. Copper tubing with expanded ends and fins not more than $\frac{1}{16}$ in. high is available for this purpose.

The hot gas is cooled to the condensing temperature by the evaporation of some of the liquid refrigerant as it drips from the tubes. It is

[1] See Appendix 6.

usually preferable that the water enter the condenser through the top tubes in order that as much condensation as possible will take place at the top of the condenser. If a shell-and-tube condenser is preceded by a discharge-line oil separator, and if the water is maintained in a clean condition, film coefficients as given in foregoing formulas will be closely achieved.

Double-tube Condensers. Condensing units of 10 hp or less are often equipped with a continuous copper double-tube condenser. Water flows through the inner tube, and the refrigerant condenses in the outer tube. Sometimes these condensers are mistakenly called *counterflow condensers*. However, the term *counterflow* has no meaning after condensation starts, since condensation is at constant temperature. The best results will be obtained if counterflow of the refrigerant and water is not used. The heat-transfer rate is very low until condensation starts. If both water and refrigerant are entered at the top, connection will start quicker, and a greater portion of the condenser will be used in the condensing process. Because cooling of the superheated gas takes appreciable heat-exchange surface, allowance for this factor must be made in the design of double-tube condensers.

In the past many ammonia condensers were double-tube steel condensers, with removable return bends on the water circuit. The condenser could be easily cleaned by removing the return bends and scraping the tubes. Water flowed through the inner tubes and the refrigerant flowed through the outer tubes. The outer tubes were interconnected alternately at the two ends so that, in effect, a continuous tube was formed. Often they were mistakenly connected to obtain counterflow, with the water entering at the bottom and the hot gas entering at the top. But, as pointed out previously, counterflow has no meaning after condensation starts. Condensation starts more quickly if both water and hot gas enter at the top of the condenser. As before, additional surface over that required in a shell-and-tube condenser was necessary in order to allow for the low heat-transfer rate before condensation starts. This type of condenser is easily constructed, easily cleaned, and is satisfactory in all respects except that it requires more space than a shell-and-tube condenser. It should be equipped with all the connections shown in the diagram of the shell-and-tube condenser.

Shell-and-coil Condenser. The shell-and-coil condenser consists of a steel shell with welded heads and one or more copper coils mounted inside. The tubes may be either bare or finned. Water flows inside the tubes, and refrigerant condenses on their outer surfaces. Condensation and cooling of the hot gas down to the condensing temperature occur as in a shell-and-tube condenser. The field of application of the shell-and-coil condenser is the same as that of the continuous copper double-tube condenser.

Evaporative Condensers. The evaporative condenser is a forced-draft cooling tower with a condensing coil mounted inside. Its construction is shown diagrammatically in Fig. 5-2. When the evaporative condenser was first developed, the condensing coil was usually of the

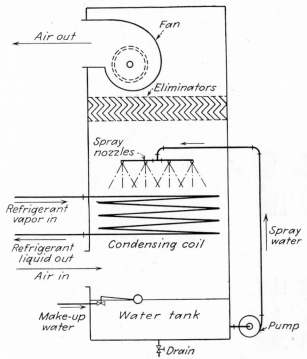

Fig. 5-2. Functional view of evaporative condenser.

finned type, but these gave so much scale trouble, especially in hard-water sections, that the design tendency has been toward bare-tube condensing coils. Finned coils have a further disadvantage: when wet with water they offer high resistance to air flow, and excessive power is required by the fan. Only the design of evaporative condensers with bare-tube condensing coils will be considered here.

No satisfactory formula has been developed for the conductance of the condensing film inside tubes, since the ease with which the liquid refrigerant drains is involved. In general, the conductance of this film is lower than when condensation occurs on the outside of the tubes. With good drainage, it is of the order of 300 Btu/(hr)(sq ft)(°F) for Freon 12 and 1,400 Btu/(hr)(sq ft)(°F) for ammonia. The water-film conductance on the outside depends upon the spray density and the velocity and turbulence of the air. With good design it will be between 300 and 400 Btu/(hr)(sq ft)(°F). With Freon 12, the heat-transfer advantage of the finned tube over that of the bare tube is not great enough to warrant the use of fins even in those districts where scale difficulties are not involved. With ammonia, fins noticeably increase the rate of heat transfer per unit length of tube; however, the tendency has been toward bare tubes because of scale trouble and because of

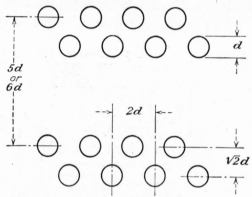

Fig. 5-3. Suggested arrangement of tubes in an evaporative condenser.

difficulties involved in the manufacture of finned steel or aluminum tubing.

For either Freon 12 or ammonia, the coil is usually constructed of ¾- or 1-in. standard-weight pipe. Return bends are made with a hydraulic pipe bender. The only welds required are at the top hot-gas header and the bottom liquid-refrigerant header. Tubes should be continuously sloped so that the refrigerant will drain easily toward the liquid-refrigerant header.

Tubes should be staggered and placed close together. Alternate rows of tubes should be unevenly spaced to increase the air turbulence. A hydraulic pipe bender will bend pipe on a centerline radius equal to five times the outside diameter of the pipe. Six to eight rows of pipe are normally used. Figure 5-3 shows a suggested arrangement of pipes.

A spray density of 3 gpm/sq ft, 15 psi gauge pressure on the sprays, and an air velocity of 600 fpm approaching the coil are satisfactory. Higher spray densities have little value. Higher air velocities will draw moisture through the eliminator plates.

If we consider the evaporative condenser as a spray chamber, one designed as suggested, with high turbulence through the condensing coil, will have a saturation efficiency of about 80 per cent.

The performance of an evaporative condenser may be predicted as follows: The wet-bulb temperature of the leaving air may be found from the total weight of the air pumped, the quantity of heat that is added to it, and the initial enthalpy of the air. The temperature of the water will be slightly higher, depending on the saturation efficiency of the spray. It can be found from the psychrometric chart as follows: Draw a line on the chart from the point representing the condition of the entering air, across the wet-bulb-temperature line of the leaving air, to the saturation curve, in such a manner that the distance from the initial point to the leaving wet-bulb line, divided by the distance from the initial point to the saturation curve, equals the saturation efficiency of the spray chamber. The temperature indicated on the saturation curve will be the temperature of the water in the condenser. Its temperature will be nearly constant as it passes over the condensing coils. With the water temperature known, the condensing coil may be considered as a water-cooled condenser.

EVAPORATORS AND ROOM COOLERS

Evaporators are ordinarily used for cooling air, water, or brine; on rare occasions they are used for cooling other gases or liquids. In the refrigerating of spaces used to store foods, if the heat is transferred from the air through the metal of the tubes of the coil to the refrigerant, the evaporator is called a *direct-expansion evaporator*. If the heat is transferred from the air through the metal of the tubes to the brine, the system is called a *brine system*. The evaporator used to chill the brine is called a *brine cooler*. Systems using direct-expansion evaporators generally operate with a higher suction temperature than systems using a brine cooler, and the power required is generally less than with brine systems. Where the piping required to handle the refrigerating medium is extensive, the piping of brine offers fewer problems than the piping of a refrigerant. Where hazardous refrigerants are used, brine systems are safer than direct-expansion systems. With the development of refrigerants that are nontoxic, nonflammable, and not injurious to the foodstuffs, direct-expansion systems are becoming increasingly popular.

Headers and Accumulators. Friction in an evaporator lowers the suction pressure, and hence reduces the quantity of refrigerant pumped by the compressor. In order that the pressure drop be a minimum, it is necessary that the evaporator have many tubes, each tube being connected to one or two headers, which are in turn connected to the liquid and suction lines. If the tubes are all connected to a liquid header at one end and to a vapor header at the other end, all the flash gas must pass through the tubes carrying the evaporating refrigerant. In such cases, the system is called a *dry-expansion system*. This term is misleading, since a properly designed dry-expansion coil operates nearly filled with a liquid refrigerant. The flow of refrigerant to dry-expansion systems is usually controlled by a thermostatic expansion valve; however, if the system has only one evaporator, a high-side float valve may be used. The liquid header in such a system must be carefully designed so that an equal portion of refrigerant will be distributed to each tube. Various devices such as metering tubes, orifices, and centrifugal headers are used to accomplish this. The coil may be arranged with the liquid header at the top, bottom, or one side of the coil. In any of these positions, there is little difference in the heat transfer, since the velocity of the refrigerant is the same, and there is the same proportion of refrigerant and vapor.

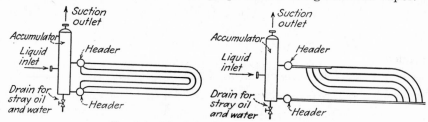

FIG. 5-4.   Flooded coil with an accumulator.

If the liquid and vapor headers are connected together by a large chamber, and if the liquid level in this chamber is maintained above the top header by means of a float valve, the system is called a *flooded system*. The vertical chamber with the float valve is called an *accumulator*. With such a device, the flash gas does not pass through the coils but goes directly to the suction line. Figure 5-4 shows a flooded coil with an accumulator. In such a system the tubes are short and installed at a slope so that the vapor will flow readily to the top of the accumulator. The heat transfer is usually a little higher in the flooded system than in a dry-expansion system; however, there is little difference if the tubes in the dry-expansion system are short and of ample size. Accumulators cannot be used with oil-solvent refrigerants satisfactorily unless the accumulator is equipped with an oil-separating device to return the oil to the suction line.

Direct-expansion Evaporators. With direct-expansion evaporators, the refrigerant flows inside the tubes, and air passes over the outside.

The film conductance of air is noticeably low either with gravity or with forced circulation. Good practice therefore demands the use of fins on the outside of the tubes and forced circulation of air. In Chap. 1 it was found that most comestibles have an optimum storage temperature above freezing of 30 to 32°F and a desirable storage temperature below freezing of 0°F. At either of these temperatures the coil will freeze solid if the fins are spaced too closely together. Not more than four fins to the inch should be used. The coils should further be equipped with a defrosting device. Water defrosting is usually the most satisfactory, although in some cases hot-gas defrosting is used. The defrosting methods will be discussed in Chap. 7.

Direct-expansion evaporators for oil-solvent refrigerants are generally of the dry-expansion type to avoid the danger of the oil "logging." A sufficient number of parallel tube paths, together with a suitable distributing header to distribute the refrigerant evenly to these tubes, must be provided so that the total pressure drop through the coil does not exceed 2 or 3 psi. Greater pressure drops will lead to improper action of the thermostatic expansion valve when adjusted for low superheat. The evaporator contains both liquid and vapor so that an accurate prediction of the pressure drop cannot be made. For calculating purposes, an assumption that the refrigerant is in the liquid form in the header and in the vapor form in the tubes will give a safe valve except in cases where the header is extremely restricted.

Direct-expansion coils for use with ammonia may be either the dry-expansion or flooded type. A closer control of both humidity and temperature can be maintained with the flooded type than with the dry-expansion type if the suction pressure is controlled by a back-pressure valve. With the flooded type, the number of parallel tube paths must be sufficient, and the tube size ample, so that negligible friction occurs through the coil. All tubes must be sloped so that the vapor may rise easily to the top of the accumulator.

Tubes should be in staggered formation to obtain maximum air turbulence. About six or eight rows of tubes are generally used. One row of $\frac{5}{8}$-in. tubes spaced $1\frac{3}{4}$ in. on centers with a plate-type fin 2 in. wide, spaced four fins to the inch, will have a contact factor of about 0.18. The air velocity has little effect upon the contact factor for the velocities used with forced-draft cooling coils. The contact factor for n rows of tubes arranged in staggered formation may be computed as follows:

$$1 - CF_n = (1 - CF_1)^n \qquad (5\text{-}15)$$

where CF_n is the contact factor for n rows of tubes and CF_1 is the contact factor for one row of tubes.

Since the contact factor is nearly independent of velocity, the heat-transfer rate will increase as the air velocity increases. However, velocities must be kept low enough that excessive friction will not occur, water will not be blown from the coil when maintaining temperatures above 32°F, and excessive circulation will not be produced in the room if the air blows through the coil directly into the room.

A moderate-speed disk fan will work against a resistance pressure of approximately ⅛ in. of water and will produce face velocities of about 600 fpm over an eight-row coil with four fans to the inch. High-speed disk fans will work against a resistance pressure of ½ in. of water and will produce a face velocity of 1,200 fpm over the same coil.

Face velocities up to 700 fpm may be used with finned coils having four plate fins to the inch without blowing condensed water from the coil. With spiral or spined fins, the velocity should not exceed 500 fpm. Lower velocities should be used with closer spacing of fins. If room temperatures of 32°F or lower are maintained, water will not be blown through the coil at any velocity.

Small cooling units equipped with disk fans that blow the air through the coil directly into the room may produce excessive air circulation in rooms containing exposed comestibles if the air velocity leaving the unit is above 600 fpm. The unit should be equipped with vanes to direct the air upward at an angle toward the ceiling to avoid direct impingement of the air on the produce. Units that blow the air radially produce milder circulation of air than those that blow in a single direction.

Large floor-mounted units with centrifugal fans may use face velocities over the coil not exceeding 600 fpm for temperatures above 32°F, but may use face velocities up to 1,500 fpm for air temperatures below 32°F.

Direct-expansion coils may also be pipe coils, plate coils, or finned-type coils for gravity circulation of air. Pipe coils are usually constructed of 1½- or 2-in. standard-weight steel pipe mounted at the ceiling in staggered formation in banks not more than 6 ft wide. An equal space between banks and sufficient space above the coil should be allowed for adequate circulation of air. Pipe coils are used for maintaining temperatures below 34°F. Pipes should not be spaced closer than 8 in. on centers since they are operated with an appreciable ice coating and may not be defrosted for 1 or more years.

Refrigerated plates, from 8 to 36 inches wide, in shelf formation are used for quick freezing of produce in small freezer plants. Direct contact with the packaged produce gives a greater heat-transfer rate than can be obtained with any other method, and hence higher evaporating temperatures may be used. Satisfactory freezing of produce in small packages may be accomplished at evaporating temperatures from −10 to −20°F. Refrigerated plates are also placed vertically at the ceiling as gravity-flow coils. They may be easily defrosted by brushing the frost from them before it has hardened. They have little advantage over bare-pipe coils, are more costly, and tend to maintain a lower humidity at given room and refrigerant temperatures.

Gravity-flow finned coils mounted at the ceiling are sometimes used where very low circulation of air is required. Not more than two or three fins to the inch are used. Sufficient space above them must be allowed for proper air circulation. When maintaining temperatures above 34°F, they should be equipped with water-collecting troughs. Hot-gas defrosting is generally used. Gravity-flow finned coils are becoming somewhat obsolete, since low circulation of air can also be obtained with forced-draft units which blow the air radially, or with bare-pipe coils.

Brine Systems. If ammonia is used as the refrigerant, brine systems are often preferred to direct-expansion systems because of the danger of escaping ammonia, with consequent damage to comestibles, and fire

TABLE 5-3. SOME PHYSICAL PROPERTIES OF SODIUM CHLORIDE SOLUTIONS*

Per cent NaCl	Specific gravity at 60°F	Weight, lb/gal	Weight, lb/cu ft	Freezing point, °F	Specific heat at	
					14°F	32°F
6	1.044	8.71	65.1	25.5	.....	0.924
8	1.058	8.82	66.0	22.9	.....	0.902
10	1.073	8.95	66.9	20.2	.....	0.882
12	1.088	9.08	67.8	17.3	.....	0.865
14	1.104	9.22	69.8	14.1	.....	0.848
16	1.119	9.33	69.8	10.6	0.827	0.834
18	1.135	9.47	70.8	6.7	0.815	0.821
20	1.151	9.60	71.8	2.4	0.804	0.809
22	1.167	9.74	72.8	−2.5	0.794	0.798
24	1.184	9.88	73.8	−1.4	0.784	0.788

* MARKS, L. S., ED., "Mechanical Engineers' Handbook," 4th ed., p. 2166, McGraw-Hill Book Company, Inc., New York, 1941.

hazard. If an oil-solvent refrigerant such as Freon 12 is used, brine is often preferred to avoid oil complications, which may occur in excessively long refrigerant lines. Other advantages of brine systems are that the amount of required refrigerant is less and there is usually a considerable mass of refrigerated brine that may be drawn on in emergency.

Two kinds of brine find common use in refrigerating systems—sodium chloride and calcium chloride. Sodium chloride is used with nearly all brine-spray systems, since calcium chloride is hygroscopic and extracts moisture from the air. Sodium chloride is also used for ice making and for other purposes where calcium chloride may contaminate the product.

The properties of sodium chloride and calcium chloride brines and water are given in Tables 5-3 to 5-8.

TABLE 5-4. VISCOSITY OF SODIUM CHLORIDE SOLUTIONS*

Per cent NaCl	Temperature, °F			
	5	14	21	32
	Viscosity, centipoises			
5.9	.....	.....	.....	1.849
8.0	.....	.....	2.297	1.912
10.2	.....	.....	2.403	1.991
12.3	.....	.....	2.525	2.091
14.5	.....	3.320	2.682	2.224
16.7	.....	3.575	2.874	2.391
19.0	4.830	3.908	3.148	2.592
21.2	5.291	4.310	3.454	2.820
23.5	5.865	4.791	3.817	3.091
25.9	.....	.....	.....	3.433

* *Refrigerating Data Book*, p. 140, The American Society of Refrigerating Engineers, New York, 1941.

TABLE 5-5. SOME PHYSICAL PROPERTIES OF CALCIUM CHLORIDE SOLUTIONS*

Per cent CaCl₂	Specific gravity	Weight, lb/gal	Weight, lb/cu ft	Freezing point, °F	Specific heat at		
					−4°F	14°F	32°F
6	1.050	8.76	65.52	28.0			
8	1.069	8.93	66.70	24.2	.....	.....	0.882
10	1.087	9.08	67.83	21.4	.....	.....	0.853
12	1.105	9.23	68.95	18.2	.....	.....	0.825
14	1.124	9.38	70.08	14.4	.....	.....	0.799
16	1.143	9.54	71.26	9.9	.....	0.768	0.775
18	1.162	9.70	72.51	4.7	.....	0.745	0.752
20	1.182	9.85	73.63	− 1.0	.....	0.723	0.731
22	1.202	10.04	75.00	− 7.3	0.695	0.604	0.711
24	1.223	10.21	76.32	−14.1	0.678	0.686	0.693
26	1.244	10.38	77.56	−22.0	0.663	0.670	0.677
28	1.265	10.56	78.94	−32.0	0.649	0.656	0.662
30	1.287	10.75	80.35	−46.0	0.638	0.643	0.648

* MARKS, L. S., Ed., "Mechanical Engineers' Handbook," 4th ed., p. 2166, McGraw-Hill Book Company, Inc., New York, 1941.

TABLE 5-6. VISCOSITY OF CALCIUM CHLORIDE SOLUTIONS*

Per cent CaCl₂	Temperature, °F				
	−13	−4	5	14	32
	Viscosity, centipoises				
1.6	......	......	......	.....	1.804
3.4	......	......	......	.....	1.854
5.0	......	......	......	.....	1.922
6.8	......	......	......	.....	2.001
8.7	......	......	......	.....	2.104
10.5	......	......	......	.....	2.211
12.2	......	......	......	.....	2.334
14.1	......	..... .	......	.....	2.491
16.0	......	......	......	4.217	2.677
17.8	......	......	......	4.521	2.888
19.8	......	......	6.296	4.894	3.119
21.8	......	8.522	6.816	5.335	3.413
23.7	11.449	9.326	7.478	5.850	3.761
25.7	12.901	10.513	8.399	6.585	4.217
27.6	14.955	12.013	9.601	7.571	4.854
29.7	......	14.269	11.165	8.860	5.688

* Refrigerating Data Book, p. 138, The American Society of Refrigerating Engineers, New York, 1940.

TABLE 5-7. VISCOSITY OF WATER*

Temperature, °F	Viscosity, Centipoises
32	1.7921
50	1.3077
68	1.0050
86	0.8007
104	0.6560
122	0.5494
140	0.4688

* Smithsonian Physical Tables, 8th rev. ed., p. 205, The Smithsonian Institution, Washington, D. C., 1934.

Brine Coolers. Brine coolers are usually of the shell-and-tube flooded type for both ammonia and the oil-solvent refrigerants. A discharge-line oil separator must be used at the compressor when an oil-solvent refrigerant is used. Other precautions to avoid oil difficulties will be discussed subsequently.

TABLE 5-8. THERMAL CONDUCTIVITIES OF BRINES*

Brine	Concentration, per cent salt	Temperature, °F	k
CaCl₂.....................................	30	86	0.32
	15	86	0.34
NaCl.....................................	25	86	0.33
	12.5	86	0.34
Water.....................................	....	32	0.330
	....	86	0.356

* McADAMS, W. H., "Heat Transmission," 2d ed., p. 389, McGraw-Hill Book Company, Inc., New York, 1942.

A brine cooler for an ammonia system is constructed like an ammonia condenser except that it is advisable to connect the suction line to a dome at the top of the cooler as shown in Fig. 5-5. When this is done, the cooler may be operated nearly filled with liquid refrigerant without danger of its entering the suction line in the liquid phase. Since any oil

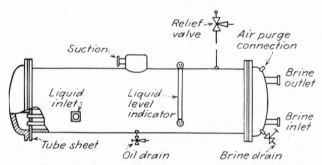

FIG. 5-5. Construction of an ammonia brine cooler.

or water that may get into the cooler will collect at its bottom, a valved oil drain must be provided. Film conductances with boiling ammonia are high; hence no fins are required on the tubes. Tubes are arranged in passes so that suitable brine velocities through the tubes are maintained. Since brine has a higher viscosity than water, slightly lower velocities are used than with water. Other constructional details and tube data are given in Appendix 6.

It is almost imperative that brine coolers using Freon 12 or other oil-solvent refrigerants have finned tubing. The film conductance of the boiling refrigerant is not high, and it is imperative that the volume of the cooler be a minimum so that it will not contain excessive refrigerant. The cost of Freon 12 and other oil-solvent refrigerants is extremely high per unit volume when compared to the cost of ammonia. Copper tubes with low fins, not more than $\frac{1}{16}$ in. high are used. These tubes are placed as close together as possible. The tubes are expanded at one end so that they will fit into the tube sheet. The cooler is constructed as shown in Fig. 5-6 with a suction header at the top and a liquid header at the bottom. The suction header may have a finned liquid line passing through it and function as a heat exchanger. The float valve is placed so that the shell will be maintained nearly full of liquid refrigerant at all times. If the cooler sometimes has to operate on greatly reduced loads,

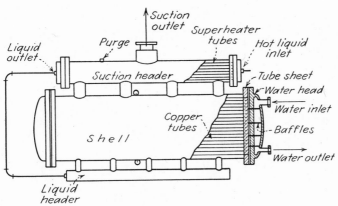

FIG. 5-6.   Freon 12 brine cooler.

oil may tend to collect in it. In this case, the suction line should be extended to a position below the cooler, and a small lead should be run from it to a position high on the shell, but below the liquid level. With Freon 22, the connection should be at the liquid level, since excess oil will collect on top the refrigerant. This connection should be equipped with a hand valve and a magnetic valve. The hand valve should be adjusted to allow a small amount of the refrigerant to pass, and the magnetic valve should have its electrical connections made in such a way that it will open automatically when one or more compressors are in operation.

For small Freon 12 or ammonia installations, double-tube dry-expansion brine coolers are satisfactory. The refrigerant boils in the outer tube, and the brine flows through the inner tube. The flow of refrigerant is controlled by a thermostatic expansion valve, which may be located at either the top or bottom of the coil. This type of brine cooler is satisfactory in every respect and involves no oil problem. Its one disadvantage is that for large capacities it requires more space than the shell-and-tube brine cooler.

In all types of brine coolers, it is economical to use enough brine that

the drop in temperature through the brine cooler, or the rise in temperature through the room cooler, will not exceed 5°F.   It is also economical
to use sufficient heat-transfer surface in the brine cooler so that the mean
temperature difference between the brine and the refrigerant will not
exceed 10°F.

Brine Room-cooling Coils.   Modern brine coils are usually of the fin
type, with forced circulation of air.   They are similar to direct-expansion

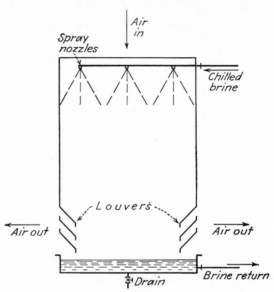

Fig. 5-7.   Simple spray-type unit.

coils except that brine instead of the boiling refrigerant flows inside the
tubes.   Brine coils are selected and operated like direct-expansion coils.
Slightly better control of temperatures and humidities can be maintained
with brine coils than with direct-expansion coils.

Brine Room-cooling Spray Units.   Brine room cooling spray units
are of three general types: spray units that induce a flow of air by their
downward spray action; spray units equipped with a fan that draws the
air counterflow to the brine spray and supplied with brine from an external
brine cooler; and spray units equipped with a fan and pump in which the
air is drawn counterflow to the brine spray, and the brine is sprayed over
the evaporating coils in the unit by its pump.

Figure 5-7 shows a simple brine-spray unit in which the air is induced
at the top by a downward spray.   It is supplied with chilled brine from a
brine cooler outside the refrigerated space.   Small spray nozzles handling
1 or 2 gpm of brine at 15 psi gauge pressure are normally used.   Enough

nozzles are used so that the spray density is about 2 gpm/sq ft. With an active height of 6 ft (distance between the sprays and the water in the pan), a saturation efficiency of about 70 to 80 per cent is obtained, and the air will flow through the unit at about 200 to 250 fpm. A very slight mist of unevaporated brine leaves the unit; this cannot be avoided, for eliminator plates do not work satisfactorily at velocities below 300 fpm.

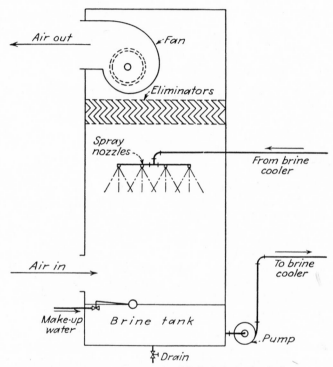

FIG. 5-8. Brine spray unit with forced-air circulation.

This small quantity of unevaporated brine is not detrimental to produce and has a definite preservative action with meats. It also assists in maintaining a high humidity within the refrigerated space.

A vertical brine-spray unit equipped with a fan is shown in Fig. 5-8. It is supplied with brine from a brine cooler outside the refrigerated space. The air flows counter to the direction of the brine spray. Small centrifugal brine nozzles are used, handling about 2 gpm each at 15 psi gauge pressure. Spray densities from 2 to 3 gpm/sq ft are used. The most satisfactory air velocity through the spray is from 500 to 600 fpm. Higher velocities tend to draw brine through the eliminator plates. With such a design the saturation efficiency will be about 70 to 80 per cent.   Horizontal spray chambers of similar design will have considerable lower saturation efficiencies.

A third type of spray cooling unit is similar to the evaporative condenser in all respects except that the refrigerant boils rather than condenses inside the pipe coil.   When designed like the evaporative condenser described in this chapter, it will have a saturation efficiency of about 80 per cent.

SELECTION OF ROOM-COOLING UNITS

In the selection of cooling units, there are four factors to consider. They are

1. Temperature to be maintained
2. Humidity to be maintained
3. Air distribution and circulation
4. Physical adaptability to the space

Temperature.   In Chap. 1 it was found that most comestibles have an optimum storage temperature above freezing of about 30 or 32°F, and a desirable storage temperature below freezing of 0°F.

Finned-type coils with forced circulation of air have become popular for the maintenance of either of these temperatures.   Fins should not be spaced closer than four fins to the inch for either temperature, or excessive trouble will be had with the formation of ice between fins.   Means for easily defrosting the coils should be supplied with all finned coils.   For maintaining temperatures above 35°F, six or seven fins to the inch are often used; however, for all temperatures below 40°F the most satisfactory results will be obtained if not more than five fins to the inch are used.

Bare-pipe coils may be used satisfactorily for maintaining any temperature, but they are heavy, bulky, and more costly to install.

Brine-spray units are seldom used for maintaining temperatures below 15°F.   Sodium chloride brine should be used, since calcium chloride is hygroscopic and extracts moisture from the air.   With any brine-spray unit there is a very small quantity of brine that will enter the air stream.   This is not detrimental but actually beneficial where meats are stored, since sodium chloride has a mild germicidal action.   The brine should be maintained slightly alkaline by adding a few pellets of sodium hydroxide when needed.   Brine-spray units avoid all defrosting difficulties.

Humidity.   With only a few exceptions, the most desirable storage condition is that in which the relative humidity of the air equals the percentage moisture content of the product stored.[1] The optimum relative humidity for fruits is usually between 80 and 90 per cent. For leafy vegetables and root crops, the relative humidity should be about 90 to 95 per cent. For other vegetables, 85 to 90 per cent is usually satisfactory.

The matter of maintaining the proper humidity is primarily one of using enough coil. If the coil temperature is below the dew-point temperature of the room, moisture will condense and freeze on it. If enough cold surface is provided so that the coil does not extract excessive moisture from the air, the humidity in the room will build up to the optimum humidity for the product stored.[1] For produce requiring humidities above 90 per cent, such as leafy vegetables, it is not practical to install enough coil to avoid extraction of moisture. In such cases the humidity may be increased by occasionally sprinkling the floor.

In the selection of coils, two types of storage conditions will be considered: long storage, where the produce will be chilled within a few days after loading and will be stored for several months, and short storage, in which produce will be continuously entering and leaving the room. A cold-storage warehouse is an example of the first type, and a walk-in refrigerator in a grocery store is an example of the second type of storage. The optimum humidity must be maintained in the first type, whereas it is nearly impossible to control the humidity accurately with the second type. Let us first consider the maintenance of the optimum humidity in a room of a cold-storage warehouse.

In cold-storage warehousing, produce enters the rooms at various temperatures. Usually the room is loaded at one time. This may take several days. The produce is chilled as rapidly as possible in order that the heat of evolution will be reduced to a minimum. Auxiliary fans are often operated to hasten the process. A great deal of heat and considerable moisture is given up during the process. Accurate control of humidity cannot be maintained, but it will be sufficiently high if the coil is selected to maintain an optimum humidity during the storage period.

In selecting the coil for the storage period, the maximum storage load must be considered. This load consists of heat gains due to transmission, infiltration, ventilation, respiration of the product, lights, motors, etc., but does not include the load due to the chilling of the product, since this process has already been completed. If sufficient coil is used, its surface temperature will not be appreciably below the dew-point temperature of the room, in which case it will extract little moisture, and the relative humidity will build up to the optimum for the product considered. For pipe coils operating with a thick coat of ice it has been found that if the

[1] Rose, D. H., R. C. Wright, and T. M. Whiteman, The Commercial Storage of Fruits, Vegetables, and Florists' Stocks, *U. S. Dept. Agr. Circ.* 278, November, 1941.

rooms are maintained at 31 or 32°F, with a refrigerant temperature of 26°F, the relative humidity will build up to the optimum for most produce.[1] Relative humidities between 90 and 95 per cent for leafy vegetables such as lettuce may also be maintained with the same coil selection by occasionally sprinkling the floor.

The maintenance of the proper humidity with finned coils is similar to the problem with the bare-pipe coil with a heavy ice coating. Both have a greatly extended outside surface, and hence the surface temperature is higher than that of the refrigerant. Finned coils will give satisfactory operation for cold-storage-warehouse work if selected on a 6°FTD between the room and the refrigerant temperature, based on the maximum-storage heat gain, not including the heat removed in chilling the produce to the room temperature.

The selection of coils for walk-in refrigerators or other rooms in which the produce is continuously changed is somewhat different. A high, irregular chilling load is encountered. To assist in the maintenance of high humidity during high loading periods, there is large infiltration. The warm outside air has a much higher absolute humidity than the room air, and hence the room humidity tends to remain high in spite of the high chilling load. It has been found by common practice that if the coil is selected on a 10°FTD between room air and refrigerant, based on the average maximum hourly heat gain for the warmest day, satisfactory conditions will be maintained for short-storage conditions.

Selection of Controls for Cooling Coils. Pipe coils have proved satisfactory over a long period of time for warehousing. They provide a mild circulation of air, and since they are operated with a thick coat of ice, they have great heat-storage capacity. Because of this heat capacity, the control of temperature and humidity is relatively simple. The temperature of the ice coat is not quickly changed by changes in load.

Brine coils are usually equipped with a hand valve, but may be equipped with an automatic control valve. The quantity of brine circulated through the coil is usually based on a 3 or 4°F rise in temperature, based on the maximum heat gain during the storage period. During the chilling period, the temperature rise may be more than double this amount.

Direct-expansion pipe coils in warehouses invariably use ammonia as the refrigerant because of its greatly lower comparative cost with the large amount of refrigerant required. They are usually equipped with a hand expansion valve and a suction-pressure control valve. The suction-pressure control valve controls the temperature of the evaporating

[1] *Ibid.*

refrigerant in the coil. A hand expansion valve usually controls the flow of refrigerant to the coil. Usually the two valves are adjusted so that the coil is maintained nearly full of the boiling refrigerant at a temperature suitable for maintaining the proper room temperature. With sufficient coil the humidity usually approaches the optimum humidity for the product. With a few products low humidities are required. The suction-pressure control valve is then set for a low suction pressure, and the hand expansion valve is adjusted so that the refrigerant evaporates in a limited length of coil.

Forced-draft finned coils have several advantages over bare-pipe coils. They require less space, are more easily installed, and do not add as much weight to the building. Finned coils may be either brine or direct-expansion coils. With brine systems, any refrigerant may be used. With direct-expansion systems, ammonia is used in large warehouses, while Freon 12, Freon 22, or ammonia may be used in small warehouses. The Freons do not lend themselves readily to application in large direct-expansion installations because of their high cost and their oil-solvent properties. Unless extreme precaution is taken in the design of a large direct-expansion system using an oil-solvent refrigerant, it may be difficult to find the location of the oil. With small direct-expansion installations, the Freons lend themselves readily to automatic control, provide no fire hazard and no damage to produce in case of leakage. Finned coils using Freon usually cost less than those using ammonia, since they may be constructed of copper rather than of aluminum or steel. Copper is quite malleable and lends itself readily to the manufacture of finned coils.

The flow of brine through a finned coil can be controlled by a hand valve, but an automatic valve is preferable. The control of temperature and humidity is similar to that when a pipe coil is used, except that the finned coil is operated with as little ice coating as possible and hence has little heat-storage capacity. If a hand valve is used with a finned coil, the temperature of the room must be watched more closely than when a pipe coil is used.

Direct-expansion coils may be of the flooded or dry-expansion types. Either type may be used with ammonia. Dry-expansion coils only are used with Freon to avoid oil complications. With flooded-type evaporators, the room temperature is often controlled by adjusting the suction-pressure control valve. Automatic control may be had by using a magnetic stop valve in the suction line, controlled by a room thermostat. A magnetic stop valve in the liquid line will do little to control temperature since flooded coils with their accumulators contain so much refrigerant. The most desirable control is obtained with a suction-pressure control valve and a thermostatically controlled magnetic stop valve in the suction line from the coil.

When dry-expansion coils are used, the room temperature is controlled by a thermostatically controlled magnetic stop valve in the liquid line. The flow of refrigerant is further controlled by a thermostatic expansion valve so that, if the magnetic stop valve is open, the coil will be maintained nearly full of boiling refrigerant. This type of automatic control costs less than any other type. It has one disadvantage: it is difficult to adjust a thermostatic expansion valve for less than 6°F superheat, particularly if there is appreciable pressure drop through the coil. This means that the temperature differences between the room air and the refrigerant must be greater with dry-expansion coils than with flooded systems. High humidities must be maintained by intermittent operation of the coil. The coil will be selected to have the same heat-transfer capacity as that of the flooded coil but will operate a lesser period of time at a greater temperature difference between the air and the refrigerant. During the off cycle, some of the extracted moisture will be returned to the atmosphere if the fan is allowed to run continuously.

We will explain the selection procedure more explicitly. We will connect the fan so that it runs continuously. It has been previously stated that cooling coils should be selected on a 6°FTD if the optimum humidity is to be maintained for most produce. The selection will be the same for dry-expansion coils as for flooded coils, but the operation will be different. The dry-expansion coil will operate on a 9°FTD two-thirds of the time and will have the refrigerant completely shut off the other third of the time. Operating suction pressures are therefore lower for dry-expansion coils than for flooded coils. A suction-pressure control valve will help greatly in controlling the suction temperature and maintaining a desirable humidity in the room.

Walk-in refrigerators for grocery stores or meat markets invariably use direct-expansion methyl chloride or Freon 12 blower-type coils. These coils are selected on a 10°FTD between the room air and the boiling refrigerant, based upon the total heat gain during the warmest day, including the heat given up by the product in the chilling process. They are usually operated on a 15°FTD for two-thirds of the time, and the refrigerant is shut off during the other third of the time. During the off cycle, the frozen moisture on the coil tends to sublimate, melt, and evaporate, thus returning some of the extracted moisture to the air and defrosting the coil. The fan runs continuously. If a single evaporator is connected to a single compressor, the compressor must be sized for 50 per cent excess capacity in order to have automatic defrosting.

With any direct-expansion system the control devices and the connecting pipes must be of sufficient size to allow the proper flow of refrigerant during the period of maximum load. In warehouse work, the chilling period will require at least twice the capacity of the storage period, and the coil will operate on correspondingly greater temperature differences. If the coil is to work on two-thirds-time operation, the control devices must have a capacity 50 per cent greater than for continuous operation.

Air Distribution and Circulation. Good distribution consists of delivering the refrigerated air to all parts of the room, producing equal temperature and humidity conditions throughout the product zone. Distribution usually takes place above the product.

With gravity-flow coils, the air may drift directly from the coils over the product. For maximum circulation, the air path should have as little obstruction as possible. Baffles may be useful in collecting the water condensate from the coils, but they cannot create circulation since they have no motive power. Circulation of air within the product zone is necessary in order to carry the heat away from the product. For good distribution and circulation, the distance between the banks of coils should be about the same as the distance across the bank of coils. There is very little danger of getting too much circulation with gravity coils.

With blower-type cooling units, the air should never be blown directly at the product. Circulation around the product should occur on the return of the air to the cooling unit. Distribution of the air should occur above the product. Cold air has a tendency to drop, hence the blower unit should be equipped with louvers to direct the air slightly upward. If maximum circulation of air is desired, all blower units should blow in the same direction. If minimum circulation is desired, a blower unit that blows the air radially in all directions should be used. For all products in the chilling process, or for ice cream in the hardening process, circulation should be high. For products in long-term cold storage that are directly exposed to the air, circulation should be low but positive, in order to avoid excessive drying, and yet high enough to avoid accumulation of free moisture on the product, which might induce spoilage. For products that are boxed or packed, circulation should be moderately high in order to prevent local warm spots.

Physical Adaptability of the Cooling Unit. Because of the small space requirements of the blower-type cooling unit and the brine-spray unit, they are generally preferred to gravity-flow coils, except where very low circulation of air is required. Where very low circulation is necessary, gravity coils of either the fin or plate type require less space than bare-pipe coils. Low circulation requirements may also be met by forced-draft units with radial blow.

COOLING TOWERS

Cooling towers are divided in two main groups: those using natural flow of air and those using forced circulation. Those using natural circulation of air are termed *atmospheric cooling towers,* and those using forced circulation are called *forced-draft,* or *induced-draft, cooling towers,* depending on whether the air is blown or drawn through them. Where the wind is mild but steady, atmospheric cooling towers have lower first cost and operating cost. They are not satisfactory when placed in restricted areas. In many localities there is practically a dead calm on the warmest days. In this case forced circulation should be used. Forced- and induced-draft cooling towers have more dependable action, better appearance, and require less space than the atmospheric tower; they are therefore becoming increasingly popular.

If it were possible to determine the size of the water drops in a tower, rational formulas could be derived to predict their performance. However, many factors influence the droplet size. The size of the drops is affected not only by the type of spray nozzles and the pressure on them, but also by their spacing and by the dimensions of the tower. Design of towers must therefore be made on an empirical basis, keeping in mind the factors that affect the rate of evaporation of the water.

Rate of Evaporation. The rate of evaporation from a free water surface is controlled by three factors:[1]

1. The vapor tension of the water corresponding to its temperature
2. The vapor pressure of the moisture in the air corresponding to the dew-point temperature
3. The effective velocity of the air over the surface

These factors have been summed up concisely for air in transverse flow with water, in the following formula:[1]

$$w = \frac{201 + 0.88v}{h_{fg}} (e_w - e_a) \tag{5-16}$$

where w = lb of water evaporated/(sq ft)(hr)

v = velocity, fpm

e_w = vapor tension of the water corresponding to its temperature

e_a = vapor pressure in the air corresponding to its dew point

h_{fg} = latent heat of evaporation of 1 lb of water

In designing a cooling tower, the square feet of surface is not determinable, and hence prediction of the tower's performance cannot be made by Eq. (5-16); however, if a test is made on a tower operating under

[1] CARRIER, W. H., Temperature of Evaporation, *Trans. ASHVE,* vol. 24, p. 39, 1918.

one set of conditions, it will be useful in determining what it will do under other conditions, provided that the spray system and the quantity of water handled by it are not changed. A more convenient method of predicting a cooling tower's performance is to use the cooling-tower efficiency as described by Eq. (5-14). With forced-draft cooling towers, the saturation efficiency [Eq. (5-12)] and the heat balance [Eq. (5-13)] are also useful.

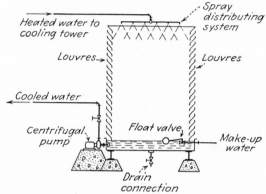

FIG. 5-9. Spray-type atmospheric tower.

Spray-type Atmospheric Cooling Towers. The spray-type cooling tower is shown diagrammatically in Fig. 5-9. The tower should be used only when it can be located in an open space or on top of a building where air currents are not obstructed. It has been previously pointed out that accurate ratings can be determined only by actual test; however, the following approximations may be used in designing a tower of this type. With a wind velocity of 3 mph, an efficiency of approximately 50 per cent is obtained with a cooling tower having louvers set at an angle of 45° with the horizontal, having one nozzle per square foot of horizontal cross-sectional area, each nozzle delivering 2 gpm when working at a head of 15 ft of water, and having approximately the following active heights:

Gpm	Active height, ft	Gpm	Active height, ft
15	7	90	11
30	8	120	12
45	9	150	13
60	10	200	14

The above table is based on towers having a square horizontal cross section. If the cross section is rectangular with the broad side facing the wind, both the efficiency and the drift loss will be increased.   Higher pressure on the nozzles, with the same spray density, also increases both the efficiency and the drift loss.   To increase the efficiency to 75 per cent, it is necessary to double the active volume of the tower without changing the water quantity or the pressure on the sprays.   This is usually done by increasing both the horizontal cross-sectional area and the height.

The Deck-type Atmospheric Tower.   The deck-type tower is shown in Fig. 5-10.   It is similar to the spray-type tower except that water-distributing troughs are used instead of spray nozzles, and the water is

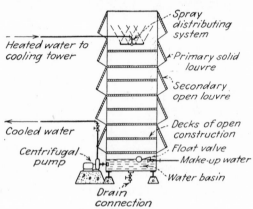

FIG. 5-10.   Deck-type atmospheric tower.

broken into small drops by decks made of hardware cloth or wood slats. The decks are usually placed about 2 ft apart.   Decks are made of $\frac{1}{8}$-in.-mesh hardware cloth and are satisfactory for small towers if corrosive conditions are not encountered.   Decks for larger towers are generally made of wood slats, because of the difficulty of supporting hardware cloth over a wide span.   If wood slats are used, they should be rather narrow and placed fairly close together.   Wood slats 2 in. wide placed on 3-in. centers are satisfactory.   On each succeeding deck the slats should run at right angles to the slats on the deck preceding it.   For a carefully designed tower of this type, the efficiency of a deck-type tower will be approximately the same as a spray-type cooling tower of the same size and handling the same water quantity.

Forced-draft and Induced-draft Cooling Towers.   A diagram of a forced-draft tower is shown in Fig. 5-11, and a diagram of an induced-draft tower is shown in Fig. 5-12.   The action of both is the same, so we will refer to both in this discussion as forced-draft towers.   If the saturation efficiency of any spray chamber is known, its performance as a forced-draft tower can be predicted from the mathematical definition of saturation efficiency and the heat balance [Eq. (5-13)]. Since forced-draft towers are tall and the air and water flow counter to each other, the temperature at the top of the tower is used when considering the satura-

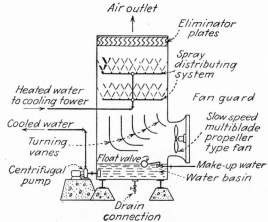

FIG. 5-11. Forced-draft cooling tower.

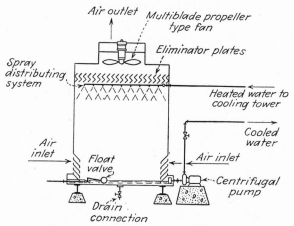

FIG. 5-12. Induced-draft cooling tower.

tion efficiency. Within the range of temperatures used in refrigeration work, their performance can also be predicted by their cooling efficiency [Eq. (5-14)].

Cooling towers are often designated with a pattern similar to the following:

Water pressure at nozzles = 8 psi gauge
Spray density = 2.5 gpm/sq ft

Spacing of nozzles = one or more per square foot
Air velocity = 300 fpm
Air friction = approximately ⅛ in. of water
Active heights as follows:

Gpm	Active Height, Ft
10	6
20	7
40	8
80	9
160	10

A tower with such a design will have a saturation efficiency of about 68 per cent and a cooling efficiency for refrigerating purposes of about 65 per cent. Eliminator plates are not required if the tower is placed outside the building. When no eliminator plates are used, the water pressure at the nozzles should not exceed 10 psi gauge, nor should the air velocity exceed 300 fpm.

Greater spray densities and air velocities may be used if the tower is equipped with eliminator plates and if the air is pumped with a centrifugal fan. The evaporative condenser is essentially a cooling tower of this type having condensing coils located within it.

Problems

1. Find Re for water flowing at 6 fps through a 1¼-in.-o.d. No. 12 B.w.g. condenser tube.

2. Find Re for a 12 per cent solution of sodium chloride brine at 20°F flowing at 6 fps through a 1¼-in.-o.d. No. 12 B.w.g. tube.

3. Find the film conductance for ammonia condensing on the outside of a 2-in.-o.d. tube if the temperature difference between the metal and the condensing vapor is 5°F.

4. Find the film conductance for Freon 12 condensing on the outside of a 2-in.-o.d. tube if the temperature difference between the metal and the condensing vapor is 5°F.

5. Find the film conductance for water at 80°F flowing at 6 fps through a 1¼-in.-o.d. No. 12 B.w.g. condenser tube.

6. Find the over-all transmittance U for an ammonia condenser if 80°F water flows at 6 fps through its 1½-in.-o.d. No. 12 B.w.g. tubes, if the condenser is to be used with hard water (15 g/gal).

7. A Freon 12 water cooler has ⅝-in.-i.d. copper finned tubes. The outside surface has three times the area of the inside surface. Water flows through the inside at 4 fps, and the refrigerant condenses on the outside. Assume that the metal offers no appreciable resistance to the heat flow. Find the over-all heat transmittance U based upon the outside surface area.

8. Brine enters a cooler at 5°F and leaves at 0°F. The evaporating temperature is −10°F. Find the mean temperature difference.

9. A finned coil cools air from 31 to 25°F. Brine enters the coil at 20°F and leaves at 24°F. The brine and air flow in opposite directions. Find the mean temperature difference.

10. Derive the expression for mean temperature difference for parallel flow of two fluids.

11. Find the number of 1¼-in.-o.d. No. 13 B.w.g. tubes required, and the number of tubes per pass, for an ammonia condenser to fit the following specifications:

Capacity = 40 tons ime
Power required by compressor = 45 bhp
Length of tubes = 16 ft
Entering water temperature = 80°F
Water velocity = approximately 6 fps
Water quantity = 120 gpm
Water hardness = 10 g/gal
Condensing temperature = 100°F

12. Find the saturation efficiency of a spray chamber if the entering air temperature is 32°F, the leaving air temperature is 26°F, and the leaving brine temperature is 24°F.

13. Air enters a brine spray chamber at 40°F. The leaving brine temperature is 30°F, and the saturation efficiency of the chamber is 70 per cent. What is the temperature of the leaving air?

14. An atmospheric cooling tower has an efficiency of 50 per cent when handling 50 gpm of water. It is connected to a refrigerating system that has a capacity of 15 tons ime and uses 21 bhp. If the wet-bulb temperature is 70°F, what are the temperatures of the entering and leaving water?

15. A forced-draft cooling tower has a saturation efficiency of 75 per cent in terms of the water at the top of the tower. The velocity of the air through it is 500 fpm, and the spray density is 3.5 gpm/sq ft. The water is to be cooled through a 12°F range in temperature. If the wet-bulb temperature is 72°F, what will be the entering and leaving water temperatures? What will be the cooling efficiency of the tower?

CHAPTER 6

THE EXPANSION VALVE AND THE ACCUMULATOR

The expansion valve is the valve that controls the flow of refrigerant to the evaporator. An ideal expansion valve will maintain the evaporator nearly full of boiling refrigerant. The degree to which the coil is filled with boiling refrigerant determines, to a considerable extent, the rate of heat transfer of the coil. Very little heat transfer takes place after the refrigerant has completely evaporated. A coil that is only half filled with the boiling refrigerant has only slightly more than half the heat-transfer rate of a coil that is completely filled. If, on the other hand, the expansion valve allows the liquid refrigerant to enter the suction line, it may be carried back to the compressor and cause "slugging." The quality of an expansion valve is therefore determined largely by the completeness with which it maintains the coil filled with the boiling refrigerant without allowing it to enter the suction line in the liquid phase. To accomplish this result, the following expansion valves are used:

1. Hand expansion valve
2. Low-pressure float valve
3. High-pressure float valve
4. Pressure-regulating valve
5. Capillary tube
6. Thermostatic expansion valve

The accumulator is a device that must be used with certain types of expansion valves if they are to function efficiently in maintaining certain types of evaporators full of refrigerant without allowing some of it to enter the suction line in the liquid phase. Accumulators will therefore be discussed in conjunction with expansion valves.

EXPANSION VALVES

The Hand Expansion Valve. The hand expansion valve is used in bypass connections with both high- and low-pressure float valves. It is also used to control the liquid flow directly to evaporators that have a nearly constant load for a period of a day or more. It will maintain

242

the coil full of liquid refrigerant only if it is used in conjunction with an accumulator.

Low-pressure Float Valve. The low-pressure float valve controls the liquid level in the evaporator directly by a float placed in the evaporator, in the accumulator, or in a float chamber connected to the evaporator or accumulator by a set of equalizing connections. Figure 6-1 shows a float valve with suitable equalizer connections for use with ammonia on a brine cooler. The float operates the valve by lever action. For small systems, the hand expansion valve will be closed during operation except

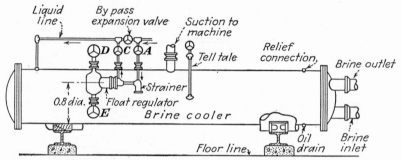

For float operation:
Valves *A*, *C*, and *E* open
Valve *B* closed

Fɪɢ. 6-1. Low-pressure float valve with brine cooler.

in case of emergency. The float chamber will then be isolated by means of the valves, and regulation will be secured by means of the hand expansion valve. For large systems, closer regulation of the liquid level will be obtained with the hand expansion valve partially open, since a minimum of boiling will then occur in the float chamber. The line from the expansion valve to the evaporator or accumulator should have a separate connection so that flow through it will in no way interfere with the operation of the float valve.

The float valve and connections for a small Freon 12 system may be arranged as in the ammonia system if the major portion of the refrigerant passes through the hand expansion valve rather than the float valve. Freon 12 has such a low latent heat of evaporation that the amount of refrigerant that flashes into vapor during the throttling process is excessive and interferes with the action of the float. Two better methods of regulation may be used. The float valve may be placed directly in the evaporator or accumulator, or a pilot-operated valve may be used. With a pilot-operated valve, evaporation does not occur in the float chamber. The small valve in the float chamber is opened or closed by lever action. The small amount of refrigerant that passes regulates another valve, external to the float chamber, that controls the flow of refrigerant to the evaporator. Flash vapor passes along with the liquid refrigerant to the bottom of the brine cooler or accumulator and bubbles to the top.

High-pressure Float Valve. The high-pressure float valve controls the liquid level in an evaporator or accumulator indirectly. It maintains a definite liquid level in the condenser or receiver. With the proper amount of refrigerant in the system, the liquid level in the brine cooler or accumulator will be correct. A shortage of refrigerant will starve the evaporator, and a surplus of refrigerant will overflood the evaporator.

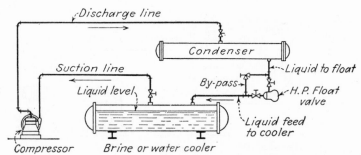

FIG. 6-2. High-pressure float valve with shell-and-tube brine or water cooler.

Only one high-pressure float valve may be used on a system. If the system has several evaporators at the same level, they may all be connected to the same accumulator. The float chamber in a high-pressure float valve is at the condensing temperature. Often a float-type steam trap is used as a high-pressure float valve. Figure 6-2 shows a high-pressure float used with a brine cooler. The type of valve and the necessary connections are simple and are the same for use with any refrigerant. The system is operated with the hand expansion valve closed except in case of emergency.

Pressure-regulating Valve. This type of valve is arranged so that pressure in the evaporator works on a diaphragm, tending to close the valve, while spring tension tends to hold it open. The valve holds a set pressure in the evaporator regardless of what the load may be. If the coil is working at a light load, the coil tends to be full of refrigerant. It is used on a heavy load, the coil tends to become starved. It is used only on small equipment, such as household refrigerators.

Capillary Tube. The capillary tube is a tube of small diameter. It is used primarily on household refrigerators with sulfur dioxide as the refrigerant. The capillary tube allows the liquid refrigerant to pass, but passes gas with difficulty because of its high specific volume. Systems of this type have no receiver. The capillary tube must be equipped with a good filter to prevent clogging.

Thermostatic Expansion Valve. The thermostatic expansion valve regulates the flow of refrigerant to the evaporator so that nearly constant superheat is maintained in the vapor leaving the coil. With this type of valve the coil is maintained nearly full of boiling refrigerant. The super-heating of the vapor takes place in only a small portion of the coil near

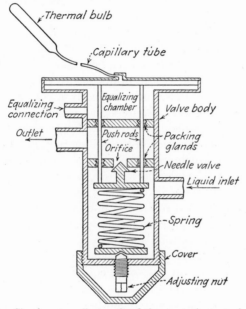

FIG. 6-3. Simple externally equalized thermostatic expansion valve.

its outlet. Figure 6-3 shows a thermostatic valve with an equalizer connection. The diaphragm is sealed from the refrigerant that flows through the valve. The diaphragm works on a stem that opens or closes the valve. The thermostatic bulb is clamped to the outlet of the evaporator and contains the same fluid that is used as a refrigerant in the system, usually in sufficient quantity that, with a rise in temperature, it does not completely vaporize. The pressure in this bulb is carried to one side of the diaphragm by a small-diameter tube. The equalizer connection carries the pressure from the outlet of the coil to the other side of the diaphragm. An adjustable spring acts on the same side of the diaphragm as the pressure from the coil outlet. This spring maintains a constant pressure difference between the pressure at the coil outlet and the pressure in the thermostatic bulb. Since the evaporating temperature is a function of the pressure in the coil, and since the pressure in the bulb is a function of the outlet-coil temperature, a constant temperature difference is maintained between the evaporating temperature and the temperature at the end of the coil.   Since the temperature at the outlet of the coil approximates the gas temperature at the point, it can be said that a constant superheat is maintained in the vapor leaving the evaporator.

In order to ensure that dry gas is returned to the compressor, the spring is usually adjusted to maintain approximately 9°F superheat. When the evaporator is selected to operate on low temperature differentials between the coil and the room temperature (12°F or less), it is necessary to adjust the valve for lower superheat.   When the expansion valve is maintaining low superheat in the vapor leaving the coil, a heat exchanger should be used to transfer heat from the liquid line to the suction line and ensure the return of dry gas to the compressor.

For very small coils that work on nearly a constant load and have very little friction (less than 2 psi pressure drop), the equalizer connection may be eliminated, in which case the diaphragm is not sealed off from the suction vapor.   The friction of the boiling refrigerant passing through the tubes will be approximately the same as if the same weight of dry vapor were passing through the tubes.   It is difficult to estimate the pressure drop in the header of the coil.   In case it is constructed with small tubes or orifices to regulate the flow, the pressure drop will often exceed 2 psi.   It is good practice in case of doubt concerning friction to use the equalizer connection, since closer regulation will always be obtained with its use.   A valve designed for use with an equalizer connection will not function unless the equalizer connection is made.

Valves for air-conditioning systems are often equipped with thermostatic bulbs having a limited charge so that when the temperature in the bulb rises to about 50°F, all the fluid completely vaporizes.   The pressure of the vapor in the coil rises faster with a rise in temperature than does the pressure of the dry gas in the bulb.   As the pressure rises in the system, it works in conjunction with the spring and closes the valve. Valves of this type usually close completely at about 55°F.   These valves perform their intended function of closing off only when the temperature of the coil during its off period never drops below the temperature at which the expansion valve is supposed to shut off.

With the thermostatic expansion valve, the flash gas must pass through the cooling coils before entering the suction line.   Also, the heat-transfer rate is low in that portion of the coil in which superheating of the vapor takes place.   Because of these two factors, the heat-transfer rate of a coil using the thermostatic expansion valve is somewhat lower than that of a coil using a float valve and an accumulator.   However, with oil-solvent refrigerants, the dry-expansion coil with the thermostatic valve has the great advantage that oil does not settle out in the evaporator, but is carried directly to the suction line and returned to the compressor without oil-separation or distilling devices. The thermostatic valve is also gaining favor on ammonia blower-type cooling units. The additional amount of coil required usually costs less and occupies less space than an accumulator with a float valve.

Installation of Thermostatic Expansion Valves. The valve should be installed as close to the evaporator as possible and may be either inside or outside the refrigerated space. Most valves may be installed in any position. There should never be a restriction of any kind between the valve and the evaporator except a distributing header or proportioning device for multifeed coils.

Most expansion valves are equipped with a small strainer. These strainers should not be depended upon to do the major portion of the filtering. A separate strainer or scale trap should be installed ahead of the expansion valve. In case there are many expansion valves used on a system, a master strainer should be installed in the main liquid line.

To ensure tight closing of the valve when the compressor stops, the bulb must be clamped on the coil or suction line in a location where the bulb temperature will be the same as the evaporator temperature during the off cycle. On direct-expansion systems, the bulb should always be inside the refrigerated space. On brine tanks or water coolers, the bulb should be below the liquid surface, at the coldest point in the tank. If, for practical reasons the bulb must be located where the temperature is higher than the evaporator temperature, a magnetic stop valve should be used ahead of the thermostatic expansion valve.

For suction lines 2 in. or less in diameter, the bulb should be clamped to the top of the suction line. For suction lines above 2-in. diameter, slightly better action is obtained if the bulb is clamped to the side of the suction line. The bulb should be clamped on with the clamps provided by the manufacturer. The pipe surface on which the bulb is clamped must be smooth and clean. Where iron pipe is used, it should be painted with aluminum paint before the bulb is applied. It is essential when the bulb is clamped on a horizontal pipe to have the capillary tubing toward the top and the charging end toward the bottom. On a vertical pipe the capillary tube should project from the top. The bulb should not be covered with insulation unless it is located where it is subjected to high temperatures. Hair felt should not be used. Use cork and make certain that it is well sealed to prevent water from condensing and freezing on the pipe and bulb underneath the insulation. If the bulb is on a brine coil below the liquid surface, the capillary tube should be painted with tar immediately above and below the liquid surface in order to prevent corrosion at this point.

Never locate the bulb in a liquid trap or pocket in the coil or suction line. Liquid boiling out of the trap will keep the bulb cold and the valve closed, when it should be feeding additional refrigerant to the coil. It should not be located where it may be affected by suction vapor from some other unit on the system. Each bulb should be subjected only to the temperature of the suction vapor of the unit that particular valve is controlling. If the bulb must be installed on a branch suction line close to the point where it taps into the main suction line, the branch should "gooseneck" into the main to prevent liquid from another unit dropping into the branch line by gravity and affecting the bulb.

On long commercial coils it is advisable, wherever possible, to clamp the bulb to the coil away from the outlet end by a distance 5 to 10 per cent of the length of the coil. The coil beyond the bulb will act as a drier to ensure that dry vapor returns to the compressor.

Valves should be ordered with an equalizer outlet where the pressure drop of the evaporator and its header exceeds 1 or 2 psi. Valves ordered with an equalizer will not operate unless the external equalizer connection is made. Run ⅛-in. pipe or ¼-in.-o.d. tubing, of material suitable for the refrigerant used in the system, from the equalizer outlet in the valve body to the suction line or end of the evaporator. This connection should be made on the compressor side of the thermostatic bulb.

Do not, under any circumstances, apply heat to the bulb or diaphragm case. If soldering, brazing or welding is done on the suction line after the valve is installed, be sure to remove the bulb while the work is being done.

In testing the system for leaks, do not permit the pressure to go above 150 psi gauge pressure for Freon or methyl chloride valves, or above 200 psi gauge pressure for ammonia valves, as higher pressures may rupture the diaphragms.

Most thermostatic expansion valves are adjusted at the factory for 9°F superheat. This adjustment will prove satisfactory in nearly all cases. Where the coil is selected to operate on a low temperature differential between the refrigerant and air temperature (less than 12°F), it will be necessary to readjust the valve. Adjustment of the valve should never be made until the system has been operating several hours. There is only one adjustment, the small stem that is normally covered by a seal cap. On most valves, screwing in the stem increases the superheat and backing it out decreases the superheat. Very few valves will work satisfactorily at a superheat of less than 6°F. Where it is necessary to adjust the valve for low superheat, a heat exchanger should be used to transfer heat from the liquid to the suction line.   After the adjustment has been made, it is seldom necessary to readjust the valve.

Capacity of Expansion Valves.   The capacity of an expansion valve varies with the pressure available to force the liquid refrigerant through the orifice of the valve.   This pressure should be calculated as the difference between the liquid-line pressure at the inlet to the valve and the evaporator pressure.   The available pressure may be computed as follows:

$$p = p_c - (p_e + p_a + p_l + p_v) \qquad (6\text{-}1)$$

where p = pressure drop across the valve
$\quad p_c$ = condensing pressure
$\quad p_a$ = pressure drop across all accessories between the tubes of the evaporator and the condenser, such as distribution header, magnetic stop valves, hand valves, strainer, etc.
$\quad p_l$ = pressure drop due to friction in the liquid line
$\quad p_v$ = pressure drop due to a vertical lift of the refrigerant

The condensing pressure p_c should be the lowest condensing pressure at which the system normally operates.   The evaporating pressure p_e should be the highest pressure at which the system normally operates. The suction pressure at the compressor may be slightly lower than the evaporating pressure at the coil, owing to friction in the suction line. The pressure drop across the header for the evaporator of a dry-expansion coil seldom exceeds 3 psi.   Magnetic stop valves are usually sized for a pressure drop of less than 5 psi.   The pressure drop through a clean strainer seldom exceeds 1 psi.   The liquid line should be sized for a friction not to exceed 5 psi.   The pressure drop p_v is a function of the density of the refrigerant and the height through which it is pumped. Since the density of a refrigerant in the liquid phase varies only slightly with temperature, the pressure drop per foot of lift will be nearly independent of temperature.   The pressure drop per foot of lift for various refrigerants in the liquid phase at 90°F is given in Table 6-1.

TABLE 6-1.   PRESSURE DROP PER FOOT OF LIFT FOR VARIOUS LIQUID REFRIGERANTS AT 90°F

Refrigerant	p_v, psi	Refrigerant	p_v, psi
Ammonia	0.26	Methyl chloride	0.39
Freon 12	0.56	Sulfur dioxide	0.58
Freon 22	0.50		

A drop in pressure by any of the foregoing causes will result in a portion of the liquid flashing into vapor.   When flashing occurs, the friction increases through subsequent accessories, thus causing further flashing. In order to avoid excessive flashing, provision should be made to subcool the liquid either in the condenser or in a separate subcooler whenever the pressure drop $p_a + p_l + p_v$ exceeds 5 psi.

After the available pressure drop across the expansion valve has been determined, the size of the expansion valve can be ascertained from catalogue ratings.   The following tables give the capacities of Sporlan thermostatic expansion valves for use with Freon 12, methyl chloride, and ammonia.

TABLE 6-2. CAPACITIES OF SPORLAN THERMOSTATIC EXPANSION VALVES IN TONS OF REFRIGERATION WHEN USING FREON 12

Port, in.	Pressure drop across valve, psi				
	20	40	60	80	100
$\frac{1}{16}$	0.3	0.4	0.5	0.55	0.6
$\frac{7}{64}$	0.6	0.85	1.0	1.1	1.2
$\frac{3}{16}$	2.0	3.0	3.5	4.0	4.5
$\frac{1}{4}$	3.5	5.5	6.5	7.5	8.5
$\frac{9}{32}$	5.0	8.0	10.0	11.5	13.0
$\frac{5}{16}$	5.0	8.0	10.0	12.0	14.0
$\frac{3}{8}$	8.0	12.5	15.0	18.0	21.0
$\frac{7}{16}$	10.0	16.0	20.0	24.0	27.0

TABLE 6-3.   CAPACITIES OF SPORLAN THERMOSTATIC EXPANSION VALVES IN TONS OF REFRIGERATION WHEN USING METHYL CHLORIDE

Port, in.	Pressure drop across valve, psi				
	20	40	60	80	100
$\frac{1}{16}$	0.85	1.0	1.1	1.2	1.3
$\frac{7}{64}$	1.3	1.7	2.0	2.3	2.4
$\frac{3}{16}$	4.0	6.0	7.0	8.0	9.0
$\frac{1}{4}$	7.0	11.0	13.0	15.0	17.0
$\frac{9}{32}$	10.0	16.0	20.0	23.0	26.0
$\frac{5}{16}$	10.0	16.0	20.0	24.0	28.0
$\frac{3}{8}$	16.0	25.0	30.0	36.0	42.0
$\frac{7}{16}$	22.0	32.0	40.0	48.0	54.0

TABLE 6-4. CAPACITIES OF SPORLAN EXPANSION VALVES IN TONS OF REFRIGERATION WHEN USING AMMONIA

Port, in.	Discharge-tube orifice	Tons
$\frac{1}{16}$	$\frac{1}{32}$	0–1
$\frac{1}{16}$	$\frac{1}{16}$	1–2
$\frac{7}{64}$	$\frac{5}{64}$	2–5
$\frac{3}{16}$	$\frac{7}{64}$	5–10
$\frac{3}{16}$	$\frac{1}{8}$	10–15
$\frac{5}{16}$	$\frac{1}{8}$	15–20
$\frac{5}{16}$	$\frac{5}{32}$	20–30
$\frac{5}{16}$	$\frac{3}{16}$	30–50
$\frac{3}{8}$	...	50–75
$\frac{7}{16}$	...	75–100

ACCUMULATORS

The purpose of an accumulator is to accumulate the surges of liquid returned by the evaporating coils or to maintain the coils completely filled with liquid refrigerant and provide a space above the liquid level so that liquid refrigerant will not enter the suction line and be carried back to the compressor. Three types of accumulators are in common use—the pressure type, the gravity type, and accumulators with liquid pumps.

Pressure-type Accumulator. The pressure-type accumulator is a heat exchanger having ample volume within its shell to hold any surges of liquid that may slop over from the evaporating coils. It is extensively used in large cold-storage warehouses and ice plants where many hand expansion valves may be used. Figure 6-4 shows a pressure-type accumulator. The hot liquid from the receiver passes through the coil inside the shell on its way to the hand expansion valves. Nearly all the refrigerant evaporates in the evaporator coils; however, a small portion may surge back to the accumulator. Heat transfer occurs between the hot liquid in the accumulator coil and the cool liquid that has returned from the evaporator coil, causing the returned liquid to evaporate. The dry vapor is carried back to the compressor through the suction line located at the top of the accumulator. The level of the returned liquid is indicated by the frost line on a piece of bare pipe used as a liquid-level indicator. As the liquid level rises, the hand expansion valves on those coils which are frosted back to the vapor-return header should be closed slightly.

While the main function of the pressure accumulator is to prevent liquid refrigerant from returning to the compressor, with consequent "slugging" at the compressor head, it has two other functions. It assists in removing water and stray oil from the system, and it subcools the liquid refrigerant before the latter enters the expansion valve. Subcooling of the liquid refrigerant reduces the amount of flash vapor in the coil and thereby increases the heat-transfer rate. Any water or oil present collects at the bottom of the accumulator, since both are heavier than the liquid ammonia. The hot coil distills a portion of the ammonia from the

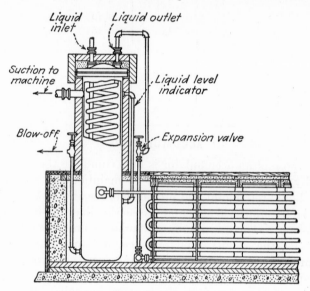

Fig. 6-4.   Pressure-type accumulator.

collected water and oil, and the residue may be drained from the system at the blowoff valve.

The coil in a pressure accumulator should be large enough to cool the liquid passing through it to within 10°F of the evaporating temperature. The shell should be ample in size, extending at least above the submerged portion of the coil. Often the coil is extended above the liquid level to ensure that dry gas is returned to the compressor.

Gravity-type Accumulator. The gravity accumulator is a header system in which the liquid level is maintained above the outlet of the coil by a float valve, but with a space above the liquid level so that liquid refrigerant will not enter the suction line. Gravity accumulators are the most common type, especially on small systems. They may be either vertical or horizontal, and have either an internal or an external float valve. Figure 6-5 shows several gravity-type accumulators.

The gravity accumulator has two other functions. The throttling process occurs entirely in the accumulator; therefore the evaporator coil has a minimum amount of flash vapor and has a maximum heat-transfer rate. Water and stray oil tend to collect at the bottom of the accumulator and may be removed at the blowoff valve.

Accumulators with Liquid Pumps. In large cold-storage plants, a large gravity accumulator with a float valve or hand expansion valve may

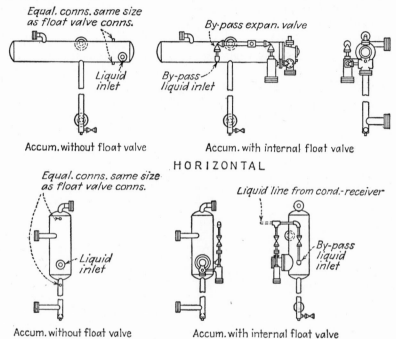

HORIZONTAL

VERTICAL

Fig. 6-5. Ammonia accumulators.

be used with a rotary pump that draws the liquid ammonia from near the bottom of the accumulator and circulates it to the various cooling coils throughout the plant. The flow through each of the coils is regulated by a hand expansion valve. The accumulator must be located well above the pump (at least 5 ft) so that it will not develop a vapor lock. With an arrangement of this type it matters little if the ammonia slops over from some of the coils since it will be returned to the accumulator and be recirculated.

With another arrangement, the ammonia that slops over from the coils collects in a large tank equipped with a float switch. As the ammonia rises to a certain level, the float switch closes the circuit for a liquid pump that pumps the excess liquid into the condenser or receiver.

If the refrigerant is pumped to the receiver, the latter should be large enough to accommodate any situation that might arise in the plant.

In determining the size of an accumulator from which the liquid is pumped to the high side of the system, it is well to consider that about 1 gpm of ammonia will be returned for each 75 tons of plant capacity. The size of the pump should be selected so that it will not operate more than 75 per cent of the time. The accumulator size should be selected so that the pump will not need to start more than twice per hour.

All accumulators should be constructed in accordance with the American Standard Safety Code for Mechanical Refrigeration.[1]

[1] See Appendix 6.

CHAPTER 7

ACCESSORIES

There are four parts without which a refrigerating system cannot operate. They are the compressor, the condenser, the expansion valve, and the evaporator. These parts have all been described in detail. There are many other parts required on some systems to make them operate safely, smoothly, and at high efficiency. These auxiliary parts will be discussed in this chapter.

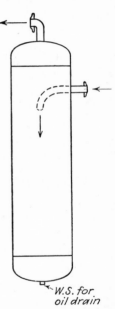

Receivers. The receiver is a refrigerant storage tank, located below the condenser, to hold a surplus of refrigerant or to hold the refrigerant that may need to be pumped from any part of the system in case of repair work. On small systems, or systems having a single evaporator, it is usually advisable for the receiver to hold the entire charge of the system plus about a 25 per cent surplus. With large systems, the receiver should hold the charge of the largest evaporator and refrigerant lines with at least a 50 per cent surplus. The receiver should be equipped with connections for the following: liquid inlet, liquid outlet, gauge glass, safety valve, and purge valve. The liquid inlet should be at least one pipe size larger than the liquid outlet. All pressure vessels should be constructed in accordance with the American Standard Code for Mechanical Refrigeration.[1]

W.S. for oil drain

FIG. 7-1. Discharge-line oil trap for ammonia.

Ammonia Discharge-line Oil Trap. An ammonia discharge-line oil trap may be constructed as shown in Fig. 7-1. It is a chamber of large size as compared to the discharge line. Its diameter should not be less than five times the diameter of the discharge line, and its length should be about three times its diameter. It may be equipped with a gas discharge connection at the top and a gas inlet connection turned downward at its center. Many variations in design occur.

The discharge gas from an ammonia compressor is highly superheated.

[1] See Appendix 6.

This superheat is used in distilling the ammonia from the stray oil. The oil collects on the walls and flows to the bottom, from whence it is occasionally drained by a hand valve.

Not all ammonia systems have a discharge-line oil trap. Often the receiver is arranged with a pocket at its bottom from which the oil may be drained. This is not good practice, especially on very low temperature systems, since the oil separation is not as complete as when the superheat of the discharge gas is used to distill the ammonia from the stray oil. Part of the oil is bound to be carried over to the evaporator and collect on the tubes, especially if the evaporator temperature is near or below the pour point of the oil.

Discharge-line Oil Trap for Freon 12 and Other Oil-solvent Refrigerants. Freon 12 and methyl chloride are highly soluble in oil; sulfur dioxide and Freon 22 are moderately soluble, and ammonia is the only refrigerant in common use having low solubility in oil. Refrigerants that are moderately or highly soluble in oil readily circulate oil throughout the system. Only that oil which stays in the compressor lubricates it. The stray oil has no function, but retards the flow of heat in both the condenser and the evaporator. Furthermore, when there is excessive oil in circulation, the oil in the crankcase becomes diluted and impairs the lubrication of the compressor. Several factors contribute to excessive oil in circulation—adjustment of the expansion valve for low superheat, excessive friction in the evaporator, excessive oil in the system, worn piston rings, and running the compressor at higher speed than that for which it was designed.

Several partial remedies for excessive oil circulation may be applied. With systems for which the expansion valve must be adjusted for low superheat, a heat exchanger between the liquid and suction lines may be installed. For systems having an excessively long evaporating coil, the coil may be divided so that each refrigerant pass will have a shorter length. Excessive oil in the system is very hard to diagnose if the system does not have a discharge-line oil trap and if the system has some other factor contributing to excessive oil circulation. Excessive oil in the system leads to excessive oil in circulation, which in turn leads to dilution of the oil, which in turn leads to excessive oil leaving the crankcase. Therefore an excess of oil in the system may, in extreme cases, result in shortage of oil in the crankcase when the compressor is running and "slugging" at the head of the compressor when it starts. The adjustment of the expansion valve should always be checked before adding or removing oil from the system. Worn piston rings on a Freon 12 system or other system using an oil-solvent refrigerant need hardly be considered as a contributing factor to oil difficulties. Invariably, the wrist pins and wrist-pin bushings become worn and noisy before the rings are worn. When these are replaced, the rings are usually replaced with them. Oil difficulty is, therefore, seldom caused by worn piston rings. Running the compressor at higher speeds than that for which it was designed leads to excessive churning in the crankcase, with excessive oil in circulation. This difficulty is seldom met except in systems of very small size. With systems of appreciable size, changing pulleys and motor is rather costly and hence is seldom done.

Systems that have more than two compressors connected in parallel or have compressors that may be operated on less than 50 per cent of their capacity should be equipped with a discharge-line oil trap to avoid an oil problem. Unless the number of coils in operation varies as the number of compressors in operation, the expansion valves become extremely oversized on the excessively reduced loads. This leads to inaccurate regulation of the superheat by the expansion valves, with consequent varying amounts of oil in circulation.

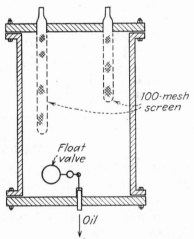

Fig. 7-2. Discharge-line oil trap for oil-solvent refrigerants.

Systems using oil-solvent refrigerants with flooded evaporators *must* use a discharge-line oil trap with each compressor. With a dry-expansion system, part of the oil is returned to the compressor in a vapor form, and part is carried by friction of the vapor with the oil film on the sides of the tube. The friction in a flooded evaporator is negligible, and some of the oil will settle out unless it is removed before reaching the evaporator. Flooded evaporators for systems using oil-solvent refrigerants have the tubes placed as close together as possible so that the boiling action will cause extreme turbulence and the oil will be carried into the suction line in a vapor form.

Systems that operate at evaporating temperatures near or below the pour point of the oil must be equipped with a discharge-line oil trap to prevent the oil from forming a film on the evaporator tubes. When a discharge-line oil trap is used, evaporating temperatures far below the pour point of the oil can be maintained without oil difficulties.

The discharge-line oil trap should not be considered a cure-all for oil difficulties; however, the lubrication of a compressor is always better on a system having one. With proper selection of equipment and proper adjustment of the expansion valve, the oil stays in the crankcase of the compressor where it belongs.

A discharge-line oil separator for an oil-solvent refrigerant is shown in Fig. 7-2. It differs from the ammonia oil separator in many respects. The amount of oil involved is much greater; the trap must, therefore, be equipped with a float valve and an oil tube to return the oil to the crankcase. The superheat involved is low, particularly with Freon 12; therefore the trap must be insulated. The required volume for a given discharge-line size is about double that of the ammonia trap. Distribut-

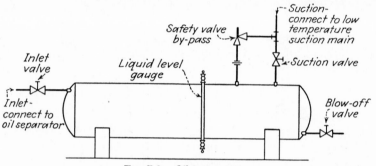

FIG. 7-3.   Oil regenerator.

ing tubes of 100-mesh screen or finer, about two pipe sizes larger than the discharge line, distribute the flow of the incoming and outgoing vapor, thus reducing the turbulence.

Oil Regenerators. Oil from an ammonia oil separator cannot be directly returned to the compressor crankcase, since it contains considerable ammonia and would only lead to greater amounts of oil leaving the crankcase. With new compressors, the stray oil is small, but as the compressors become worn, the amount increases. The cost of this oil becomes appreciable unless the ammonia is driven from it so that it can be used over again.

The most simple regenerator consists of a drum made from a piece of standard-weight 6- or 8-in. pipe, 2 or 3 ft long, equipped with the following: oil inlet valve, oil blowoff valve, safety valve, suction valve, and liquid-level gauge. Figure 7-3 shows such a regenerator. Lines lead from the bottoms of the oil separator, the receiver, and the evaporator to the oil inlet valve. Another line leads from the suction valve of the regenerator to the suction main for the lowest temperature system having an evaporating pressure above atmospheric pressure in the plant. All connections may be half inch. To operate the regenerator, close the suction valve, open the inlet valve, and drain all the oil from the oil separator, receiver, and evaporators. Then close the oil inlet valve and open the suction valve. The ammonia boils out of the valve slowly. The reclaimed oil is drained by closing the suction valve and opening the blowoff valve. More rapid action may be obtained if the regenerator has a jacket through which hot water may be circulated.

Liquid-ammonia De-oiler. With an ammonia evaporator at a temperature near the pour point of the oil, there is a tendency of the stray

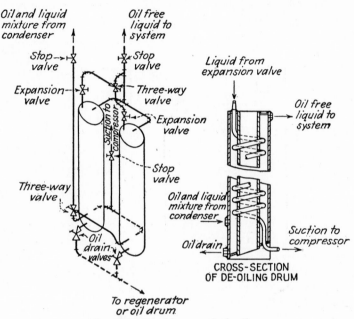

FIG. 7-4. Liquid ammonia de-oiler.

compressor-lubricating oil to form a film and congeal on the cooling surface. This film greatly reduces the heat-transfer rate and should be avoided. One method is to use liquid-ammonia de-oiling drums. A liquid-ammonia de-oiler consists of two shell-and-coil coolers for cooling the liquid ammonia to such a temperature that the stray oil collects on the surface of the cooling coil. One cooler collects the stray oil, while the other cooler is allowed to rise to room temperature. With the rise of temperature, the oil will drop to the bottom of the cooler and may be drained from the system. Figure 7-4 shows such a set of coolers with suitable connections. Each cooler is constructed in an annular shape from two pieces of standard-weight pipe with a dry-expansion evaporating coil placed between them. The evaporating coil is connected so that it uses de-oiled liquid ammonia.

Liquid-ammonia Filter and Oil Injector.   Oil may be removed from liquid ammonia by filtering it through steel wool.   This oil may be removed from the steel wool or from the tubes of the evaporator by injecting a very low viscosity oil with a very low pour point, or kerosene, into the system at the filter or evaporator.   The light oil or kerosene will cut loose the congealed oil, and the resulting oil solution will collect at the

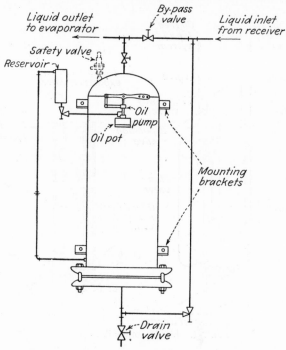

FIG. 7-5.   Liquid ammonia filter and oil injector.

bottom of the evaporator, from whence it may be drained or sent to the regenerator.   The reclaimed oil should be discarded.   Figure 7-5 shows a liquid-ammonia filter and oil injector.

To put the system in operation, open the angle valve between the pump and the reservoir, and inject kerosene into the reservoir until it is filled.   Subsequent fillings may require $\frac{1}{4}$ or $\frac{1}{2}$ pt of kerosene.   After the reservoir is filled, the angle valve should be tightly closed.

To remove the oil solution from the evaporator, it is necessary to build up the evaporator pressure 10 or 20 psi above the normal suction pressure.   The line from the evaporator to the regenerator is then opened and the oil solution allowed to drain to the regenerator, from whence it is discarded.

Noncondensable-gas Purgers. Systems in which the evaporator may operate at a vaccum all or part of the time are subject to air leakage from the outside, although some modern pressure-lubricated shaft seals have greatly reduced this tendency. This air is noncondensable and will collect in the condenser or receiver. Air that collects in the condenser will form a film on the surface of the condenser tubes and impair their heat-transfer rate, thus causing a rise in condensing temperature.

The air may be purged as follows: Stop the compressor and close the inlet valve to the condenser. Allow the cooling water to continue running through the tubes for a few minutes. Close the valve between the condenser and the receiver. Open the purge valve at the top of the condenser until the pressure in it is reduced nearly to atmospheric pressure. With ammonia, the purged gas must be bubbled through water or relieved to the outside. Methyl chloride is combustible and should be relieved to the outside. The Freons are noncombustible and cause no distress if relieved directly to the room. After purging, the condenser shutoff valves may be opened and operation resumed. In extreme cases the operation may need repeating. Air diffuses readily in the refrigerant' vapor and cannot be easily eliminated.

A better method of purging employs an automatic purger. Figures 7-6A and 7-6B show such a device[1] with the necessary connections. Its operation is as follows. With valves AA, AB, B', C, and D closed, prime the purger by opening valve AA and cracking valve D. Open valve C wide and crack valve A until purger is well frosted. Then open valves B and D wide. Valve A should be adjusted to keep the frost line at the top of the purger.

Refrigerant gas and air in the inverted bucket will bubble up through the vent in its top and rise through the surrounding liquid to strike the baffle, which diverts the gas against the chilled inner wall of the refrigerating jacket. The refrigerant vapor promptly condenses. Air, however, cannot condense, but rises and collects above the liquid refrigerant. As the air collects at the top of the purger, the liquid level is depressed, allowing the ball float to drop and open the air discharge valve.

The liquid refrigerant in the purger enters the inverted bucket, causing it to sink at regular intervals and open the valve leading to the liquid line. A small amount of liquid is discharged; then gas again floats the bucket, and the purging operation continues.

After purging from the receiver, valve B should be closed and valve B' opened, and the purging operation will proceed for the condenser. Air will collect in the receiver, the condenser, or both. With an evapora-

---

[1] Armstrong Machine Works, Three Rivers, Mich.

tive or double-tube condenser, it is more apt to be found in the receiver. With a shell-and-tube condenser, it may be found in either place. Do not try to purge from both condenser and receiver simultaneously. The gas and vapor will follow only one of the paths, leaving the other path blocked off.

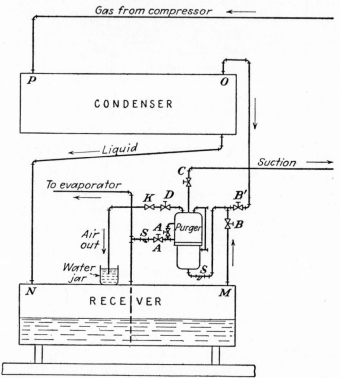

Fig. 7-6A.   Diagrammatic sketch of hookup for straight purging service.

Defrosting by Interrupted Refrigerant Flow. The most common method for defrosting blower-type cooling units operating at room temperatures above 35°F is intermittent operation. The fan is allowed to run continuously while the refrigerant flow is interrupted.

As previously stated, the optimum relative humidity of storage spaces for most produce is between 80 and 90 per cent. This humidity is maintained by using sufficient coil so that the temperature difference between the refrigerant and the room air does not exceed 10°F, with continuous operation, during the period of maximum heat gain. If the fins are not too closely spaced (less than six fins to the inch for 35°F), automatic defrosting may be had by selecting the coil on a 10°FTD for maximum load and operating it on a 15°FTD two-thirds of the time, with the fan running continuously. Much of the moisture that has been extracted from the air during the running period will be given back to the air during the off period. The net result is approximately the same as if

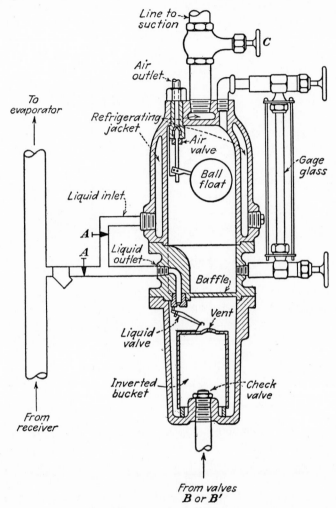

Fig. 7-6B. Cross section of refrigerant gas purger.

the coil operated continuously at the 10°FTD. There are two common methods of interrupting the refrigerant flow.

If the system has a single compressor and a single evaporator, the compressor is selected for 50 per cent excess capacity and its running time controlled by a thermostat. It is difficult to control the temperature or humidity accurately by this method without excessive cycling of the compressor. A suction-pressure control valve will smooth the operation appreciably.

If the system has two or more dry-expansion evaporators, intermittent flow of refrigerant can be obtained by the use of a magnetic stop valve controlled by a thermostat in the liquid line to each evaporator. For accurate control of humidity or temperature, a suction-pressure control valve is also required in the suction line from each evaporator. If flooded evaporators are used, the magnetic stop valves should be placed in the suction line rather than the liquid line from each evaporator.

When two or more evaporators are involved, the compressors should be selected on the basis of about 25 per cent excess capacity above the probable maximum load. The probable maximum load may differ appreciably from the sum of the maximum loads of the various evaporators, since it may be very improbable that the maximum loads will occur simultaneously. The compressors should be selected at the lowest suction pressure for which any of the suction-pressure control valves may be set.

For room temperatures below 35°F, defrosting cannot be satisfactorily accomplished by intermittent flow of refrigerant. Since the optimum storage temperature above freezing of most produce is between 30 and 32°F, other types of defrosting should be considered for most coils. Three common methods are used: water defrosting, hot-gas defrosting, and mechanical defrosting. Of these, water defrosting is the most common and usually the most satisfactory.

Defrosting with Water. Water defrosting may be used with blower-type cooling units at any temperature. The procedure is as follows: The fan motor is stopped. With dry-expansion coils, the flow of refrigerant is interrupted by closing the liquid line with a hand valve or magnetic stop valve. For flooded systems, both liquid and suction lines should be closed. Normal-temperature water is distributed over the coil by a water-distributing header, or set of sprays, in sufficient quantity to melt the ice. At least 2 gpm of water per square foot of face area of the coil should be used for this service if the evaporating temperature is below 0°F. The valves are then opened and operation resumed.

The drain connection must be of ample size, with a trap outside the refrigerated space. The water-supply pipe should be equipped with a three-way valve installed in such a manner that the water will drain out of the line when the flow is stopped.

Water defrosting cannot be used satisfactorily with coils having gravity circulation of air, since the spray header system would be too extensive and the water-collecting pan would interfere with the flow of air. In this case hot-gas defrosting or mechanical defrosting must be used.

Defrosting with Hot Gas. Hot discharge gas from the compressor may be used to defrost any dry-expansion coil quickly, provided that proper piping connections are made. Figure 7-7 shows suitable connections for a system having several evaporators. The method of defrosting each of the coils is similar. We will start with the system in normal operation

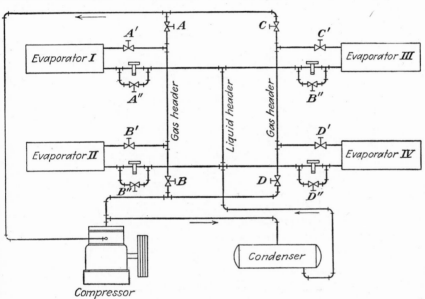

Fig. 7-7. A typical hot-gas defrosting system.

and defrost evaporators 1, 2, 3, and 4, in order. For normal operation, valves A, C, A', B', C', and D' will be open, and valves B, D, A'', B'', C'', and D'' will be closed. Close valves A, A', and B', and open valve B. The left-hand gas header will then be filled with hot discharge gas, and we may defrost evaporators 1 and 2. To defrost evaporator 1, open valves A' and A''. The coil will function as a condenser, and liquid will flow from it into the liquid line. When the frost has completely melted, close valves A' and A'', and open valves B' and B'' until evaporator 2 is defrosted. Shift all valves of the left-hand gas header and evaporators to their normal position, and repeat the entire operation for the right-hand gas header and evaporators.

Mechanical Defrosting. Refrigerated plates mounted in a vertical position at the ceiling may be easily defrosted by brushing the frost from them before it has hardened. Bare-pipe coils in refrigerated warehouses have wide spacing and are operated with a thick coating of ice. They have a much greater surface when operated in this manner, and higher humidities may be maintained.   They may operate several years without defrosting.   When defrosting is required, the refrigerant is pumped out and the ice is chopped from them.

Liquid-ammonia Injection.   Automatic liquid injection into the suction line should be used with all ammonia compressors having clearance pockets or other capacity-reduction devices and on all ammonia compressors operating with a discharge temperature above 250°F.   With

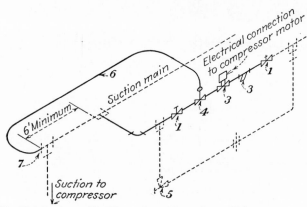

Fig. 7-8.   Liquid injection.   (1) Stop valve, (2) strainer, (3) magnetic stop valve, (4) thermal valve, (5) by-pass valve, (6) thermal valve tubing, (7) thermal valve bulb and insert well.

ammonia, the vapor superheats greatly upon compression.   The superheated temperature may be found by consideration of the particular refrigerating cycle that is involved.   Liquid injection into the suction main will prevent excessively high discharge temperatures, with consequent carbonizing of the lubricating oil at the discharge valves.   Injection should occur at least 6 ft from the compressor, and only enough ammonia should be injected to bring the discharge temperature within reason.   With excessive liquid injection, the droplets do not completely evaporate during the compression stroke, but also evaporate on the suction stroke of the piston.   This greatly reduces volumetric efficiency. The accessories necessary for ammonia liquid injection, with the necessary connections, are shown in Fig. 7-8.

Ammonia Intercooler.   An intercooler is a heat exchanger for a two-stage system that cools the liquid and the discharge gas of the lower temperature stage to the evaporating temperature of the higher temperature stage, or just slightly above it.   The increased efficiency, reduced displacement, and reduced discharge temperatures have been discussed in Chap. 3. Figure 7-9 shows an intercooler that cools the liquid ammonia nearly to the evaporating temperature of the higher temperature stage by means of a heat-exchange coil and condenses the discharge vapor from the lower temperature stage at the evaporating temperature of the higher temperature stage by bubbling it through liquid ammonia of the higher temperature stage.

Freon Intercooler. With oil-solvent refrigerants, the discharge vapor of the lower temperature stage cannot be bubbled through the liquid of

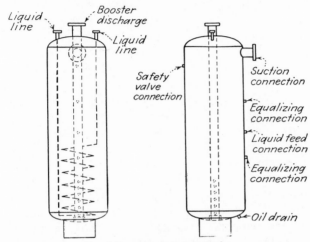

Fig. 7-9. Ammonia intercooler.

the higher temperature stage as with ammonia. The oil would tend to settle in one or the other of the compressor crankcases, depending on the adjustment of the expansion valves. With flooded evaporators, the oil tends to settle in the lower temperature crankcase. A Freon intercooler must entirely separate the refrigerants of the two stages. The intercooler is therefore a simple heat exchanger, and may be of the shell-and-coil, shell-and-tube, or double-tube type. Freon intercoolers are generally designed with a 10°FTD between the refrigerants of the two stages.

Pressure Controls. The high-pressure cutout is a safety pressure switch that opens the control circuit of the magnetic starter for the compressor motor if the condensing pressure rises abnormally. It is usually set to cut out at about 20 psi above the normal condensing pressure. High-pressure cutouts should be used on all systems of 1 hp or above.

The low-pressure cutout is sometimes used as a safety pressure switch and sometimes used as a control switch to control the suction pressure. When used as a safety switch, it is set to open the control circuit at slightly above atmospheric pressure. When used as a suction-pressure control switch, the cutin and cutout points are set above and below the desired suction pressure by sufficient margin so that short cycling of the compressor does not occur. The low-pressure cutout should not be used to control temperatures within refrigerated spaces.

The dual-pressure control combines the functions of both high- and low-pressure cutouts in one instrument.

Magnetic Stop Valves. When more than one evaporator is used with a compressor, control of temperatures in spaces served by these evaporators can be obtained by means of magnetic stop valves in the liquid lines to each evaporator. These stop valves are controlled by thermostats within the refrigerated spaces. Magnetic stop valves are also used on intermittently run systems to avoid flooding of the refrigerant into the evaporator during shutdown periods.

Suction-pressure Control Valves. When two or more evaporators are operating at different suction pressures, it is necessary to install pressure-regulating valves in the suction lines of all evaporators. There are two general types—the gradual-acting and the two-pressure snap-acting. Both operate from the pressure in the evaporator, opening when the suction pressure is high and closing when the suction pressure is low. If close control of the suction pressure is desired, the gradual-acting valve should be used. If only two evaporators are used, the snap-acting valve will give more economical operation. The two-pressure snap-acting valve is arranged with a double seat so that the compressor operates on only one coil at a time. It operates on the higher pressure coil until the suction pressure pulls down to the desired point. The valve then closes the suction line to the higher pressure coil and opens the suction line to the lower pressure coil. When the pressure has pulled down to the setting of the low-pressure cutout, the compressor stops. During the off period, the pressure in the higher pressure coil builds up so that the valve shifts its position, shutting off the suction line to the lower pressure coil and opening the suction line to the higher pressure coil. If the two-temperature snap-acting valve is used, the evaporators should be selected for 12 hours' operation per day, and the compressor for 16 hours' operation per day.

Dryers and Strainers. All mechanical parts of a refrigerating system should be protected by an ample-sized dryer or strainer. All dryers are equipped with suitable filter screens so that strainers are not necessary if dryers are used. Silica gel is used more than any other drying agent. Silica gel is a very porous form of silicon dioxide, which readily adsorbs moisture on the large amount of surface in its pores. Containers should be kept tightly sealed when not in use, since silica gel readily absorbs moisture from the air. Silica-gel dryers may be used with any refrigerant; however, it is questionable how much moisture they will extract from sulfur dioxide. With flooded ammonia systems, dryers are not required, since water collects at the bottom of the accumulator, from which it can be drained. Strainers or dryers should be used to protect control valves, expansion valves, and compressors. If there are several expansion valves on a system, a single master strainer may be used in the liquid line. Compressors are usually equipped with suction strainers. If this precaution has not been taken, one should be installed, except on fractional-horsepower systems.

Thermostats. Nearly all thermostats used on refrigerating systems are electrical. Thermostats control temperatures by starting and stopping compressors, or by opening and closing magnetic valves. If a single-phase fractional-horsepower motor is used, it is connected in series with the thermostat and pressure control. If a three-phase motor or single-phase motor of 1 hp or more is used, a magnetic starter will be required, and the thermostat will be in the control circuit. If the thermostat is used in the control circuit, the mercury-switch type will give more dependable action. If the thermostat is used in series with the motor, a metallic-contact-switch type is necessary, since heavy arcing in the mercury bulb will develop sufficient mercury-vapor pressure to break it.

Water-regulating Valves. When space requirements do not allow the use of a cooling tower and the system is too large for an air-cooled condenser to be practical, water from the city main is used through the condenser and discharged to the sewer. In such cases, the water quantity is controlled by an automatic valve operated by the condensing pressure. The valve opens gradually as the condensing pressure builds up and closes as the condensing pressure drops.

Surge Tanks. Surge tanks are installed in the suction line of multiple-evaporator systems operating on a single compressor to prevent short cycling of the compressor when most of the control valves have closed. Surge tanks are simply large tanks with both connections made at the bottom of the tank so that oil cannot trap out in it. They are seldom used on systems above 5-ton capacity. On larger systems, multiple compressors are generally used, arranged so that the system will operate on one or more compressors, as required. A tank having a capacity of about 2 cu ft/(ton refrigeration) will usually prevent excessive cycling on Freon 12 or methyl chloride systems.

Auxiliary Heat Exchangers. Auxiliary heat exchangers are used for many purposes. Three of the more important uses of auxiliary heat exchangers are

1. To increase the capacity of the system by subcooling the liquid refrigerant with water

2. To avoid use of insulation on the suction line

3. To avoid flashing of liquid refrigerant into vapor within the liquid line

Noticeable increase in capacity can be obtained by cooling the liquid refrigerant with water below its saturation temperature. This matter was discussed in Chap. 3.

Heat transferred through the suction line outside the refrigerated space causes expansion of the vapor, reducing the capacity and slightly raising the power required. To avoid this loss, the size of the liquid line can be increased and the suction line run inside it. (Special interchanger tees are made for this purpose.) In this case, heat transfer results in cooling the liquid refrigerant. The net result is that a slight increase in capacity is obtained, rather than a loss. This matter has also been discussed in Chap. 3.

If excessive pressure drop exists in the liquid line and the liquid is not subcooled, it will flash into vapor, thus causing a further increase in friction. The effect is cumulative and may result in greatly reduced capacity. Pressure drop may be due to vertical lift or due to friction through the pipe and accessories. To avoid this difficulty, the liquid refrigerant should be cooled below the saturation temperature corresponding to the reduced pressure. This may be done with water or with suction vapor. When suction vapor is used, the suction line is usually run inside the liquid line for the entire height through which the liquid is lifted.

Liquid-level Gauges. With vessels containing any liquid refrigerant below 25°F, the gauge may consist of a single pipe exposed to the atmosphere and connected to the refrigerant vessel at the top and bottom of the pipe. Frost will appear on the pipe up to the refrigerant level. This type of gauge is satisfactory if sudden changes in liquid level do not occur.

Gauges made of a single glass tube with automatically closing shutoff valves at its top and bottom are satisfactory for determining the oil level in ammonia compressor crankcases or the liquid level in an ammonia vessel at a temperature above 32°F. The shutoff valves have a ball check so that, upon breakage of the glass, the ball check will close. For temperatures below 32°F, the tube must be of double glass construction with the air evacuated between the two tubes. This type of gauge is not satisfactory for use with any of the oil-solvent refrigerants, since the packing will not keep them from leaking at junction between the glass and the valve.

Gauges with a float and indicator are satisfactory for ammonia or oil-solvent refrigerants at any temperature.

All gauges for temperatures above 32°F on systems using oil-solvent refrigerants are generally of the bull's-eye type. This gauge is not as subject to leaking as the glass tubular type. Gauges in the receiver are seldom used. In order to tell if the system has sufficient refrigerant, a bull's-eye gauge is placed in the liquid line at the outlet from the receiver. A shortage of refrigerant will cause a frothing condition of the refrigerant. A bull's-eye gauge should always be used in the compressor crankcase at the proper oil level.

Pressure-relief Devices. A pressure-relief device may be a safety valve, a rupture disk, or a fusible plug. A safety valve is a spring-loaded pressure-relief valve set to open at 25 per cent above the working pressure for which the vessel that it protects is designed. A rupture disk is a member designed to rupture at a pressure just slightly less than two times the pressure for which the vessel is designed. A fusible plug is a threaded plug with an insert of metal having a low melting point. The fusible metal should melt at a temperature corresponding to a saturation pressure 25 per cent above the pressure for which the vessel was designed.

In accordance with the Standard Safety Code,[1] each refrigerant-containing vessel that has a gross volume of more than 5 cu ft, exclusive of vessels whose diameter is less than 6 in., and that may be shut off by valves, should be protected by a relief valve in parallel with a rupture member. Each vessel having a volume of 5 cu ft or less that may be shut off by valves should be protected by a pressure-relief valve or fusible plug. No shutoff valves should be used in series with relief valves.

Compressors operating above 15 psi gauge and having a displacement exceeding 100 cfm cu ft per min should be equipped with a pressure-relief valve of adequate size to prevent rupture of the compressor. This valve should be placed between the compressor and its discharge cutoff valve and may be vented to the outside of the building or to the low-pressure side of the system.

Pressure-relief devices and fusible plugs in all systems containing more than 30 lb of refrigerant, except those devices used to protect compressors and those that are vented to the low side, should discharge to the outside of the building.

[1] American Standard Safety Code for Mechanical Refrigeration. Approved by ASA, 1939. Sponsored by ASRE. See Appendix 6.

CHAPTER 8

PIPING FOR REFRIGERATING SYSTEMS

The design of piping systems involves consideration of the following factors: materials, method of assembly, strength, size, expansion, vibration, and supports. In addition, if there is danger of having liquid present in a pipe carrying vapors, special precautions should be taken to ensure proper flow of the liquid.

Pipe Material. Pipe material should be selected from the standpoint of cost, strength, and ability to resist corrosion. The common materials used in the piping of water, brine, and refrigerants are steel, zinc, wrought iron, brass, and copper.

Black steel pipe is satisfactory for use with ammonia, methyl chloride, or any of the Freon refrigerants. With ammonia there is little danger of corrosion even if water is present, since ammonia is base-forming and inhibits the formation of acids from the action of air and water on the oil. With methyl chloride, or any of the Freons, there is no corrosion problem if water is not present. Since systems using these refrigerants do not operate satisfactorily with water present, there is no particular corrosion problem. Steel is the most commonly used material for refrigerant pipe sizes above 2-in. diameter. Black steel pipe has been used satisfactorily on water and brine piping where corrosive conditions of water are not encountered, or where the brine is maintained in a slightly alkaline condition. It corrodes readily on the outside when buried underground or when exposed to a moist atmosphere. For this reason, galvanized steel piping is generally preferred for water or brine piping.

Zinc is an excellent protective coating for steel pipe. It is highly resistant to oxidation. Since it has a very slightly higher potential than iron in the electrochemical series, any galvanic action that might occur would tend to corrode the zinc rather than the iron. Since the electrochemical potentials of zinc and iron are nearly the same, the coating of iron with zinc does not lead to excessive galvanic action. Since it has a fairly high potential, it is readily attacked by acids. Galvanized steel pipe is produced by dipping black steel pipe in a molten bath of pure zinc. It is used extensively for water and brine piping; however, certain precautions should be considered. When carbon dioxide is present in the water supply, it is usually well to consider other types of piping. Brine should be maintained in a slightly alkaline condition by the addition of small quantities of sodium hydroxide when needed. When galvanized iron piping is used on a brine system, all parts of the system should be iron or zinc in order to reduce galvanic action to a minimum. If it is necessary to use a pump with either a runner or housing of bronze, it should be separated from the pipe by a rubber connection. Wrought-iron pipe is more resistant to corrosion than either black steel or galvanized steel pipe. Wrought iron has about 2 per cent of siliceous slag in a finely divided and uniformly distributed state. In the original hand-puddling process of manufacture, a charge of pig iron and scrap iron is melted in a puddling furnace and most of the carbon is driven off. The silicon, phosphorus, and manganese become oxidized and unite in a slag. The molten metal is vigorously stirred and reaches a pasty state so that it can be removed for rolling into bars. Rolling causes the included slag to be drawn into thin layers and threads in the iron to produce a fibrous structure. Following the initial rolling, the bars are reheated for rolling into pipe. Other methods of puddling have been developed, which produce pipe similar to that produced by the hand-puddling process.

There is little difference in appearance between wrought iron and black steel pipes; however, several simple tests can be made to identify the materials. By hammering a piece of pipe flat, one can readily observe the fracture. The fracture of wrought iron is ragged, dull gray, and fibrous. The fracture of steel is bright and crystalline. Wrought iron, when threads are cut, gives a crumbled chip, whereas the steel gives a long spiral chip. Wrought iron is relatively soft, since it has low carbon and manganese contents. It sells at a considerably higher price than black steel or galvanized steel pipe but is often used because of its greater resistance to corrosion.

Copper and copper alloys offer high corrosion resistance to a widely varying group of corroding agents. Alloys of copper are often more corrosion resistant than pure copper. Copper is more highly resistant to acids than any common metal. It is satisfactory in the piping of methyl chloride, all the Freons, and sulfur dioxide. Copper or copper compounds are not satisfactory with ammonia. The ASA B31 Piping Code bars the use of aluminum-base alloys with Freon 12 or Freon 114 and of magnesium-base alloys with any Freon refrigerant. It also bars the use of zinc, aluminum, die castings, and magnesiums alloys with methyl chloride. Brass containing more than 15 per cent zinc is readily attacked by acids. Red brass (85 per cent copper, 15 per cent zinc) offers high corrosion resistance in nearly all cases.

Sea water presents special corrosion problems.[1] Copper and red

---

[1] Anaconda Publication B28, 8th ed., 1945.

brass offer good corrosion resistance. Yellow brass (63 per cent copper, 37 per cent zinc) is subject to dezincification. Several special alloys have been developed. Admiralty alloy (70 per cent copper, 29 per cent zinc, 1 per cent tin) offers good corrosion resistance with low water velocities. Arsenical admiralty (70 per cent copper, 28.9 per cent zinc, 1 per cent tin, 0.05 per cent arsenic) is more resistant to dezincification than plain admiralty. Aluminum brass (76 per cent copper, 21.95 per cent zinc, 2 per cent aluminum, 0.05 per cent arsenic) is more resistant than admiralty to sea water at higher velocities; it also shows excellent resistance to polluted harbor waters. Super-Nickel (70 per cent copper, 30 per cent nickel) has proved to be the best available material for marine use. It is resistant to corrosion at relatively high velocities.

Method of Assembly. Flared compression fittings are permitted by the ASA B31 Piping Code for refrigerant lines not over $3/4$ in. in outside diameter using annealed copper tubing, provided all such joints are exposed for visual inspection.

Screwed joints are limited by the ASA B31 Piping Code to not over 3 in. for refrigerant pressures 250 psi or less, $1\frac{1}{4}$ in. for refrigerant pressures above 250 psi, and not over 4 in. for brine lines. Screwed joints are more subject to leakage than soldered or welded joints. When it is necessary to use screwed joints on oil-solvent refrigerant lines, they should be made with specially prepared joint compound, or litharge and glycerine. The joint compound should be applied to the male thread only. If litharge and glycerine are used, they should be dried by heating them separately to a temperature above 300°F before mixing. Screwed fittings are commonly used on water and brine piping up to 6-in. diameter, although for sizes 4 in. and above, considerable time may be saved by welding. Screwed joints should be left exposed for visual inspection.

Welding is the most suitable method of assembling steel refrigerant lines. It is also the most suitable method of assembly of large steel and wrought-iron piping used for handling water or brine. Galvanized pipe should not be welded because of the flaking of the zinc and also because of the poisonous fumes formed. Rules for qualification of welding procedures and operators are given in the ASA B31 Piping Code.

The most suitable method of assembling hard-drawn copper tubing is sweat fittings and hard solder. Hard-soldering is also called *silver brazing*. Hard solder is ordinarily a silver-base alloy melting above 1000°F, whereas soft solder is a tin-base alloy melting below 500°F. The piping code requires the use of hard solder for field joints in refrigerant lines except for tubes of $\frac{1}{2}$ in. nominal size and less in systems containing less than 20 lb of refrigerant.

Pipe Strength. The thickness of a given material required for a given pressure is fixed by the Piping Code as follows:

$$t_m = \frac{PD}{2S} + C \tag{8-1}$$

where t_m = minimum pipe-wall thickness, in.

P = maximum internal service pressure, psi gauge

D = outside diameter of the pipe, in.

S = allowable stress in material due to internal pressure in psi as given in Table 8-1

C = allowance for threading, for mechanical strength, and for corrosion, as follows:

Pipe	*Allowance, In.*
Threaded steel, wrought-iron,	
or nonferrous, $\frac{3}{8}$ in. or larger......................	0.05
$\frac{1}{2}$ in. and larger..............................	Depth of thread
Plain-end steel or wrought-	
iron, 1 in. and smaller..........................	0.05
Larger than 1 in..............................	0.065
Plain-end nonferrous............................	0

TABLE 8-1. ALLOWABLE STRESS FOR USE IN EQ. (8-1)

Material	Specification	S, psi
Steel pipe:		
Seamless, Grade A......................	ASTM A53	12,000
	ASTM A120	
	ASTM A106	
	API 5L	
Seamless, Grade B......................	ASTM A53	15,000
	ASTM A106	
Lap-welded............................	ASTM A53	9,000
	ASTM A106	
	ASTM A120	
	API 5L	
Butt-welded..........................	ASTM A53	6,800
	ASTM A120	
Electric-resistance-welded..............	ASTM A135	10,200
Wrought iron:		
Lap-welded............................	ASTM A72	8,000
	API 5L	6,000
Butt-welded..........................	ASTM A72	
Brass pipe, seamless red brass.............	ASTM B43	4,700
Copper pipe, seamless....................	ASTM B42	4,000
Copper tubing, seamless.................	ASTM B88	4,000

The ASA Safety Code for Mechanical Refrigeration sets forth the following rules for refrigerant piping:

1. Refrigerant working pressure shall not exceed 250 psi in Schedule 40 ferrous pipe, and butt-welded pipe shall not exceed 2 in. in size.

2. Refrigerant liquid ferrous pipe 1½ in. and smaller shall be Schedule 80.

3. Copper tubing shall not be lighter than Type L for field assembly or Type M for shop assembly.

4. Soft annealed copper tubing erected on the premises shall not be used in sizes above ¾ in.

5. Pipe thinner than Schedule 40 ferrous or brass shall not be threaded.

Pipe Dimensions. The dimensions of commonly used pipe, copper tube, and steel condenser tube are given in Tables 8-1 to 8-4 inclusive. Pipe sizes are given in nominal sizes, in which case the inside diameter of the pipe is approximately the same as the nominal size of the pipe. The inside diameters of various strengths of pipes of the same nominal size vary in order that the fittings may be standardized. Tube sizes are always given in outside diameters, designated OD, and are accurately the size given.

TABLE 8-2. DIMENSIONS OF WELDED AND SEAMLESS STEEL PIPE, INCHES*

Nominal pipe size	O.d.	Nominal wall thicknesses		Nominal pipe size	O.d.	Nominal wall thicknesses	
		Schedule No. 40†	Schedule No. 80‡			Schedule No. 40†	Schedule No. 80‡
⅛	0.405	0.068	0.095	2½	2.875	0.203	0.276
¼	0.540	0.088	0.119	3	3.5	0.216	0.300
⅜	0.675	0.091	0.126	3½	4.0	0.226	0.318
½	0.840	0.109	0.147	4	4.5	0.237	0.337
¾	1.050	0.113	0.154	5	5.563	0.258	0.375
1	1.315	0.133	0.179	6	6.625	0.280	0.432
1¼	1.660	0.140	0.191	8	8.625	0.322	0.500
1½	1.900	0.145	0.200				
2	2.375	0.154	0.218				

* Wrought Iron and Wrought-Steel Pipe, ASA B36.10, American Standards Association, New York, 1939.

† Schedule 40 pipe is identical with standard-weight pipe in former lists.

‡ Schedule 80 pipe is identical with extra-strong pipe in former lists.

TABLE 8-3. DIMENSIONS OF BRASS PIPE, INCHES*

Size of pipe	O.d.	Pipe thickness	
		Standard	Extra strong
⅛	0.405	0.0620	0.100
¼	0.540	0.0825	0.123
⅜	0.675	0.0905	0.127
½	0.840	0.1075	0.149
¾	1.050	0.1140	0.157
1	1.315	0.1265	0.182
1¼	1.660	0.1460	0.194
1½	1.900	0.1500	0.203
2	2.375	0.1565	0.221
2½	2.875	0.1875	0.280
3	3.500	0.2190	0.304
3½	4.000	0.2500	0.321
4	4.500	0.2500	0.341
4½	5.000	0.2500	0.375
5	5.563	0.2500	0.375
6	6.625	0.2500	0.437
7	7.625	0.2815	0.500
8	8.625	0.3125	0.500

* ASTM Specifications B42-33 and B43-33.

TABLE 8-4. DIMENSIONS OF COPPER TUBING, INCHES*

Nominal size	Actual o.d.	Wall thickness	
		Class K	Class L
⅜	0.500	0.049	0.035
½	0.625	0.049	0.040
¾	0.875	0.065	0.045
1	1.125	0.065	0.050
1¼	1.375	0.065	0.055
1½	1.625	0.072	0.060
2	2.125	0.083	0.070
2½	2.625	0.095	0.080
3	3.125	0.109	0.090
3½	3.625	0.120	0.100
4	4.125	0.134	0.110
5	5.125	0.160	0.125
6	6.125	0.192	0.140

* ASTM Specification B88-33.

TABLE 8-5.   STANDARD CONDENSER-TUBE DATA*

O.d., in.	Size No., B.w.g.	Wt./ft- lb.†	Thickness, in.	I.d., in.	Surface, sq ft/ft of length		Inside sectional area, sq in.	Velocity, fps at 1 U.S. gal/min	Capacity at 1-fps velocity	
					Outside	Inside			U.S. gal/min	Lb water /hr
½	12	0.493	0.109	0.282	0.1309	0.0748	0.0624	5.142	0.1945	97.25
	14	0.403	0.083	0.334	0.1309	0.0874	0.0876	3.662	0.2730	136.5
	16	0.329	0.065	0.370	0.1309	0.0969	0.1076	2.981	0.3352	167.5
	18	0.258	0.049	0.402	0.1309	0.1052	0.1269	2.530	0.3952	197.6
	20	0.190	0.035	0.430	0.1309	0.1125	0.1452	2.209	0.4528	226.4
⅝	12	0.656	0.109	0.407	0.1636	0.1066	0.1301	2.468	0.4053	202.7
	14	0.526	0.083	0.459	0.1636	0.1202	0.1655	1.939	0.5157	258.9
	16	0.424	0.065	0.495	0.1636	0.1296	0.1925	1.667	0.5999	300.0
	18	0.329	0.049	0.527	0.1636	0.1380	0.2181	1.472	0.6793	339.7
	20	0.241	0.035	0.555	0.1636	0.1453	0.2420	1.326	0.7542	377.1
¾	10	0.962	0.134	0.482	0.1963	0.1262	0.1825	1.758	0.5688	284.4
	12	0.812	0.109	0.532	0.1963	0.1393	0.2223	1.442	0.6935	346.8
	14	0.644	0.083	0.584	0.1963	0.1528	0.2678	1.198	0.8347	417.4
	16	0.518	0.065	0.620	0.1963	0.1613	0.3019	1.063	0.9407	470.4
	18	0.400	0.049	0.652	0.1963	0.1706	0.3339	0.9611	1.041	520.5
⅞	10	1.16	0.134	0.607	0.2291	0.1589	0.2893	1.108	0.9025	451.3
	12	0.992	0.109	0.657	0.2291	0.1720	0.3390	0.9465	1.057	528.5
	14	0.769	0.083	0.709	0.2291	0.1856	0.3949	0.8126	1.230	615.0
	16	0.613	0.065	0.745	0.2291	0.1951	0.4360	0.7360	1.358	679.0
	18	0.472	0.049	0.777	0.2291	0.2034	0.4740	0.6770	1.477	738.5
1	10	1.35	0.134	0.732	0.2618	0.1916	0.4208	0.7626	1.311	655.5
	12	1.14	0.109	0.782	0.2618	0.2048	0.4803	0.6681	1.497	748.5
	14	0.887	0.083	0.834	0.2618	0.2183	0.5463	0.5874	1.702	851.0
	16	0.708	0.065	0.870	0.2618	0.2277	0.5945	0.5398	1.852	926.0
	18	0.535	0.049	0.902	0.2618	0.2361	0.6390	0.5022	1.991	995.5
1¼	10	1.74	0.134	0.982	0.3271	0.2572	0.7575	0.4236	2.362	1181
	12	1.45	0.109	1.032	0.3271	0.2701	0.8369	0.3834	2.608	1304
	14	1.13	0.083	1.084	0.3271	0.2839	0.9229	0.3477	2.877	1439
	16	0.898	0.065	1.120	0.3271	0.2932	0.9852	0.3257	3.070	1535
	18	0.675	0.049	1.152	0.3271	0.3015	1.043	0.3075	3.253	1627
1½	10	2.12	0.134	1.232	0.3925	0.3227	1.193	0.2688	3.720	1860
	12	1.76	0.109	1.282	0.3925	0.3355	1.292	0.2482	4.030	2015
	14	1.36	0.083	1.334	0.3925	0.3941	1.398	0.2292	4.362	2181
	16	1.09	0.065	1.370	0.3925	0.3585	1.473	0.2180	4.587	2294
2	10	2.94	0.134	1.732	0.5233	0.4534	2.355	0.1362	7.342	3671
	12	2.40	0.109	1.782	0.5233	0.4665	2.494	0.1287	7.770	3885
	14	1.85	0.083	1.834	0.5233	0.4803	2.643	0.1213	8.244	4122
	16	1.47	0.065	1.870	0.5233	0.4896	2.747	0.1168	8.562	4281

* McADAMS, W. H., "Heat Transmission," p. 417, McGraw-Hill Book Company, Inc., New York, Table XXVII: Standard Condenser Tube Data, prepared by T. B. Drew.

† Specific gravity of brass = 8.56; of steel = 7.8.

Friction in Pipe. Friction in pipe is usually measured in pounds per square inch pressure drop per 100 ft of pipe. Variations of the Darcy equation are commonly used to compute the friction. It is as follows:

$$\Delta P = \frac{FL\rho v^2}{2Dg} \tag{8-2}$$

where ΔP = pressure drop, psf
     F = friction factor
     ρ = density, lb/cu ft
     v = fluid velocity, fpm
     L = length, ft
     D = internal diameter, ft
     g = gravitational constant, 32.2 ft/sec^2

The Darcy equation may be expressed in a more convenient form for engineering purposes as follows:

$$\Delta p = 0.000336\frac{FW^2}{\rho d^5} \tag{8-3}$$

where Δp = pressure drop, psi/1000 ft of pipe
     F = friction factor
     W = rate of flow, lb/hr
     ρ = density, lb/cu ft
     d = internal diameter of the pipe, in.

The friction factor F is a function of Re, of the diameter of the pipe, and of its roughness. The diameter of the pipe has no effect on the friction factor for smooth pipe. Pigott[1] tested the assumption that roughness of the surface had the effect of entangling a thicker film of fluid and reducing the effective pipe diameter. Since the change of diameter affects the pressure loss as the fifth power of the diameter, a small roughness would have a noticeable effect on the friction. This assumption was checked by data from numerous sources, and the correlation was found to be very good for various steel pipes with Re from 20,000 to 600,000. Figure 8-1, with its accompanying table, gives friction factors for various pipes as compiled by Pigott and Kemmler.[2]

The determination of pipe sizes for Eq. (8-3) is rather tedious where numerous pipe sizes are concerned. Friction tables have therefore been prepared for the common refrigerants, water and brine. In the construction of these tables, a table was first prepared for the flow of fluid at

---

[1] PIGOTT, R.-J. S., The Flow of Fluids in Closed Conduits, *Mech. Eng.*, August, 1933.

[2] KEMMLER, EMORY, A Study of the Data on the Flow of Fluids in Pipes, *Trans. ASME*, vol. 55, p. 2, 1933.

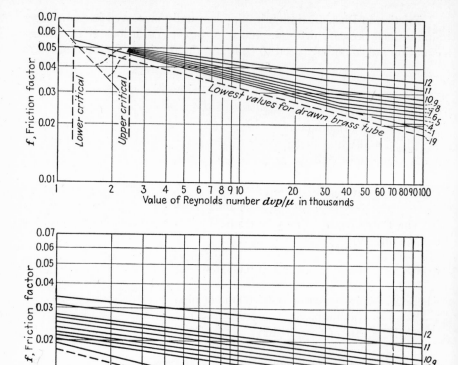

FIG. 8-1.   Friction factors.

Curve	Clean steel or wrought iron, diameter, in.	Clean galvanized, diameter, in.
19	Lower limit, brass tube, above .35 in. diameter	
1	Upper limit, brass tube, above .35 in. diameter	
4	6–12	10–24
5	4– 5	6– 8
6	2– 3	3– 5
7	1.5	2.5
8	1– 1.25	1.5– 2.0
9	.75	1.25
10	.50	1
11	.37	.75
12	.25	.50

various pressures, or temperatures, that would give 1 psi pressure drop per 100 ft of 2-in. Schedule 40 steel pipe. Two other tables were then prepared. One gave the ratio of the carrying capacity at other pressure drops to the carrying capacity at 1 psi pressure drop per 100 ft of pipe, and the other gave the ratio of the carrying capacity of other sizes of pipe to that of the 2-in. pipe. By use of the three tables, pipe size may be selected for a wide range of capacities and pressure drops.

TABLE 8-6. SATURATED VAPORS, FLOW FOR 1 PSI PRESSURE DROP PER 100 FT OF 2-IN. SCHEDULE 40 (STANDARD) STEEL PIPE*

Absolute pressure	Ammonia			Freon (F-12)			Methyl chloride			Sulfur dioxide		
	Temp. sat. vapor	Lb/ hr†	Tons refrig.‡	Temp. sat. vapor	Lb/ hr†	Tons refrig.‡	Temp. sat. vapor	Lb/ hr†	Tons refrig.‡	Temp. sat. vapor	Lb/ hr†	Tons refrig.‡
In. Hg.												
5	−83.0	219	8.0									
10	−63.7	310	11.6							−26.2	593	6.9
15	−51.3	380	14.4							−12.5	727	8.5
20	−41.9	439	16.7	−38.0	1,238	4.8				− 2.0	840	9.9
25	−34.3	490	18.8	−29.0	1,383	5.4	−18.5	838	10.3	6.6	945	11.1
Psi												
15	−27.3	540	20.8	−20.8	1,525	6.1	−10.0	927	11.4	14.4	1,040	12.3
20	−16.6	623	24.2	− 8.2	1,753	7.2	2.9	1,073	13.4	26.4	1,202	14.3
25	− 8.0	696	27.2	2.2	1,953	8.3	13.3	1,204	15.2	36.3	1,345	16.0
30	− 0.6	762	30.0	11.1	2,135	9.2	22.3	1,325	16.9	44.8	1,472	17.6
35	5.9	822	32.5	18.9	2,305	10.1	29.7	1,430	18.3	52.2	1,595	19.1
40	11.7	877	34.8	25.9	2,465	11.0	36.6	1,535	19.8	58.8	1,707	20.4
50	21.7	980	39.2	38.3	2,760	12.6	48.4	1,720	22.4	70.4	1,915	22.8
60	30.2	1,072	43.1	48.7	3,020	14.1	58.6	1,892	24.8	80.3	2,095	24.9
80	44.4	1,239	50.0	66.3	3,495	16.8	76.1	2,220	29.4	96.9	2,445	
100	56.0	1,386	56.2	80.9	3,925	19.3	88.7	2,440		110.2	2,750	
120	66.0	1,520	62.0	93.4	4,320		101	2,655		121.5	3,040	
140	74.8	1,643	67.2	104.5	4,710		111	2,805		131.6	3,310	
160	82.6	1,760	72.2	114.5	5,070		120	2,910				
180	89.8	1,868		123.7	5,420		128	3,140				
200	96.3	1,970		132.1	5,770		140	3,325				
250	110.8	2,195										
300	123.2	2,390										
400												

* This table, prepared by M. B. Golber, is found in Chap. 21 by A. B. Stickney in The Refrigerating Data Book, 5th ed., p. 294, The American Society of Refrigerating Engineers, New York, 1943.

† Pounds per hour is the flow in 2-in. Schedule 40 steel pipe with 1 psi pressure drop per 100 linear feet.

‡ Tons of refrigeration is based on 86°F liquid up to expansion valve.

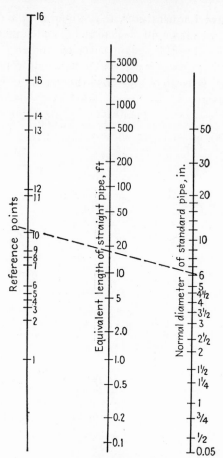

Fig. 8-2. Friction equivalents for standard fittings.
(ft of pipe)

Gate valve:		Sudden enlargement:		Sudden contraction:	
¾ closed............	16	$d/D = \frac{1}{4}$..........	9	$d/D = \frac{1}{4}$..........	3
½ closed............	14	$d/D = \frac{1}{2}$..........	6	$d/D = \frac{1}{2}$..........	2
¼ closed............	10	$d/D = \frac{3}{4}$..........	5	$d/D = \frac{3}{4}$..........	1
Open................	1				
Globe valve, open......	15	Close return bend......	12	Standard elbow........	9
Angle valve, open......	13	Standard tee..........	11	Square elbow..........	11
Ordinary entrance......	4	Tee reduced ½........	9	Medium sweep elbow..	7
Borda entrance........	8	Tee reduced ¼........	7	45° elbow.............	3
				Long sweep elbow......	6

Friction through Valves and Fittings. Friction through valves and fittings may conveniently be stated in terms of equivalent length of straight pipe. Figure 8-2[1] gives equivalent lengths of pipe for various valves, fittings, and changes of flow.

[1] Prepared by the Crane Co.

Valves and Valve Locations. Valves for brine and water may be of the globe, angle, or gate type. The globe and angle valves provide tighter shutoff than the gate valve; however, the gate valve offers less resistance to flow. For use with water, the valves are usually brass. For use with brine, it is preferable that the valve be made of the same material as the pipe.

TABLE 8-7. FREON 22 SATURATED VAPOR FLOW GIVING A 1-LB FRICTION LOSS PER 100 FT OF SCHEDULE 40 (STANDARD) STEEL PIPE*

Temperature of saturated vapor, °F	Pressure of saturated vapor, psi absolute	Flow, lb/hr	Tons†
−40	15.31	1,320	7.16
−35	17.40	1,400	7.71
−30	19.69	1,490	8.28
−25	22.22	1,580	8.88
−20	25.00	1,670	9.52
−15	28.00	1,770	10.2
−10	31.34	1,880	10.9
− 5	34.95	1,990	11.6
0	38.87	2,100	12.4
5	43.12	2,200	13.2
10	47.66	2,320	13.9
15	52.88	2,440	14.7
20	58.00	2,560	15.6
25	63.98	2,680	16.4
30	69.97	2,810	17.6
35	76.27	2,950	18.6
40	83.72	3,090	19.4
45	91.12	3,230	20.1
50	99.40	3,360	20.6

* KNOKEY, C. R., "Friction-loss Tables for Freon 22 Liquid, Saturated Vapor, and Superheated Vapor Lines," unpublished thesis for B.S. degree, California State Polytechnic College.

† Tons of refrigeration based on 86°F liquid temperature and saturated vapor at temperature shown.

The Piping Code provides that refrigerant valves shall be of the globe, angle, or needle type. Gate valves and cocks are barred, except in industrial plants having competent operating men constantly in charge. Refrigerant valves having valve-stem packing must be of the backseating type to permit packing under pressure. Either packed or packless types of valves are permissable. Stop valves are required by the Code as follows:

In systems having more than 20 but less than 100 lb of refrigerant:

1. At each inlet and outlet pipe of each compressor
2. At each outlet of each liquid receiver

In systems having 100 lb or more of refrigerant:

1. At each inlet and each outlet pipe of each compressor
2. At each inlet and each outlet pipe of each liquid receiver
3. At each liquid and each suction-branch header

Stop valves used with soft annealed copper tubing of ¾ in. nominal size or smaller must be securely mounted independent of tubing fastening or supports.

TABLE 8-8. SUPERHEATED VAPORS, FLOW FOR 1 PSI PRESSURE DROP PER 100 FT OF 2-IN. SCHEDULE 40 (STANDARD) STEEL PIPE*

Abso-lute pres-sure	Ammonia			Freon (F-12)			Methyl chloride			Sulfur dioxide		
	Temp. comp. vapor†	Lb/ hr	Tons refrig.‡	Temp. comp. vapor†	Lb/ hr	Tons refrig.‡	Temp. comp. vapor†	Lb/ hr	Tons refrig.‡	Temp. comp. vapor†	Lb/ hr	Tons refrig.‡
In. Hg												
25										8	938	13.1
Psi												
15										28	1,021	14.1
20										57	1,144	15.4
25							25	1,203	17.8	81	1,254	16.6
30				13	568	12.1	45	1,283	18.6	98	1,325	17.2
35	7	822	38.6	22	601	12.7	65	1,367	19.5	115	1,413	18.0
40	22	869	40.4	31	636	13.3	75	1,448	20.4	132	1,522	19.1
50	47	965	44.0	45	691	14.1	100	1,612	22.1	158	1,667	20.4
60	69	1,027	46.0	58	747	14.8	125	1,760	23.6	179	1,835	21.9
80	105	1,153	50.1	78	833	16.0	155	1,990	25.6	215	2,030	23.3
100	135	1,260	53.3	94	916	16.8	180	2,215	27.5	243	2,210	24.5
120	160	1,354	56.1	109	987	17.2	200	2,430	29.2	265	2,405	26.0
140	182	1,440	58.5	121	1,050	17.7	220	2,550	29.8	284	2,550	26.8
160	201	1,520	60.6	133	1,110	18.0	235	2,680	30.5			
180	219	1,595	62.5	143	1,170	18.1	250	2,805	30.9			
200	235	1,660	64.0	153	1,227	18.2	270	2,940	29.8			
250	270	1,820	67.5									
300	300	1,955	70.1									
400												
500												
600												

* This table, prepared by M. B. Golber, is found in Chap. 21 by A. B. Stickney in The Refrigerating Data Book, 5th ed., p. 295, The American Society of Refrigerating Engineers, New York, 1943.
† Temperature of compressed vapor is based on isentropic compression from saturated vapor at 5°F.
‡ Tons of refrigeration is based on liquid at temperature corresponding to pressure to saturated vapor at 5°F.

Refrigerant-pipe Size. The pipe size affects the capacity of a refrigerating system, its cost, and the power it uses. Reducing the pipe size does not necessarily reduce the first cost of a system per unit of capacity. In order to study this problem, let us first consider a Freon 12 system operating at 110 psi condensing pressure and 35 psi evaporating pressure. The compressor, furthermore, will be assumed to have a constant displacement. The effect of friction in the suction pipe is given in Table 8-14. All ratios are in reference to a system with negligible pipe friction.

TABLE 8-9.   FREON 22 SUPERHEATED VAPOR FLOW GIVING A 1-LB FRICTION LOSS PER
        100 FT OF SCHEDULE 40 (STANDARD) STEEL PIPE*

Pressure, psi absolute	Temperature of compressed vapor, °F†	Flow, lb/hr	Tons‡
16	−36.6	1,400	11.6
20	−20.0	1,540	12.3
30	11.4	1,800	14.0
40	37.1	2,020	15.0
50	57.0	2,220	16.4
60	71.0	2,400	17.0
70	84.6	2,580	17.6
80	96.6	2,740	18.3
90	107.4	2,900	18.9
100	117.1	3,050	19.3
110	126.1	3,200	19.9
120	134.4	3,340	20.2
130	142.2	3,470	20.5
140	149.5	3,600	20.7
150	156.5	3,720	20.9
160	162.9	3,840	21.0
170	169.1	3,960	21.1
180	174.9	4,070	21.2
190	180.5	4,170	21.4
200	185.9	4,270	21.6
210	191.0	4,370	21.8
220	196.0	4,470	22.0
240	205.5	4,660	22.3
260	214.3	4,820	22.6

* KNOKEY, C. R., "Friction-loss Tables for Freon 22 Liquid, Saturated Vapor, and Superheated Vapor Lines," unpublished thesis for B.S. degree, California State Polytechnic College.

† Temperature of compressed vapor based on isentropic compression of saturated vapor at −40°F to pressures shown.

‡ Tons of refrigeration based on liquid at a condensing temperature corresponding to the pressures shown and saturated vapor at −40°F.

TABLE 8-10.   LIQUIDS, FLOW FOR 1 PSI PRESSURE DROP PER 100 FT OF 2-IN. SCHEDULE 40 (STANDARD) STEEL PIPE*

Fluid	Temperature, °F	Density, lb/cu ft	Flow		Tons†
			Lb/hr	Gpm	
Water..........................	32	62.4	15,900	31.8	
	100	62.0	17,100	34.5	
	212	59.8	17,800	37.2	
Water, average pipe‡.............	....	....	......	25.0	
Sodium brine:					
10% NaCl...................	25	67.2	16,200	31.2	
15% NaCl...................	15	69.9	16,100	28.8	
	25	69.8	16,300	29.2	
20% NaCl...................	5	72.7	15,500	26.6	
	15	72.5	15,900	27.4	
	25	72.2	16,350	28.3	
Calcium brine:					
10% CaCl₂...................	30	68.2	16,350	30.0	
20% CaCl₂...................	0	74.7	15,200	25.4	
	15	74.5	15,800	26.5	
	30	74.3	16,500	27.7	
30% CaCl₂...................	−15	81.9	13,500	20.6	
	0	81.7	14,600	22.3	
	15	81.5	15,400	23.6	
	30	81.3	16,100	24.7	
Ammonia......................	86	37.2	14,100	....	556
Freon (F-12)...................	86	80.6	21,000	....	89.3
Methyl chloride................	86	56.3	17,400	....	218
Sulfur dioxide................	86	84.4	21,300	....	251

* STICKNEY, A. B., ASRE Data Book, 5th ed., p. 296, The American Society of Refrigerating Engineers, New York, 1943.

† Tons of refrigeration based on 5°F evaporation, saturated gas, and 86°F liquid.

‡ Water pipe is subject to scale, corrosion, and tuberculation. This value gives a close approximation to the Williams and Hazen tables, using $C = 100$.

Let us now consider a Freon 12 system operating at 110 psi condensing pressure and 15 psi evaporating pressure. The effect of friction in the suction pipe is given in Table 8-15.

From Tables 8-14 and 8-15 it will be seen that for a given system, friction in the suction pipe reduces the capacity appreciably, while the horsepower is only slightly reduced. The net effect is that the horsepower per unit capacity is appreciably increased. It will further be seen from these tables that this effect becomes greater as the suction is low-

TABLE 8-11. FREON 22 LIQUID FLOW GIVING A 1-LB FRICTION LOSS PER 100 FT OF SCHEDULE 40 (STANDARD) STEEL PIPE*

Condensing temperature, °F	Condensing pressure, psi absolute	Flow, lb/hr	Tons†
40	83.72	20,820	137
45	90.56	20,750	134
50	99.40	20,680	131
55	108.30	20,610	128
60	117.20	20,540	125
65	127.20	20,460	122
70	137.20	20,380	119
75	148.45	20,310	116
80	159.70	20,230	112
85	172.26	20,160	108
90	184.8	20,070	104
95	198.7	19,990	101
100	212.6	19,900	98
105	228.0	19,820	95
110	243.4	19,720	92
115	260.1	19,620	89
120	277.3	19,500	86

* KNOKEY, C. R. "Friction-loss Tables for Freon 22 Liquid, Saturated Vapor, and Superheated Vapor Lines," unpublished thesis for B. S. degree, California State Polytechnic College.
† Tons of refrigeration based on liquid temperature shown and saturated vapor at −40°F.

TABLE 8-12. RATIOS OF THE FLOW AT OTHER PRESSURE DROPS TO THE FLOW AT 1 PSI PER 100 FT OF PIPE*

Pressure drop, psi	Tenths				
	0	2	4	6	8
Units	Ratios				
0	0.00	0.42	0.61	0.77	0.89
1	1.00	1.10	1.20	1.29	1.37
2	1.45	1.52	1.60	1.67	1.73
3	1.80	1.86	1.92	1.98	2.04
4	2.10	2.15	2.21	2.26	2.31
5	2.36	2.41	2.46	2.51	2.56

* STICKNEY, A. B., ASRE Data Book, 5th ed., p. 296, The American Society of Refrigerating Engineers, New York, 1943.

ered.   The problem of sizing pipe, therefore, becomes one of selecting a size with friction low enough that the size of the equipment will not have to be increased appreciably, and yet maintaining the pipe size small enough that excessive money will not be spent on pipe, fittings, and valves.   Obtaining a rigorous mathematical solution of this problem would be extremely difficult; an approximate balance between these factors will usually be obtained with methyl chloride or Freon 12 if the suction pipe is sized on the basis of a pressure drop of 2 psi/100 ft of pipe for suction temperatures of 20°F or above, and 1 psi/100 ft of pipe for suction temperatures of 0°F or below.   For ammonia and Freon 22, slightly higher values can be used, such as 1 psi/100 ft of pipe for suction temperatures −10°F or lower, and 2 psi/100 ft of pipe for suction temperatures above −10°F.

TABLE 8-13.   RATIOS OF THE FLOW FOR OTHER PIPE SIZES AND TYPES TO THAT OF 2-IN. SCHEDULE 40 STEEL PIPE FOR THE SAME PRESSURE DROP*

Nominal size, in.	Steel or wrought iron		Brass		Copper tubing		
	Schedule 40 Standard	Schedule 80 Extra strong	Regular	Extra strong	Type K	Type L	Type M
⅛	0.0041	0.0022	0.0052	0.0022	0.00175	0.0021	0.0021
¼	0.0090	0.0055	0.0115	0.0059	0.0068	0.0071	0.0077
⅜	0.021	0.0138	0.025	0.0157	0.0138	0.0166	0.0188
½	0.039	0.028	0.047	0.032	0.029	0.032	0.036
⅝	....	....	....	....	0.052	0.055	0.060
¾	0.086	0.064	0.098	0.073	0.075	0.086	0.094
1	0.164	0.127	0.193	0.144	0.162	0.176	0.190
1¼	0.33	0.27	0.38	0.31	0.29	0.30	0.32
1½	0.51	0.42	0.57	0.48	0.47	0.49	0.50
2	1.00	0.84	1.13	0.95	0.99	1.02	1.04
2½	1.65	1.37	1.90	1.55	1.77	1.83	1.80
3	2.8	2.4	3.3	2.8	2.8	2.9	3.0
3½	4.2	3.6	4.6	4.2	4.2	4.4	4.5
4	5.9	5.1	6.6	5.8	6.0	6.2	6.3
5	10.7	9.5	12.1	10.6	10.6	11.0	11.2
6	17.5	15.3	19.9	16.9	16.8	17.6	17.9
8	36	32	40	35	35	36	37
10	67	58	71	66	61	64	66
12	108	93	114	....	97	103	104

* STICKNEY, A. B., ASRE Data Book, 5th ed., p. 294, The American Society of Refrigerating Engineers, New York, 1943.

TABLE 8-14. EFFECT OF FRICTION IN THE SUCTION PIPE FOR A FREON 12 SYSTEM OPERATING AT 110 PSI CONDENSING PRESSURE AND 35 PSI EVAPORATING PRESSURE*

Pipe friction, psi	Capacity ratio	Horsepower ratio	Horsepower ratio per unit capacity
0	1.00	1.00	1.00
1	0.98	1.00	1.02
2	0.95	0.99	1.04
5	0.88	0.98	1.11

* Computed by use of the following formulas for adiabatic processes:

$$\frac{V_2}{V_1} = \left(\frac{P_1}{P_2}\right)^{\frac{c_v}{c_p}} \quad \text{and} \quad W = \frac{P_2V_2 - P_1V_1}{1 - \frac{c_p}{c_v}}$$

TABLE 8-15. EFFECT OF FRICTION IN THE SUCTION PIPE FOR A FREON 12 SYSTEM OPERATING AT 110 PSI CONDENSING PRESSURE AND 15 PSI EVAPORATING PRESSURE

Pipe friction, psi	Capacity ratio	Horsepower ratio	Horsepower ratio per unit capacity
0	1.00	1.00	1.00
1	0.94	0.99	1.04
2	0.88	0.94	1.08
5	0.71	0.86	1.21

Friction in the discharge pipe results in an increase in power used. The effect on capacity is usually negligible. With a Freon 12 system operating on 110 psi condensing pressure and 35 psi evaporating pressure, a friction of 2 psi in the discharge pipe causes less than 2 per cent increase in power over what it would be with no friction. Here the problem of balancing first cost against operating cost is simple, since the capacity of the system is not affected. Usually an economical balance is obtained when discharge lines are sized on about 2 psi/100-ft length of pipe for Freon 12 and methyl chloride, and about 3 psi/100-ft length for ammonia and Freon 22.

Friction in the liquid line has no effect upon the capacity or horsepower of a system if the liquid is sufficiently cooled below its condensing temperature so that flashing of the liquid into vapor does not occur. If the liquid is not subcooled and an appreciable pressure drop occurs in the liquid line, due either to friction or to a vertical lift, the liquid will flash into vapor. Vapor present in the liquid line increases its friction abnormally, so that the effect is cumulative. Excessive flashing will reduce the capacity of the system greatly. Liquid lines are usually sized on about 5 psi pressure drop/100-ft length of pipe. If the total pressure drop in the liquid line, including the pressure drop due to vertical lift, exceeds 5 psi, the liquid should be subcooled so that excessive flashing will not occur.

When a system using an oil-solvent refrigerant has two or more compressors working in parallel, there should be an interconnecting oil line with its center at the level of the oil in the crankcases. This line should be not less than 1 in. in diameter, or the oil will not flow freely. If it is necessary to place the line below the oil level, there should also be a ¾-in. line connecting the crankcases above the oil line in order to equalize the vapor pressures in the crankcases. Compressors of various sizes or designs may be interconnected, providing that the heights of the bases are adjusted so that the oil level will be the same in each of the compressors.

Brine- and Water-piping Size. It is usually economical to size brine or water piping on the basis of a drop in pressure of 2 to 4 psi/100 ft of pipe. A liberal safety factor should be used with steel pipe where corrosive condition of water may exist.

Precautions for Avoiding Trapping or Slugging of Oil and Refrigerant. Oil-solvent refrigerants often present special piping problems. Refrigerants of this type carry with them oil that may trap out unless the pipe is properly sized and correctly laid out. If automatic oil traps are installed in the discharge line, the problem is greatly simplified. The problem will first be discussed from the standpoint of systems having no oil traps in their discharge lines.

When discharge-line oil traps are omitted, oil may trap out in either discharge or suction pipe if the friction in these lines drops below ½ psi/ 100 ft of pipe. When multiple compressors connected in parallel are concerned, the pipe should have friction not less than this amount when only a single compressor is operating. Loops having a short section of pipe at the bottom should be avoided in either discharge or suction lines. Oil and condensed refrigerant may collect in these loops during off periods and cause liquid hammer to occur at the fittings and at the head of the compressor when it starts. Branch suction connections should drain downward into the main suction pipe so that oil and condensed refrigerant cannot run into the evaporators. When multiple compressors in parallel are used, the suction line should be manifold at the compressors so that the returning oil will flow equally to all compressors. Long discharge lines from the compressor should be arranged so that refrigerant and oil that may condense in them during the off cycle will not drain back into the head of the compressor.

If discharge-line oil separators are used with systems using oil-solvent refrigerants, the problem is more simple. No special precautions need be considered in the discharge pipe. In the suction pipe there will be no oil problem; however, with unfavorable conditions liquid refrigerant may be present. Loops having a short section of pipe at the bottoms should be avoided.

Systems using relatively non-oil-solvent refrigerants, such as ammonia, usually are equipped with discharge-line oil separators. In this case no special precautions need be considered in the discharge line except that the oil separators shall be located near the compressors. Short loops in which refrigerant may collect in the suction line under unfavorable conditions should be avoided. If the system has no discharge-line oil separator, and the discharge line is long, care should be taken that condensed refrigerant during the off cycle cannot flow back into the head of the compressor.

CHAPTER 9

MOTORS AND THEIR CONTROLS

This chapter will deal with the application of various types of electric motors commonly used in the refrigerating industry. Only those principles which are necessary to understand these applications will be discussed. The design of motors is beyond the scope of this chapter.

Nearly all motors used for refrigerating application use alternating current because of the difficulty of transmitting direct current. Fractional-horsepower motors generally use single-phase current, while multiple-horsepower motors generally use three-phase current. Motors from 1 to 100 hp are generally three-phase induction motors. Motors above 100 hp are either three-phase induction or three-phase synchronous motors. In order to understand these motors, a few basic principles must first be discussed.

POWER IN ALTERNATING-CURRENT CIRCUITS

Apparent Power and Active Power. In a d-c circuit, if voltage E is impressed across the terminals and a current of I amperes flows, the power used in the circuit is $W = EI$, where W is measured in watts. In an a-c circuit, the product of instantaneous values of volts and amperes gives the power at that particular instant. With alternating current, however, the voltage and current are rapidly varying, usually going through 60 complete reversals per second. Moreover, the current may not be in phase with the voltage. Average values of volts times amperes, therefore, may not give the average power available. The cycles of alternating current are so rapid that a-c voltmeters and ammeters read only average magnitudes, not considering the direction of flow. In a circuit containing only resistance, the voltage and current are in phase with each other, and the power consumed is $W = EI$, where E and I are voltmeter and ammeter readings. The product EI, thus measured, of any a-c circuit is called the *apparent power* of the circuit. Alternating-current circuits are well represented as a sine curve. Figure 9-1 shows the current, voltage, and watts of a purely resistive circuit.

Unfortunately, no a-c circuit is purely resistive; all a-c circuits contain either inductance or capacitance. Usually they contain both. In a circuit having only pure inductance, the current lags the voltage by

90°. In a circuit having only pure capacitance, the current leads the voltage by 90°. If the inductive reactance equals the capacitive reactance, the current will be in phase with the voltage and the circuit will act as one having pure resistance. Figure 9-2 shows the current, voltage,

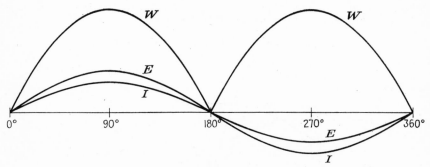

FIG. 9-1. Phase relations in a purely resistive circuit.

and power of a purely inductive circuit. Figure 9-3 shows the current, voltage, and power of a purely capacitive circuit. Figure 9-1 represents a circuit in which the inductive reactance equals the capacitive reactance. In all cases, the instantaneous power is the vector product of volts and

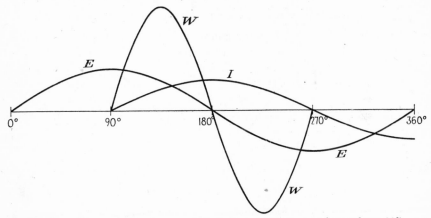

FIG. 9-2. Phase relations in a purely inductive circuit (current lags voltage 90°).

amperes. The power is positive when voltage and current are in phase, and negative when the current and voltage are out of phase. The net, or active, power is zero in all circuits having current and voltage 90° out of phase with each other.

Figure 9-4 shows a circuit in which the current lags the voltage by 30°. The instantaneous power is largely positive, but also has a negative part.   The active power is the vector sum of the positive and negative components and is given by the equation

$$\text{Active power} = EI \cos \varphi \qquad (9\text{-}1)$$

where E and I represent average values and $\cos \varphi$ is the angle of lag, called the *power factor*.

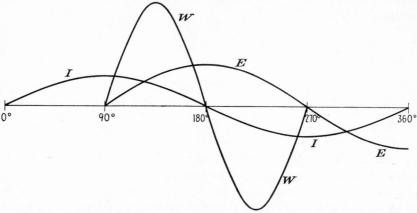

Fig. 9-3.   Phase relations in a purely capacitive circuit (current leads voltage 90°).

Power-factor Measurement.   The usual method of determining power factor is to use voltmeter, ammeter, and wattmeter.   The watt-meter gives the active power in the circuit.   For a single phase, the

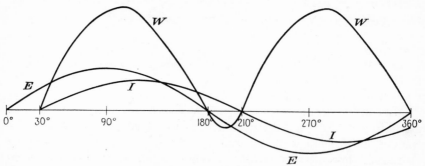

Fig. 9-4.   Phase relations in a circuit in which the current lags the voltage 30° (power factor = cos 30°).

product of volts and amperes gives the apparent power.   The power factor is then the ratio of active power to apparent power.

For a three-phase circuit, the apparent power is $\sqrt{3}\, E_L I_L$, where E_L is the voltmeter reading between any two of the three terminals, and I_L is the current flowing through any of the three terminals.   A three-phase wattmeter gives the active power. The power factor is, again, the active power divided by the apparent power.

Current Required by an Alternating-current Motor. If all electric energy involved were transformed to mechanical energy, a motor would require 746 watts/hp. This is not possible, since heating and other losses occur. The actual input will therefore be $(746 \times hp)/e$, where e is the efficiency of the motor. For a single-phase motor, this equals $EI \cos \varphi$; therefore

$$I = \frac{746 \times hp}{eE \cos \varphi} \tag{9-2}$$

For a three-phase motor

$$I = \frac{746 \times hp}{e \sqrt{3} \, E \cos \varphi} \tag{9-3}$$

I²R Losses. The power used in overcoming resistance is $W = EI$, where E is the voltage drop across the resistance and I is the current through the resistance. Substituting $E = IR$ in this equation, we obtain $W = I^2 R$. This power is dissipated in heat and is not available as motive power. From the foregoing discussion on power factor, it is apparent that as the angle of lag or lead varies from 0°, there will be an increase in current required for a given amount of power. Low power factors therefore result in high transmission losses and in heating of the motors, and are undesirable from the standpoint of both the power companies and the users. Power companies often give lower rates where motors are selected for high power factors or for leading power factors when the neighboring equipment is largely inductive.

THE POLYPHASE INDUCTION MOTOR

The polyphase induction motor is the most common type of motor used for refrigerating purposes. Its action is similar to that of a polyphase transformer. The primary coils are in the stator, and the secondary coils are in the rotor. Since both stator and rotor are subject to alternating fields, each of these parts is constructed of laminations. The windings in the slots of the stator are connected to the power line. The windings in the rotor slots are not connected to any power line but receive their current by induction. The stator winding is usually three-phase. The rotor is wound for the same number of phases or is a squirrel-cage winding. In the former, the conductors of the rotor winding are insulated and are brought out to slip rings that are connected to a starting or control device. In the squirrel-cage rotor, the conductors are not insulated; they consist of bare copper or aluminum conductors set in slots. These conductors are connected solidly by a ring at each end. An induction motor with an insulated rotor winding is called a *slip-ring motor*. The one with the bare conductors is called a *squirrel-cage induction motor*.

Speed of an Induction Motor. The windings in the stator of a polyphase induction motor are arranged to produce a rotating magnetic field. This rotating magnetic field induces a rotating field in the rotor that is similar but of opposite polarity. The magnetic field of the rotor is pulled around by the rotating magnetic field of the stator. The speed of rotation of the magnetic field of the stator is called its *synchronous speed*. If n is the rpm, p is the number of stator poles (per phase), and f is the frequency of the line current, the synchronous speed is as follows:

$$n = \frac{120f}{p} \qquad (9\text{-}4)$$

The number of poles must always be an even number.

At no load, the speed of the rotor will be nearly the synchronous speed, under which condition the motor uses very little current. As the load increases, the rotor slows down, inducing greater currents within it and causing more current to be drawn from the line through the stator. The full-load speed of a polyphase induction motor is about 3 or 4 per cent less than the synchronous speed of the motor. Four-pole motors are the most common. These run at 1,800 rpm synchronous speed on 60-cycle current (approximately 1,750 rpm full-load speed). Slower speed motors are more costly, since they must produce higher torques and, hence, have larger frames and bearings. A 7½-hp 1,800-rpm motor uses the same frame and costs the same as a 5-hp 1,200-rpm motor.

The Slip-ring Motor. The slip-ring motor is an induction motor with a polyphase-wound rotor. The rotor is wound for the same number of poles and phases as the stator. Leads from the rotor windings are brought out at one end to slip rings. Collector brushes run on these rings. At full speed the rotor windings are short-circuited by direct connection between these brushes. Reduced speeds down to 50 per cent of full speed are obtained by introducing resistance between the brushes by an external rheostat. Wound-rotor induction motors are available with both constant- and adjustable varying-speed characteristics. The constant-speed motor has application where there is frequent starting or reversing under full load, or where exceptionally high starting torques are required. Adjustable varying-speed characteristics mean that speed can be adjusted to any value over a considerable range and, when adjusted, will vary only with a change in load. Wound-rotor induction motors are the same for both constant- and adjustable varying-speed services. The speed characteristics desired are obtained by selecting controllers of the proper types.

The slip-ring motor is inherently a high-starting-torque motor. By introducing resistance into the rotor circuit through slip rings, the rotor currents may be brought more nearly into phase with the induced voltage and a higher torque obtained. Too much resistance, however, reduces the starting torque because of the reduced current flowing in the rotor. In order that the starting torque continue to have the same value as at the start, the rheostat resistance must be reduced as the speed increases.

The power required by a wound-rotor induction motor varies as the torque and is independent of the speed. The mechanical power produced, however, is directly proportional to the speed at constant torque.

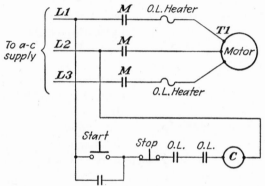

Fig. 9-5. Wiring diagram of a three-phase, magnetic, nonreversing line starter.

The efficiency therefore drops as the speed is reduced. Reciprocating refrigerating compressors usually require the same torque at reduced speeds as at maximum speeds. Wound-rotor induction motors are therefore unsatisfactory for speed reduction on this type of service. Centrifugal compressors and blowers require less torque at reduced speeds. With this type of equipment the current therefore decreases as the speed decreases; hence wound-rotor motors are satisfactory for this type of service.

Controls for Slip-ring Motors. The magnetic starter is used to make or break the circuit from the power line to the stator. Figure 9-5 shows a schematic wiring diagram of a magnetic, three-phase, nonreversing line starter. Momentarily pressing the start button energizes the main contactor coil C; this closes the main contacts M. The control contacts CC also close, shunting the start button and maintaining current through C. The overload relay opens the circuit through C on continued overload. Pressing the stop buttons opens the control circuit, de-energizing coil C, and the main contacts M fall out. The overload relays consist of resistance heater coils in two of the three legs of the circuit to the motor, together with bimetallic thermostatic elements that open the control circuit if the resistance coils produce too much heat.   The heater elements are closely selected so that a continuous overload of not more than 25 per cent will open the thermostatic switches.   This does not interfere with the starting operation, since an overload of several hundred per cent for a few seconds will not cause the heating elements to generate enough heat to throw open the thermostatic switches.

To adjust the resistance of the rotor for low starting current, slow

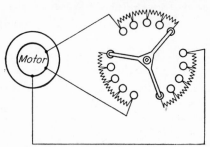

acceleration, or speed control, a speed-regulating rheostat is used. For sizes up to 25 hp, this consists of resistors connected in Y formation by a three-legged contactor arm. Figure 9-6 shows this type of rheostat schematically.

When the motor is started, the contactor arm is placed so that there is maximum resistance in the rotor circuit.   The push button on the magnetic starter is then closed.

FIG. 9-6.   Diagram of a three-phase wound-rotor controller for starting and speed control.

Resistance in the rotor circuit is then decreased until the desired speed or starting torque is obtained.

If the wound-rotor motor is used only because of its high-starting-torque and low-starting-current characteristics, a magnetic controller may be used.   This controller consists of the ordinary magnetic switch with heater relays for the stator and a switching arrangement for the rotor that introduces resistance in the rotor circuit for a few seconds, after which time the rotor is short-circuited.   The entire operation is automatic.   This type of controller can be furnished when necessary with one additional accelerating contactor to decrease the accelerating current peaks or to increase the time of the accelerating period if the motor drives a very high inertia load.

The Squirrel-cage Induction Motor.   Because of its simplicity, low first cost, and ease of maintenance, and the few required controls for its operation, the squirrel-cage induction motor is the most popular type of electric motor in sizes above 1 hp.   It is satisfactory wherever constant-speed constant-torque motors are required.   The operation of a squirrel-cage motor is similar to that of a wound-rotor motor, except that the resistance of the rotor is not subject to adjustment, and hence neither the starting torque nor speed are adjustable by this method.   The squirrel-cage motor has, therefore, a relatively low starting torque unless specifically designed otherwise.

It is impossible externally to increase the resistance of the rotor of a squirrel-cage motor in order to increase the starting torque and, at the same time, decrease the current, as can be done with a slip-ring motor. The increase in resistance for high-torque starting must be provided by electrical and magnetic means rather than by mechanical means. The resistance of the squirrel-cage rotor must be low in order to avoid excessive I^2R losses at normal speed; therefore, the conductor bars must be large and made of low-resistance material such as aluminum or copper. In order to increase the rotor resistance at starting, the skin effect is used.

The magnetic field of the rotor follows the same pattern as that of the stator, but is of opposite polarity. The induced current has the same number of phases as that in the stator, but the frequency differs. Current is induced in the rotor by rotating magnetic lines cutting the conductors. At zero speed, the cutting of the conductors is a maximum, the current is a maximum, and the frequency in the rotor is the same as that in the stator. As the speed of the rotor is increased, the bars of the rotor more nearly follow the magnetic lines; the induced current reduces, and the induced frequency becomes less. At synchronous speed the induced current and frequency would be zero. Owing to skin effect, the current tends to flow only in the top of the bars at high frequency. As the frequency reduces, the current flows equally through the top and bottom portions of the bars. The resistance of the rotor is therefore highest when starting, and decreases as the motor comes up to its normal speed. In order to make maximum use of the skin effect, high-starting-torque squirrel-cage motors are wound with deep bars, or with a double-cage rotor. In the double-cage rotor, each conductor is divided in two parts: one part in the outer cage and the other part in the inner cage. These parts are connected by a thin strip of metal between them.

Speed Regulation of Squirrel-cage Induction Motors by Changing the Number of Poles. Assuming constant line frequency, speed variation in a few steps may be obtained by varying the number of poles of the motor. It is possible to obtain two speeds with a single stator winding so arranged that the coils may be regrouped. One grouping will have double the number of poles of the other grouping and, hence, half the speed. Motors are also made that operate at three-fourths full speed, but these require two separate windings in the stator. A four-speed motor having two stator windings is also made.

NEMA Classifications of Squirrel-cage Induction Motors. The NEMA Class A general-purpose squirrel-cage induction motor is the most widely used of all industrial power motors. It is sometimes listed as a normal-starting-torque, normal-starting-current motor. The starting torque varies with the number of poles, but is between 115 and 150 per cent of the torque at full speed when started at full voltage. In order to meet power-company restrictions on starting current, it may be started at reduced voltage if starting-torque requirements can be met. The starting current at full voltage will be between 500 and 1,000 per cent, depending on size and speed rating. This motor has a very high pull-out torque and will therefore operate through high peak loads, but if they are sustained, over-heating results. The characteristics of this motor are obtained by a low-resistance squirrel-cage rotor, with medium slots partly or completely closed at the top. Whenever possible, this motor is used because of its low first cost, low maintenance, high efficiency, high power factor, and low slip. It is suitable for fan, centrifugal-pump, and centrifugal-compressor service, but cannot be used to drive reciprocating refrigerating compressors unless they are unloaded when starting.

The NEMA Class B, normal-starting-torque, low-starting-current motor usually has a slightly greater starting torque than the Class A motor, with about 75 per cent of its starting current. The characteristics of this type of motor are obtained by using thinner, but deeper, rotor bars placed in deeper slots, or by using a double-cage rotor winding with the resistance bars for starting in the outer cage. The Class B motor has a slightly lower pull-out torque and power factor than the Class A. It is used where the higher starting current of Class A motors limit their use. The cost of this motor is slightly greater than that of the Class A motor.

The NEMA Class C, high-starting-torque, low starting-current motor has a slightly lower starting current than the Class B motor, but the starting torque is much higher. The starting torque is about 240 per cent of the normal running torque. The pull-out torque is less than that of Class A or Class B. With Class A and Class B motors, the pull-out torque exceeds the starting torque, while Class C motors produce their maximum torque at starting. The efficiency, power factor, and overload capacity are less, and the slip is greater than with a Class A motor. Class C motors are useful in handling loads of high inertia, such as reciprocating refrigerating compressors. This motor, if started at a reduced voltage on loads requiring moderate starting torque, may be used instead of the wound-rotor motor, to reduce starting current and produce smooth acceleration.

Controls for Three-phase Squirrel-cage Induction Motors. Practically all squirrel-cage induction motors are designed so that they may be started at full voltage. Power-company restrictions, however, sometimes limit the size that can be started in this manner. Where no limitations exist, nearly all three-phase induction motors are started with a magnetic across-the-line starter. For single-speed motors, the magnetic starter with its overload relay arrangement is shown in Fig. 9-5 and described on the accompanying page.

For two-speed motors a special magnetic switch is used, having two sets of contactors and two sets of overload relays. The two sets of contactors are mechanically or electrically interlocked, so that when one set makes contact, the other set is open. The two sets of overload relays must be selected separately for the power required at the two speeds. For two-winding motors, two three-pole contactors are used. For a one-winding motor, one three-pole and one five-pole contactor are used. When these starters are automatically controlled and used in connection with equipment of high inertia, such as refrigerating compressors, it is necessary that the starter be equipped with a deceleration time relay to furnish a time delay in transferring from the high-speed to the slow-speed connections.

Where it is necessary to start the motor on reduced voltage to limit the starting current, the autotransformer is generally used. The autotransformer is also called a *starting compensator*, or an *autostarter*. It contains induction coils so arranged and tapped that the voltage on starting is reduced to 80 per cent, 65 per cent, or 50 per cent of the line voltage. Both the line current and the starting torque are reduced as the square of the voltage at the motor terminals. Shifting from starting voltage to line voltage is usually done with a hand lever but may be done magnetically. Magnetic control is very expensive with this type of starter. In order to obtain the proper starting torque on reduced voltage, it is usually necessary to use a Class C high-starting-torque, low-starting-current motor.

SINGLE-PHASE INDUCTION MOTORS

Split-phase Induction Motor. The split-phase induction motor is a constant-speed single-phase motor having two sets of windings in its stator. The alternating current produces an oscillating magnetic field by means of the main winding. To change this field to a rotating magnetic field, a high-resistance starting winding is placed to produce poles between the main poles. The resistance of the main winding is low, while its inductance is high. The resistance of the starting winding is high, while its inductance is relatively low. The current in the starting winding will, therefore, be out of phase with the current in the main winding, and a rotating magnetic field is produced. In order to avoid overheating, the starting winding is cut out by a centrifugal switch when the rotor reaches its normal speed.

The winding of the rotor is of the squirrel-cage type, consisting of copper or aluminum bars short-circuited by heavy end rings. A current is induced in this winding that sets up in the rotor a magnetic field having opposite polarity to that in the stator. As the magnetic field in the stator rotates, the magnetic field in the rotor is pulled around by it.

When the rotor has reached its normal speed, the starting winding in the stator cuts out, and the magnetic field in the rotor attempts to keep in step with the oscillating field of the stator. When pulling no load, the magnetic field in the rotor nearly keeps up with the oscillating field in the stator, and very little current is induced in the rotor. On full load there is a slip between these magnetic fields so that the rotor moves at a slightly slower speed than the magnetic field in the stator. Most fractional-horsepower split-phase induction motors are designed to operate at 1,750 rpm on full load and at nearly 1,800 rpm on no load. They are usually designed for low or normal starting torque and are satisfactory for use on small fans or centrifugal pumps up to $\frac{1}{3}$ hp.

Capacitor-start Motors and Capacitor Motors. Capacitor-start induction motors are constructed like split-phase induction motors except they have a capacitor in series with the starting winding. The starting winding, as with the split-phase motor, is disconnected by a centrifugal switch when the rotor comes up to 70 per cent of its rated speed. The capacitor causes the current in the starting winding to lead the terminal voltage. The phase difference is much greater than with the split-phase induction motor. With an appropriate capacitor, the phase angle may approach 90°, so that the motor acts nearly the same as a two-phase squirrel-cage induction motor. As a result, higher starting torques at lower starting currents than with the split-phase motor are available. Capacitor-start induction motors are standard with starting torques up to 400 per cent of the normal running torque, in sizes from $\frac{1}{8}$ to 10 hp, and at sychronous speeds from 600 to 3,600 rpm. The running speed at full load of a high-starting-torque motor is about 4 to 5 per cent less than the sychronous speed.

With the capacitor-start motor, the starting winding is disconnected by a centrifugal switch when the rotor reaches about 70 per cent of its normal speed. However, the starting winding with its capacitor can be used for permanent operation, in which case the motor is called a *capacitor motor* or a *capacitor-run motor*. For satisfactory running performance, a capacitor of small size is necessary. If low starting torque is required, the small running capacitor is adequate for starting also, but if normal or high starting torques are required, the motor will have two capacitors, one for starting and one for running. These motors are intended to serve those fields where minimum operating noise and minimum radio interference are vital. In order to obtain quiet operation, these motors should be loaded at least 50 per cent of full load.

Repulsion-start Induction Motor. The repulsion motor is a single-phase a-c motor with a d-c armature with commutator and brushes. The brushes are short-circuited, and current flows through the armature by induction. The stator winding is like the running winding of a single-phase capacitor motor. The motor has a very high starting torque with a very low starting current. The torque can be adjusted or the direction of rotation reversed by shifting the brushes. The greatest torque occurs when the brush axis and the main-field axis make an angle of 90° with each other. When the motor has reached about 70 per cent of its synchronous speed, a centrifugal mechanism short-circuits the commutator segments and lifts the brushes from the commutator concurrently, after which time the armature acts as the ordinary squirrel-cage rotor in a single-phase stator. The motor is very satisfactory for high-starting-torque requirements such as starting refrigerator compressors, but it is gradually being replaced by the capacitor motor. It is obtainable in sizes up to 10 hp, usually at synchronous speeds of 1,800 or 1,200 rpm. The rotor slip is about the same as for other types of single-phase induction motors.

Controls for Single-phase Motors. For fractional-horsepower single-phase motors, starting and stopping may be accomplished by a simple snap switch with a single heater relay. This switch can also be used in conjunction with metallic-contact thermostats, passing the entire line current through these instruments. Mercury-contact thermostats or pressure controllers will not handle enough current for this service.

For multiple-horsepower single-phase motors the magnetic starter is used. Thermostats and pressure controllers are used in the control circuit only. Either mercury-bulb or metallic-contact thermostats and pressure controllers may be used for this service.

THE SYNCHRONOUS MOTOR

The synchronous motor has a three-phase stator winding like that of a three-phase induction motor. The rotor is wound with the same number of poles as the stator and is supplied with direct current from its exciter through its slip rings. The exciter is a d-c generator attached, or belted, to the shaft of the motor. The d-c winding of the rotor is called the *field*. Since the rotor field is supplied with direct current, its magnetic field is stationary with respect to the rotor. In order for the stator to exert a force on it, the rotor must turn at such speed that the fixed poles of the d-c rotor field will follow exactly the rotating magnetic field of the stator. The synchronous motor must therefore run at exactly synchronous speed. Any deviation from this speed will destroy all torque; hence suitable controls must be arranged to prevent damage to the motor during such a failure.

In order to make it possible for a synchronous motor to start by itself, it must be equipped with a starting or damper winding in the rotor. This winding is similar to a squirrel-cage winding of an induction motor. At synchronous speed the rotating magnetic field cannot induce any current in this winding, since the rotating magnetic stator field is stationary with respect to the rotor. It is quite different, however, during the starting period when the speed of the rotor is less than that of the rotation field. A high current is induced in the damper winding and a high voltage is induced in the rotor field winding, which may lead to breakdown of the insulation. In order to protect the main rotor winding, it is closed through a resistor during starting. The exciter is disconnected from the main winding during this operation. During starting the damper winding and the main winding, therefore, behave like an induction motor with a double cage. Owing to skin effect, the damper winding acts as the outer cage and largely governs the starting torque; the field winding acts as the inner cage and has its greatest effect as the rotor nears synchronous speed. It governs the pull-in torque of the motor.

The motor, of course, does not reach synchronism as an induction motor. However, when the slip is small, d-c excitation may be applied to the field, and the motor will pull into synchronism. The resistor that closes the main rotor winding is disconnected in the same operation. Before the direct current is connected, the induction torque balances the load torque. As soon as the direct current is applied, a synchronous torque appears that tends to decrease or increase the slip, depending on the position of the d-c field poles with respect to the poles of the rotating magnetic field. There is a most favorable position of the field poles at which the pulling into step occurs with a minimum direct current and a minimum disturbance of the a-c line. A synchronizing relay finds this position. This relay disconnects the resistance, which closes the field circuit and connects the d-c excitation simultaneously.

The induction windings are not designed for continuous operation of the motor. A damper-winding relay is therefore used to shut off the motor if it runs too long at nonsynchronous speeds. This relay is sensitive only to alternating current induced in the d-c field winding at nonsynchronous speeds. If this alternating current continues too long, the relay will open the main circuit to the motor.

Controls for the Synchronous Motor. Synchronous motor controllers are available in four types—full-voltage magnetic, full-voltage semimagnetic, reduced-voltage magnetic, and reduced-voltage semimagnetic. Magnetic controllers are operated with push buttons, while semimagnetic are operated with manual starting devices. The full-voltage magnetic controllers are equipped with a magnetic switch for connecting the motor to the line, and the semimagnetic is equipped with a manually operated circuit breaker. The reduced-voltage magnetic controllers are furnished with starting and running contactors and an autotransformer for supplying reduced voltage to the motor in starting. The reduced-voltage semimagnetic controllers are like the magnetic type except that starting and running devices are manually operated. All magnetic controllers are equipped with a time relay to determine the accelerating time.

The following equipment is commonly used on all types of synchronous motor controllers: a-c line ammeter; d-c field ammeter; d-c field-applying contactor; d-c field-discharge contactor with discharge resistor; sequence relays for maintaining the proper sequence in the application and removal of field excitation; power-factor field-removal relay, which operates on lagging power factors to remove d-c field excitation during the first slip cycle out of synchronism; temperature overload relay for the stator; and temperature relay protecting the squirrel cage.

All synchronous motor controllers are designed to work with a specific size and design of motor. A synchronous motor controller for one make of motor will not necessarily operate with another make of motor of the same size and starting characteristics.

Power Factor of Synchronous Motors. Synchronous motors with their required controls usually cost more than twice as much as squirrel-cage induction motors. They are often used, however, in sizes of 100 hp or above, because of their power-factor characteristics. Induction motors have a lagging power factor, and if there are several on the line, they will lower the power factor throughout the plant or district. Synchronous motors have unity power factor or a leading power factor and can be used to correct the poor power factor caused by induction motors.

The power factor of an induction motor is determined by the excitation of the d-c field. By overexciting the d-c field, the motor will have a leading power factor. Synchronous motors are available with unity power factor and 0.8 leading power factor. Motors with 0.8 leading power factor have higher starting torques, higher pull-in torques, and higher pull-out torques than those with unity power factor. Motors with unity power factor have slightly higher efficiency and are slightly smaller in size than motors with 0.8 leading power factor. Motors with 0.8 power factor are commonly used because of the lower electric rates obtainable from the power companies. The lowest electric rates are obtainable if a motor of 0.8 power factor is used, running continuously, with the driven equipment being engaged by clutching devices.

Application of Synchronous Motors in the Refrigerating Industry. Synchronous motors are commonly used to drive large refrigerating compressors in cold-storage warehouses, ice-making plants, breweries, etc., where at least some of the compressors are operating at all times. Reciprocating compressors are usually driven by slow-speed directly connected motors, mounted so that the rotor of the motor becomes the flywheel of the compressor. The rotor is designed so that it has a moment of inertia equal to or greater than that of the flywheel that is regularly used. Slow-speed synchronous motors (less than 514 rpm) are not standard with high starting torque and high pull-in torque. Reciprocating compressors are therefore unloaded when starting by opening by-pass valves from the discharge to the suction of the compressor. The motors generally used for this service have an 0.8 leading power factor.

Centrifugal compressors are often driven by 3,600-rpm, directly connected synchronous motors, or by 1,800-rpm motors connected through a set of set-up gears. This type of compressor has peculiar power requirements. Although starting does not require high torque, the moment of inertia that must be overcome in bringing the compressor up to speed is high because of the high rotative speed of the compressor. High-starting-torque motors are therefore commonly used to produce the desired acceleration. The vapor-pumping capacity of a centrifugal compressor increases rapidly as the suction pressure increases. Since the compressor usually starts at high suction pressures, the power required as the compressor comes up to full speed, and shortly thereafter, is excessively high. A high pull-in torque and a high pull-out torque are therefore required. If the compressor is equipped with a suction damper, this damper should be closed when starting. Synchronous motors with an 0.8 power factor are commonly used for this service.

TABLE 9-1. STARTING TORQUES, PULL-IN TORQUES, PULL-OUT TORQUES, AND STARTING CURRENTS OF NEMA STANDARD SYNCHRONOUS MOTORS

Type of motor	Rpm	Torque, per cent			Starting current at full voltage
		Starting	Pull-in	Pull-out	
General purpose:					
Unity power factor..........	1,800	110	110	150	550–750
Up to 200 hp..............	514–1,200	110	110	175	550–750
0.8 power factor............	1,800	125	125	200	500–700
Up to 150 hp..............	514–1,200	125	125	250	500–700
Large high-speed:					
Unity power factor, 250–500 hp....................	514–1,800	110	110	150	550–700
600 hp and above..........	514–1,800	85	85	150	550–700
0.8 power factor, 250–500 hp	514–1,800	125	125	200	500–700
600 hp and above..........	514–1,800	100	100	200	500–700
Low-speed:					
Unity power factor..........	Less than 514	40	30	140	300–500
0.8 power factor............	514	40	30	200	250–400

CHAPTER 10

REFRIGERATION APPLICATIONS

The cold-storage field has widened until it now includes all phases of the handling of comestibles from the time they are harvested until the time they are consumed. Refrigeration is applied to such services as are offered by cold-storage warehouses, meat-packing plants, refrigerated railway cars and trucks, locker storage plants, retail walk-in boxes, display cases for frozen produce, and household refrigeration.

In addition to cold-storage applications, there are numerous others, such as ice-cream making, bakery refrigeration, wine cooling, ice making, cooling of drinking water, etc.

Many of these fields require men specifically trained for their respective jobs. The selection and handling of fruits and vegetables requires men trained in the field of agriculture. The selection and processing of meats requires trained butchers and packers. Men employed in the various phases of dairy manufacturing must be highly skilled in their field. The various phases of the processing are beyond the scope of this text. We will discuss only those phases of the refrigerating problem directly connected with the design of equipment or refrigerating systems for a few of the more important applications.

THE COLD-STORAGE WAREHOUSE

The cold-storage warehouse provides such services as the storage of comestibles either above or below freezing, and the quick-freezing thereof.

Design Condition for Rooms Holding Produce above Its Freezing Point. It is usually impractical to design separate rooms for each type of produce. The type of produce in a particular room will vary from season to season or year to year. Sometimes many types of produce are stored in a single room. When this is done, care must be taken that the optimum storage condition is nearly the same for the various types of produce concerned. Most produce has an optimum storage temperature between 30 and 32°F. The optimum humidity is usually between 80 and 90 per cent, depending on the moisture content of the product. If sufficient cooling coil is used and the room is loaded with a single product, the room humidity will tend to come to the optimum humidity for that product. If the room has sufficient coil to maintain the room tempera-

307

ture at 32°F with a refrigerant temperature of 26°F, the humidity will tend to approach its optimum for that product.[1] Tests indicating this fact were made with bare coils heavily coated with ice; such coils have a large outside surface and maintain approximately the same humidity as finned coils if both are operated at the same refrigerant temperature.

Certain produce, notably lettuce and other leafy vegetables, requires humidities of 90 to 95 per cent. These humidities may be maintained by occasionally sprinkling the floor. With certain other produce, notably lemons, avocados, and bananas, the optimum storage temperature is considerably above 32°F. The higher temperature can be maintained in a room designed for general storage without lowering the relative humidity if the coil is equipped with a suction control valve in addition to whatever temperature-control device it may have.

Cooling-coil Selection. Both bare coils with gravity circulation of air and finned coils with forced circulation of air are commonly used. The method of selecting either type was discussed in Chap. 5. Pipe coils are operated with a thick coat of ice and have great heat-storage capacity. They may be operated several years without defrosting. Because of their heat-storage capacity, they lend themselves to manual control. They have proved satisfactory over a long period of time; however, they add much weight to the building, occupy considerable storage space, and are costly to install. If finned coils are used, the fin spacing should be not more than four to the inch, and a suitable defrosting device must be provided. The air should enter the room at a velocity not greater than 600 fpm, and care should be taken that it does not directly impinge on any product. Auxiliary fans should be provided to increase the circulation during the chilling period.

Freezing of Comestibles. Quick-freezing helps to retain the vitamin content of all comestibles. Vitamin C (ascorbic acid) is the vitamin that is most easily lost in any product, either above or below its freezing point. Its retention is often taken as a criterion of the value of frozen foods, since if it is retained, other vitamins and palatability are likely to be retained.[2]

Vitamin C is lost both by solution and by oxidation. It is the most soluble of all known vitamins. Blanching or cooking should therefore be done with a minimum quantity of water, or with live steam. Oxidation is hastened by heat, whether it be in storage above freezing, in blanching

---

[1] Rose, Dean H., R. C. Wright, and T. M. Whiteman, The Commercial Storage of Fruits, Vegetables, and Florists' Stocks, *U. S. Dept. Agr. Circ. 278*, p. 5, 1941.

[2] Tressler, D. K., Bacteria, Enzymes, and Vitamins—Indices of Quality in Frozen Vegetables, *Refrig. Eng.*, vol. 36, p. 319, 1939.

previous to freezing, in cooking, or in holding at high temperatures after cooking. Produce should therefore be blanched as quickly as possible after harvesting, frozen immediately, stored in a frozen condition until ready for cooking, cooked as quickly as possible in a covered vessel, and served immediately after cooking. Properly handled frozen comestibles have a much higher vitamin content than so-called "fresh produce" obtained at the grocery store.

Vegetable tissues differ from animal tissues in that animal tissues are dead upon arrival at the quick-freezing plant, while vegetable and fruit tissues are very much alive and subject to enzyme reaction. To stop this reaction, sugar or corn syrup is added to most fruits before freezing, while vegetables are blanched in vigorously boiling water or live steam. Live steam is preferable, since less of the mineral and vitamin content is leached from the product by this method. The time of blanching must be sufficient so that the vegetable is heated nearly to the boiling point throughout. The time required is between 1 and 4 min for most vegetables. This partial cooking has no detrimental effect on the food product.

For sanitary reasons, nearly all produce is packaged before freezing. For retail trade, the packages are usually waxed cardboard cartons containing 12 to 16 oz of fruit or vegetables. Freezing is accomplished by contact with a refrigerated plate, or the package is placed in a cold air blast. When the refrigerated plate is used, its temperature is usually -10 or $-20°F$. When the air-blast method is used, the air is usually $-20°F$ or lower. Contact with the refrigerated plate gives faster freezing and, hence, a slightly better product than the air-blast method if the temperatures are the same; however, the handling of a large number of packages is easier with the air-blast method. With high air velocity and slightly lower temperature, the air-blast method will produce a product equivalent to that of the contact method. The contact method is generally used in small plants, while the air-blast method is generally used in large plants.

For restaurant and institutional use, vegetables are sometimes packed in $2\frac{1}{2}$-, 5-, and 10-lb waxed cardboard containers. In such cases the produce is frozen before packaging on either moving belts or trays placed in an air-blast freezing tunnel.

Berries, cherries, and other small fruits for the bakery, soda fountain, or ice-cream trade are often packed in 20-, 30-, or 50-lb slip-cover tin cans. The fruit is packed with sugar or corn syrup and frozen in the container at about 0°F. Quick-freezing is not necessary with this type of produce.

Fish are frozen by the contact method, the air-blast method, or by the brine-spray method. With the contact or the air-blast method, the fish are usually filleted and packaged before freezing. With the brine-spray method, sodium chloride brine is sprayed directly on the fish. They are packaged after freezing. Large fish are usually frozen by the brine-spray method. After the fish are removed from the freezer, they are dipped into a tank of cold water. The temperature of the fish is low enough to freeze a thin coating of ice over the surface. This is known as *glazing*. The fish are then piled in stacks in the storage room. The fish can be sprayed with cold water after piling in order to cover them with an additional glaze in case the regular glaze has been cracked in handling. Fish are ordinarily frozen and stored at about 0°F.

Meat is usually cut and wrapped before freezing. Freezing is accomplished by contact with cold plates, or by the air-blast method.

The freezing temperature is usually about −20°F, and the storage temperature is about 0°F. Meat is always chilled before entering the freezer, but not necessarily aged. Pork is usually taken directly from the chilling room to the freezing room. Beef and lamb are usually aged about a week, at a temperature of about 35°F, before freezing; however, it is sometimes taken directly from the chilling room to the freezer. The required time for aging in any case is less for meat that is to be frozen than it is for meat that is to be marketed directly.

Storage of Frozen Comestibles. No comestible is ever completely frozen. The average freezing point given in Tables 1-3 and 1-4 is the temperature at which most of the free water, with its dissolved minerals, is frozen. At this temperature the product becomes hard. Further lowering of temperature increases the percentage of frozen water; however, most of the chemically combined water is never frozen. Any change in temperature causes a partial thawing or freezing of the product. It is therefore essential that frozen produce be held at a constant temperature throughout the storage period.

In the freezing process, the temperature of the contact plate or the air blast is about −20°F, while the product is stored at 0°F. Lower temperatures are required during the freezing process in order that the product be lowered as rapidly as possible to its storage condition.

If properly frozen and stored at a uniform temperature of 0°F or below, most fruits, vegetables, and meats will keep their vitamin C, bright color, and fresh flavor for 1 year. Furthermore, at this temperature there is no bacterial growth. The most dangerous bacteria are *Clostridium botulinum* and *Eberthella typhi*. *Clostridium botulinum* is probably present in most nonacid vegetables. It is not pathogenic but produces a toxin that, in sufficient quantities, may cause sickness or death. It is not completely destroyed in freezing but does not develop in frozen produce.[1] Considering *Eberthella typhi*, there is little danger of typhoid with produce that has been frozen and stored at 0°F.[2]

Direct-expansion Systems. Direct-expansion systems operate at higher suction temperatures and require less equipment than do brine systems; hence they require less power and are lower in first cost. Brine systems are more easily controlled, avoid certain complications in the design of the refrigerating equipment, avoid danger of damage to the product in case of leakage of the refrigerant, and reduce the fire hazard.

With relatively small warehouses (three stories or less) handling produce above its freezing point, such as is often the case with warehouses for oranges, apples, or pears, a direct-expansion Freon 12 system has very desirable characteristics, but care should be taken in the design of the system. In case of leakage, Freon 12 does not damage produce and involves no fire hazard. The equipment lends itself to automatic control and is moderate in cost. Certain precautions should be taken. To avoid an oil problem, discharge-line oil traps should be used at each compressor; dry-expansion, finned blower coils should be used, and the refrigerant lines should be as short as possible. An oil-equalizing line should also be used between the crankcases of the compressors, and the suction and discharge lines at the compressors should be interconnected. The refrigerant has a high density and is subject to flashing in the liquid line at vertical lifts. For vertical lifts of more than 10 ft, the suction line should be run inside the liquid line. The refrigerant has no odor; hence leaks may occur without notice. All lines, therefore, should be exposed and not insulated. If the suction line is run at the side of the refrigerated space near the wall, no damage due to moisture condensation will occur. To avoid transmission gain to the suction vapor, the suction line should be run through refrigerated space, or a heat exchanger between the suction and liquid lines should be used. Welded steel pipe is more rigid and less subject to physical damage than copper tubing.

Small or moderate-sized warehouses (three stories or less) engaged in the freezing of comestibles and their storage, above or below freezing, may use either ammonia or the Freons. A moderate-sized plant using direct-expansion coils with Freon 12 in the upper stage and Freon 22 in the lower stage is practical. In case of leakage, neither refrigerant will damage the product or involve a fire hazard. The heat exchanger between stages and the refrigerant are more expensive with the Freons

[1] TANNER, F. W., P. R. BEAMER, and J. C. RICKER, Further Studies on the Development of Clostridium Botulinum in Refrigerated Foods, *Food Research*, vol. 5, p. 323, 1940.

[2] PRESCOTT, S. C., and F. W. TANNER, Microbiology in Relation to Food Preservation, *Food Research*, vol. 3, pp. 192–193, 1938.

than with ammonia; however, the over-all cost of the system may be less because of the lower cost of Freon compressors and suitable cooling coils.

Ammonia is commonly used in warehouses of all sizes where multiple-stage refrigeration is required. The interchangers between stages are more simple and less costly than those for Freon. The pipe sizes are small, and the piping system is relatively simple, since the latent heat of evaporation of ammonia is high, and it involves no oil problem. The density of the liquid refrigerant is low; hence, excessive flashing in the liquid line will not occur unless the refrigerant is lifted more than three stories. If higher lifts are involved, the liquid should be cooled in a heat exchanger using boiling refrigerant as the cooling agent. Suction vapor should not be used for this cooling, since ammonia superheats greatly upon compression. Suction lines should pass through refrigerated spaces near the wall, or they should be insulated.

Brine Systems. Brine systems are generally preferred for all storage rooms, above or below freezing, in large cold-storage warehouses. Quick-freezing rooms generally use direct-expansion coils. Brine piping is simple—any number of stories may be supplied without complication; temperatures are easily controlled, and the brine has a large heat-storage capacity, which may be drawn on in case of emergency. Calcium chlorride brine is generally preferred, since it is less corrosive and requires a lesser amount of salt to lower the freezing point than is required for sodium chloride brine.

Ammonia is the common refrigerant. The ammonia brine cooler and the ammonia intercooler are simpler and less costly than those of other refrigerants. Film conductances during evaporation and condensation are higher with ammonia than with other refrigerants.

To avoid corrosion, the piping and other parts of the brine circuit should be made of a single material, or from materials having nearly the same potential in the electromotive series. The following materials are common: pipe of steel or galvanized steel, valves with an iron body and steel disks, pump with an iron body and an iron runner. It is also possible to make the entire brine circuit out of copper alloys, but it is better not to mix copper alloys and iron alloys on the same brine circuit. Iron and iron alloys are generally used, since condenser and evaporator tubes are always steel when ammonia is used as the refrigerant.

Piping is nearly always arranged as shown in Fig. 10-1. This is called a *three-pipe system.* The brine is pumped through the condenser, through the supply lines, through the coils, to a line that leads to the balance tank on the roof. As many supply lines as are needed may be used. The refrigerant returns from the balance line to the pump through a single return line.

Condensing Equipment. In selecting equipment, it should be kept in mind that the produce stored in a cold-storage warehouse at one time has greater value than the refrigerating machinery. The compressors and condensers should have sufficient capacity to operate the plant under maximum capacity, including the maximum storage load and the probable

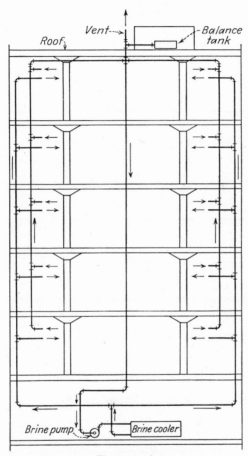

Fig. 10-1. Three-pipe brine system.

maximum chilling load. In addition, stand-by capacity is desirable. The probable maximum chilling load will not be the sum of the maximum chilling loads for the separate rooms, since loading in all rooms will not occur at one time. The loading may be nearly steady or may be seasonal, depending on the location of the plant. Stand-by equipment may be installed when the plant is built, or provision may be made with regard to space and piping connections so that it may be installed later.

The refrigerating system should have multiple condensers connected in parallel with suitable valves so that one condenser at a time may be cleaned or repaired without interruption of operations.   Each storage-temperature range should have at   least two compressors.   If two compressors are used, each should have sufficient capacity to carry the maximum storage load, but need not have extra capacity to do any chilling.   At least one of the compressors should be equipped with clearance or other capacity-reduction devices.

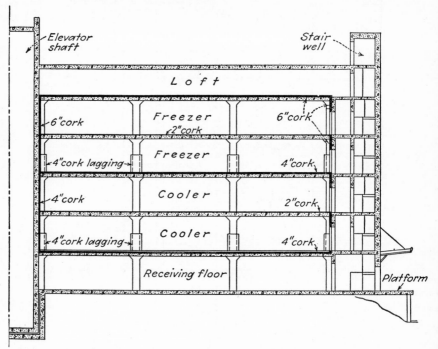

Fig. 10-2.   Warehouse with curtain-wall construction.

Arrangement of the Plant.   For low first cost and low operating cost, the plant should be as nearly a cube as possible.   Staircases, elevators, and corridors should be adjacent to the outside walls to keep heat leakage at a minimum.   Quick-freezing and freezer rooms should be well above the ground level so that the water in the ground will not freeze and destroy the footings.   Freezers must be separated from coolers by insulation to prevent freezing of the produce in the coolers during cold weather.   It is better that the freezer be located beside the cooler rather than above it, since there will be less area common to both rooms.   It is usually desirable to have about the same amount of freezer space as cooler space; however, this problem must be considered separately for each warehouse.

The usual allowance for receiving and shipping area, including platforms, is about 5 per cent of the total cold-storage floor area. The quick-freezing plant should be located adjacent to freezer storage rooms and never adjacent to cooler rooms. The rooms for public cold storage should be as large as possible without incurring excessive structural cost. Rooms having 5,000 to 10,000 sq ft of floor area are common. About 50 sq ft of elevator floor area is required for each 30,000 sq ft of storage floor area.

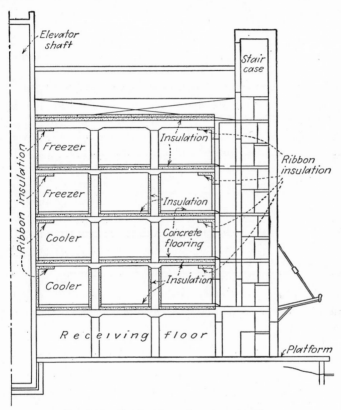

Fig. 10-3. Insulated-warehouse construction.

Construction and Insulation. Fireproof construction is necessary to obtain low insurance rates and low depreciation. The walls and floors are usually reinforced concrete. There are two general types of construction—the curtain-wall construction, as shown in Fig. 10-2, and the insulated-warehouse construction, as shown in Fig. 10-3.

In the curtain-wall construction, the floors, ceiling, and interior columns form one structure, which is surrounded by the independent exterior walls. The interior structure may be anchored to the exterior structure as shown in Fig. 10-6. The insulation forms a continuous envelope between the inner and outer shells. Rooms of different temperature must be separated by insulation. Rooms of the same temperature must be separated by at least half as much insulation as is used in the outside walls, since temperatures are subject to adjustment, and under certain conditions some rooms may be inoperative for a period of time. Curtain-wall construction may be insulated with board-type insulation or loose-fill insulation. When the board type of insulation is used, it should be supported at every other floor with a horizontal wood or steel rail bolted to the outside wall. If loose-fill insulation is used, provision must be made for adding insulation at the top of the wall after a few years.

Insulated-warehouse construction requires more insulation than the curtain-wall construction and is more expensive for warehouses of large size because of this reason. Small warehouses or storage rooms are usually of the insulated-warehouse construction. Ribbon insulation is used on the ceiling at the outer walls, as shown in Fig. 10-3. The width of the ribbon should be such that the concrete slab to which it is attached will have a conductance edgeways not less than that of the insulation on the outside wall. The insulation must be thoroughly protected from moisture. Insulation may be kept dry, but if it does become wet it cannot be dried. In order to keep it dry, it must be kept from breathing outside air. The moisture-holding capacity of air approximately doubles with each 20°F increase in temperature. The outside air in summer has a much higher moisture content than is possible for the inside air. Air that leaks into the insulation from the outside will therefore condense in the insulation near the inside surface, causing it to become wet and lose its insulating value. The outside wall must therefore be thoroughly sealed against air leakage. Whenever possible one course of Foamglas or other vaporproof material should be used against the outside wall. An effective flashing, about 12 in. deep, for roofing against parapet walls must be provided. For added safety, the interior and top of the parapet wall should be waterproofed with hot tar. Any leakage of moisture at this point will cause serious damage to the insulation. Board-type insulations, such as corkboard, Foamglas, and rock cork, installed with hot tar, are more moisture-resistant than loose-fill insulations and are generally preferred.

The Air Conditioning and Refrigerating Machinery Association recommends that the walls be insulated with not less than the amounts of insulation given in Table 10-1.

These recommended thicknesses are based on the assumption that the insulation is properly applied and remains in a reasonably dry condition over years in service.

Ceilings on the top floor should be insulated at least 2 in. thicker than the walls. Partitions should have nearly the same amount of insulation as the outside walls, since there will be times when adjoining rooms will not be in operation.

TABLE 10-1.

Room temperature, °F	Equivalent thickness of corkboard, in.	Minimum transmission coefficient, Btu/(24 hr) (sq ft)(°F)
−19 to −10	8	1.00
−9 to −5	7	1.14
−4 to +5	6	1.33
6 to 20	5	1.60
21 to 35	4	2.00
36 to 45	3	2.67
46 and over	2	4.00

Method of Applying Insulation to Walls. Slab insulation may be applied to masonry walls as shown in Fig. 10-4. The wall should be thoroughly cleaned of dirt, dust, loose mortar, etc., and where necessary,

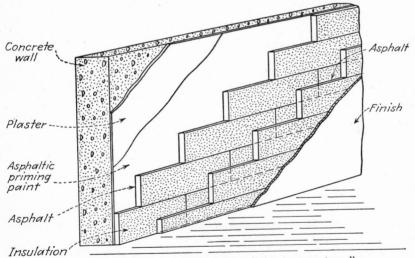

FIG. 10-4. Method of applying slab insulation to concrete walls.

made true and even with back plaster. After the wall has thoroughly dried, the wall should be primed with two coats of asphalt priming paint. The first layer of insulation is applied directly to this surface with hot asphalt. The second layer should be also applied in hot asphalt and secured to the first layer with treated wood skewers. All joints must be tight and the joints of successive layers broken with respect to each other. The exposed surface may be finished with cement plaster or mastic. Cement plaster can be painted with enamel, and mastic can be painted with varnish-base aluminum paint.

Where only one layer of insulation is required, apply it as described for the first layer.

Slab insulation may be applied to wood walls or ceilings as shown in Fig. 10-5. Directly against the sheathing, one layer of roofing paper is applied with the edges lapped and tarred for not less than 3 in. The first layer of insulation is applied in hot asphalt and secured to the wood with galvanized box nails. The second layer is applied and finished as previously described for masonry walls.

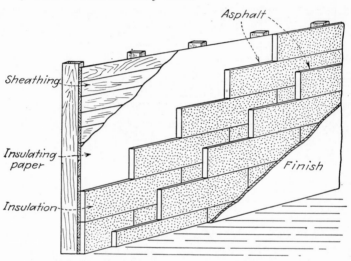

FIG. 10-5.   Method of applying slab insulation to wood walls.

Figure 10-6 shows a method of insulating a warehouse using curtain walls.[1] Foamglas or other moistureproof insulation is applied to the masonry wall. Moisture-resistant insulation of low thermal conductivity is then applied to the moistureproof insulation. All layers are applied as described for masonry walls.

Loose-fill insulation may be applied to masonry walls as shown in Fig. 10-7. The inside face of the masonry wall should be thoroughly brushed and cleaned. The wall should then be sealed against moisture leakage with two coats of asphalt fibered emulsion or one coat of asphalt primer and two coats of hot asphalt. The horizontal furring may be fastened to the masonry wall with expansion bolts or inserts installed when the wall was constructed. The studs are then erected, and the

[1] Armstrong's Insulator, Armstrong Cork Co.

loose-fill insulation is installed as the inner course of tongue-and-groove lumber is applied.

For rooms above 32°F, walls or partitions may be insulated as shown in Fig. 10-8. For partitions, two layers of a good quality of asphalt-impregnated kraft paper should be installed under the tongue-and-groove

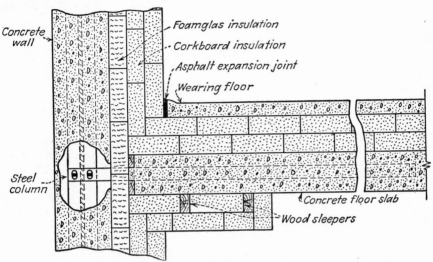

Concrete wall

Foamglas insulation

Corkboard insulation

Asphalt expansion joint

Wearing floor

Steel column

Concrete floor slab

Wood sleepers

FIG. 10-6. Method of applying slab insulation with curtain-wall construction.

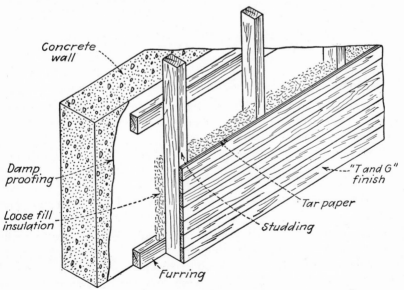

Concrete wall

Damp proofing

Loose fill insulation

"T and G" finish

Tar paper

Studding

Furring

FIG. 10-7. Method of applying loose-fill insulation to concrete walls.

lumber on both sides.   The layers of vaporproof paper should be installed so that each sheet overlaps each preceding sheet slightly more than 50 per cent, to provide at least two thicknesses of paper at all points.   Seams should be sealed with asphalt.   For walls, the two layers should be installed under only the outer course of wood.   The loose-fill insulation should be installed and mildly tamped as the wood sheathing and paper are applied.

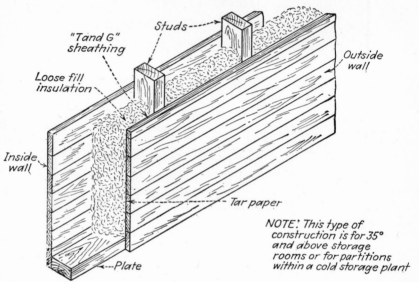

FIG. 10-8.   Method of applying loose-fill insulation in wood walls for temperatures above 30°F.

For rooms below 32°F, walls, partition, and ceiling may be constructed as shown in Fig. 10-9.   Studs and ceiling joists are staggered so that there will be little wood contact from the inner to the outer surface.   Insulation and vaporproof paper should be installed as described in the preceding paragraph.

Insulation may be applied to a concrete floor as shown in Fig. 10-10. Slab insulation should be used.   Loose-fill insulations cannot be kept dry in the floor.   The concrete floor on which the insulation is to be laid must be smooth, clean, and level.   The first layer is applied in hot asphalt.   The second layer is also applied in hot asphalt.   After all joints have been filled, the top surface is heavily flooded with hot asphalt, or a waterproof membrane is applied consisting of two layers of 15-lb roofing felt, each layer being mopped in place with hot asphalt.   The membrane should be flashed up 9 in. high along the walls and around the columns.   On top of the membrane install a 3-in. concrete wearing floor.

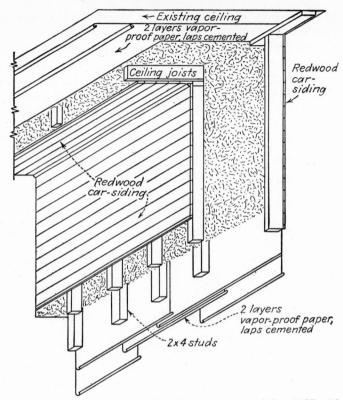

Fig. 10-9. Insulation of walls and ceiling for temperatures below 32°F with loose-fill insulation.

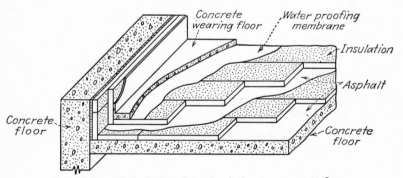

Fig. 10-10. Method of applying insulation to a concrete floor.

Insulation may be applied to a wood subfloor in the same manner as to a concrete floor, except that the wood subfloor must first have a layer of roofing paper mopped in place with hot asphalt.

Slab insulation may be applied to a concrete ceiling as shown in Fig. 10-11. The ceiling is cleaned of all dirt, dust, loose plaster, etc., and primed with asphalt priming paint. Wood sleepers, 1.62 in. wide and equal in thickness to the first layer of insulation, are fastened to the under side of the concrete slab with expansion bolts or inserts that were installed when the concrete slab was cast. The sleepers are spaced so that the insulation fits tightly between them, but not more than 18 in.

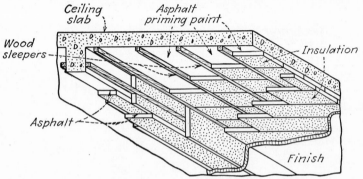

FIG. 10-11.   Method of applying slab insulation to a concrete ceiling.

apart. The first layer of insulation is applied in hot asphalt and toenailed to the sleepers with galvanized nails. The second layer of insulation is applied in hot asphalt and nailed to the first layer and to the wood sleepers with galvanized nails. The surface is finished with cement plaster or mastic. The ceiling plus the roof insulation should be at least 2 in. thicker than the insulation used on outside walls. With fireproof construction, it is less expensive to apply this insulation above the concrete slab.

Slab insulation may be applied to a concrete roof as follows: The concrete must be smooth, clean, and level. Prime the surface with asphalt primer or thinned asphalt emulsion. Apply the insulation in hot asphalt. On top the insulation, apply two layers of 15-lb roofing felt mopped in place with hot asphalt, and flash up along the fire walls about 1 ft. Apply the roofing paper with hot asphalt and paint with aluminum paint.

In the insulation of a wood roof, a membrane should first be installed, the membrane consisting of two layers of roofing felt nailed in place and mopped with hot asphalt. The insulation may then be installed as described in the preceding paragraph.

Self-supporting partitions as shown in Fig. 10-12 may be used. These partitions may be constructed as follows: Erect temporary 2- by 4-in. studs on 18-in. centers in alignment as a guide for the self-supporting partition. Erect the first layer with hot asphalted edges against the temporary studs. Toenail each slab to the abutting one, and also to the walls, floor, and ceiling, with wood skewers or galvanized nails, where necessary. Erect the second layer against the first layer in hot asphalt, and also secure it to the first layer with treated wood skewers. Finish the exposed surfaces with cement plaster or mastic, as desired.

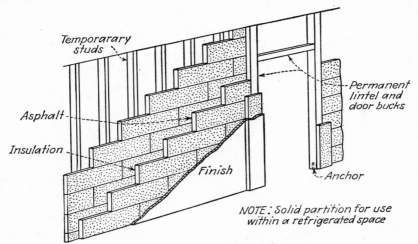

Fig. 10-12.   Self-supporting insulated partition.

Columns that may conduct heat from the outside or from a room of higher temperature must be insulated. Round or square columns may be used. The round column is less subject to damage by trucks but is more expensive to construct and insulate. If square columns are used, the corners must be adequately armored to prevent damage by trucking.

Round columns may be insulated as shown in Fig. 10-13. Insulation is applied as follows: Prime the columns with asphalt priming paint. Apply the lags, properly beveled to fit the column, in hot asphalt, and toenail each cork lag to the abutting one with treated wood skewers. Where necessary to protect the insulation, install around the column a 20-gauge galvanized sheet-metal guard 4 ft 6 in high, before the finish is applied. Finish the column with cement plaster or mastic.

Square columns may be insulated as shown in Fig. 10-14. The insulation is applied as follows: Prime the surface with an asphalt priming paint. Apply the first layer of insulation in hot asphalt. Apply the second layer in hot asphalt and secure it to the first layer with treated wood shewers.   Successive layers must be cross-broken on the flat surfaces and at the corners.   Apply corner protective angles, constructed of a 20-gauge galvanized sheet iron, with each leg 6 in. wide, at each of the four corners before applying the finish.   Finish with cement plaster or mastic.

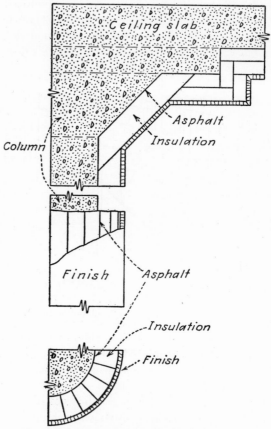

Fig. 10-13.   Method of applying insulation to a round column.

Portland-cement back plaster may be mixed in the proportions

1 part Portland cement
3 parts clean sharp sand
5 per cent hydrated lime

Immediately before the application of plaster, wet the walls with clear water.   Apply the plaster to 0.25-in. minimum thickness on high points, straighten with a straightedge, and float it smooth.   Where necessary, the wall surface should be roughened or hacked before applying the plaster, to ensure a good bond.

Portland-cement finish plaster may be mixed in the proportions

1 part Portland cement
2 parts clean plaster sand
8 per cent hydrated lime

The first coat must be keyed to the insulation, scratched in two directions, and allowed to dry before the second coat is applied. The second coat is brought to an even surface with a straightedge and troweled smooth. To reduce the cracking to a minimum, score the second coat into approximately 4 ft squares before it has hardened. Cracking may also be reduced by reinforcing the plaster with galvanized wire netting fastened to the insulation with 1.25-in. galvanized staples. All salient corners should be protected with a corner bead fastened in place before the insulation is applied.

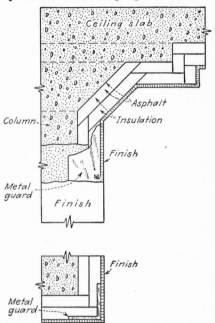

FIG. 10-14. Method of applying insulation to a square column.

An asphalt-mastic plaster may be composed of the following:

50 gal asphalt emulsion
175 lb asbestos float
275 lb (2.75 cu ft) dry, screened plaster sand
15 gal clean water

These ingredients are thoroughly mixed together until the mixture is uniform in color throughout. Use only the smallest quantity of water necessary to give the proper troweling consistency. Apply this plaster directly to the insulation surface in two coats, each approximately 0.125 in. thick. All cracks must be filled with the mixture before applying the first coat. The first coat must be dry to the hand before the second is applied. The second coat is troweled smooth and may be scored in 4-ft squares.

Portland-cement plaster finishes may be painted with a flat undercoat and two coats of white enamel. A varnish-base aluminum paint may also be used as an undercoat.   Asphalt finishes may be finished with two coats of varnish-base aluminum paint.   Most other paints will not adhere to the asphalt.

MEAT PACKING

Meat should be chilled as quickly as possible, aged for tenderness, and stored at a low temperature until ready for use.   For short storage, the meat may be aged slowly at a temperature just above freezing.   For long storage, the aging period is shortened, and the meat is quickly frozen and stored at about 0°F.

Chilling-room Air Temperatures.   Meats of all types should be placed in the chilling room immediately after dressing and chilled quickly to avoid bacterial action.   The room should be 31 or 32°F before loading and should not exceed 38°F during the chilling process.   The relative humidity will be 95 per cent or higher during the first part of the chilling process owing to the vapor from the hot carcasses.   At the end of the chilling period, it should be about 85 to 90 per cent.   The air circulation should be moderate in order to remove the vapor and prevent condensation, but not excessive so that drying of the product will occur at the end of the chilling period.   The chilling period is usually about 24 hr, during which time lambs and light hogs are chilled to within 5°F of the room temperature, while beeves will be chilled to within about 10°F of the room temperature.

Aging-room Air Conditions.   Beeves are usually aged at temperatures between 33 and 36°F at relative humidities between 86 and 92 per cent. The required time will depend on the temperature of the room and the toughness of the meat.   At 33°F the time will be about 10 or 12 days, while at 36°F the time will be about 7 days.   The longer aging time with the lower temperature will give a superior product.   Aging at temperatures above 36°F for less than 7 days is sometimes accomplished with the aid of ultraviolet light to retard the bacterial action; however, bloom, color, and keeping qualities are adversely affected.   If it is desired to store the beef for 1 month to 6 weeks, it may be aged at its optimum storage temperature and humidity for this period of time.

Although the foregoing discussion is for beef, it also applies to mutton and lamb; however, the temperature should be somewhat lower and the time of aging shorter.   Aging for mutton and lamb is best accomplished at near the optimum storage temperature and humidity.   Pork usually needs very little aging.

If the meat is to be frozen, the aging time may be taken as approximately half of that required for nonfrozen meats.   Pork requires no aging but should be thoroughly chilled before cutting.

Weights and Spacing of Carcasses. The approximate weights of dressed carcasses are as follows:

	Maximum	Minimum	Average
Beeves...............................	800	400	500
Lambs...............................	100	30	45
Hogs................................	400	100	180

Beeves are split when dressed, while the entire carcasses of hogs and lambs are handled in one piece. In either the chilling or aging room, the rails are spaced 32 to 36 in. apart and have a minimum height of 8 ft 6 in. above the floor. Average-weight hogs, or halves of beef, may be placed 2 ft on center, while average-weight lambs may be placed 18 in. on center.

Cooling-unit Selection for Chilling Rooms. Forced circulation of air is desired, since it will give quicker chilling of the carcasses and will remove excess moisture, avoiding condensation on the meat. The rate of giving up moisture is not constant. It is highest at the beginning of the chilling period and tapers off as the meat is reduced to its storage temperature. More than 30 per cent of the heat at the beginning is in the form of evaporated moisture. When the meat has become completely chilled down to its storage temperature, the latent heat drops to about 20 per cent of the total. Circulation should be moderately high during the period of latent heat gain and should be reduced as the latent heat load reduces. This is accomplished by partially damping the air flow through the unit.

Finned-coil units or brine-spray units may be used. If a finned-coil unit is used, it should be equipped with a suitable defrosting device so that the coil may be defrosted quickly and often. Brine-spray units are preferable, since they solve the defrosting problem. A very small quantity of brine enters the air stream, but this is beneficial, since salt is mildly antiseptic. The unit may have either a finned- or a bare-tube coil located within it, or the brine may be cooled in an external brine cooler. The saturation efficiency of the unit may be from 70 to 90 per cent, depending on its design. The saturation efficiency affects the required air quantity but does not affect the required brine temperature.

The unit is primarily selected for the conditions at the close of the chilling period. These have been given as 35°F and 85 per cent relative humidity. The air quantity is based on the average hourly heat quantity for the 24-hr period. This will give a slightly greater air quantity than is required at the close of the period, but this is desirable, since it will make available a greater air quantity at the beginning of the period. The unit may be damped to obtain the required amount at the close of the period.   An example will be given to illustrate the selection of the unit.

Example: Find the required quantities of brine and air and their respective temperatures per 1,000 Btu/hr of capacity for a brine-spray unit in a meat chilling room.   The unit will use 15 per cent sodium chloride brine solution, will have a saturation efficiency of 80 per cent, and the brine temperature will rise 5°F in the spray.   We will assume that the meat has been sufficiently chilled so that the latent heat gain is 25 per cent of the total heat gain.

Solution: The brine will leave the unit at the dew-point temperature of the leaving air.   This temperature is called the *apparatus dew point.* It must be found by a "cut-and-try" process.   We will assume it to be 24°F and check our assumption.   The air that leaves the unit may be divided into two parts—that which contacts the spray and becomes saturated at the brine temperature, and that which passes through the spray without contacting it.   It will be recalled from Chap. 5 that *contact factor* and *saturation efficiency* have the same meaning.   The contacted air quantity will be the sensible heat divided by its temperature change and its specific heat.

$$\frac{750}{8 \times 0.24} = 390 \text{ lb/hr of contacted air}$$

Since 250 Btu/hr of latent heat must also be removed, the equivalent grains of moisture per hour will be

$$\frac{250 \times 7,000}{1,070} = 1,640 \text{ g/hr}$$

The moisture per pound of contacted air to be removed is

$$\frac{1,640}{390} = 4.2 \text{ g/lb}$$

The specific humidity at the apparatus-dew-point temperature will be the specific humidity at the room dew point minus the grains of moisture per pound of air that must be removed.

$$22.4 - 4.2 = 18.2 \text{ g/lb}$$

This specific humidity corresponds to the 24°F assumed apparatus dew point.   Therefore, our assumption has been checked and found to be true.   The brine will leave the spray chamber at 24°F and will be cooled to 19°F in the brine cooler.   Its quantity per 1,000 Btu/hr will be

$$\frac{1,000}{5 \times 0.835} = 240 \text{ lb/hr}$$

or

$$\frac{240}{9.30 \times 60} = 0.430 \text{ gpm}$$

The air temperature leaving the unit may be found from the units saturation efficiency

$$e = \frac{t_i - t_o}{t_i - t_b}$$

$$0.80 = \frac{32 - t_o}{32 - 24}$$

$$t_o = 25.6$$

The air quantity handled by the unit will be the sensible heat gain divided by the temperature change of the air and its specific heat.

$$\frac{750}{6.4 \times 0.24} = 487 \text{ lb/hr}$$

or

$$\frac{487 \times 12.3}{60} = 100 \text{ cfm}$$

Cooling-coil Selection for Aging Rooms. The circulation of air in the aging room should be low in order to avoid excessive shrinkage, but positive in order to avoid the appearance of slime on the product. Gravity coils, blower-type cooling units, and brine-spray units have all proved satisfactory when properly selected. If forced circulation of air is used, slightly higher humidities should be maintained. Brine-spray units are often preferred, since there is no defrosting problem and the small amount of brine that is carried into the air is mildly antiseptic. Either the blower type or the spray-induced-air type of brine-spray unit may be used. When the latter type is used, it is usually made about 1 ft wide, 6 or 8 ft high, and is backed against one of the walls. It will usually extend nearly the entire distance along the wall. Figure 10-15 shows such a unit. This arrangement produces a mild positive circulation that is desirable for the aging of meat, and a minimum space is required above the rails. The blower-type brine-spray unit is also satisfactory. The heat gain in the aging room is low, so the required air quantity is small. Blower-type units, therefore, do not produce excessive circulation. Ample space must be provided above the rails so that the air may spread over the room without impinging against the meat. Usually a space 3 ft high is satisfactory.

Since conditions at which meat is aged vary considerably and may be modified by the packer at any time, it would seem good practice to select the equipment for the optimum storage temperature and humidity. This is approximately 32°F and 88 per cent relative humidity for most meats. If selected for these conditions, the equipment may be adjusted for higher temperatures if the packer desires.

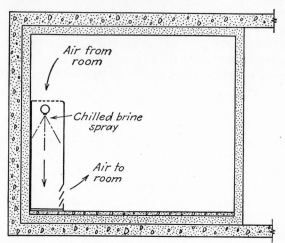

FIG. 10-15.　Simple brine-spray unit for a meat-aging room.

LOCKER STORAGE

Locker storage plants are increasingly popular in cities of up to 100,000 population, particularly in meat-raising areas. Usually only a small part of the stored produce is fruits or vegetables. Preparation of the latter prior to quick freezing is handled by the customer. The plant should be operated by a good butcher, since much processing of meats is involved. Beef is weighed, chilled, aged, cut, wrapped, frozen, and stored in the customer's lockers. Lamb may follow this route, but the aging period is shortened or omitted. Pork is weighed, chilled, cut, wrapped, frozen, and stored; or, after chilling, it may be cured, smoked, rechilled, cut, wrapped, frozen, and stored in the customers' lockers. The locker plant should have the following rooms: chilling and aging room, pork-curing room, smoke room or cabinet, cutting room, quick-freezing room or cabinet, and locker storage room. These rooms will be described in detail.

Chilling and Aging Room. A trolley rail extends above the doorway to the loading platform at one end of the room and to the cutting room at the other end. The rails in the room are spaced on 32- to 36-in. centers at a height 8 ft 6 in. above the floor.

The cooling unit is selected to maintain 35°F temperature with 85 per cent relative humidity. A direct-expansion blower-type unit with a water-defrosting header is satisfactory. The room is not usually large enough to warrant the expense of a brine-spray unit. The unit is selected on a 10°FTD between room and refrigerant, based on the entire chilling and storage load. In estimating the chilling load, it may be assumed that the entire contents of the locker storage room will change every 3 months. All of it except the fruits and vegetables will pass through the chilling room. The fruits and vegetables are seldom more than 10 per cent of the total produce stored. The temperature range through which the meat will be chilled will depend on the operation of the plant. Usually, at least 75 per cent of the meat will be purchased from meat packers, in which case the meat will have been previously chilled. Sometimes as much as 95 per cent of the meat will come from meat packers. The temperature of the previously chilled meat will seldom be above 45°F. The rest of the meat may be assumed to be received at body temperature.

Cutting and Wrapping Room. The cutting and wrapping room resembles a butchershop and contains saws, grinders, cutting blocks, and worktables. Often it is further equipped with refrigerated cases for sale of frozen fruits, vegetables, cheese, etc., to the customers. The meats are cut and packaged according to the owner's instructions. Pork may be cut preparatory to curing. After curing it is returned to the aging and wrapping room for packaging. For sanitary reasons, the smoke cabinet should be in a separate room.

Curing Room. The two methods of curing pork with salt are known as *pickling* and *dry-salting*. In pickling, the cut meat is submerged in pickle or brine and kept under the surface with weights or other devices so that the salt in the pickle is diffused through the meat. This causes the strength of the pickle to decline so that the meat must occasionally be removed and placed in a vat of restrengthened pickle. The time required is about 1 month.

In dry-salting the cuts of meat are rubbed with salt and piled in layers with the salt sprinkled freely between them. The meat is left for about 10 days, when it is rubbed again and repiled. The time required for the dry-salt method is about the same as for the pickling method.

Hams, shoulders, bacon, and side meats are generally smoked after curing. In smoking, the pieces are hung in a smoking cabinet; heat is produced by a low gas flame, and the smoke is produced by hickory chips placed on a grate well above the gas flame. The meat is held at nearly its cooking temperature for several hours, after which the gas is turned off and the meat allowed to cool. Usually it is allowed to cool overnight before returning it to the curing room for chilling. After chilling, the meat is returned to the cutting and wrapping room for further cutting or slicing and wrapping. It is then frozen and stored in the customer's locker.

The size of the curing room will depend on the amount of pork raised in the district. In pork-raising sections, it may constitute one-third of the plant capacity.

Temperatures in the curing room should be between 35 and 40°F, depending on the plant operator's desires. Humidities should be 85 to 90 per cent, and the air circulation should be low so that a minimum shrinkage of the smoked meats will occur during chilling. Pipe coils or blower-type cooling units with radial diffusion may be used. Blower coils that blow in a single direction tend to produce too much air circulation.

Quick-freezing Room or Cabinet. Small locker plants may use refrigerated plates arranged as shelves and screened from the locker room. This is an ideal arrangement for a small plant, since the refrigerant temperature can be the same as for the locker-room unit. Heat transfer is greater by direct contact than by any other method; therefore, a refrigerant temperature of -10 or $-15°F$ is satisfactory.

For large plants, the air-blast method is more convenient. The wrapped meats are placed on a truck that is wheeled into the quick-freezing room. After freezing, the truck is wheeled into the locker room, and the packages are placed in the customers' lockers.

The temperature maintained in a quick-freezing room should be $-20°F$ or lower. The air velocity around the product should be 500 fpm or higher. Because of the high heat-transfer rate of the finned coil in a blower unit, it is invariably used. It is economical to use face velocities through the coil of 1,000 fpm or higher. The several methods of producing high circulation in the room are using a high-velocity unit, using auxiliary disk fans, and jet action.

With the high-velocity unit, a 3,500-rpm disk fan blows the air through a finned coil, with wide spacing of fins, directly into the room at a high velocity.

Auxiliary fans are a convenient method of producing high circulation. Disk fans are placed on each side of the outlet from the blower-type cooling unit, and they blow in the same direction as the unit.

Jet action is the best method of obtaining high, even circulation if the cooling unit is of sufficient size to require a centrifugal fan. With jet action, an air-distributing duct is placed near the ceiling and extends along the entire end wall of the room. To this duct are attached conical-shaped air nozzles about 3 in. in diameter at the tip, 4.5 in. in diameter at the base, and 8 in. long. For even distribution of air to these nozzles, the air velocity in the header should not exceed 1,200 fpm. The air should leave the tip of the nozzle at about 2,000 to 2,500 fpm. This method will give a high, even circulation throughout the room.

Locker Storage Room. Locker storage rooms are held at a uniform temperature of 0°F. At this temperature all foods retain their desired qualities of taste, texture, appearance, and vitamin content for 6 months or more. Most locker rooms are equipped with sheet-metal lockers, common sizes of which are given in Fig. 10-16. The three bottom lockers are usually of the drawer type, and the top two of the door type. One key to the locker is retained by the management, while the other is

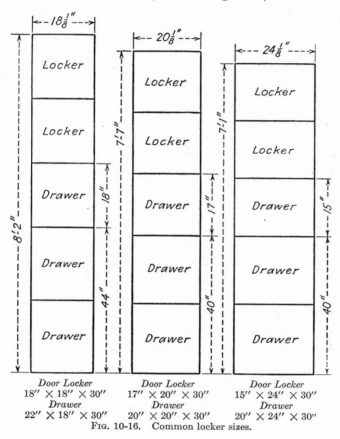

Fig. 10-16. Common locker sizes.

Door Locker	Door Locker	Door Locker
18″ × 18″ × 30″	17″ × 20″ × 30″	15″ × 24″ × 30″
Drawer	*Drawer*	*Drawer*
22″ × 18″ × 30″	20″ × 20″ × 30″	20″ × 24″ × 30″

held by the customer. Usually, the top locker is held as an overflow locker. The four bottom lockers are rented on a yearly basis, while the top is rented on a monthly basis as required by the customer. The lockers are 30 in. deep, and the aisles between them should be about 36 in.

Circulation of air in the room should be low so that the customers will not get too cold; however, distribution of the air must be good in order that a uniform temperature will be maintained throughout the room. Overhead pipe coils or refrigerated plates placed edgeways at the ceiling are satisfactory. A very good method of using a blower-type unit is shown in Fig. 10-17. A subceiling is placed about 1 ft below the regular ceiling. The blower unit discharges the chilled air into the furred space at one end of the room. An open space in the subceiling extends across the other end of the room. The air drifts into the storage space through this slot and returns to the blower unit.

The cooling load consists of the transmission and infiltration gains plus the heat given off by the lights, people, and fan motor. There is no chilling load, since all produce has been previously frozen and brought to

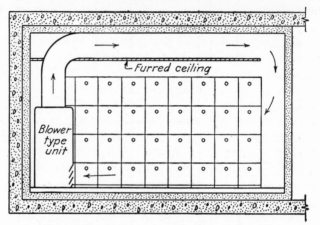

Fig. 10-17.   Locker room with blower-type unit.

an average temperature of 0°F.   Coils are selected on a 10°FTD between room air and refrigerant temperature.

All coils should be equipped with a suitable defrosting device.   Pipe coils may be operated for a long period of time without decreasing the rate of heat transfer, because of the increased outer surface.   They will, however, eventually need defrosting.   Since locker plants have continuous operation, this defrosting must be quick so that the room temperature is not affected.   Hot-gas defrosting is suitable for this purpose.

Since an ice coating reduces the rate of heat transfer of refrigerated plates, the frost should be brushed from them regularly before it hardens. Coils of this type should be further equipped with hot-gas defrosting.

Blower-type coils should be equipped with a water-defrosting header. This is the most simple and satisfactory of all defrosting methods where it can be used.

Condensing Equipment. Small locker plants having refrigerated plates for quick freezing may have only two compressors: one for the aging and curing rooms, and one for the quick-freezing plates and locker room. Either ammonia or Freons 12 and 22 may be used, but the Freons are preferable. They will not damage the produce in case of leakage, and they offer no fire hazard. Freon 12 may be used for the higher temperature system, and either Freon 12 or Freon 22 may be used for the lower temperature system.

Each compressor should be equipped with a spare set of belts and shaft seal. If the plant is sufficiently large to warrant the expense, two compressors connected in parallel should be used for the lower temperature system. In case one compressor needs repairing, the quick freezing may be temporarily discontinued, and the other compressor will maintain the proper temperature in the locker storage room.

If the plant has sufficient size to warrant an air-blast quick-freezing room, a two-stage system should be used. Often large plants are operated in connection with an ice plant, a cold-storage warehouse, or a quick-freezing establishment, in which case the refrigerant is ammonia, or brine is used. The aging, curing, and locker rooms may use brine, while the quick-freezing room uses direct-expansion ammonia. This is a very satisfactory arrangement and precludes danger of damage to produce or of fire in case of leaks.

For plants that operate independently of any other business, the Freons are preferable. Two interconnected compressors should be used for the higher temperature stage. The lower temperature stage should have one compressor for the locker room and one compressor for the quick-freezing room. The two lower temperature compressors should have crossover connections so that the compressor for the quick-freezing room may be used for the locker room. With this arrangement, repairs can be made without affecting the temperatures in the locker, aging, and curing rooms.

ICE MAKING

The greatest demand for ice is in the shipping of produce. It also has extensive use in fish storage, bakeries, creameries, soda fountains, restaurants, and hospitals. Nearly all ice is made from clear water; however, carbon dioxide ice is becoming increasingly popular. In this discussion, the term *ice* will mean water ice, unless otherwise indicated.

Forms of Ice. Ice is commonly sold in 300-lb cakes (or divisions thereof), cracked ice, cubed ice, and flaked ice. All these forms except flaked ice are first manufactured in 300-lb cakes. Flaked ice is produced by a special process in which the flakes are shaved from an evaporating drum. Flaked ice has many uses and is becoming increasingly important.

The Ice-plant Building. Unless the cost of land is high, the building should be one story with the ice-tank-room floor and the engine-room floor set on the ground.   The ice storage room should be adjacent to the ice-tank room, and its floor should be slightly below the top of the lids of the ice cans to provide a slope for the ice slide.   The engine room is also adjacent to the tank room, with no partition between the two rooms. The top of the ice-can lids is usually 4 or 5 ft above the engine-room floor.

The Ice Tank.   The ice tank is usually constructed of 0.25-in. welded steel, although lighter metal may be used if properly backed with wood. Electric welding should be used to avoid distortion of the steel plates. The plate assembly is welded while set in place upon the cork insulation. A 0.12-in. opening is left between the butted sheets.   Beneath the open joint is placed a 2-in.-wide flat strap of steel, and the gap is electrically welded.   Necessary tank partitions for directional flow of brine are lock-nut bolted to the tank bottom and sides.   After fabrication, the tank is painted with two coats of asphalt-emulsion paint.   Tank depths are about 52 in.   In the design of the tank, care must be taken to avoid excessive passage of brine under the cans and near the sides of the tank. The brine level should be about $1\frac{1}{2}$ in. above the top of the ice when the freezing is over.   The insulation under the tank should be at least 5 in. of corkboard.   If the floor rests on unexcavated ground, the ground should be well drained, and about 12 in. of gravel should be supplied as a base for the floor.   Freezing of the ground may cause buckling of the tank. About 12 in. of granulated cork should be used at the sides of the tank.

In the modern freezing tank, all the wood framing is eliminated. Cans are spaced on about 15- by 25-in. centers in grids so that a half row or a full row may be pulled at a time.   These grids are steel holding frames weighing 45 to 50 lb per can to keep them from floating.   Grids should preferably be hot-galvanized after fabrication, since they are located above the brine level.

Wooden ice covers rest directly over the grids.   The covers are usually 2 or 3 in. thick and cover several cans.

Ice Cans.   Ice cans are usually 11 by 22 by 52 in. and hold 320 lb of water.   An extra 20 lb is allowed for melting.   The cake produced is called a 300-lb cake.   The cans have a 1-in. taper to facilitate dumping. Cans are constructed of 14-gauge galvanized iron and are either riveted and soldered or welded.   If welded, they are galvanized after fabrication. Around the top of the can is a galvanized-iron band 0.25 in. by $1\frac{1}{2}$ in. to provide stiffness and means for lifting and attaching the grids.

Brine.   The usual brine is sodium chloride brine with specific gravity 1.14 to 1.17.   Sodium chloride brine costs less than calcium chloride brine and will remain clear with years of operation.   The usual circulation of brine is about 30 fpm.   Brine movement is caused by the hydraulic gradient, best designed for about 1.25 to 1.5 in. in the tank length.   It is important to maintain brine movement, ensuring a temperature as uniform as possible. A variation of not more than 1°F is allowable.

Time of Freezing. The time of freezing is proportional to the square of the thickness of the ice cake and inversely proportional to the temperature difference between the freezing water and the brine. The time of freezing is reduced as the brine velocity increases, but the relationship has

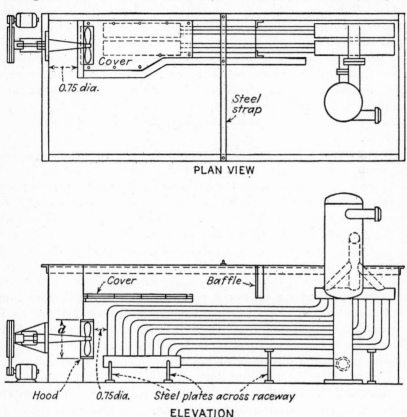

PLAN VIEW

ELEVATION

Fig. 10-18.   Raceway coil with horizontal agitator.

not been accurately determined. Empirical formulas have been devised for the time of freezing, but they do not usually take into consideration the effect of brine velocity, and hence do not give consistent results. Usually, at brine temperatures between 12 and 15°F, with brine velocity by the cans of about 30 fpm, the time for freezing the standard 300-lb cake is 36 to 42 hr.

Brine Coolers and Agitators. The brine cooler is either a bare-pipe flooded coil extending along a raceway, or is an open single-pass shell-and-

tube brine cooler submerged in the brine.   In either case, brine is forced
through with an agitator.   An agitator is a propeller-type pump designed
to move large quantities of brine at a low head.

Figure 10-18 shows a bare coil in a raceway with its agitator.   The
evaporator tubes are nested in the raceway so that about one-third of the
entire cross-sectional area is occupied by the tubes.   Brine velocities of
100 to 150 fpm are used.   With a well-designed coil, the heat transmittance U is about 85 Btu/(sq ft)(°FTD)(hr) at 100 fpm velocity, and is
about 120 Btu/(sq.ft.)(°FTD)(hr) at 150 fpm velocity.

Open single-pass shell-and-tube brine coolers are equipped with an
agitator and a pressure hood between the agitator and the brine cooler to
direct the flow of brine.   Somewhat higher velocities and lower brine
quantities are used than with the raceway coil.   The method of computing the heat-transfer rate with a shell-and-tube brine cooler was given in
Chap. 5.

Water and Liquid-ammonia Forecooling.   The equipment size and
the required horsepower may be appreciably reduced by forecooling the
water used for ice making, and cooling the liquid ammonia to an intermediate temperature before it is piped to the brine cooler.   Usually, the
water is cooled to about 40°F, and the liquid ammonia is cooled to about
30°F.   The cooling of the liquid ammonia may be done in the accumulator of the water cooler.   A separate compressor will maintain 30°F
suction temperature in this accumulator.   The savings may be illustrated
as follows: At 90°F condensing temperature and 30°F evaporating
temperature, about 0.8 hp/ton is required, while at 90°F condensing
temperature and 5°F evaporating temperature about 1.3 hp/ton is
required.   Assuming 70°F water for ice making, about 28 per cent of the
entire load can be taken care of at the higher suction temperature.   The
capacity per unit of displacement is approximately 1.9 times greater at
the higher suction temperature than at the lower suction temperature.

Air Agitation.   In order to produce clear ice, it is necessary to agitate
the water in the cans during the freezing process.   Agitation of the water
in the cans by bubbling air through it brings the dissolved salts to the
unfrozen core.   It is usual to pump the core and replace it with chilled
clear water.   Two types of air agitation are in common use—high-pressure and low-pressure.

High-pressure air systems compress the air to about 25 psi, at which
pressure a large portion of its moisture is removed.   Unit volume of air
will hold the same quantity of moisture at any pressure.   The air after
compression may be cooled to various temperatures by water, brine, or
refrigerant.   The two latter cooling mediums are preferable, since more
moisture will be removed and the air will enter the cans at a lower temper-

ature. The air should be cooled to as low a temperature as is practical without forming ice on the cooling coils. The condensate is removed from the heat exchanger by a float-type steam trap. The dehydrated compressed air is expanded to about 15 psi gauge pressure, which reduces the relative humidity. The treated air is conducted by headers down the tank sides or center. Air laterals attached to each grid are readily connected to the main headers by a rubber tube and a brass, tapered friction fitting with a check valve. Air enters the can through a tube extending down its center. The grid lateral and the drop tubes are lifted out at the time of pumping out the cores and not replaced when the core is filled. High-pressure systems supply a minimum of $\frac{1}{7}$ cfm of air per can, measured at atmospheric pressure.

Low-pressure air systems compress the air to 2 or 3 psi gauge pressure, filter it with surface filters, and deliver it to the cans. The air may be cooled, providing that all pipes are installed so that moisture cannot collect in low spots. One-half a cubic foot of air per minute per can is supplied.

A reciprocating air compressor is used for the high-pressure system, and a rotary air compressor is used for the low-pressure system. Less power is used for air compression with the low-pressure system, but because of the greater volume of air that must be chilled, more power is required by the refrigerating compressors.

Core pumps are usually of the rotary type handling about 15 gpm. Core water is drawn through a flattened tube connected by a 1-in.-i.d. heavy hose. Core water is replaced through another similar hose and tube.

Ice-handling Equipment. Cranes are usually powered by three electric motors and have longitudinal transverse and lifting motions. For full-row lifting, the transverse motion may be dispensed with, and only two motors are required. Cranes are selected for the ice load plus the weight of the cans and grids. Groups of cans are carried by the crane to the dip tank, where they are submerged in water whose temperature is approximately 70°F. After the ice thaws free from the cans, they are raised and carried to the dump. Several types of can dumps are employed. In one, the can group is rested off balance on a tilting table, and the crane is used to tilt the table and right it again. When the crane is used for this purpose, it is equipped with a two-speed motor and is operated at high speed for lowering the cans. The pitch of the run is 1 to 3 in./ft to start, and tapers off to $\frac{1}{2}$ in./ft. The run leads directly into the ice storage room. After the cans have been dumped, they are refilled with can fillers that measure the required amount of water accurately.

Ice Storage Room.   The size of ice storage rooms should be governed by the type of demand for ice.   If there is a nearly steady demand throughout the summer season, a room that will hold the entire output of the plant for 3 days is sufficient.   If the ice is used for refrigerated railway cars in districts where, owing to the type of crop handled, there is an extreme demand for short periods of time, the storage room may take the entire output of the plant for a month.   Where only 3-day storage is required, the ice cakes are placed on end only one tier high.   Where seasonal storage is required, the ice may be stacked 20 ft high or more with a portable tiering machine.   A temperature of about 26°F is maintained by pipe coils at the ceiling.   Low circulation of air is required to keep sublimation at a minimum.

Condensing Equipment.   Ammonia compressors of either the single-acting vertical type or the double-acting horizontal type are satisfactory; however, the single-acting vertical type is increasingly used.   At least two main compressors are used, and it is desirable to use another compressor for forecooling the water and the liquid ammonia.   The third compressor increases the efficiency of the plant and adds considerably to the flexibility of its capacity.   Compressors of less than 75 hp are usually driven by three-phase induction motors.   If 75 hp or more is required, it is usually advisable to use a synchronous motor because of the lower electric rate available.   Horizontal double-acting compressors are direct connected to a slow-speed synchronous motor, while single-acting vertical compressors may be direct connected to or belt-driven by a high-speed synchronous motor.   The high-speed synchronous motor has the more desirable operating characteristics.   In some cases, two compressors are direct connected to a single synchronous motor through magnetic or hydraulic clutches.   All compressors using synchronous motors must be unloaded for starting unless clutches are used.

The diesel engine is a very satisfactory source of power and is sometimes used.   Ice plants in outlying districts that supply ice to the railroad are often powered in this manner.   Diesel engines may be operated at full speed or at speeds down to 75 per cent of full speed.   With two compressors separately driven, almost any desired capacity may be obtained.

Horizontal or vertical shell-and-tube condensers may be used.   If horizontal condensers are used, there should be sufficient numbers connected in parallel so that one at a time can be cleaned without interfering with the operation of the plant.   Vertical shell-and-tube condensers can be cleaned while in operation.

Most plants use an atmospheric cooling tower; however, forced-draft towers should be used if air flow is at all restricted by adjoining buildings.   The cost of the two types is about the same, but the forced-draft type has more dependable performance.

Flakice and Pakice. Flakice and Pakice are trade names for similar products. Flakice is formed on the outside of a rotating drum partially immersed in water. The sheets are peeled off with a curved scraper whose curvature is less than that of the cylinder. As the product is formed, it is dropped into a storage container. Because of the curvature of the pieces, it does not tend to congeal. In handling, the ice flows readily and may be passed through inclined ducts.

Pakice is formed on the inside of a stationary cylinder and is scraped off with Stellite faced scraper blades. The water is sprayed on the inside of the cylinder in small droplets. The ice is soft in texture, making possible close packing around bottles and produce.

Flakice and Pakice have the same applications. They are used in fish icing, icing vegetables for transport, milk-bottle icing, in bakeries for dough mixing to keep from overheating, etc.

Dry Ice. Solid carbon dioxide has its greatest application in the transportation of ice cream and other frozen comestibles. Its physical properties are as follows:

TABLE 10-2. PROPERTIES OF CARBON DIOXIDE*

Density of solid CO_2	95 lb/cu ft
Temperature when surrounded by its own gas at 14.7 psi	$-109.3°F$
Temperature when surrounded by air at 14.7 psi	$-220°F$
Critical temperature	$87.8°F$
Critical pressure	1,069.4 psi
Triple point	$-69.9°F$
Triple point	75.0 psi
Heat of sublimation at $-109.3°F$	246.3 Btu/lb
Specific heat of the vapor at constant pressure	0.2025

* QUINN, ELTON L., and CHARLES L. JONES, "Carbon Dioxide," ACS Monograph Series No. 72, Reinhold Publishing Corporation, New York, 1936.

From the foregoing table it will be seen that the temperature of dry ice in its own atmosphere or in the open air is far below any desirable temperature. The dry ice must therefore be kept from contact with the product. Insulated compartments or bags in the container must be used. The cold CO_2 gas formed by sublimation diffuses throughout the container, keeping the contents uniformly cooled. Temperatures are maintained by the amount of dry ice put in the product container and the thickness of the insulation of the container that separates it from the product. Satisfactory methods of closely controlling the temperature have not been developed.

Carbon dioxide is available from many sources, such as by-products from the chemical industry, fermentation, CO_2 gas wells, calcium and magnesium carbonates treated with acid, etc. Carbon dioxide forms an appreciable proportion of the natural gas from many oil wells. The CO_2

lowers the heat content of the gas and sometimes makes it necessary to add butane to bring it up to a standard heat content. The removal of the CO_2 raises the heat content and makes available large quantities of CO_2. Separation of the CO_2 from the natural gas is therefore being contemplated.

The means of separating CO_2 from other constituents is beyond the scope of this book. The methods of solidifying it will be discussed briefly. The gas is first liquefied. This may be done by multiple-stage compression of CO_2 with water intercooling between stages and condensation with water after compression, at pressures from 900 to 1,000 psi, or the gas may be condensed at relatively low pressures, using two-stage ammonia refrigeration to condense the CO_2. The first method can be used only where cooling-water temperatures are rather low, since the critical temperature is 87.8°F, and carbon dioxide compressors work inefficiently as the condensing temperature approaches the critical temperature. After the CO_2 is liquefied, it is expanded in a cold well-insulated chamber at a pressure only slightly above atmospheric pressure. A portion of liquid CO_2 is solidified in the form of snow, and the remainder is vaporized and carried back to the CO_2 compressor for recondensation. The CO_2 snow is compressed into cakes by hydraulic means.

Because of the low temperatures involved in the production of dry ice, it is much more costly to produce per unit of cooling effect than water ice. Its application is therefore limited to the production of temperatures below 32°F.

TABLE 10-3. TEMPERATURES FOR HOLDING, MANUFACTURING, AND STORING DAIRY PRODUCTS*

Name of product	*Temperature recommended, °F*
Fluid milk and skim milk:	
Not pasteurized:	
To be held under 12 hr after milking	50 or below
To be held under 24 hr after milking	40
To be held under 48 hr after milking	34
Pasteurized:	
To be held 24 hr or less	40
To be held up to 6 days	34
Fluid milk heated to pasteurizing temperatures and held without cooling up to 6 hr	142–145
Cream, not pasteurized, to be held 24 hr or less	40
Fluid milk and cream pasteurizing temperatures	140–145
Cream, pasteurized:	
To be held up to 10 days	34
To be frozen and held up to 3 months	25
Whey, not pasteurized, to be held 6 hr or less	50

TABLE 10-3. TEMPERATURES FOR HOLDING, MANUFACTURING, AND STORING DAIRY
PRODUCTS*.—(*Continued*)

Cultured buttermilk:	
Pasteurizing temperature before inoculating..............	170–190
Lactic type:	
Inoculating temperature...........................	68
Incubating temperature............................	68
Bulgaricus type:	
Inoculating temperature...........................	98
Incubating temperature............................	98
Either type, holding temperature......................	45–50
Buttermilk cultures, either lactic or *bulgaricus* type, in water,	
holding temperature...................................	35
Ice-cream mix, to be held for 24 to 96 hr..................	32–40
Ice cream, hardening and holding temperatures.............	0–5
Evaporated milk:	
Hot-well temperatures.................................	160–212
Temperature in vacuum pan...........................	125–140
Before processing:	
When canned immediately after condensing...........	60
When canned 24 hr after condensing.................	42
When canned 48 hr after condensing.................	40
After processing:	
When held before packing to develop leakers...........	68
If consumed within 2 months after manufacture........	Ordinary temperature
When held in storage for 1 year or less................	35–40
Sweetened condensed milk:	
Hot-well temperatures.................................	160–212
Pan temperatures.....................................	125–140
Temperature at which to barrel or can....................	About 74
When held for early consumption......................	Ordinary temperature
When held in storage for 1 year or less..................	35–40
Bulk unsweetened condensed milk, for consumption inside of	
1 week...	40
Butter churning temperatures:†	
Summer..	48–53
Winter, average about 56°F...........................	52–60
Butter in cold storage...................................	−10
Cheese:	
Best temperature for action of rennet in making Cheddar	
cheese..	86–88
High curing temperature, Cheddar cheese................	60–68
Low curing temperature, Cheddar cheese................	45–50
In storage...	35
Temperature at which milk powder can be heated during	
manufacture, without impairing flavor..................	140
Milk powder in storage...................................	35–40

* MOJONNIER, TIMOTHY, and CHARLES HUGH TROY, "The Technical Control of Dairy Products,"
pp. 877–878, Caspar Book Emporium, Milwaukee, 1925.

† Where cottonseed meal is fed and under certain feed and breed conditions, higher churning temperatures may be used.

DAIRY REFRIGERATION

Refrigeration is required at nearly every step of handling or processing dairy products, from the time the milk is taken from the cow until the products are delivered to the customer.   A glance at Table 10-3 will show the extent to which refrigeration is used.

Specific Heat of Dairy Products.   To compute the quantity of heat involved in changing the temperature of dairy products, their specific

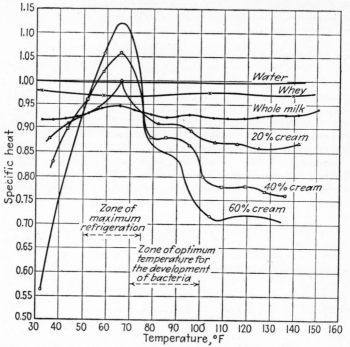

Fig. 10-19.   Specific heats of some dairy products.

heats and specific gravities must be known.   For dairy products containing butterfat, the specific heat changes rapidly with the temperature. All frozen products have a much lower specific heat after freezing than before freezing.   Figure 10-19 gives the specific heats of some dairy products.[1]

The specific heats of other dairy products are approximately as follows:

[1] Bowen, John T., Refrigeration in the Handling, Processing, and Storing of Milk and Milk Products, *U. S. Dept. Agr. Misc. Pub. 138,* p. 26, March, 1932.

Butter...	0.56
Cheese...	0.64
Condensed milk...	0.94
Whey..	0.97
Skim milk...	0.95
Ice-cream mix:	
Above freezing..	0.9
Below freezing..	0.46

The specific heat of ice cream below freezing is its specific heat after it has been hardened. Ice cream leaves the freezer in a half-frozen condition; therefore, its specific heat at this time will be 0.68.

Specific Gravity. The usual range of specific gravity of milk is from 1.029 to 1.035. In the case of a mixed herd, 1.032 may be taken as an average. This corresponds to 8.59 lb/gal. Table 10-4 gives the specific gravity of milk and cream at 68°F. The values were determined by adding fat to skim milk.[1] The density of ice-cream mix before freezing is

TABLE 10-4. SPECIFIC GRAVITY OF MILK AND CREAM CONTAINING VARIOUS PERCENTAGES OF BUTTERFAT AT 68°F

Percentage of fat	Specific gravity	Percentage of fat	Specific gravity
0.025	1.037	21	1.012
1	1.036	22	1.011
2	1.035	23	1.010
3	1.034	24	1.009
4	1.032	25	1.008
5	1.031	26	1.008
6	1.030	27	1.007
7	1.029	28	1.006
8	1.027	29	1.005
9	1.026	30	1.004
10	1.025	31	1.003
11	1.024	32	1.002
12	1.022	33	1.001
13	1.020	34	1.000
14	1.019	35	0.999
15	1.018	36	0.999
16	1.017	37	0.998
17	1.016	38	0.997
18	1.015	39	0.996
19	1.014	40	0.995
20	1.013		

[1] *Ibid.*, p. 27.

about 9.0 lb/gal.   Its density after freezing with 100 per cent overrun is 4.5 lb/gal.   The latent heat of fusion of ice cream is about 90 Btu/lb.

Milk Cooling on the Farm.   Raw milk should be cooled immediately after being drawn from the cow to 50°F or less and so maintained until delivered to the customer.[1]   The surface type of cooler is generally used. It is a cooler about 16 tubes high in which water is used as a cooling medium in the top eight tubes, and boiling refrigerant is used as the cooling medium in the bottom eight tubes.   Counterflow of milk and the cooling medium is used in both bottom and top sections.   The outside surface of the cooler is corrugated to allow space for the tubes and is without seams or sharp corners in which dirt can collect.   The milk is entered over the cooler through a distributing trough at the top and is collected at the bottom by another trough.   Troughs may be stainless steel or tinned copper.   If ammonia is used as the refrigerant, the coil is steel, but the outside corrugated surface is tinned copper.   If methyl chloride or Freon 12 is used as the refrigerant, the entire coil is copper except for the tinned surface.   The film conductance of the milk on the outside is about 220 Btu/(sq ft)(°FTD)(hr).   The over-all transmittance for the various refrigerants is about as follows:

Refrigerant	Btu/(sq ft)(°FTD)(hr)
Ammonia	190
Methyl chloride	155
Freon 12	130

On the farm, methyl chloride or Freon 12 is generally used as the refrigerant because of the less expensive equipment required.

Sanitary conditions must be maintained during milking and milk cooling.   The following precautions should be taken:[2]   The milk cooling room should be adjacent to the milk room.   The milk from the cows should be received in a receiving tank on the outside wall of the milk room.   The wall behind the milk tank should be smooth cement plaster. The pouring platform should be constructed of masonry, concrete, or steel so installed to avoid all corners and pockets difficult to clean.   A rustless pipe with appropriate flanges should be placed in the wall to carry the milk conductor pipe.   The hole in the wall should be equipped with an outside swinging shutter to exclude the flies.   Compressor, boiler, milking-machine motor, etc., should not be located in the milk room. The cooler must be thoroughly cleaned after each time it is used with steam, hot water above 170°F, or a chlorine solution.

[1] Extracts from the Agricultural Code of California and Dairy Regulations, p. 12, 1944.

[2] *Ibid.*, pp. 95–98.

The cooling of milk on the farm is generally done in two periods, night and morning. The milk is immediately cooled from body temperature to around 45°F. Shortly after the milking is finished, the cooling is completed. The time available for cooling is about 1 to 1½ hr for each milking; consequently ample refrigeration must be available to do the work in this time. The milk from the cooler is caught in cans for storage or immediate transportation to market. The night's milk, after being run over the cooler, is stored overnight either in a tank of chilled water or in a storage room where the temperature is further reduced.

Market Milk Plants. Market milk is milk that is sold for household purposes. Nearly half the milk produced is used in this manner. Market milk plants are located in cities and receive their supply of milk by trucks or trains from the farmers or from receiving stations. If the milk is not received at the city plant at a satisfactory temperature, it is rejected. Usually, the milk is delivered to the plant before noon. It is then pasteurized, cooled, bottled, stored overnight, and delivered to the customers early next morning. Processing the milk begins as soon as it is received. The first step is to pasteurize the milk.

Two methods of pasteurization are commonly used—the holding method and the flash method. For the holding method, the milk is heated to about 143°F for 30 min. For the flash method, the milk is heated to 160°F for at least 15 sec. In the cooling of milk from the pasteurizing to the bottling temperature, usually a regenerator or heat exchanger is employed to transfer heat from the hot milk to the cold milk entering the pasteurizer. Usually, the temperature of the milk is reduced to about 90°F at the outlet of the regenerator. The milk is then cooled in the water section of the surface milk cooler to within 5°F of the entering water temperature, and to about 40°F in the refrigerated section. It is then bottled and stored in a refrigerated room overnight at about 35°F. For delivery, Pakice or Flakice is put around the bottles so that its temperature is low when it is delivered to the customer.

Creameries. A creamery is a plant having for its primary object the manufacture of butter. When whole milk is received at the creamery, it is heated to a temperature between 90 and 100°F and run through a cream separator to separate the cream from the skim milk. The cream is then pasteurized like milk, cooled immediately to about 40°F and held for 3 hr or overnight before it is churned. After the holding period it is churned at a temperature of 45 to 55°F. The temperature of the butter when removed from the churn is usually between 50 and 60°F.

The lower the temperature at which butter is stored, the better it will keep. For short storage, such as a week or 10 days, the butter may be stored at 35°F, but when stored for several months the temperature should be 0°F or lower. The relative humidity should be maintained at about 80 per cent. Such a humidity will prevent the growth of molds and will also prevent excessive drying of the butter.

Cheese Plants. In the manufacture of cheese, the temperature and humidity must be under close control for satisfactory results. At different stages of manufacture it is necessary to change both temperature and humidity for proper growth of bacteria and mold.

In the curing of Roquefort cheese made from cow's milk, effort is made to maintain the conditions stated in Table 10-5. The cheese should be held at 46 to 48°F until consumed.

TABLE 10-5. CONDITIONS FAVORABLE TO CURING ROQUEFORT CHEESE MADE FROM COW'S MILK*

Period	Temperature, °F	Relative humidity, per cent	Ventilation
First week..........................	65–68	85–90	Slight
Second week.......................	48–50	80–90	Considerable
Third and fourth weeks..............	48–50	80–90	Considerable
Second and third months............	46–48	90–95	Moderate
Fourth and fifth months.............	46–48	80–90	Considerable

* BOWEN, JOHN T., Refrigeration in the Handling, Processing, and Storing of Milk and Milk Products, *U. S. Dept. Agr. Misc. Pub.* 138, March, 1932.

In the manufacture of Camembert cheese, it has been found desirable to maintain conditions as listed in Table 10-6. After the cheese is fully cured, a temperature of 50 to 52°F is advisable until the cheese is consumed. A "considerable" relative humidity probably would be 88 to 92 per cent, a "moderate" humidity 85 to 88 per cent, and a low humidity 80 to 85 per cent.

TABLE 10-6. CONDITIONS FAVORABLE FOR MAKING CAMEMBERT CHEESE FROM UNCUT CURD

Period	Temperature, °F	Relative humidity	Ventilation	Mold development
First period, 4 days	50	Considerable	Very little	Starting of penicillium in acid medium
Second period, 10 to 12 days	55–58	Moderate	Moderate	Development of penicillium in acid medium
Third period, 2 to 4 days	55	Low	Very active	Termination of the penicillium; the acid has disappeared, the medium is alkaline, and the cheese becomes firm

Desirable conditions in the manufacture of Swiss cheese are stated in Table 10-7.

TABLE 10-7. CONDITIONS FAVORABLE FOR MAKING SWISS CHEESE*

Period	Temperature, °F	Relative humidity, per cent	Ventilation
2 weeks in salt room....................	52–59	85–90	Moderate
6 to 8 weeks in warm room..............	65–72	85–90	Moderate
Cold storage...........................	50–55	80–85	Moderate

* BOWEN, JOHN T., Refrigeration in the Handling, Processing, and Storing of Milk Products, *U. S. Dept. Agr. Misc. Pub.* 138, March, 1932.

American or Cheddar cheese is cured from 4 to 10 days at a temperature of 55 to 60°F with plenty of ventilation. This allows the bacteria to develop properly. For long storage (4 to 12 months), it should be placed in a cold room at a temperature from 32° to 35°F. For short storage, 40° to 45°F is satisfactory. When it is to be placed upon the market as soon as possible, it should be held at 50° to 60°F until it reaches a marketable condition.

Condenseries. A condensary is a plant for concentrating milk by evaporating a part of the contained water. The evaporation usually takes place under vacuum. Refrigeration is used to cool the product after it leaves the vacuum pan for storing. It is also used for holding the raw milk at a temperature of 35 to 45°F until it is to be processed.

Sweetened condensed milk contains sufficient cane sugar to preserve it. The proper cooling of sweetened condensed milk is very important, for upon it depends, to a great extent, the smoothness of texture of the product.[1] The rate of cooling from vacuum-pan temperature down to that of forced crystallization should be as rapid as practicable. The milk comes from the vacuum pan at from 125 to 140°F and, at this temperature, is a saturated solution of sugar. As the temperature is lowered, the solution becomes supersaturated, and the milk sugar begins to crystallize out. Should the cooling be slow, the crystals will be large, and the texture of the milk will be coarse. This is known as *sandy* or *gritty*. With rapid cooling and agitation, the crystals are very small, giving the desired smooth velvety texture. Crystallization is slow at first, but reaches a maximum rate at about 86°F. From this point down to 75°F is the critical range through which the forced circulation is accomplished. The time required to lower the temperature through the range (86 to 75°F) is from 15 to 30 min. Cooling should be continued to about

[1] BOWEN, *op. cit.*

65°F, at which temperature it should be canned.   If it is to be stored for a considerable period, it should be kept at a temperature of 35 to 40°F.

Plain condensed milk is simply the raw product concentrated by evaporation without the addition of sugar.   When the proper concentration has been obtained, the milk is drawn from the vacuum pan and cooled at once to about 60°F if it is to be canned immediately.   If it is to be sold in bulk, it should be cooled to at least 40°F and maintained at this temperature until used.   It should never be allowed to freeze, as freezing would cause the separation of the constituent parts.   Plain condensed milk is used largely by ice-cream and candy makers and by bakers. Since the demand is not always steady, it is often necessary to hold it under refrigeration for a considerable time.

Evaporated milk is the term generally applied to sterilized, unsweetened, condensed milk.   Since all bacterial and yeast spores are supposed to be destroyed by the application of heat in the sterilizing process, refrigeration would seem unnecessary.   This result is not always achieved, so it is common practice, for long storage, to store the milk at a temperature between 35 and 45°F.

Milk-powder Plants.   Milk powder is the product resulting from evaporation of practically all the water contained in the milk.   Refrigeration is limited to storing the fresh milk in case it is not to be used immediately, and to storing the finished product.   The fresh milk is held at a temperature of about 45°F until it is used.

The milk powder should be stored in a refrigerated space.   Between 68 and 86°F, oxidation of the fat in the powder is comparatively rapid. As the temperature is lowered, oxidation is reduced.   Milk powder is stored at 35 to 45°F.   Owing to the hygroscopic nature of the powder, the relative humidity should be as low as possible.   In order to maintain low relative humidity, room air may be circulated over a small bed of calcium chloride flakes having adequate drainage.

Ice-cream Plants.   In the manufacture of ice cream, refrigeration is employed in cooling the mix after pasteurization, in holding the mix, and in freezing and hardening it.   It is also used in storage of materials, in distributing the ice cream to retailers, and in holding low temperatures in the retail cabinets.   Refrigeration is required at every step of the manufacture and distribution of ice cream, from the preparation of the mix to its consumption, and at no time may the temperature of the product rise materially without damage to the product.

The mix is first pasteurized to safeguard health, to check fermentation, and to destroy most of the bacteria.   From the pasteurizer the mix is put through a homogenizer or viscolizer to break up the fat globules and give a greater dispersion of butterfat, which results in an increased viscosity and smoother texture of the ice cream.

When the mix is delivered into the aging vats, it is immediately cooled and held between 35 and 40°F for 24 to 36 hr. The aging is done in a special type of vat that keeps the mix stirred and prevents the settling out of the heavier ingredients. The aging increases the viscosity and gives a smoother texture to the mix and assists in obtaining and maintaining the proper overrun.

The overrun is the percentage increase in volume of the ice cream during the freezing process. It is due in part to the expansion of the ingredients, but largely to the inclusion of air by the beating or whipping action of the freezer dashers. The desired overrun for vanilla and fruit ice creams is approximately 100 per cent. A proper amount is very important. Insufficient overrun will cause the ice cream to be heavy and soggy. Too much will cause it to be fluffy and more or less grainy and brittle.

Most ice-cream freezers are of the batch type. For very large outputs, the continuous freezer is used. The modern batch freezer consists of a refrigerated drum of 40- to 100-qt capacity, mounted on a base, with a motor drive that turns a dasher, scrapers for removing the ice cream from the refrigerated surface, and a beater for whipping air into the ice cream. It is also fitted with a fruit hopper for adding fruits and flavors. The ice cream is frozen to a 50 per cent frozen condition; then the refrigeration is turned off, and air is whipped into the ice cream until the desired overrun is obtained. The mix is drawn from the freezer at about 21 or 22°F. The suction temperature is usually about −5°F. The time of freezing is about 5 to 7 min. Ammonia is used as the refrigerant, since it has a much higher boiling-film conductance than any other refrigerant.

The power required by a batch freezer increases rapidly as the freezing progresses, so that the power required at the end of the process is about ten times that required at the beginning. This increase in power offers a convenient means of judging the state of freezing. By installing a suitable wattmeter in the motor circuit, the time for drawing the frozen cream can be accurately determined by noting the power consumption.

The continuous freezer works on the same principle as the batch freezer except that the machine freezes the ice cream under pressure. It is equipped with a dasher motor, which drives the dashers and the air compressor, and a pump motor, which drives the mix pump and the ice-cream pump. The principle of operation is as follows: If the ratio of the volume pumped by the ice-cream pump to the volume pumped by the mix pump were fixed, the percentage overrun would automatically be fixed. The percentage overrun is controlled by changing the capacity ratios of these two pumps. This can most easily be accomplished by changing the pressure on the freezing cylinder and hence changing the pressure at the inlet to the ice-cream pump. Air is supplied by a sanitary-type diaphragm compressor that operates at a maximum gauge pressure of about 40 psi. The pressure is reduced to the proper pressure to give the desired overrun.

Continuous freezers, when used for fruit-flavored ice creams, must be equipped with a fruit feeder for injecting fruit continuously into the finished ice cream. Two types are in common use. One forces fruit into the pressure line carrying the stiff ice cream and mixes it to form the finished product. The other meters the fruit and drops it by gravity on a rotating star wheel, which, in turn, carries it around to meet a ribbon of ice cream, picking up the ice cream in the same pockets of the star wheel. The two materials are then carried to the bottom of the feeder case, mixed, and forced out by the pump action of the lower scraper and star wheel through the usual delivery tubes and nozzles.

After the ice cream is about 50 per cent frozen, it is drawn into containers and taken to the hardening room. Its temperature in this condition is about 22°F. The temperature in the hardening room is generally from −10 to −20°F, although lower temperatures are used when the air circulation is low. The time of hardening may be cut in half by using high air circulation in the room. A modern ice-cream-hardening room resembles an air-blast quick-freezing room for fruits or vegetables, and the process is similar in all respects to the quick-freezing process. The air velocity throughout the room should be uniformly above 500 fpm. With the air-blast method of hardening, a 10-qt container may be hardened in a minimum of about 5 hr although double this time should be used unless the plant is extremely rushed.

Ice-cream products are transported in refrigerated trucks or in insulated trucks with the ice-cream packages cooled by dry ice. Small insulated containers are used to hold the dry ice so that it will sublimate more slowly. The cold CO_2 vapor diffuses around the ice-cream containers, keeping them at a uniform temperature. Upon arriving at retail stores, they are put in retail cabinets where they are held at 8 to to 10°F until sold.

APPENDIX 1

COMMERCIAL STORAGE OF FRUITS AND VEGETABLES[1]

Apples. (Temperature, 30° to 32°F; relative humidity, 85 to 88 per cent.) There is a wide variation in the storage quality of the different varieties of apples, and of the same variety grown in different regions. For example, McIntosh grown in the Middle Atlantic States is practically an early fall apple not suitable for more than 2 or 3 weeks' storage, whereas if grown in northern New York or New England it can be held for as long as 4 or 5 months. Such varieties as Northern Spy, Baldwin, and Rhode Island Greening grown in the Cumberland-Shenandoah Valley district or in the hot, irrigated valleys of the Pacific Northwest behave like fall varieties and are short-lived in storage, although suitable for winter storage when grown in New England, New York, Michigan, and other northern producing districts.

The keeping quality of apples in storage is also definitely related to the cultural and orchard sanitation practices of the grower, who alone is responsible for the production of sound, properly matured fruit. To have good keeping quality, apples should be mature and well colored. When they have reached this stage, they are less likely to scald in storage and are in better condition generally to be held in storage for the maximum period than if they are either immature or overmature.*

To insure soundness and good keeping quality, apples must be not only properly grown and at the proper stage of maturity, they should also be handled in all the operations of picking, grading, packing, and hauling with that degree of care necessary to prevent serious bruising, skin punctures, or other mechanical injuries; and they should be stored as quickly as possible after they are picked.

Apples should not be handled while frozen, if such handling can possibly be avoided. Water core does not develop or spread in storage, and in varieties such as Yellow Newton and Winesap it may actually disappear after a few months' storage, especially if originally present only in a mild form. When large portions of the flesh are affected, especially in soft-textured varieties like Jonathan, Delicious, Stayman Winesap, and Rome Beauty, there is danger of subsequent break-down, and prompt disposal of the fruit is advisable. The diseases of apples in storage are discussed in Farmers' Bulletin 1160* and Miscellaneous Publication 168.*

For the storage of most varieties of apples the best results are obtained by maintaining a temperature of 30° to 32°F and a relative humidity of 85 to 88 per cent. However, as the storage temperature approaches the freezing point of the fruit the hazard of freezing increases unless the temperature is well controlled and there is good air circulation. Yellow Newton apples from the Pajaro Valley, Calif., and McIntosh and Rhode Island Greening apples from New York should be held at 35° to 38°F rather than at 32° to prevent the development of internal browning or brown core. Grimes Golden apples should be held at 34° to 36° instead of at lower temperatures* in order to avoid soggy break-down. It should be remembered, however, that at these

[1] ROSE, DEAN H., R. C. WRIGHT, and T. M. WHITEMAN, The Commercial Storage of Fruits, Vegetables and Florists' Stocks, *U. S. Dept. Agr. Circ.* 278, November, 1941. (Where * appears in Appendix 1, this bulletin may be referred to for literature cited.)

higher temperatures the fruit cannot be held as long as when stored at 30° to 32°, because of the possible development of Jonathan spot and internal break-down.

If air-cooled storage is used, the temperature obtainable will usually not be much lower than the average of the prevailing outside temperatures. The nearer this is to 32° the better.*

The length of time apples can be held successfully in cold storage will vary with the variety and with the district where grown, as well as with their condition when harvested. Table 4 shows the normal or average storage period and the maximum storage period for the more important apple varieties when picked at proper maturity and stored immediately at 30° to 32°F.

Table 4. Normal and maximum storage period for important apple varieties

Variety	Storage period	
	Normal months	Maximum months
Jonathan	2–3	4
Grimes Golden	2–3	4
McIntosh	2–3	4–5
Golden Delicious	3–4	5
Cortland	3–4	5
Delicious	3–4	6
Rhode Island Greening	3–4	6
Yellow Newton	5–7	8
Baldwin	3–5	6–7
Stayman Winesap	4–5	5–6
York Imperial	4–5	5–6
Arkansas (Black Twig)	4–5	6
Northern Spy	4–5	6
Rome Beauty	4–5	6–7
Ben Davis	4–5	8
Winesap	5–7	8

In determining when to remove apples from storage the dealer must, of course, consider the market, but he must also allow for the more rapid softening that takes place at the higher temperatures to which they will usually be removed. Investigations by the United States Department of Agriculture* have shown that apples soften approximately twice as fast at 70° as at 50°F, twice as fast at 50° as at 40°, and about twice as fast at 40° as at 32°, whereas at 30° the rate is about three-fourths that at 32°.

Apples in cold storage should be inspected frequently, in order that they may be removed and sold while still in good condition. It is highly desirable that apples intended for storage be wrapped in oiled paper or packed in shredded oiled paper, in order to reduce damage by scald as much as possible.* Apples should not be stored in the same room with potatoes because of the danger that the former will absorb undesirable odors. On the other hand, the odors given off by apples are readily absorbed by dairy products; consequently the two should not be stored in the same room.*

Avocados. (Temperature, see text; relative humidity, 85 to 90 per cent.) Investigations in California* on the storage of avocados have shown that the best temperature for all varieties grown there, except the Fuerte, is about 40°F. The Fuerte discolors internally at this temperature but holds up well at 45°. At temperatures below 40° all the varieties investigated are likely to become discolored internally and do not soften when removed to a higher temperature. When properly stored, the Dickinson, Royal, Taft and Queen are said to hold up well for about 2 months, the Spinks, Sharpless, and Challenge for 5 to 6 weeks, and the Rey, Fuerte, and Kist for about 4 weeks. Most of these varieties are of the Guatemalan race.

No general recommedations can be made concerning the storage of varieties of avocados grown in Florida, Central America, or the West Indies, because of the wide variation among them in susceptibility to injury by low temperatures. Many varieties of the West Indian race are injured by exposure to temperatures of 50° to 53°F for 15 days,* whereas others (Pollock, Trapp) remain in good condition for 3 weeks when held at 42°.* Varieties of the Guatemalan race are more resistant to cold, and those of the Mexican race are the most resistant of all. Some of the varieties that are least affected by cold (Lula, Taylor) can safely be held at 37° to 42° for 4 weeks.*

At the higher temperatures mentioned above, anthracnose, a fungus disease of avocados, will probably be an important factor in the storage of this fruit. At the lower temperatures decay is not likely to be troublesome except after long storage.

Bananas. (Temperature: ripening, 62° to 70°F; holding ripe fruit, 56° to 60°; relative humidity: green fruit, 90 to 95 percent; ripe fruit, somewhat reduced but not below about 85 percent.) The banana is one of the fruits that must be shipped to market green, because in this condition it can be handled for a longer time without becoming overripe and without serious injury from bruising during the marketing process. Furthermore, bananas of the Gros Michel variety, which make up the great bulk of banana shipments into this country, if allowed to ripen on the plant become mealy, lack flavor, and are subject to splitting, with subsequent decay.

The bunches of green bananas as they are received from the Tropics are usually ripened at a temperature of about 64°F, with a relative humidity of 90 to 95 percent or higher. If it is desired to hasten the ripening process, a higher temperature can be used (up to 70°) for the first 18 to 24 hours, but temperatures should then be reduced to about 66°. In any case relative humidity should be kept at 90 to 95 percent or higher until the fruit becomes thoroughly colored. After this it should be reduced slightly, but not below about 85 percent. Prolonged exposure to high temperatures will cause poor color and flavor and weak necks and will hasten decay.

The lowest temperature at which green bananas can safely be held in order to delay ripening is about 56°; below this they suffer an injury known as chilling—a form of peel injury to which both green and ripe bananas are susceptible, caused by low but not freezing temperatures. Ripe fruit is slightly less susceptible to chilling injury then green fruit. Fruit chilled in the green stage does not develop a bright-yellow color on ripening, but instead a smoky dull color. Fruit chilled after ripening will develop a dull-brown color when later exposed to higher temperatures and is very susceptible to handling marks, the slightest bruising causing discoloration.

The best holding temperature for ripe bananas is generally considered to be between 56° and 60°. At this temperature they will retain their good appearance and flavor and remain edible for a week or 10 days, although ordinarily they will not keep firm enough for shipment more than half that time.*

Dates. (Temperature, 28° to 32°F; relative humidity, 65 to 75 percent; or 28°F and no humidity control for cured grades.)   Dates absorb moisture and odors readily from the air.   The rate of absorption is much less at temperatures below 32°F than at those above 32°.   Deterioration caused by humidity above 75 percent is slow at storage temperatures below 28°.   The dates of commerce are of three grades with respect to storage life—dried, cured, and noncured.   The cured and noncured grades are perishable.   A temperature as low as 0° has no deleterious effect upon dates but is actually beneficial to them.

Dates are of two different types, and fruits of each type are likely to be either dry, cured, or noncured.   The "cane sugar" type is usually firm, light-colored, and comparatively dry, whereas the "invert sugar" type is usually softer, darker colored, and inclined to be slightly sticky or sirupy.

Deglet Noor, the most important variety grown in this country, is of the cane-sugar type.   Dates of this variety, cured grade, keep well until March at 28° to 32°F and for a year at 24° to 26° or lower, whereas the noncured grade requires 18° or lower for storage until March, and 0° to 10° for a year.   In Deglet Noor dates that have become overripe or have been held under unfavorable storage conditions the cane sugar is inverted and the dates become soft, sirupy, and darker in color.   Such dates are commonly graded as "dark soft."   If they can be dried down somewhat, they can be stored at 28° to 32° until Christmas without becoming objectionably dark and sirupy, although a temperature of 0° to 10° will be needed if they are to be stored until March.   If such dates are not cured, a temperature of 0° to 10° is necessary for even short-time storage.*

Halawy, Khadrawy, Zahidi, and Saidy dates are all of the invert-sugar type, and the cured grades can be kept until Christmas at 28° to 32°F without forming sugar spots but require a temperature of 18° or lower if stored until March.   Noncured grades of these varieties require 0° to 10° for even short storage.   After Christmas it is well to shift all dates of the invert-sugar type remaining in storage to "freezers" at 0° to 10°F.*

Grapefruit.   (Temperature, see text; relative humidity, 85 to 90 percent.)   Storage rooms for grapefruit should have a relative humidity of 85 to 90 percent.   Lower humidities are favorable to pitting, and higher ones may increase decay.

For short-time storage, grapefruit can be held satisfactorily at a temperature of 32°F.   For longer periods the temperature to be used will depend on the character of the fruit and the troubles most likely to be encountered.   For fruit grown in sections where stem end rot is prevalent, this disease is likely to be the determining factor; it will generally be advisable to use a comparatively low temperature range (32° to 34°). On the other hand if the fruit is grown in regions where stem end rot is not prevalent, the limiting factors are likely to be storage pitting and watery break-down, which develop most seriously at temperatures of 40° or lower.   For fruit from these regions a temperature of 45° to 55° is satisfactory, and the more rapid development of undesirable high color and the increase in blue mold and green mold rots at the higher temperatures have not been found as objectionable on such fruits as the pitting that results from storage at lower temperatures.

Sound fruit that is not overmature or likely to suffer from stem end rot can usually be held for 6 weeks without serious spoilage at the higher temperature ranges mentioned above, and this storage period can sometimes be doubled with satisfactory results.   Weak or overmature fruit requires close watching from the time it is removed from the tree, regardless of storage conditions.

The percentage of stem end rot in Florida and Texas grapefruit will be greatly reduced if the fruit is properly treated with borax or sodium metaborate, pulled from the tree instead of being clipped,* and precooled before being shipped. The disbuttoning that may occur during handling and packing is also effective in reducing loss from stem end rot. As compared with stem end rot, blue mold and green mold rots are relatively less important on Florida grapefruit in storage. Stem end rot is not known to occur on California and Arizona fruit.*

Oranges. (Temperature, 32° to 34°F; relatively humidity, 85 to 90 percent.) Although oranges are ordinarily stored at about 38°F, experimental results have shown that for long storage (8 to 10 weeks) a range of 32° to 34° gives better results. However, within this range some decay, chiefly blue mold rot or green mold rot, may occur during storage of 2 months or more, and some fruit may begin to show pitting and brown stain of the rind. If stored for longer periods, decay increases, and the spotted fruit may gradually turn brown over all or most of the surface. Watery break-down may develop, as in grapefruit. Stem end rot is likely to develop in Florida fruit if the storage temperature is higher than about 34°. Among California varieties, Washington Navel oranges are more subject to decay (blue mold and green mold rots) than Valencia oranges. The Washington Navel is also subject to alternaria rot.

Careful handling is necessary at all times to avoid injury to the fruit and the decay, chiefly blue mold rot or green mold rot, that frequently follows injuries.

A free circulation of air around the boxes is desirable for oranges, as for other citrus fruit. A relative humidity of 85 to 90 percent is sufficient to hold the shriveling of packed oranges to a minimum and retards decay more than does a higher humidity.

Oranges should not be stored with eggs or butter in places where it is possible for the orange odor to penetrate into eggs or butter storage rooms. It is desirable that oranges in storage be examined regularly and often to avoid loss from the development of pitting or decay. After such examinations, a decision as to how long the fruit can safely be left in storage should take account of the fact that if pitting and decay are found they may increase rapidly after the fruit is removed to higher temperatures.*

Pears. (Temperature: Bartlett pears, 29° to 30°F; fall and winter pears, 30° to 31°; relative humidity for all varieties, 85 to 90 percent.)

Bartlett pears. The successful storage of Bartlett pears* depends not only on the temperature and humidity in the storage room but also on the condition of the fruit when stored. If the highest quality is to be obtained, Bartlett pears for storage should not be removed from the tree until the ground color begins to lighten and the lenticels have corked over. If picked before reaching that stage, they have a marked tendency to wilt, scald, and break down in storage. They also tend to break down in storage if picked when too ripe. The most desirable temperature for the storage of Bartlett pears is 29° to 30°F. The relative humidity should range from 85 to 90 percent. The maximum period for storage for canning and local fresh markets is about 90 days and for storage at shipping point and at terminal markets, 45 to 60 days.

Fall and winter pears. For fall and winter varieties of pears* such as Anjou, Bosc, Clairgeau, Comice, Easter Beurre, Hardy, Seckel, and Winter Nelis, the most desirable storage temperature is 30° to 31°F. A relative humidity of 85 to 90 percent is most commonly used. However, a relative humidity of 90 to 95 percent is maintained in some pear storage rooms in order to prevent shriveling. Such humidities are maintained in connection with air velocities of 100 to 200 feet per minute. The length of time for which it is safe to store these pears depends on the variety and when it is picked and also on whether the fruit is shipped directly to a consuming center and there stored or is stored at the shipping point for a time and later shipped to market. Information on these points is given in Table 5. In using the table it should be remembered that wide differences in keeping quality are often found in pears from various producing sections of the country. If Bosc, Flemish Beauty, and Comice pears are held in cold storage beyond their season they do not ripen satisfactorily or they may not ripen at all.* For best ripening, these and other varieties of fall and winter pears should be held at a temperature somewhere in the range from 60° to 70°, preferably about 65°.

The commonest and most serious decays of fall and winter pears in storage are gray mold rot, caused by the fungus Botrytis, and blue mold rot, caused by the fungus Penicillium. Gray mold rot is able to spread from decaying to sound healthy fruit and for that reason is frequently called nest rot. Losses from this rot can be reduced by the use of paper wrappers impregnated with copper.* In the Pacific Northwest blue mold rot, in the form known as pinhole rot, is sometimes more important on pears, particularly Winter Nelis, than gray mold rot. Losses from blue mold can be greatly reduced by careful picking and handling, prompt storage at 30° to 31°F after harvest, and the use of paper wrappers to prevent direct contact between diseased and sound fruit.

Table 5. Length of time at 30° to 31°F for safe storage of certain varieties of pears at shipping point and after shipment to market*

Storage treatment and variety	Length of storage period, months	End of storage period
Stored immediately after harvest:		
Hardy	2–3	Sept.–Nov.
Comice	2–3	Nov.–Dec.
Bosc	3–3½	Nov.–Dec.
Clairgeau	6	Feb.
Winter Nelis	6–7	Mar.–May
Easter Beurre	5–7	Mar.–May
Anjou	5–6	Mar.
Stored after 12-day transit period (not precooled):		
Anjou	4–5	Jan.–Feb.
Bosc	1–2	Oct.–Nov.
Clairgeau	2–6	Oct.–Feb.
Winter Nelis	2–4	Oct.–Jan.
Easter Beurre	4–6	Jan.–Mar.
Stored after 12-day transit period (precooled):		
Anjou	4–5	Mar.
Hardy	2–3	Sept.–Nov.
Comice	2–3	Nov.–Dec.
Bosc	2–3	Nov.–Dec.
Clarigeau	3–6	Nov.–Feb.
Winter Nelis	6–7	Mar.–May

Kieffer pears, if they are sound, firm, and still green when stored and are held under the conditions recommended for other fall and winter pears, can be expected to keep satisfactorily for 2 or 3 months. If intended for storage, they and other varieties should be handled with extreme care during the picking process, because even slightly bruised or rubbed places are very likely to turn black and seriously damage the sales value of the fruit. Recent investigations* by the United States Department of Agriculture have proved that a ripening temperature of 60° to 65°F is essential for the attainment of maximum quality in Kieffer pears for either dessert or canning purposes.

Dried fruits. (Temperature and relative humidity, see text.) For the preservation of natural color in storage, cut dried fruits and dried berries that are not subject to sugaring are held at 26°F with no humidity control, or at 32° with a relative humidity of 70 to 75 percent.

Figs and prunes are best stored at 40° to 45°F. The relative humidity should not be over 70 to 75 percent, to prevent excessive absorption of moisture. Dried apples, apricots, and peaches keep best at 26° to 32°. Raisins should be stored at 40° to 45° and require a relative humidity of 50 to 60 percent to keep them from absorbing moisture. The holding of dried fruit in high humidity at temperatures above 32° is likely to result in mold. The dried fruits mentioned can be kept in marketable condition for 9 to 12 months at the temperatures and humidities specified.

Dried fruit can be tightly stacked, without stripping, in large solid blocks in storage rooms without injurious effect, and this method of handling the packages minimizes the absorption of moiture from the storage-room air. When nonventilated packages, such as those used for dried fruit and dates, are removed from cold rooms, the sweating that results occurs mostly on the outside of the package and the moisture can be prevented from penetrating into the fruit by allowing the packages to warm up before they are opened.*

Frozen fruits and vegetables. (Temperature, see text.) Frozen fruits should be held at −10° to 0°F if they are to be stored for several months.

For the freezing of fruits a temperature of 0°F or lower is desirable for both small containers and barrels. If freezing takes place too slowly the same undesirable conditions may develop that are encountered if the fruit is stored at too high a temperature after being frozen.

For best results frozen fruits should be held in airtight containers.*

The best temperature for freezing vegetables is from −10° to −5°F. For storage after freezing −10° to 0° is satisfactory if ample provision is made for rapid cooling until the product reaches the freezing point.

Corn (green). (Temperature, 31° to 32°F; relative humidity, 85 to 90 percent.) Green corn is seldom stored, although there are occasions during the southern shipping season when it may be desirable to put an excess supply of this commodity temporarily into cold storage; however, storage for more than a few days will result in serious deterioration. The sugar content, which so largely determines quality in this product and which rapidly decreases at ordinary temperatures, is reduced very little if the corn is quickly cooled and kept at a relatively low temperature. In order to keep this loss of sugar to a minimum and preserve the flavor, corn in the husks as it comes from the field for consumption in the fresh state should be cooled as quickly as possible. This is sometimes done by submerging it in tanks of ice water immediately after removal from the field to reduce the temperature to as near 32° as possible.

Corn should not be handled in bulk because of its tendency to heat but should be put in baskets or crates, which allow air circulation and the more rapid removal of field heat and heat produced by respiration. This commodity as it usually arrives on the market should not be expected to keep in marketable condition in cold storage for more than 4 to 8 days.

Peppers: Chili (dry). (Temperature, see text; relative humidity, 70 to 75 percent.) Chili peppers are usually picked when ripe and then dried and allowed to equalize in moisture content in covered piles.   Water is usually added to the peppers after drying, and as a result they become less brittle.   They are then packed tightly by tamping into sacks holding 200 to 300 pounds and stored in nonrefrigerated warehouses for 6 to 9 months.

The temperature of the warehouses depends to some extent on their construction and the way in which they are managed but chiefly on the outside temperature.   In southern California, where a large part of the commercial crop of Chili peppers is produced, the outside temperature ranges from 50° to 80°F during the usual storage period.

The moisture content of Chili peppers when stored is generally low enough (10 to 15 percent) to prevent mold growth; the chief storage trouble is insect infestation. Sometimes manufacturers of Chili pepper products hold part of their supply of the raw material in cold storage, but they prefer to grind the peppers as soon as possible and store them in the manufactured form in airtight containers.

Potatoes.   (Temperature, 36° to 50°F; relative humidity, 85 to 90 percent.) Potatoes are stored in cold or common storage, but the greater part of the crop that is stored is held in common storage.*   Like most other vegetables that can be held for relatively long periods in common storage, potatoes can be successfully kept through the fall and winter months only in those regions where a sufficiently cold winter climate prevails.   In either cold or common storage a temperature of 40°F is as low as table or seed stock need be kept during the first few months after harvest.   At temperatures below this, there is a tendency for potatoes to become undesirably sweet. However, if sweetening occurs, a few days' exposure to ordinary living-room temperature will partly restore the natural flavor.   At 40° potatoes will remain dormant 3 to 5 months after harvest, depending on the variety.   If it is desired to keep them longer than this, as is often the case with seed stock, the temperature may be lowered to 36° or 38°F, where they should remain dormant indefinitely.   A storage temperature as low as 32° is unnecessary and detrimental.

Investigations have indicated that potatoes stored at 50° to 60°F have better texture, color, and flavor when cooked or made into chips than the same stock stored at lower temperatures,* although the higher temperatures are not suitable for long-time storage.   When potatoes are stored at these higher temperatures, sprouting will occur more quickly.   A limited amount of sprouting does not injure potatoes for food purposes, but it makes the stock difficult to market because usually only dormant potatoes are wanted.   If sprouting has started it can be checked by lowering the storage temperature.

The relative humidity of a potato-storage house should be 85 to 90 percent, to prevent undue shrinkage through loss of water.   In cold storage potatoes are generally kept in sacks holding from 100 to 150 pounds net; in common storage they are usually placed in bins holding from 150 to as much as 1,000 bushels or more.   In Maine and northern New York, where the average temperature is sufficiently low, the large-bin storage is used with success, but in the milder climate of States in the latitude of Pennsylvania potatoes should not be stored in such large units.   Potatoes are readily injured by even slight freezing, which takes place at about 29°F or slightly below; hence common-storage buildings should be sufficiently insulated to prevent freezing. Insulation will also prevent the condensation of moisture on the walls and ceilings, and the consequent undesirable wetting of stored stock, which favors the development of decay.   Common storages should be provided with sufficient ventilation to take advantage of the cool night air in mild weather; this will aid in removing excess moisture, accumulating especially soon after potatoes are stored in the fall, and will maintain a lower average temperature. Ventilators should never be opened, however, when the outside temperature is higher than that inside the storage house. In addition to damage to potatoes, condensed moisture caused by improper ventilation or inadequate insulation may also cause serious impairment to the building structure.*

Potatoes intended for storage should be handled carefully to avoid bruises and cuts; otherwise they are likely to be damaged by various forms of decay before the end of the storage period.

Sweetpotatoes. (Temperature, 55° to 60°F; relative humidity, 75 to 80 percent.) The requirements for the successful storage of sweetpotatoes differ from those recommended for most vegetable crops. When freshly dug sweetpotatoes are to be stored for any length of time they should be given a preliminary curing treatment to permit the healing of all wounds or abrasions incident to harvesting and handling, in order to prevent the entrance of decay organisms.

The curing and storing are done in the same house so that the potatoes do not have to be moved after the curing treatment. When commercial lots are handled, the storage house is generally of special construction with sufficient insulation to maintain a uniform temperature and some means of ventilation that will insure the desired humidity. Provision should be made for heating the building during the curing process and for holding the proper storage temperature afterward. The curing process ordinarily takes from 10 to 14 days, during which the house is kept at a temperature of 80° to 85°F, with a relative humidity of 85 to 90 percent. After the curing period the storage temperature is allowed to drop to about 55°, with a humidity of 75 to 80 percent. Short periods of a few hours at temperatures somewhat lower than 50° need not cause alarm, but prolonged periods of low temperature should be avoided because of the danger from certain types of decay, which are more likely to develop at temperatures below the range given.* Under the recommended conditions, properly cured stock should keep satisfactorily for 4 to 6 months.

Only well-matured stock that is practically free from mechanical injury or decay should be used for storage. Sweetpotatoes are usually stored in slat crates of about a bushel capacity or in bushel baskets. Shallow bins are sometimes used. The roots should be handled as little as possible during storage.

Tomatoes. (Temperature: ripe, 40° to 50°F; mature green, 55° to 70°; relative humidity, 85 to 90 percent). Ripe tomatoes are held in storage only temporarily and should not be stored at temperatures lower than 40°F. At 40° to 50°, if not already soft ripe, they will keep in good condition for a week to 10 days; at temperatures lower than this they sometimes show a tendency to break down.

Green tomatoes are best kept at a temperature not lower than 55°F. At this temperature ripening progresses slowly but satisfactorily, and mature green tomatoes can be kept for 3 to 5 weeks before becoming overripe. At temperatures much below 55° green tomatoes do not ripen well and if kept there more than about 8 days and then moved to a warmer place usually do not ripen satisfactorily; on the other hand, if they are to be kept for less than 8 days they can be held at 40° or even somewhat lower. If fairly rapid ripening is desired, temperatures from 60° to 70° should be used. At 70° or slightly above, ripening is accelerated, but so also is the development of decay, which will be found difficult to control. At about 80° coloring will be uneven since the development of the red pigment is inhibited at this temperature or above. The relative humidity of tomato-storage or tomato-ripening rooms should be from 80 to 85 percent.*

APPENDIX 2

INTERNAL ENERGY OF A FLUID

Fluids are composed of an aggregation of molecules that are moving continuously in random directions. According to the kinetic theory of gases, it is the impact of these molecules on a surface that accounts for the pressure of gases. A gas in a closed flask may appear stagnant, but it possesses a considerable amount of kinetic energy due to the translational motion of its molecules. In addition, polyatomic molecules possess rotational energy, and also vibrational energy of the atoms within the molecule. The rotational and vibrational energies are also forms of internal kinetic energy.

In addition to the internal kinetic energy, a fluid has also internal potential energy. There is an attractive force between molecules, and if anything happens to change the distance between the molecules, there will be a change in the internal potential energy. As an illustration of such a change, let us consider 1 lb of water being boiled at atmospheric pressure. As water it occupies 0.016 cu ft. Upon evaporation it occupies 27 cu ft. To move the molecules apart against their attractive forces requires a large amount of energy, which is stored in the steam as part of its internal energy.

In a gas the molecules are widely separated so that the attraction between them is small. Compression or expansion can therefore take place with only a small change of internal potential energy. With an ideal gas a change of state produces no change of internal potential energy. For a perfect gas the internal energy is therefore a function only of its temperature.

APPENDIX 3

TRANSFERRED HEAT

Transferred heat may be defined as follows:

$$Q = w\int c\, dT$$

where Q = transferred heat
    w = weight
    c = specific heat
    T = temperature, °R

The quantity c is the specific heat for the type of process involved. Depending on the type of process, it may have a value of c_p, c_v, or a value between c_p and c_v.

Transferred heat may also be defined by the simple energy equation

$$Q = \Delta U + W$$

or

$$dQ = dU + \frac{P\, dV}{J}$$

where U = internal energy
    W = work
    P = the pressure, psf
    V = volume, cu ft
    J = mechanical equivalent of heat (778)

APPENDIX 4

PRESSURE AND VOLUME RELATION FOR ADIABATIC COMPRESSION

Let us first consider the relation between c_p and c_v for any process.

$$W = \int P\, dV = P \int_{v_1}^{v_2} dV$$
$$W = P(v_2 - v_1)\text{ft-lb}$$

or

$$W = \frac{P(v_2 - v_1)}{J} \qquad \text{Btu}$$

but

$$PV = wRT$$

therefore

$$W = \frac{wR(T_2 - T_1)}{J} \qquad \text{Btu}$$

The heat transferred in a constant-pressure process is

$$Q = wc_p(T_2 - T_1)$$

But for any process the change of internal energy is $wc_v(T_2 - T_1)$.
Substituting these values in the simple energy equation, $Q = \Delta U + W$, we obtain

$$wc_p(T_2 - T_1) = wc_v(T_2 - T_1) + \frac{wR(T_2 - T_1)}{J}$$

or

$$c_p = c_v + \frac{R}{J} \qquad (a)$$

Now let us consider the relation between P and V for an adiabatic process. In an adiabatic process there is no transferred heat. The internal energy is converted into work, or work is converted into internal heat energy.

$$Q = \Delta U + W = 0$$

and hence

$$wc_v\, dT = -\frac{P\, dV}{J} \qquad (b)$$

Next, differentiate the equation $PV = wRT$. Since P, V, and T vary

$$P\, dV + V\, dP = wR\, dT$$

or

$$dT = \frac{P\, dV + V\, dP}{wR} \qquad (c)$$

364

Combining Eqs. (*b*) and (*c*),

$$-\frac{P\,dV}{J} = \frac{c_v P\,dV + c_v V\,dP}{R}$$

Multiplying both sides of the equation by R/PV,

$$-\frac{R\,dV}{JV} = c_v\frac{dV}{V} + c_v\frac{dP}{P}$$

$$-\left(\frac{R}{J} + c_v\right)\frac{dV}{V} = c_v\frac{dP}{P}$$

From Eq. (*a*)

$$\frac{R}{J} + c_v = c_p$$

$$-c_p\frac{dV}{V} = c_v\frac{dP}{P}$$

$$-c_p\int_{v_1}^{v_2}\frac{dV}{V} = c_v\int_{P_1}^{P_2}\frac{dP}{P}$$

$$-c_p\log_e\frac{V_2}{V_1} = c_v\log_e\frac{P_2}{P_1}$$

$$-\frac{c_p}{c_v}\log_e\frac{V_2}{V_1} = \log_e\frac{P_2}{P_1}$$

Taking the antilog of both sides of the equation,

$$\left(\frac{V_1}{V_2}\right)^{c_p/c_v} = \frac{P_2}{P_1}$$

Designate $\dfrac{c_p}{c_v} = \gamma$

Then

$$P_1 V_1{}^\gamma = P_2 V_2{}^\gamma = \text{constant}$$

APPENDIX 5

WORK REQUIRED FOR ADIABATIC COMPRESSION

The work required for any process is

$$W = \int P \, dV \tag{a}$$

But for an adiabatic process $P = C/V^\gamma$ (see Appendix 4). Substituting this value in Eq. (a),

$$W = C \int_1^{v_2} \frac{dV}{V^2} = \left[\frac{C V^{-\gamma+1}}{-\gamma + 1} \right]_{v_1}^{v_2}$$
$$= \frac{C V_2^{1-\gamma} - C V_1^{1-\gamma}}{1 - \gamma}$$

But

$$C = P_2 V_2^\gamma = P_1 V_1^\gamma$$

Therefore

$$W = \frac{P_2 V_2 - P_1 V_1}{1 - \gamma} \qquad \text{ft-lb}$$

or

$$W = \frac{P_2 V_2 - P_1 V_1}{J(1 - \gamma)} \qquad \text{Btu}$$

APPENDIX 6

AMERICAN STANDARD SAFETY CODE FOR MECHANICAL REFRIGERATION[1]

Section 1. Scope and Purpose.

1.10. The application of this Code is intended to insure the safe design, construction, installation, operation, and inspection of every Refrigerating System employing a fluid which is vaporized and liquefied in its refrigerating cycle, which may be used for the extraction of heat, including the preparation and preservation of food, the cooling and dehumidification of air for industrial purposes and for comfort, and as an aid to or a part in a chemical process.

1.20. This Code shall apply to Refrigerating Systems installed subsequent to its adoption and to parts replaced or added to systems installed prior to its adoption.

1.30. This Code is intended to provide reasonable safeguards to life, limb, health, and property; to correct certain practices which are inconsistent with safety; and to prescribe standards of safety which will properly influence future progress and developments in Refrigerating Systems.

Section 2. Definitions.

2.10. *Approved*—Acceptable to the authorities having jurisdiction.

2.11. *Brazed Joint*—For the purpose of this Code, a brazed joint is a gas-tight joint, obtained by the joining of metal parts with alloys which melt at temperatures higher then 1,000 F but less than the melting temperatures of the joined parts.

2.12. *Brine*—Any liquid, used for the transmission of heat without a change in its state, having no flash point or a flash point above 150 F determined by American Society for Testing Materials method D56-36.

2.13. *Compressor*—A mechanical device used in a Refrigerating System for the purpose of increasing the pressure upon the refrigerant.

2.14. *Condenser*—A vessel or arrangement of pipe or tubing in which vaporized refrigerant is liquefied by the removal of heat.

2.15. *Condensing Unit*—A specific refrigerating machine combination consisting of a motor-driven compressor, a condenser, a liquid receiver, and the regularly furnished accessories.

2.16. *Container*—A cylinder for the transportation of refrigerant constructed to conform to the Specifications of the Interstate Commerce Commission as contained in their "Regulations for the Transportation by Rail of Explosives and other Dangerous Articles in Freight, Express and Baggage Services, including Specifications for Shipping Containers" effective October 1, 1930, with supplements 1 to 18 inclusive.

2.17. *Department Store*—The entire space occupied by one tenant or more than one tenant in an individual store where more than 100 persons commonly assemble on other than the street level floor for the purpose of buying personal wearables and other merchandise used in the home.

[1] ASRE Circ. No. 15, ASA B9-1939.

2.18. *Design Working Pressure*—The maximum allowable working pressure for which a vessel is designed.

2.19. *Duct*—A tube or conduit used for conveying air.

2.20. *Evaporator*—That part of the system in which liquid refrigerant is vaporized to produce refrigeration.

2.21. *Expansion Coil*—An evaporator constructed of pipe or tubing.

2.22. *Fusible Plug*—A device having a predetermined temperature fusible member for the relief of pressure. .

2.23. *Generator*—Any device equipped with a heating element used in the Refrigerating System to increase the pressure of the refrigerant in its gas or vapor state for the purpose of liquefying the refrigerant.

2.24. *Liquid Receiver*—A vessel permanently connected to a system by inlet and outlet pipes for storage of a liquid refrigerant.

2.25. *Machinery*—Refrigerating equipment including any or all of the following: compressor, condenser, generator, absorber, receiver, connecting pipe, evaporator, or complete Unit System.

2.26. *Machinery Room*—A room in which is permanently installed and operated a Refrigerating System but not including evaporators located in a cold storage room, refrigerator box, air cooled space, or other enclosed space. Closets solely contained within and opening only into a room shall be considered a part of such room.

2.27. *Machinery Room, Class T*—A room having machinery other than flame producing apparatus permanently installed and operated and also having:

a. Doors which are tight-fitting, fire-resisting, and self-closing.

b. Walls which are vapor-tight and of approved fire resistive construction.

c. An exit door which opens directly to the outer air or through a vestibule-type exit equipped with self-closing, tight-fitting doors.

d. Exterior openings which, if present, are not under any fire escape or any open stairway.

e. All pipes piercing the interior walls or floor of such room, tightly sealed to the walls or floor through which they pass.

f. Emergency remote controls located immediately outside to stop the action of the refrigerant compressor.

g. Mechanical means for ventilation.

h. Emergency remote controls for the mechanical means of ventilation located outside.

2.28. *Mechanical Joint*—For the purpose of this Code, a mechanical joint is a gas-tight joint, obtained by the joining of metal parts through a positive-holding mechanical construction.

2.29. *Piping*—Pipe or tube mains for interconnecting the various parts of a Refrigerating System.

2.30. *Pressure Limiting Device*—A pressure responsive mechanism designed to automatically stop the operation of the compressor at a predetermined pressure.

2.31. *Pressure Relief Device*—A valve or rupture member designed to automatically relieve excessive pressure.

2.32. *Pressure Relief Valve*—A valve held closed by a spring or other means and designed to automatically relieve pressure in excess of its setting.

2.33. *Pressure Vessel*—Any refrigerant containing receptacle of a Refrigerating System other than expansion coils, headers, and pipe connections.

2.34. *Refrigerant*—A substance used to produce refrigeration by its expansion or vaporization.

2.35. *Refrigerating System*—A combination of interconnected refrigerant containing parts in which a refrigerant is circulated for the purpose of extracting heat.

2.36. *Rupture Member*—A device that will automatically rupture at a predetermined pressure.

2.37. *Soldered Joint*—For the purpose of this Code, a soldered joint is a gas-tight joint, obtained by the joining of metal parts with metallic mixtures or alloys which melt at temperatures below 1000 F and above 350 F.

2.38. *Stop Valve*—A shut-off for controlling the flow of refrigerant.

2.39. *Tenant*—As herein used a tenant shall be construed as a person, firm, or corporation possessed with the legal right to occupy premises.

2.40. *Welded Joint*—For the purpose of this Code, a welded joint is a gas-tight joint, obtained by the joining of metal parts in the plastic or molten state. (Abbreviated from American Standards Association Code for Pressure Piping, B31.1—1935.)

Section 3. Building Occupancy Classification.

3.10. *Locations* in which Refrigerating Systems may be placed are grouped by occupancy as follows:

3.20. *Institutional* occupancy shall apply to that portion of a building in which persons are harbored to receive medical, charitable, educational, or other care or treatment, or in which persons are held or detained by reason of public or civic duty, including among others, hospitals, asylums, sanitariums, police stations, jails, court houses with cells, and similar occupancies.

3.30. *Public Assembly* occupancy shall apply to that portion of the premises in which persons congregate for civic, political, educational, religious, social, or recreational purposes; including among others, auditoriums, assembly rooms, armories, ball rooms, bath houses, broadcasting studios, colleges, court houses without cells, churches, dance halls, department stores, exhibition halls, fraternity halls, lodge rooms, mortuary chapels, museums, schools, libraries, passenger depots, subway stations, bus terminals, theatres, skating rinks, and similar occupancies.

3.40. *Residential* occupancy shall apply to that portion of a building in which sleeping accommodations are provided for more than two families, including among others, multiple story apartments, tenements, hotels, lodging houses, dormitories, convents, studios, club houses, and similar occupancies.

3.50. *Commercial* occupancy shall apply to that portion of a building used for the transaction of business; for the rendering of professional services; for the supplying of food, drink, or other bodily needs and comforts; for manufacturing purposes or for the performance of work or labor, except as included under "Industrial" occupancies, including among others, office buildings, professional buildings, markets, restaurants, laboratories, bake shops, fur storage, loft buildings, stores other than department stores, and similar occupancies.

3.60. *Industrial* occupancy shall apply to an entire building when used by a single tenant for manufacturing, processing, or storage of materials or products, including among others, chemical, food, candy and ice cream factories, ice making plants, meat packing plants, refineries, perishable food warehouses, and similar occupancies, where a single tenant is defined as a single authority which operates and maintains the entire building and the Refrigerating System.

3.70. *Mixed* occupancy shall apply to a building occupied or used for different purposes in different parts. When the occupancies are cut off from the rest of the building by tight partitions, floors and ceilings and protected by self-closing doors, the requirements for each type of occupancy shall apply for its portion of the building.

When the occupancies are not so separated, the occupancy carrying the more stringent requirements shall govern.

Section 4.   Refrigerating System Classification by Type.

4.10. *Refrigerating Systems* shall be divided into classes, descriptive of the method employed for extracting heat as follows:

4.20. *Direct System* is one in which the evaporator is in direct contact with the material or space refrigerated or is located in air circulating passages communicating with such spaces.

4.30. *Unit System* is one which has been assembled and tested prior to its installation and which is installed without connecting any refrigerant containing parts.

4.40. *Indirect System* is one in which a liquid, such as brine or water, cooled by the refrigerant, is circulated to the material or space refrigerated or is used to cool air so circulated.   Indirect Systems which are distinguished by the type or method of application are as follows:

4.41. *Indirect Open Spray System* is one in which a liquid, such as brine or water, cooled by an evaporator located in an enclosure external to a cooling chamber, is circulated to such cooling chamber and is sprayed therein.

4.42. *Indirect Closed Surface System* is one in which a liquid, such as brine or water, cooled by an evaporator located in an enclosure external to a cooling chamber, is circulated to and through such a cooling chamber in pipes or other closed circuits.

4.43. *Indirect Vented Closed Surface System* is one in which a liquid, such as brine or water, cooled by an evaporator located in a vented enclosure external to a cooling chamber, is circulated to and through such cooling chamber in pipes or other closed circuits.

4.44. *Double Indirect Vented Open Spray System* is one in which a liquid, such as brine or water, cooled by an evaporator located in a vented enclosure, is circulated through a closed circuit to a second enclosure where it cools another supply of a liquid, such as brine or water, and this liquid in turn is circulated to a cooling chamber and is sprayed therein.

4.45. *Indirect Absorptive Brine System* is an Indirect Vented Open Spray System in which the brine will chemically absorb the refrigerant in the system, and the chemical compound so formed in the solution will be stable at temperatures up to 100 F. The brine shall be of such quantity and concentration that it will absorb twice the total quantity of refrigerant in the system.   An approved automatic device shall be provided for shutting down the system when the brine concentration becomes such that the brine will absorb only one and one-half times the total quantity of refrigerant in the system.

4.46. *Double Refrigerant System* is one in which a refrigerant is used in the secondary circuit instead of brine or water.   For the purpose of this Code, each circuit shall be considered as a separate Direct Refrigerating System.

4.50. The Direct and various Indirect Systems referred to above are illustrated in Fig. 1.

Section 5.   Refrigerant Classification.

5.10. Refrigerants shall, for Safety Code purposes, be divided into groups as follows:

5.11.

Group 1	Chemical Formula
Carbon dioxide	CO_2
Dichlorodifluoromethane (Freon 12)	CCl_2F_2
Dichloromonofluoromethane (Freon 21)	$CHCl_2F$
Dichlorotetrafluoroethane (Freon 114)	$C_2Cl_2F_4$
Dichloromethane (Carrene No. 1) (Methylene chloride)	CH_2Cl_2
Trichloromonofluoromethane (Freon 11) (Carrene No. 2)	CCl_3F

5.12.

Group 2	Chemical Formula
Ammonia	NH_3
Dichloroethylene	$C_2H_2Cl_2$
Ethyl chloride	C_2H_5Cl
Methyl chloride	CH_3Cl
Methyl formate	$HCOOCH_3$
Sulphur dioxide	SO_2

5.13.

Group 3	Chemical Formula
Butane	C_4H_{10}
Ethane	C_2H_6
Isobutane	$(CH_3)_3CH$
Propane	C_3H_8

Section 6. Institutional Occupancies.

General.

6.10. No Refrigerating System shall be installed in or on public stairways, hallways, lobbies, entrances or exits.

6.11. Refrigerant piping or tubing shall not be carried through floors except that for the purpose of connecting to a condenser on the roof, it may be carried through a continuous, rigid and tight fire-resisting (four (4) hour rating) flue or shaft having no openings on intermediate floors, or it may be carried on the outer wall of the building provided it is not located in an air shaft, closed court or in other similar open spaces enclosed within the outer walls of the building.

Group 1 Refrigerants.

6.20. No Refrigerating System shall be installed in any room except Unit Systems each containing not more than ten (10) pounds of a Group 1 refrigerant, and then only when a window or other ventilation is provided, and except as otherwise permitted.

6.21. Systems each containing not more than twenty (20) pounds of a Group 1 refrigerant may be installed in kitchens, laboratories, and mortuaries.

6.22. Systems each containing more than twenty (20) pounds of a Group 1 refrigerant shall be of the Indirect type with all refrigerant containing parts, excepting parts installed outside the building, installed in a machinery room, used for no other purpose and in which for Group 1 refrigerants, excepting carbon dioxide, no flame is present or apparatus to produce a flame is installed.

6.23. When a Group 1 refrigerant, other than carbon dioxide, is used in a system any portion of which is in a room where there is an apparatus for producing an open flame, then such refrigerant shall be classed in Group 2 unless the flame producing apparatus is provided with a hood and flue capable of removing the products of combustion to the open air. Flames by matches, cigarette lighters, small alcohol lamps and similar devices, shall not be considered as open flames.

Group 2 Refrigerants.

6.30. Group 2 refrigerants shall not be used except in Unit Systems containing not more than six (6) pounds of refrigerant when installed in kitchens, laboratories, or mortuaries, or except in systems containing not more than five hundred (500) pounds of refrigerant and having all refrigerant containing parts installed in a Class T machinery room.

6.31. Group 2 refrigerants shall not be used in a system for air conditioning for human comfort, except in an Indirect Vented Closed Surface System, or in a Double Indirect Vented Open Spray System, or in an indirect Absorptive Brine System.

Group 3 Refrigerants.

6.40. Group 3 refrigerants shall not be used in Institutional occupancies.

Section 7.   Public Assembly Occupancies.

General.

7.10. No Refrigerating System shall be installed in or on public stairways, hallways, lobbies, entrances or exits.

7.11. Refrigerant piping or tubing shall not be carried through floors except from basements to the first floor or from the top floor to a penthouse or the roof, or except that for the purpose of connecting to a condenser on the roof it may be carried through a continuous, rigid and tight fire-resisting (four (4) hour rating) flue or shaft having no openings on intermediate floors, or it may be carried on the outer wall of the building provided it is not located in an air shaft, closed court or in other similar open spaces enclosed within the outer walls of the building.

Group 1 Refrigerants.

7.20. The maximum quantity of a Group 1 refrigerant in a Direct System used for air conditioning for human comfort shall be limited by the volume of the space to be air conditioned as shown in the table on page 373.

7.21. A system containing more than fifty (50) pounds of a Group 1 refrigerant, other than carbon dioxide, and which includes air ducts shall be of the Indirect type unless it conforms to requirements as follows:

a. Positive automatic fire damper or dampers shall be provided to cut off the refrigerant containing apparatus from the duct system.

b. Automatic means shall be provided to close the dampers and to stop the fan when the temperature of the air in the duct at the damper location reaches 210 F when the damper is on the discharge side of a system containing a heating coil and at 125 F when the damper is on the suction side of the system, or on the discharge side of a system containing no heating coil.

7.22. A system containing more than one thousand (1000) pounds of a Group 1 refrigerant shall be of the Indirect type with all the refrigerant containing parts, excepting parts mounted outside the building, installed in a machinery room used for no other purpose and in which for Group 1 refrigerants, excepting carbon dioxide, no flame is present or apparatus to produce a flame is installed.

7.23. When a Group 1 refrigerant, other than carbon dioxide, is used in a system, any portion of which is in a room where there is an apparatus for producing an open

Refrigerant		Maximum quantity in lbs per 1000 cu ft of air conditioned space*
Name	Chemical formula	
Carbon dioxide..............................	CO_2	12
Dichlorodifluoromethane (Freon 12)...............	CCl_2F_2	30
Dichloromethane (Carrene No. 1)................	CH_2Cl_2	6
Dichloromonofluoromethane (Freon 21)...........	$CHCl_2F$	13
Dichlorotetrafluoroethane (Freon 114)............	$C_2Cl_2F_4$	40
Trichloromonofluoromethane (Freon 11)...........	CCl_3F	35

* Notes.

a. When the refrigerant containing parts of a system are located in one or more enclosed spaces, the cubical contents of the smallest enclosed space other than the machinery room, shall be used to determine the permissible quantity of refrigerant in the system.

b. When the evaporator is located in a duct system, the cubical content of the smallest enclosed space served by the duct system shall be used to determine the permissible quantity of refrigerant in the system unless the airflow to any enclosed space served by the duct system cannot be reduced below ¼ of its maximum, in which case the cubical contents of the entire space served by the duct system shall be used to determine the permissible quantity of refrigerant in the system.

flame, then such refrigerant shall be classed in Group 2 unless the flame producing apparatus is provided with a hood and flue capable of removing the products of combustion to the open air. Flames by matches, cigarette lighters, small alcohol lamps and similar devices, shall not be considered as open flames.

Group 2 Refrigerants.

7.30. Group 2 refrigerants shall not be used except in Unit Systems containing not more than twelve (12) pounds of refrigerant, or except in systems containing not more than one thousand (1000) pounds of refrigerant and having all refrigerant containing parts installed in a Class T machinery room

7.31. Group 2 refrigerants shall not be used in a system for air conditioning for human comfort, except in an Indirect Vented Closed Surface System, or in a Double Indirect Vented Open Spray System, or in an Indirect Absorptive Brine System.

Group 3 Refrigerants.

7.40. Group 3 refrigerants shall not be used in Public Assembly occupancies.

Section 8.   Residential Occupancies.

General.

8.10. No Refrigerating System shall be installed in or on public stairways.

8.11. No Refrigerating System shall be installed in public hallways, lobbies, entrances, or exits, except Unit Systems containing not more than four (4) pounds of a refrigerant, provided free passage is not obstructed.

8.12. Refrigerant piping shall not be carried through floors except as follows:

a. It may be carried from basements to the first floor or from the top floor to a penthouse or the roof.

b. For the purpose of connecting to a condenser on the roof it may be carried through an approved, rigid and tight continuous fire-resisting flue or shaft having no openings on intermediate floors, or it may be carried on the outer wall of the building provided it is not located in an air shaft, closed court, or in other similar open spaces enclosed within the outer walls of the building.

c. In systems containing Group 1 refrigerants and used for air conditioning for human comfort, the refrigerant piping may be carried through floors provided it is enclosed in an approved, rigid and tight continuous fire-resisting flue or shaft where it passes through any intermediate space not served by the air conditioning system. The flue shall be vented to the outside or to a space served by the air conditioning system. Such systems shall conform to the requirements of paragraph 8.20.

Group 1 Refrigerants.

8.20. The maximum quantity of refrigerant in a Direct System used for air conditioning for human comfort, shall be limited by the volume of the space to be air conditioned as shown in the table of paragraph 7.20.

8.21. A system containing more than fifty (50) pounds of a Group 1 refrigerant, other than carbon dioxide, and which includes air ducts shall be of the Indirect type unless it conforms to requirements as follows:

a. Positive automatic fire damper or dampers shall be provided to cut off the refrigerant containing apparatus from the duct system.

b. Automatic means shall be provided to close the dampers and to stop the fan when the temperature of the air in the duct at the damper location reaches 210 F when the damper is on the discharge side of a system containing a heating coil and at 125 F when the damper is on the suction side of the system, or on the discharge side of a system containing no heating coil.

8.22. A system containing more than one thousand (1000) pounds of a Group 1 refrigerant shall be of the Indirect type with all the refrigerant containing parts, excepting parts mounted outside the building, installed in a machinery room used for no other purpose and in which for Group 1 refrigerants, excepting carbon dioxide, no flame is present or apparatus to produce a flame is installed.

Group 2 Refrigerants.

8.30. No system containing more than six (6) pounds of a Group 2 refrigerant shall be located in sleeping rooms, or spaces directly connected to sleeping rooms.

8.31. No system containing a Group 2 refrigerant shall be used for air conditioning for human comfort unless it is of the Indirect Vented Closed Surface, Double Indirect Vented Open Spray, Indirect Absorptive Brine, or primary circuit of a Double Refrigerant type with all the refrigerant containing parts, excepting parts mounted outside the building, installed in a machinery room used for no other purpose.

8.32. Any system containing more than three hundred (300) pounds of a Group 2 refrigerant shall have all refrigerant containing parts installed in a Class T machinery room.

Group 3 Refrigerants.

8.40. Group 3 refrigerants shall not be used except in a Unit System containing not more than six (6) pounds of refrigerant.

Section 9. Commercial Occupancies.

General.

9.10. No Refrigerating System shall be installed in or on public stairways.

9.11. No Refrigerating System shall be installed in public hallways, lobbies, entrances, or exits, except Unit Systems containing not more than four (4) pounds of a refrigerant, provided free passage is not obstructed.

9.12. Refrigerant piping shall not be carried through floors except as follows:

a. It may be carried from basements to the first floor or from the top floor to a penthouse or the roof.

b. For the purpose of connecting to a condenser on the roof it may be carried through an approved, rigid and tight continuous fire-resisting flue or shaft having no openings on intermediate floors, or it may be carried on the outer wall of the building provided it is not located in an air shaft, closed court, or in other similar open spaces enclosed within the outer walls of the building.

c. In systems containing Group 1 refrigerants and used for air conditioning for human comfort, the refrigerant piping may be carried through floors provided it is enclosed in an approved, rigid and tight continuous fire-resisting flue or shaft where it passes through any intermediate space not served by the air conditioning system. The flue shall be vented to the outside or to a space served by the air conditioning system. Such systems shall conform to the requirements of paragraph 9.20.

Group 1 Refrigerants.

9.20. Direct Systems containing more than twenty (20) pounds of a Group 1 refrigerant when used for air conditioning for human comfort, shall be limited by the volume of the space to be air conditioned as shown in the table of paragraph 7.20.

9.21. A system containing more than fifty (50) pounds of a Group 1 refrigerant other than carbon dioxide, and which includes air ducts shall be of the Indirect type unless it conforms to requirements as follows:

a. Positive automatic fire damper or dampers shall be provided to cut off the refrigerant containing apparatus from the duct system.

b. Automatic means shall be provided to close the dampers and to stop the fan when the temperature of the air in the duct at the damper location reaches 210 F when the damper is on the discharge side of a system containing a heating coil and at 125 F when the damper is on the suction side of the system or on the discharge side of a system containing no heating coil.

9.22. A system containing more than one thousand (1000) pounds of a Group 1 refrigerant shall be of the Indirect type with all the refrigerant containing parts, excepting parts mounted outside the building, installed in a machinery room used for no other purpose and in which for Group 1 refrigerants, excepting carbon dioxide, no flame is present or apparatus to produce a flame is installed.

Group 2 Refrigerants.

9.30. A system containing more than twenty (20) pounds of a Group 2 refrigerant shall not be used for air conditioning for human comfort unless it is of the Indirect Vented Closed Surface, Double Indirect Vented Open Spray, Indirect Absorptive Brine, or primary circuit of a Double Refrigerant type with all the refrigerant containing parts, excepting parts mounted inside the building, installed in a machinery room used for no other purpose.

9.31. Any system containing more than six hundred (600) pounds of a Group 2 refrigerant shall have all refrigerant containing parts installed in a Class T machinery room.

Group 3 Refrigerants.

9.40. Group 3 refrigerants shall not be used except in a Unit System containing not more than six (6) pounds of refrigerant.

Section 10. Industrial Occupancies.

10.10. There shall be no restriction on the quantity or kind of refrigerant used in an Industrial occupancy, except as specified in paragraph 10.20.

10.20. When the number of employees above the first floor exceeds one per one hundred (100) square feet of floor area, the requirements of Commercial occupancies shall apply unless that portion of the building containing more than one employee per one hundred (100) square feet of floor area above the first floor, together with its entrances and exits, be cut off from the rest of the building by vapor-tight construction with self-closing, tight-fitting doors.

Section 11. Installation Requirements.

Condensing Units.

11.10. Not more than two (2) condensing units shall be located one above the other within the same floor area between floor and ceiling.

11.11. All moving machinery shall be provided with adequate guards in accordance with the American Standard Safety Code for Mechanical Power Transmission Apparatus, B15-1927.

11.12. Adequate illumination and clear space for inspection and servicing of condensing units shall be provided.

11.13. Condensing units with enclosures shall be readily accessible for servicing and inspection.

Water Connections.

11.20. No connection shall be made with the public water supply which is inconsistent with the regulations of the public authority having jurisdiction. Water used for removing heat from a Refrigerating System shall not be discharged into any water supply where the water is used for drinking purposes.

11.21. Discharge water lines from condensers or other equipment shall not be directly connected to the waste or sewer system in such a manner as to permit siphoning of the waste water into the water supply lines. The waste or discharge from such equipment shall be over and above the rim of a properly trapped and vented plumbing fixture.

Electrical Wiring.

11.30. The installation of all electrical equipment and wiring shall be in accordance with the requirements of the latest edition of the National Electric Code, as approved by American Standards Association.

Gas Devices.

11.40. The installation of all gas fuel devices and equipment used with Refrigerating Systems shall be in accordance with the latest edition of National Board of Fire Underwriters' Pamphlet No. 54 entitled "Recommended Good Practice Requirements for Installation, Maintenance and Use of Piping and Fittings for City Gas," as approved by American Standards Association.

Open Flames.

11.50. When the quantity of refrigerant in any one Refrigerating System exceeds the amount given in the following table, for each one thousand (1000) cubic feet of room volume in which the system or any part thereof is installed, then no flame producing device or hot surfaces above 800 F shall be permitted in such room and all electrical equipment in the room shall conform to the requirements of Article 500—

Hazardous Locations Class I of the latest edition of the National Electric Code as approved by American Standards Association.

Refrigerant		Maximum quantity in lbs per 1000 cu ft of room volume
Name	Chemical formula	
Butane........................	C_4H_{10}	3
Ethane........................	C_2H_6	3
Ethyl chloride................	C_2H_5Cl	6
Isobutane.....................	$(CH_3)_3CH$	3
Methyl chloride...............	CH_3Cl	10
Methyl formate...............	$HCOOCH_3$	7
Propane......................	C_3H_3	3

Machinery Room.

11.60. Each refrigerator machinery room shall be provided with tight-fitting door or doors and have no partitions or openings that will permit the passage of the refrigerant to other parts of the building.

11.61. Each refrigerating machinery room shall be provided with means for ventilation to the outer air. The ventilation shall consist of windows or doors opening to the outer air, of the size shown in Table 1, or of mechanical means capable of removing the air from the room in accordance with Table 1. The amount of ventilation for refrigerant removal purposes shall be determined by the refrigerant content of the largest system in the machinery room.

11.62. When mechanical means are used, they shall consist of a power-driven exhaust fan, which shall be capable of removing from the refrigerating machinery room the amount of air specified in Table 1. The inlet to the fan shall be located near the refrigerating equipment. The outlet from the fan shall terminate outside of the building. When air ducts are used on either the inlet or discharge side of the fan, they shall each have an area not less than specified in Table 1.

11.63. Class T machinery rooms in basements or sub-basements shall have adequate mechanical ventilation operating continuously, which may be considered as a part of the emergency ventilation required in paragraph 11.61.

Air Duct Systems.

11.70. The installation of all Air Duct Systems of air conditioning equipment using mechanical refrigeration for human comfort shall be in accordance with the requirements of the American Standard Regulations for the Installation of Air Conditioning, Warm Air Heating, Air Cooling and Ventilating Systems Z33.2-1938 and all subsequent revisions thereof approved by American Standards Association.

Indirect Open Spray Systems.

11.80. Indirect Open Spray Systems containing more than one thousand (1000) pounds of a Group 1 refrigerant shall be provided with approved means of preventing the escape of refrigerant into the spray system, except when the vapor pressure of the refrigerant at 32 F does not exceed atmospheric pressure.

Table 1. Duct Areas and Openings

Weight of refrigerant in system, lbs	Mechanical cu ft per minute discharge	Duct area, sq ft	Open window or door area, sq ft
Up to 20	150	¼	4
50	250	⅓	6
100	400	½	10
150	550	⅔	12½
200	680	⅔	14
250	800	1	15
300	900	1	17
400	1,100	1¼	20
500	1,275	1¼	22
600	1,450	1½	24
700	1,630	1½	26
800	1,800	2	28
900	1,950	2	30
1,000	2,050	2	31
1,250	2,250	2¼	33
1,500	2,500	2¼	37
1,750	2,700	2¼	38
2,000	2,900	2¼	40
2,500	3,300	2½	43
3,000	3,700	3	48
4,000	4,600	3¼	55
5,000	5,500	4½	62
6,000	6,300	5	68
7,000	7,200	5½	74
8,000	8,000	5¾	80
9,000	8,700	6¼	85
10,000	9,500	6½	90
12,000	10,900	7	100
14,000	12,200	7½	109
16,000	13,300	7¾	118
18,000	14,300	8	125
20,000	15,200	8¼	130
25,000	17,000	8¾	140
30,000	18,200	9	145
35,000	19,400	9¼	150
40,000	20,500	9½	155
45,000	21,500	9¾	160

Section 12.[1]   Refrigerant Piping, Valves, Fittings and Related Parts.

Materials.

12.10. All materials used in the construction and installation of Refrigerating Systems shall be suitable for the refrigerant used, and no material shall be used that will deteriorate due to the chemical action of the refrigerant or the oil, or the combination of both.

Steel and Wrought Iron Pipe.

12.11. Standard weight steel or wrought iron pipe may be used for Design Working Pressures not exceeding two hundred fifty (250) pounds per square inch, provided lap welded or seamless pipe is used for sizes larger than two (2) inches (iron pipe size) and extra heavy pipe is used for liquid lines for sizes one and one-half (1½) inches (iron pipe size) and smaller.

12.12. Pipe joints may be screwed, flanged or welded. Screw joints shall conform to American Standards Association Pipe Thread Standard No. B2-1919. Exposed threads shall be tinned or otherwise coated to inhibit corrosion.

12.13. Welds shall conform to the Welding Section of the American Standards Association Code for Pressure Piping B31-1935.

12.14. Valves, flanges, and fittings may be made of cast iron, malleable iron, bronze or steel castings, hot forged or drop forged steel, wrought copper, bronze or brass, and shall be of the design and material listed by the manufacturer for the particular refrigerant service.

12.15. Cast iron shall conform to American Society for Testing Materials, designation A-126-30, Class B higher strength gray iron with not less than thirty thousand (30,000) pounds per square inch tensile strength.

12.16. Bushings may be used in fittings when the reduction is two or more pipe sizes. For single pipe size reduction, reducing fittings must be used.

Pipe Bends.

12.17. Pipe bends shall be substantially circular in section and free from injurious wrinkles, buckles, kinks and creases. This shall not be construed as barring corrugated pipe bends made of suitable material.

Brass Pipe.

12.18. Standard pipe size copper or red brass (not less than eighty (80) per cent copper) may be used.

Copper Tubing.

12.20. Copper tubing used for refrigerant piping erected on the premises shall conform to American Society for Testing Materials designation B-88-33, grades K or L for dimensions, and shall be absolutely free from scale and dirt.

12.21. Copper tubing of one-eighth (⅛), one-quarter (¼), and five-eighths (⅝) inch nominal sizes in the same standard series as grades K or L of American Society for Testing Materials designation B-88-33, shall be considered as meeting the requirements of paragraph 12.20.

---

[1] The provisions of this section apply to piping, valves, fittings and related parts for Design Working Pressure not exceeding two hundred fifty (250) pounds per square inch gauge.

Soft Copper Tubing.

12.22. Soft annealed copper tubing used for refrigerant piping erected on the premises shall not be used in sizes larger than three-quarters (¾) inch nominal size. It shall conform to grades K or L of American Society for Testing Materials designation B-88-33.

12.23. Rigid metal enclosures shall be provided for soft annealed copper tubing used for refrigerant piping erected on the premises, except that flexible metal enclosures may be used at bends or terminals if not exceeding six (6) feet in length.   No enclosures shall be required for connections between condensing unit and the nearest riser box, provided such connections do not exceed six (6) feet in length.

12.24. Threaded joints on copper or brass pipe of standard pipe size shall be made with extra heavy brass fittings which conform to Federal Specifications WW-P-461 composition B, Feb. 2, 1932.

12.25. Joints on annealed copper tubing not exceeding three-quarters (¾) inch in outside diameter may be made with flared compression fittings of approved type, provided that all such fittings shall be exposed for visual inspection.

12.26. Joints on hard drawn copper tubing, if of the sweated capillary type, may be made with an alloy having a melting point greater than 1000 F or with a solder melting at a point below 500 F, but above 350 F.

12.27. Fittings used in sweated capillary joints shall be cast red brass or die pressed brass or copper, or wrought brass or copper, or extruded brass or copper.

12.28. Soldered joints in pipe or tubing erected on the premises shall remain mechanically intact when subjected to a pull-apart test equivalent to a pressure of not less than three hundred (300) pounds per square inch gauge pressure with a temperature of not less than 800 F, except that this requirement shall not apply to soldered joints in pipe or tubing of one-half (½) inch nominal size or smaller when used in systems containing not more than twenty (20) pounds of refrigerant.

12.29. Any evaporator located in an air duct of an air conditioning system for human comfort shall be constructed to withstand without leakage a temperature of 1000 F.

Stop Valves.

12.30. Stop valves shall be installed on all systems containing more than twenty (20) pounds but less than one hundred (100) pounds of refrigerant at locations as follows:

a. Each inlet and each outlet pipe of each compressor.

b. Each outlet of each liquid receiver.

12.31. Stop valves shall be installed on all systems containing one hundred (100) pounds or more of refrigerant at locations as follows:

a. Each inlet and each outlet pipe of each compressor.

b. Each inlet and each outlet pipe of each liquid receiver.

c. Each liquid and each suction branch header.

12.32. Stop valves used with soft annealed copper tubing or hard drawn copper tubing three-quarter (¾) inch nominal size or smaller shall be securely mounted independent of tubing fastenings or supports.

12.33. Stop valves placed where it is not obvious what they control shall be suitably labelled.   Numbers may be used to label the valves provided a key to the numbers is located near the valves.

Pipe and Tube Supports.

12.40. All refrigerant piping shall be securely supported by means of metal hangers, brackets, straps, clamps or pedestals, in such manner as to relieve joints of harmful strains and vibration. The supports shall be used for no other purpose. Hangers for refrigerant piping above seven-eighths ($\frac{7}{8}$) inch outside diameter, shall not be less than 0.125 square inch cross section.

Location of Refrigerant Piping.

12.50. Refrigerant piping crossing an open space which affords passageway in any building shall not be less than seven and one-half ($7\frac{1}{2}$) feet above the floor unless against the ceiling of such space.

12.51. Refrigerant piping shall not be placed in public hallways, lobbies, stairways, elevators or dumbwaiter shafts, excepting that such refrigerant piping may pass across a public hallway if there be no joints in the section in the public hallway, and provided non-ferrous tubing of one (1) inch nominal outside diameter and less be contained in a rigid metal pipe.

12.52. Refrigerant piping, with or without insulation covering, shall be exposed to view, excepting for mechanical protection herein specified, or when located in the cabinet of a Unit System. This does not apply to refrigerant piping installed outside the building or in a flue vented to the outer air.

Section 13. Design, Construction, and Safety Devices.

Design and Construction.

13.10. Every part of a Refrigerating System, except pressure gauges and control mechanisms, shall be designed, constructed, and assembled to withstand the test pressures specified in Table 3, without being stressed beyond one-third ($\frac{1}{3}$) of its ultimate strength.

13.11. Equipment listed by a recognized engineering testing laboratory having a follow-up inspection service, shall be considered as conforming with the requirements of paragraph 13.10.

13.12. Refrigerant containing vessels which are not a part of equipment listed by a recognized engineering testing laboratory having a follow-up inspection service, shall be constructed in accordance with the rules of Section VIII (Unfired Pressure Vessel Section) of the 1937 A.S.M.E. Boiler Construction Code, except that compliance with paragraphs U-2 to U-10 inclusive and U-65 and U-66 of the aforesaid A.S.M.E. Code shall not be required.

Pressure Relief Devices.

13.20. Every system, except as provided in paragraphs 13.21, 13.22 and 13.23, shall be protected by a pressure relief device unless so constructed that pressure due to fire conditions will be relieved safely by soldered joints, lead gaskets, fusible plugs, or other parts of the system.

13.21.[1] Each pressure vessel containing liquid refrigerant and which may be shut off by valves from all other parts of a refrigerating system, shall be protected by an approved pressure relief valve in parallel with a rupture member or a second approved

---

[1] It may be necessary on large pressure vessels containing liquid refrigerant to use two or more pressure relief devices in parallel to obtain the required minimum rated capacity. In such cases the battery, of pressure relief devices shall be considered as a unit and therefore as one pressure relief device.

pressure relief valve if its gross volume exceeds five (5) cubic feet unless its diameter does not exceed six (6) inches.

13.22. Each pressure vessel having a gross volume of five (5) cubic feet or less, containing liquid refrigerant and which may be shut off by valves from all other parts of a refrigerating system, shall be protected by an approved pressure relief device or an approved fusible plug.

13.23. The requirements of 13.21 and 13.22 shall not apply to flooded evaporators located in a refrigerator cabinet.

13.24. Each pressure vessel shall have the Design Working Pressure stamped thereon if its gross volume exceeds five (5) cubic feet.

13.25. Compressors operating above fifteen (15) pounds per square inch gauge and having a displacement exceeding one hundred (100) cubic feet per minute, shall be equipped by the manufacturer with a pressure relief device of adequate size to prevent rupture of the compressor, located between the compressor and stop valve on the discharge side. The discharge from such relief device may be vented to the atmosphere or into the low pressure side of the system.

Capacity Rating.

13.30. The rated discharge capacity of a pressure relief valve, expressed in pounds of air per minute, shall be one-fifth ($\frac{1}{5}$) of its discharge capacity determined by test with the outlet open to the atmosphere and with a differential pressure across the restraining member equal to twice the marked pressure setting of the pressure relief valve.

13.32. The rated discharge capacity of rupture members and discharge piping shall be as given in Table 2.

Required Capacity.

13.33. The minimum required rated discharge capacity of the pressure relief device for a refrigerant containing vessel shall be determined by the following formula:

$$C = fDL$$

where C = Minimum required rated discharge capacity of the relief device in pounds of air per minute
D = Outside diameter of the vessel in feet
L = Length of the vessel in feet
f = Factor dependent upon kind of refrigerant as follows:

Kind of refrigerant	*Value of "f"*
Ammonia (NH_3)	0.1
Dichlorodifluoromethane (Freon 12)	0.3
All other refrigerants	0.2

Pressure Setting.

13.34. All pressure relief devices for refrigerant containing vessels shall be directly pressure actuated.

13.35. All pressure relief valves for refrigerant containing vessels shall be set to function at a pressure not to exceed 25% above the Design Working Pressure of the vessel.

13.36. All rupture members used in parallel with pressure relief valves on refrigerant containing vessels shall be set to function at a pressure not to exceed ninety (90) per cent above the Design Working Pressure of the vessel.

Pressure Setting Test.

13.37. The pressure setting of relief devices for refrigerant containing vessels shall be tested with the outlet open to the atmosphere and the relief device shall function at a pressure not more than ten (10) per cent above the pressure marked thereon, if such marking is one hundred (100) pounds per square inch or more, or at not more than ten (10) pounds per square inch above the pressure marked thereon, if such marking is less than one hundred (100) pounds per square inch.

Marking.

13.38.[1] All pressure relief valves for refrigerant containing vessels shall be set and sealed by the manufacturer. The name or trade-mark of the manufacturer, the pressure setting expressed in pounds per square inch gauge, the rated discharge capacity expressed in pounds of air per minute, and the maximum equivalent length of discharge piping that can be attached to the pressure relief valve without loss of discharge capacity, shall be cast or stamped on the device, or on a metal plate permanently attached thereto.

13.39. Each rupture member for refrigerant containing pressure vessels shall have cast or stamped on the device or on a metal plate permanently attached thereto the name or trade mark of the manufacturer and the bursting pressure of the rupture member expressed in pound per square inch gauge.

Installation Requirements.

13.40. A rupture member may be located between a pressure relief valve and a pressure vessel.

13.41. No stop valve shall be located between any automatic pressure relief device and the part or parts of the system protected thereby, except when the parallel relief devices mentioned in paragraph 13.21 are so arranged that only one can be rendered inoperative at a time for testing or repair purposes.

13.42. All pressure relief devices shall be connected as nearly as practicable directly to the pressure vessel or other parts of the system protected thereby, and shall be placed above the liquid refrigerant level.

13.43. The seats and discs of pressure relief devices for refrigerant containing vessels shall be constructed of suitable material to resist refrigerant corrosion.

Discharge from Pressure Relief Devices.

13.44. Pressure relief devices and fusible plugs on all systems containing more than thirty (30) pounds of refrigerant, except those used to protect compressors, shall discharge to the outside of the building in an approved manner.

13.45. The size of the discharge opening and pipe from the pressure relief device shall not be less than the size of the relief device inlet. The discharge from more

---

[1] The maximum length of discharge line which can be attached to a pressure relief valve without loss of discharge capacity may be determined from Table 2, using that length of line for the size of the discharge connection of the pressure relief valve which has twice the rated discharge capacity of the pressure relief valve at a Design Working Pressure equal to the pressure setting of the pressure relief valve.

Table 2. Discharge Capacity of Rupture Members and Discharge Piping in Pounds of Air per Minute

Maximum relief pressure, lbs per sq in gauge	Design working pressure, lbs per sq in gauge	Pipe length, ft	Standard weight pipe, nominal size, in.							
			½	¾	1	1¼	1½	2	2½	3
			Discharge capacity, lbs of air per min							
100	53	50	2.6	5.2	9.6	19.0	28	52	81	140
		150	2.2	4.2	7.8	16.0	23	43	66	114
		300	1.8	3.6	6.8	13.0	20	37	57	99
		75	1.6	3.0	5.4	11.0	16	30	47	81
		100	1.4	2.6	4.8	9.6	14	26	41	70
		200	1.0	2.2	4.0	7.8	11	21	33	57
125	66	50	3.2	6.4	12.0	24.0	35	65	101	175
		75	2.6	5.2	9.8	19.0	28	53	82	143
		100	2.2	4.6	8.4	17.0	25	46	72	124
		150	1.8	3.8	7.0	14.0	20	38	58	101
		200	1.6	3.2	6.0	12.0	17	33	51	87
		300	1.4	2.6	4.8	9.8	14	27	42	72
150	79	50	3.8	7.8	14.0	28	42	78	122	210
		75	3.2	6.4	12.0	23	34	64	99	171
		100	2.8	5.4	10.0	20	30	55	86	148
		150	2.2	4.4	8.2	16	24	45	70	121
		200	2.0	3.8	7.0	14	21	39	61	105
		300	1.6	3.2	5.8	12	17	32	50	86
175	92	50	4.6	9.0	17.0	33	49	91	142	244
		75	3.8	7.4	14.0	27	40	75	116	200
		100	3.2	6.4	12.0	23	34	64	100	173
		150	2.6	5.2	9.6	19	28	53	82	141
		200	2.2	4.6	8.4	17	24	46	71	122
		300	1.8	3.6	6.8	14	20	37	58	100
200	105	50	5.2	10.0	19.0	38	56	104	162	280
		75	4.2	8.4	16.0	31	45	85	132	228
		100	3.6	7.2	14.0	27	39	74	115	198
		150	3.0	6.0	11.0	22	32	60	94	162
		200	2.6	5.2	9.6	19	28	52	81	140
		300	2.2	4.2	7.8	16	23	43	66	114
250	131	50	6.4	13.0	24.0	47	70	130	206	350
		75	5.4	11.0	20.0	39	57	106	166	286
		100	4.6	9.2	17.0	34	49	92	144	248
		150	3.8	7.4	14.0	27	40	75	117	202
		200	3.2	6.4	12.0	24	35	65	102	175
		300	2.6	5.2	9.8	19	28	53	83	143

Table 2.   Discharge Capacity of Rupture Members and Discharge Piping in Pounds of Air per Minute —*(Continued)*

Maximum relief pressure, lbs per sq in gauge	Design working pressure, lbs per sq in gauge	Pipe length, ft	Standard weight pipe, nominal size, in.							
			½	¾	1	1¼	1½	2	2½	3
			Discharge capacity, lbs of air per min							
300	158	50	7.8	15.0	29	57	83	156	244	420
		75	6.4	13.0	23	46	68	128	199	342
		100	5.4	11.0	20	40	59	111	172	296
		150	4.6	9.0	17	33	48	90	140	242
		200	4.0	7.8	14	28	42	78	122	210
		300	3.2	6.4	12	23	34	64	100	171
400	210	50	10.0	21.0	38	76	111	208	324	560
		75	8.4	17.0	31	62	91	170	264	457
		100	7.4	15.0	27	54	79	148	230	396
		150	6.0	12.0	22	44	64	120	187	324
		200	5.2	10.0	19	38	56	104	163	280
		300	4.2	8.4	16	31	45	85	133	228
500	263	50	13.0	26	48	94	139	260	406	700
		75	11.0	21	39	77	114	213	330	570
		100	9.2	18	34	67	98	184	287	495
		150	6.4	13	24	47	70	130	203	350
		200	7.4	15	28	55	80	150	234	405
		300	5.2	10	19	39	57	106	166	286

than one relief device may be run into a common header, the area of which shall be not less than the sum of the areas of the pipes connected thereto.

Ammonia Discharge.

13.46. Where ammonia is used, the discharge may be into a tank of water which shall be used for no purpose except ammonia absorption. At least one (1) gallon of fresh water shall be provided for every one (1) pound of ammonia in the system. The water used shall be prevented from freezing without the use of salt or chemicals. The tank shall be substantially constructed of not less than one-eighth (⅛) inch or No. 11 U. S. gauge iron or steel. No horizontal dimension of the tank shall be greater than one-half (½) the height. The tank shall have a hinged cover, or, if of the enclosed type, shall have a vent hole at the top. All pipe connections shall be through the top of the tank only. The discharge pipe from the pressure relief valves shall discharge the ammonia in the center of the tank near the bottom.

Sulphur Dioxide Discharge.

13.47. Where sulphur dioxide is used, the discharge may be into a tank of absorptive brine which shall be used for no purpose except sulphur dioxide absorption. There shall be one (1) gallon of standard dichromate brine (two and one-half (2½) pounds sodium dichromate per gallon of water) for each pound of sulphur dioxide in the system. Brines made with caustic soda or soda ash may be used in place of sodium dichromate provided the quantity and strength give the equivalent sulphur dioxide absorbing power. The tank shall be substantially constructed of not less than one-eighth (⅛) inch or No. 11 U. S. gauge iron or steel. The tank shall have a hinged cover, or, if of the enclosed type, shall have a vent hole at the top. All pipe connections shall be through the top of the tank only. The discharge pipe from the pressure relief valve shall discharge the sulphur dioxide in the center of the tank near the bottom.

Pressure Limiting Devices.

13.50. Pressure limiting devices are required on all systems containing more than twenty (20) pounds of refrigerant and operating above atmospheric pressure, and on all Water Cooled Systems so constructed that the compressor or generator is capable of producing a pressure in excess of the test pressure.

13.51. Pressure limiting devices shall stop the action of the compressor at a pressure less than ninety (90) per cent of the pressure relief device setting but not more than ninety (90) per cent of the test pressures given in Table 3.

13.52. Pressure limiting devices shall be connected between the compressor and the stop valve on the discharge side.

Test of Refrigerant Containing Vessels.

13.60. Refrigerant containing vessels, the shells of which have been previously tested under hydrostatic pressure of not less than one and one-half times the Design Working Pressure may be finally tested with pneumatic pressure at one and one-half times the Design Working Pressure, instead of hydrostatic pressure.

Gauges.

13.70. Liquid level gauge glasses, except those of the bull's-eye type, shall have automatic closing shut-off valves, and such glasses shall be adequately protected against injury.

Motor Protection.

13.80. Motors of Refrigerating Systems shall be adequately protected against hazardous overheating under normal or abnormal operating conditions.

Section 14. Tests.

General.

14.10. Every refrigerant containing part of every system shall be tested and proved tight by the manufacturer at not less than the minimum test pressures shown in Table 3.

14.11. Every refrigerant containing part of every system that is erected on the premises, except compressors, safety devices, pressure gauges, and control mechanisms, that are factory tested, shall be tested and proved tight after complete installation and before operation at not less than the minimum pressures shown in Table 3.

Test Medium.

14.12. No oxygen or any combustible gas or combustible mixture of gases shall be used for testing.

14.13.

Table 3. Test Pressures

Refrigerant		Min. test pressure, lbs per sq in	
Name	Chemical formula	High pressure side	Low pressure side
Ammonia	NH_3	300	150
Butane	C_4H_{10}	90	50
Carbon dioxide	CO_2	1500	1000
Dichlorodifluoromethane (Freon 12)	CCl_2F_2	235	145
Dichlorotetrafluoroethane (Freon 114)	$C_2Cl_2F_2$	80	50
Dichloromethane (Carrene No. 1) (Methylene chloride)	CH_2Cl_2	30	30
Dichloromonofluoromethane (Freon 21)	$CHCl_2F$	70	50
Dichloroethylene	$C_2H_2Cl_2$	30	30
Ethane	C_2H_6	1100	600
Ethyl chloride	C_2H_5Cl	60	50
Isobutane	$(CH_3)_3CH$	130	75
Methyl chloride	CH_3Cl	215	125
Methyl formate	$HCOOCH_3$	50	50
Propane	C_3H_8	325	210
Sulphur dioxide	SO_2	170	95
Trichloromonofluoromethane (Freon 11)	CCl_3F	50	30

Refrigerants Not Listed.

14.14. For refrigerants not listed in Table 3, the test pressure for the high pressure side shall be not less than the saturated vapor pressure of the refrigerant at 150 F. The test pressure for the low pressure side shall be not less than the saturated vapor pressure of the refrigerant at 115 F. In no case shall the test pressure be less than thirty (30) pounds per square inch by gauge.

Posting of Tests.

14.15. A dated declaration of test, signed by the installer, shall be mounted in a frame, protected by glass, and posted in the machinery room. If an inspector is present at the tests he shall also sign the declaration.

Section 15. Instructions.

User's Responsibility.

15.10. All Refrigerating Systems shall be maintained in a cleanly manner, free from accumulations of oily dirt, waste, and other debris, and shall be kept readily accessible at all times.

Instructions.

15.20. It shall be the duty of the person in charge of the premises on which a Refrigerating System containing more than twenty (20) pounds of refrigerant is installed, to place a card conspicuously as near as practicable to the refrigerant condensing unit giving directions for the operation of the system, including precautions to be observed in case of a breakdown or leak as follows:

a. Instructions for shutting down the system in case of emergency.

b. The name, address and day and night telephone numbers for obtaining service.

c. The name, address and telephone number of the municipal inspection department having jurisdiction and instructions to notify said department immediately in case of emergency.

Signs.

15.30. Each Refrigerating System shall be provided with an easily legible metal sign permanently attached and easily accessible, indicating thereon the name and address of the manufacturer or installer, the kind and total number of pounds of refrigerant contained in the system, and the field test pressure applied.

15.31. Systems containing more than one hundred (100) pounds of refrigerant should be provided with metal signs having letters of not less than one-half (½) inch in height designating the main shut-off valves to each vessel, main steam or electrical control, remote control switch, and pressure limiting device. On all exposed high pressure and low pressure piping in each room where installed outside the machinery room, shall be signs as above with the name of the refrigerant and the letters HP or LP.

Marking.

15.32. Each separately sold refrigerant containing vessel larger than five (5) cubic feet in gross volume, each refrigerant condensing unit, and each refrigerant compressor shall carry a nameplate marked with the manufacturer's name and address, identification number, and name of refrigerant used.

Helmets.

15.40. One mask or helmet shall be required where amounts of Group 2 refrigerants between one hundred (100) and one thousand (1000) pounds, inclusive, are employed. If more than one thousand (1000) pounds of Group 2 refrigerants are employed, at least two masks or helmets shall be required.

15.41. Only complete helmets or masks marked as approved by the Bureau of Mines of the United States Department of the Interior and suitable for the refrigerant employed shall be used and they shall be kept in a suitable cabinet immediately outside the machinery room or other approved accessible location.

15.42. Canisters or cartridges of helmets or masks shall be renewed immediately after having been used or the seal broken and if unused, must be renewed at least once every two (2) years. The date of filling shall be marked thereon.

Refrigerant Storage.

15.50. Not more than three hundred (300) pounds of refrigerant in approved containers shall be stored in a machinery room.

15.51. No refrigerant shall be stored in a room in which less than twenty (20) pounds are used in the system.

15.52. Refrigerants on the user's premises in excess of that permitted in the machinery room shall be stored in a fireproof shed or room used for no other purpose.

Charging and Discharging Refrigerants.

15.60. When refrigerant is added to a system, except a Unit System containing not more than six (6) pounds of refrigerant, it shall be charged into the low pressure side of the system. No container shall be left connected to a system except while charging or withdrawing refrigerant.

15.61. Refrigerants withdrawn from Refrigerating Systems shall only be transferred to approved containers. No refrigerant shall be discharged to a sewer.

15.62. The containers from which refrigerants are discharged into or withdrawn from a Refrigerating System must be carefully weighed each time they are used for this purpose, and the containers must not be filled in excess of the permissible filling weight for such containers and such refrigerants as are prescribed in the Interstate Commerce Commission's "Regulations for the Transportation by Rail of Explosives and other Dangerous Articles in Freight, Express and Baggage Services including Specifications for Shipping Containers," effective October 1, 1930, with supplements 1 to 18 inclusive.

INDEX

391